FINANCE

LIFE SCIENCE

(continued inside back cover)

CALCULUS

WITH APPLICATIONS

SECOND EDITION

RONALD J. HARSHBARGER
Georgia Southern University

JAMES J. REYNOLDS
Clarion University of Pennsylvania

Custom-Published
Version

D. C. HEATH AND COMPANY
Lexington, Massachusetts   Toronto

Address editorial correspondence to:

D. C. Heath
125 Spring Street
Lexington, MA 02173

Acquisitions Editor: Charlie Hartford
Developmental Editor: Kathleen Sessa
Production Editor: Kathleen A. Deselle
Designer: Cornelia Boynton
Art Editor: Gary Crespo
Production Coordinator: Lisa Merrill
Cover photographs: Jim Olvera

Published simultaneously in Canada.

Printed in the United States of America.

International Standard Book Number: 0–669–33162–7

Library of Congress Catalog Number: 92–70799

10   9   8   7   6   5   4   3   2

A Note to Instructors and Students About Custom Publishing

Applied calculus courses are offered nationally in a variety of formats. Courses can be one or two semesters (or two to four quarters) in length and cover a wide range of topics. To meet the diverse requirements of these courses, publishers have traditionally offered two versions of their applied calculus textbooks: one short version containing just those core topics covered in virtually all courses, and another, long version containing this same core subject matter plus all the additional topics covered in the lengthiest courses. The unfortunate, but frequent result: students must purchase a book containing chapters that will not be assigned.

D. C. Heath's solution is to offer *Calculus with Applications,* Second Edition, in a custom-published format, allowing instructors to build the texts most appropriate for their courses and helping students to save money. With this format, an instructor can request that we combine any or all of the last four chapters (on differential equations, trigonometric functions, probability, and infinite series and Taylor polynomials) with the beginning eight core chapters (which include an algebra review and the topics most often covered in all courses) to create the text best suited for his or her course. And pricing is structured so that students are charged only for those chapters included in their particular books. The result: instructors select—and students pay for—only those chapters they will use.

We at D. C. Heath are working hard to provide innovative, quality products for your courses. We value your feedback.

The Publisher

PREFACE

Calculus with Applications, Second Edition, presents mathematical skills and concepts for a brief calculus course and applies them to areas that are important to students in the management, life, and social sciences. The emphasis on applications allows students to view mathematics in a practical setting relevant to their intended careers. Almost every chapter of this book includes a section or two devoted to the applications of mathematical topics. An index of these applications on the inside covers demonstrates the wide variety used in examples and exercises. Although intended for students who have completed two years of high-school algebra or the equivalent, this text begins with a brief review of algebra, which, if covered, will aid in preparing students for the work ahead.

New Features of the Second Edition

Technology Corners   Most sections of the text contain Technology Corners for which students can use a graphics calculator and/or a computer to solve more advanced applied problems, to study the concepts of the section, or to discover new relationships.

Consultant's Corners   At the end of each chapter, Consultant's Corners pose real or realistic business problems; and, like real problems, they require students, as consultants, to provide several answers based on different conditions. Students will give advice based on a mathematical analysis of a problem and make decisions about the best way to solve it. Consultant's Corners can be assigned as projects requiring a written report or as discussion items for class. The questions are not connected to a specific section of the text, but are intended to have the consultant draw different mathematical skills and concepts together to solve a problem.

Checkpoints   Each section of the text contains Checkpoint problems that permit students to check their understanding of the skills and concepts under discussion before proceeding farther in the section. Solutions to the Checkpoint problems are given at the end of the section.

Key Terms and Formulas   Each chapter contains a summary of Key Terms and Formulas from that chapter. The terms and formulas are keyed to the sections in which they occur so that students can easily review any topic as needed.

Labeled Applications   Each application problem in the exercise sets has a label identifying its subject matter. This permits the instructor to more easily assign application problems that are appropriate for the students in his or her class.

Computer-Generated Art   To ensure the accuracy of the figures and graphs, the art has been computer-generated. The graphs and axes appear in the same color, eliminating the possibility of inaccurate graphs caused by color registration problems during printing.

Precise Mathematical Language   The Second Edition continues its emphasis on concepts, problem solving, and applications rather than on formal proofs. Although the text retains its clarity and readability, the mathematical language has been honed for more precision in the Second Edition, with definitions and theorems stated accurately but in language that students can understand.

PEDAGOGICAL FEATURES RETAINED IN THE SECOND EDITION

Separate Application Sections   Offering applied topics such as cost, revenue, and profit functions in separate sections brings the preceding mathematical discussion into clear and concise focus. There are eight such sections in the book. In all, there are more than 1260 application problems and hundreds of applied examples.

Exercise Sets   The quantity of the exercise sets has been increased by more than 17% in the Second Edition. The new problems are graded better, are more challenging, and are of a wider variety. A number of problems are drawn from real-life data and are documented by references. As in the previous edition, those exercises that are best worked with a calculator are highlighted with a ▦ symbol.

Warmups   The Warmup at the beginning of each chapter invites students to test themselves on the skills needed for that chapter. They present several prerequisite problem types that are taken from parts of upcoming problems. Each prerequisite problem type is keyed to the upcoming section where that skill is needed, and students who have difficulty with any particular skill are directed to specific sections of the text for review. Instructors may find the Warmups useful in creating a syllabus.

Objectives   Every section begins with a brief list of objectives that outlines the goals of that section for the student.

Procedure/Example and **Property/Example Tables**   Placed where helpful, these tables aid student understanding by giving step-by-step descriptions of important procedures and properties with illustrative examples worked out beside them.

Boxed Information   All definitions and other important information are boxed for easy reference, and key terms are highlighted in boldface.

Review Exercises   At the end of each chapter, a set of Review Exercises offers students extra practice on the topics in that chapter. These exercises are annotated with section numbers so that students having difficulty can turn to the appropriate section for review.

CONTENT CHANGES IN THE SECOND EDITION

Significant changes within the chapters of the Second Edition include the following.

In Chapter 0, Sections 0.1 and 0.2 from the First Edition have been combined, and a discussion of intervals as special subsets of the real numbers, as well as interval notation has been added. In Section 0.6, Algebraic Fractions, we discuss complex fractions. Also, in Section 0.7, we have expanded our treatment of the solution of linear equations to include the solution of linear inequalities.

In Chapter 1, we rewrote our discussion of functions and graphs and expanded it to two sections. To the original section, we added operations with functions, including function composition. In the new Section 1.5, we look at simple polynomial, rational, and piecewise defined functions and at the special features of their graphs.

We have written a more precise presentation of limits, continuity, and the derivative in the first three sections of Chapter 2. We have moved limits involving piecewise defined functions out of Section 2.1 and have used graphs to a greater extent in the remaining material, all in an effort to make the introduction to limits more easily understood and to join the geometric and algebraic concepts of limits. There is also a greater emphasis on graphs in our discussion of continuity in Section 2.2, and this section now contains the material on limits of piecewise defined functions. Our discussion of asymptotes has been moved to a new section in Chapter 3 that covers both asymptotes and graphing. In Section 2.3, we introduce instantaneous rates of change with an example involving velocity and follow this with the discussion of marginal revenue, so that students first encounter the idea of derivative through a concept from their personal experience. This section also includes a new Procedure/Example table that clearly outlines how to use the definition of derivative to find the derivative of a function. Finally, throughout the chapter, we have increased our mathematical precision with carefully stated theorems, more proofs of the derivative formulas, and more justification in our discussions.

We have completely reorganized Chapter 3 to cover curve sketching using the first and second derivatives in Sections 3.1 and 3.2. These discussions include more justification of theory and make a stronger connection between information from the derivatives and the shape of the graph. In particular, we have introduced sign diagrams for the derivatives and mainstreamed our discussion of critical points where $f'(x)$ does not exist. Section 3.3 is a new section that covers asymptotes and curve sketching and acts as a summary section for Sections 3.1 and 3.2.

Also in Chapter 3, inventory-cost models are now discussed in the text of Section 3.5. Section 3.6 is a new section devoted to differentials. Section 3.7 now covers implicit differentiation and elasticity, followed by related rates in Section 3.8.

In Chapter 5, we have added the change of base formula to our development of logarithmic functions. In Sections 5.3 and 5.4, we have focused our discussion and theoretical development on the natural logarithm and the natural exponential functions, although derivatives of logarithmic and exponential functions with other bases are still included.

In Chapter 6, Section 6.1, we have expanded our work with a fixed number of subdivisions to approximate the area under a curve. Also, in Section 6.3, the exercises on finding areas between two curves have been reworked so that they are more interesting and will help students to conceptualize the topic better.

Chapter 7 now includes a new discussion of linear regression. This discussion introduces a technique important for many business applications, and the formula development provides an application of the max-min techniques for functions of two variables.

SUPPLEMENTS

Instructor's Guide   This guide contains four forms of a test for each chapter of the text with answers provided, solutions to the even-numbered text exercises, and transparency masters. In addition, a section containing the answers to the even-numbered text exercises is included.

Study and Solutions Guide   by Gordon Shilling. In addition to the solutions to all the odd-numbered exercises in the text, this guide contains supplementary exercises that reinforce the concepts and techniques presented in the text. Answers to these problems are also provided.

Computerized Testing   Computerized testing for the IBM PC and the Apple Macintosh is available to instructors free of charge. This test bank contains more than 1600 test items.

Test Item File   This is a printed file of all the test items and answers appearing in the computerized testing program.

Interactive Applied Calculus   by The Math Lab. For use with the IBM PC or Apple II, this software program provides labwork for business, life, and social science majors. A total of 40 labs are provided, allowing instructors to select those labs appropriate for their use. Eight of the labs are related to business and economic applications, while many others model real-life business problems and situations.

BestGrapher   by George Best. Available for the IBM PC and the Apple Macintosh, this highly accessible program and its accompanying workbook emphasize the concepts of calculus. The software can be used for graphing, evaluating functions, and symbolic differentiation among other tasks. The workbook provides activities that encourage experimentation and discovery about functions, derivatives, areas, and other topics.

RELATED TEXTS

This book is one of three covering finite mathematics and applied calculus. All three of our texts heavily emphasize real-world applications of the mathematics featured as the students in these courses are typically majoring in management or the life or social sciences. The other texts in this series are:

Finite Mathematics for Management, Life, and Social Sciences, Third Edition. This text is intended for a one-term course covering sets, matrices, inequalities and linear programming, mathematics of finance, probability, statistics, and game theory.

Mathematical Applications for Management, Life, and Social Sciences, Fourth Edition.
This text is designed for a one- or two-term course in finite math and calculus. It contains topics from *Finite Mathematics* as well as most of the calculus topics discussed in this text.

ACKNOWLEDGMENTS

We wish to thank the many people who have helped us at various stages of this project. The encouragement, criticism, and suggestions that have been offered have been invaluable to us. Our special thanks to Peter Jones, who developed the ideas and wrote the first drafts of some of the Consultant's Corner applications in this text, and to James Braselton for his assistance in developing Consultant's Corner applications and Technology Corners. We are also grateful for the assistance provided by Thomas Frost, Danielle Van Zwet, and Robert Baldwin. We would also like to thank the following colleagues, who reviewed manuscript and made many helpful comments.

Edward Arismendi, Orange Coast College; Genelle Beck, University of Texas at Austin; Roger Chitty, Southern Illinois University; Theodore Faticoni, Fordham University; Genaro Gonzalez, Texas A & I University; Chaitan Gupta, Northern Illinois University; D. J. Hartfiel, Texas A & M University; Donald King, Northeastern University; Joyce Longman, Villanova University; Michael Nasab, Long Beach City College; Carol Nessmith, Georgia Southern University; James Shirey, Ohio University; Shirleen Smith, University of Scranton; Tuong Ton-That, University of Iowa; Arnold Villone, San Diego State University; and John Welgarz, Kirkwood Community College.

Ronald J. Harshbarger
James J. Reynolds

CONTENTS

4 | EXPONENTIAL AND LOGARITHMIC FUNCTIONS 354

5 | INDEFINITE INTEGRALS 410

6 | DEFINITE INTEGRALS 446

7 | FUNCTIONS OF TWO OR MORE VARIABLES   522

CALCULUS
WITH APPLICATIONS

0 | ALGEBRAIC CONCEPTS

This chapter provides a brief review of the algebraic concepts that will be used throughout the text.

The review begins with sets and the real numbers, the number system used in the remainder of the text. Special subsets of the real numbers, including intervals, are also covered.

Exponents, rules of exponents, and radicals are then introduced. Expressions involving powers and radicals are the building blocks for algebraic expressions. Operations with algebraic expressions and factoring are reviewed and then followed by operations with and simplification of algebraic fractions.

The chapter concludes with a study of the solution of linear equations and inequalities and a look at some of their applications.

You should already be familiar with the topics covered in this chapter, but it may be helpful to spend some time reviewing them. In addition, each chapter after this one opens with a warm-up page that identifies prerequisite skills needed for that chapter. If algebraic skills are required, the warm-up cites their coverage in this chapter. Thus, you will find that the following sections are a useful reference as you study later chapters.

0.1 | SETS AND THE REAL NUMBERS

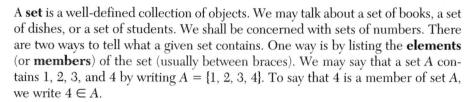

A **set** is a well-defined collection of objects. We may talk about a set of books, a set of dishes, or a set of students. We shall be concerned with sets of numbers. There are two ways to tell what a given set contains. One way is by listing the **elements** (or **members**) of the set (usually between braces). We may say that a set A contains 1, 2, 3, and 4 by writing $A = \{1, 2, 3, 4\}$. To say that 4 is a member of set A, we write $4 \in A$.

If all the members of the set can be listed, the set is said to be a **finite set.** $A = \{1, 2, 3, 4\}$ and $B = \{x, y, z\}$ are examples of finite sets. Although we cannot list all the elements of an **infinite set,** we can use three dots to indicate the unlisted members of such a set. For example, $N = \{1, 2, 3, 4, \ldots\}$ is an infinite set. This set N is called the set of **natural numbers.**

Another way to specify the elements of a given set is by description. For example, we may write $D = \{x\colon x$ is a Ford automobile$\}$ to describe the set of all Ford automobiles. $F = \{y\colon y$ is an odd natural number$\}$ is read "F is the set of all y such that y is an odd natural number."

EXAMPLE 1 | Write the following sets in two ways.

(a) The set A of natural numbers less than 6.

(b) The set B of natural numbers greater than 10.

(c) The set C containing only 3.

Solution

(a) $A = \{1, 2, 3, 4, 5\}$ or $A = \{x\colon x$ is a natural number less than 6$\}$

(b) $B = \{11, 12, 13, 14, \ldots\}$ or $B = \{x\colon x$ is a natural number greater than 10$\}$

(c) $C = \{3\}$ or $C = \{x\colon x = 3\}$

Note that set C of Example 1 contains one member, 3; set A contains five members; and set B contains an infinite number of members. It is possible for a set to contain no members. Such a set is called the **empty set** or the **null set,** and it is denoted by $\varnothing$ or by $\{\ \}$. The set of living veterans of the War of 1812 is empty because there are no living veterans of that war. Thus

$\{x\colon x$ is a living veteran of the War of 1812$\} = \varnothing$.

Special relations that may exist between two sets are defined as follows.

RELATIONS BETWEEN SETS

DEFINITION	EXAMPLE
1. Sets X and Y are **equal** if they contain the same elements.	1. If $X = \{1, 2, 3, 4\}$ and $Y = \{4, 3, 2, 1\}$, then $X = Y$.
2. $A \subseteq B$ if every element of A is an element of B. A is called a **subset** of B. The empty set is a subset of every set.	2. If $A = \{1, 2, c, f\}$ and $B = \{1, 2, 3, a, b, c, f\}$, then $A \subseteq B$.
3. If C and D have no elements in common, they are called **disjoint.**	3. If $C = \{1, 2, a, b\}$ and $D = \{3, e, 5, c\}$, then C and D are disjoint.

In the discussion of particular sets, the assumption is always made that the sets under discussion are all subsets of some larger set, called the **universal set** U. The choice of the universal set depends upon the problem under consideration. For example, in discussing the set of all students and the set of all female students, we may use the set of all humans as the universal set.

We may use **Venn diagrams** to illustrate the relationships among sets. We use a rectangle to represent the universal set and closed figures inside the rectangle to represent the sets under consideration. Figures 0.1–0.3 show such Venn diagrams.

FIGURE 0.1

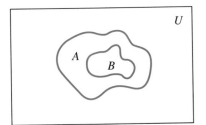

FIGURE 0.2

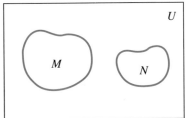

FIGURE 0.3

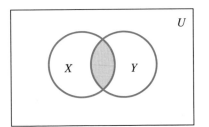

Figure 0.1 shows that B is a subset of A; that is, $B \subseteq A$. In Figure 0.2, M and N are disjoint sets. In Figure 0.3, sets X and Y overlap; that is, they are not disjoint.

The shaded portion of Figure 0.3 indicates where the two sets overlap. The set containing the members that are common to two sets is said to be the **intersection** of the two sets.

Set Intersection   The intersection of A and B, written $A \cap B$, is defined by

$$A \cap B = \{x: x \in A \text{ and } x \in B\}.$$

EXAMPLE 2   If $A = \{2, 3, 4, 5\}$ and $B = \{3, 5, 7, 9, 11\}$, find $A \cap B$.

Solution $A \cap B = \{3, 5\}$ because 3 and 5 are the common elements of A and B. Figure 0.4 shows these sets and their intersection.

FIGURE 0.4

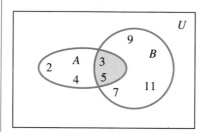

The **union** of two sets is the set that contains all members of the two sets.

Set Union   The union of A and B, written $A \cup B$, is defined by

$$A \cup B = \{x: x \in A \text{ or } x \in B \text{ (or both)}\}.*$$

*In mathematics, the word *or* means one or the other or both.

EXAMPLE 3   If $X = \{a, b, c, f\}$ and $Y = \{e, f, a, b\}$, find $X \cup Y$.

Solution $X \cup Y = \{a, b, c, e, f\}$

EXAMPLE 4   Let $A = \{x: x \text{ is a natural number less than 6}\}$ and $B = \{1, 3, 5, 7, 9, 11\}$.
(a) Find $A \cap B$.
(b) Find $A \cup B$.

Solution
(a) $A \cap B = \{1, 3, 5\}$
(b) $A \cup B = \{1, 2, 3, 4, 5, 7, 9, 11\}$

We can illustrate the intersection and union of two sets by the use of Venn diagrams. Figures 0.5 and 0.6 show Venn diagrams with universal set U represented by the rectangles and sets A and B represented by the circles. The shaded region in Figure 0.5 represents $A \cap B$, the intersection of A and B, while the shaded region in Figure 0.6 represents $A \cup B$.

FIGURE 0.5

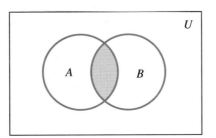

FIGURE 0.6

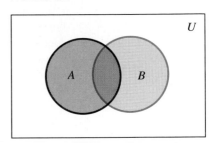

All elements of the universal set that are not contained in a set A form a set called the **complement** of A.

Set Complement

The complement of A, written A', is defined by

$$A' = \{x: x \in U \text{ and } x \notin A\}.$$

EXAMPLE 5

If $U = \{x \in N: x < 10\}$, $A = \{1, 3, 6\}$, and $B = \{1, 6, 8, 9\}$, find the following.

(a) A' (b) B' (c) $(A \cap B)'$ (d) $A' \cup B'$

Solution

(a) $U = \{1, 2, 3, 4, 5, 6, 7, 8, 9\}$ so $A' = \{2, 4, 5, 7, 8, 9\}$

(b) $B' = \{2, 3, 4, 5, 7\}$

(c) $A \cap B = \{1, 6\}$ so $(A \cap B)' = \{2, 3, 4, 5, 7, 8, 9\}$

(d) $A' \cup B' = \{2, 4, 5, 7, 8, 9\} \cup \{2, 3, 4, 5, 7\}$
$ = \{2, 3, 4, 5, 7, 8, 9\}$

We can use a Venn diagram to illustrate the complement of a set. The shaded region of Figure 0.7 represents A' and the *unshaded* region of Figure 0.5 represents $(A \cap B)'$.

FIGURE 0.7

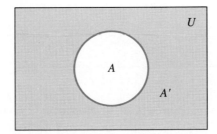

The concepts and applications of this text use the set of real numbers. We can represent the real numbers along a line called the **real number line.** This number line is a picture, or graph, of the real numbers. Each point on the number line corresponds to exactly one real number and each real number can be located at exactly one point. Thus two real numbers are said to be equal whenever they are represented by the same point on the number line. The equation $a = b$ (a equals b) means that the symbols a and b represent the same real number. Thus $3 + 4 = 7$ means that $3 + 4$ and 7 represent the same number. Table 0.1 lists special subsets of the real numbers.

TABLE 0.1 Subsets of the set of real numbers

	Description	Example
Natural numbers	$\{1, 2, 3, \ldots\}$ The counting numbers	
Integers	$\{\ldots, -2, -1, 0, 1, 2, \ldots\}$ The natural numbers, 0, and the negatives of the natural numbers.	
Rational numbers	All numbers that can be written as the ratio of two integers, a/b, with $b \neq 0$. These numbers have decimal representations that either terminate or repeat.	
Irrational numbers	Those real numbers that *cannot* be written as the ratio of two integers. Irrational numbers have decimal representations that neither terminate nor repeat.	
Real numbers	The set of all rational and irrational numbers (the entire number line).	

The properties of the real numbers are fundamental to the study of algebra. These properties follow.

Properties of the Real Numbers

1. Addition and multiplication are commutative.

   $$a + b = b + a \qquad ab = ba$$

2. Addition and multiplication are associative.

   $$(a + b) + c = a + (b + c) \qquad (ab)c = a(bc)$$

3. The additive identity is 0.

   $$a + 0 = 0 + a = a$$

4. The multiplicative identity is 1.

   $$a \cdot 1 = 1 \cdot a = a$$

5. Each element a has an additive inverse, denoted by $-a$.

   $$a + (-a) = -a + a = 0$$

   Note that there is a difference between a negative number and the negative of a number.

6. Each nonzero element a has a multiplicative inverse, denoted by a^{-1}.

   $$a \cdot a^{-1} = a^{-1} \cdot a = 1$$

   Note that $a^{-1} = 1/a$.

7. Multiplication is distributive over addition.

   $$a(b + c) = ab + ac$$

Notice that property 5 provides the means to subtract by defining $a - b = a + (-b)$ and property 6 provides a means to divide by defining $a \div b = a \cdot (1/b)$. The number 0 has no multiplicative inverse, so division by 0 is undefined.

We say that a is less than b (written $a < b$) if the point representing a is to the left of the point representing b on the real number line. For example, $4 < 7$ because 4 is to the left of 7 on the number line. We may also say that 7 is greater than 4 (written $7 > 4$). We may indicate that the number x is less than or equal to another number y by writing $x \leq y$. We may also indicate that p is greater than or equal to 4 by writing $p \geq 4$.

EXAMPLE 6

Use $<$ or $>$ notation to write

(a) 6 is greater than 5.
(b) 10 is less than 15.
(c) 3 is to the left of 8 on the number line.
(d) x is less than or equal to 12.

Solution (a) $6 > 5$ (b) $10 < 15$ (c) $3 < 8$ (d) $x \leq 12$

The subset of the real numbers consisting of all real numbers x that lie between a and b, excluding a and b, can be denoted by the *double inequality* $a < x < b$ or by the **open interval** (a, b). It is called an open interval because neither of the endpoints is included in the interval. The **closed interval** $[a, b]$ represents the set of all real numbers x satisfying $a \leq x \leq b$. Intervals containing one endpoint, such as $(a, b]$ and $[a, b)$, are called **half-open intervals.**

We can use $[a, +\infty)$ to represent the inequality $x \geq a$, and $(-\infty, a)$ to represent $x < a$. In each of these cases, the symbols ∞ and $-\infty$ are not real numbers, but represent the fact that x increases without bound (∞) or decreases without bound ($-\infty$).

TABLE 0.2   Intervals

Type of interval	Inequality notation	Interval notation	Graph
Open interval	$x > a$	(a, ∞)	
	$x < b$	$(-\infty, b)$	
	$a < x < b$	(a, b)	
Half-open interval	$x \geq a$	$[a, \infty)$	
	$x \leq b$	$(-\infty, b]$	
	$a \leq x < b$	$[a, b)$	
	$a < x \leq b$	$(a, b]$	
Closed interval	$a \leq x \leq b$	$[a, b]$	

CHECKPOINT

1. Evaluate the following, if possible. For any that are meaningless, so state.

   (a) $\dfrac{4}{0}$ (b) $\dfrac{0}{4}$ (c) $\dfrac{4}{4}$ (d) $\dfrac{4-4}{4-4}$

2. For (a)–(d), write the inequality corresponding to the given interval and sketch its graph on a number line.

   (a) $(1, 3)$ (b) $(0, 3]$ (c) $[-1, \infty)$ (d) $(-\infty, 2)$

Sometimes we are interested in the *distance* a number is from the origin (0) of the number line, without regard to direction. The distance a number a is from 0 on the number line is the **absolute value** of a, denoted $|a|$. The absolute value of any nonzero number is positive, and the absolute value of 0 is 0.

EXAMPLE 7

Evaluate the following.

(a) $|-4|$ (b) $|+2|$ (c) $|0|$ (d) $\left| -5 - |-3| \right|$

Solution

(a) $|-4| = +4 = 4$

(b) $|+2| = +2 = 2$

(c) $|0| = 0$

(d) $\left| -5 - |-3| \right| = |-5 - 3| = |-8| = 8$

Note that if a is a nonnegative number, then $|a| = a$, *but if a is negative, then $|a|$ is the positive number* $(-a)$. Thus

Absolute Value

$$|a| = \begin{cases} a & \text{if } a \geq 0 \\ -a & \text{if } a < 0 \end{cases}$$

When two or more operations with real numbers are indicated in an evaluation, it is important that everyone agree upon the order in which the operations are performed so that a unique result is guaranteed.

The following **order of operations** is universally accepted.

1. Perform operations within parentheses.

2. Find indicated powers $(2^3 = 2 \cdot 2 \cdot 2 = 8)$

3. Perform multiplications and divisions from left to right.

4. Perform additions and subtractions from left to right.

EXAMPLE 8

Evaluate the following.

(a) $-4 + 3$ (b) $-4^2 + 3$

(c) $(-4 + 3)^2 + 3$ (d) $6 \div 2(2 + 1)$

Solution

(a) -1 (b) $-16 + 3 = -13$

(c) $(-1)^2 + 3 = 1 + 3 = 4$ (d) $6 \div 2(3) = 3 \cdot 3 = 9$

CHECKPOINT

True or false:

3. $-(-5)^2 = 25$

4. $|4 - 6| = |4| - |6|$

5. $9 - 2(2)(-10) = (7)(2)(-10) = -140$

Operations with real numbers can be performed with ease on a calculator. Calculator types vary widely, from those that perform only the four arithmetic operations to those that perform many operations automatically and those that can be programmed.

Two types of internal logic (methods of computation) are used in calculators: *algebraic* and *reverse Polish*. Reverse Polish logic is highly efficient and does not require parentheses; many people feel it is better for complex problems. Algebraic logic operates in a manner consistent with the order of operations and is easy to use for most elementary problems.

The text assumes that you have a scientific calculator that can perform the four arithmetic operations and can evaluate exponential and logarithmic expressions. Many differences exist among the various models of calculators, even those that use algebraic logic, so it is important that you refer to your manual to understand how to use function keys and devise your own plan for solving each problem type. Problems 51–56 of Exercise 0.1 are provided for you to practice using your calculator.

Graphics calculators also have algebraic logic but use a slightly different keying sequence. For more information about keying and capabilities, see your graphics calculator manual.

CHECKPOINT
SOLUTIONS

1. (a) Meaningless. A denominator of zero means division by zero, which is undefined.

   (b) $\frac{0}{4} = 0$. A numerator of zero (when the denominator is not zero) means the fraction has value 0.

   (c) $\frac{4}{4} = 1$

   (d) Meaningless. The denominator is zero.

2. (a) $1 < x < 3$

   (b) $0 < x \leq 3$

   (c) $-1 \leq x < \infty$ or $x \geq -1$

   (d) $-\infty < x < 2$ or $x < 2$

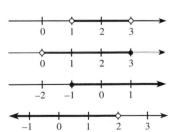

3. False. $-(-5)^2 = (-1)(-5)^2 = (-1)(25) = -25.$
   Exponentiation has priority and applies only to -5.

4. False. $|4 - 6| = |-2| = 2$ and $|4| - |6| = 4 - 6 = -2.$

5. False. Without parentheses, multiplication has priority over subtraction.
   $9 - 2(2)(-10) = 9 - 4(-10) = 9 + 40 = 49.$ ■

EXERCISE 0.1

Use $\in$ or $\notin$ to indicate whether the given object is an element of the given set in the following problems.

1. x $\{x, y, z, a\}$ 2. 3 $\{1, 2, 4, 5, 6\}$

3. 6 $\{x: x$ is a natural number less than 6$\}$

4. 3 $\varnothing$

Use $\subseteq$ notation to indicate which set is a subset of the other in the following problems.

5. $C = \{a, b, 1, 2, 3\}, D = \{a, b, 1\}$

6. $E = \{x, y, a, b\}, F = \{x, 1, a, y, b, 2\}$

7. $A = \{2, 3, 4, e\}, \varnothing$

8. $D = \{a, e, 1, 3, c\}, F = \{e, a, c, 1, 3\}$

9. From the following list of sets, indicate which pairs of sets are disjoint.

   $A = \{1, 2, 3, 4\}$

   $B = \{x: x$ is a natural number greater than 4$\}$

   $C = \{4, 5, 6, \ldots\}$

   $D = \{1, 2, 3\}$

10. If A and B are disjoint sets, what does $A \cap B$ equal?

In problems 11–18, assume

$A = \{1, 3, 5, 8, 7, 2\}, \quad B = \{4, 3, 8, 10\},$
$C = \{2, 4, 6, 8, 10\},$

and U is the universal set of natural numbers less than 11. Find the following.

11. $A \cap B$ 12. $A \cap C$

13. $B \cup C$ 14. $A \cup B$

15. A' 16. C'

17. $(A \cap B') \cup C'$ 18. $(A \cup B') \cap C$

In problems 19–20, indicate whether the given expression is one or more of the following types of numbers: rational, irrational, integer, natural. If the expression is meaningless, so state.

19. (a) $\dfrac{-\pi}{10}$ (b) -9

   (c) $\dfrac{9}{3}$ (d) $\dfrac{4}{0}$

20. (a) $\dfrac{0}{6}$ (b) -1.2916

   (c) 1.414 (d) $\dfrac{9}{6}$

Insert the proper sign $<$, $=$, or $>$ to replace $\square$ in problems 21–24.

21. $0.333 \ \square \ \dfrac{1}{3}$

22. $\dfrac{1}{3} + \dfrac{1}{2} \ \square \ \dfrac{5}{6}$

23. $|-3| + |5| \ \square \ |-3 + 5|$

24. $|-9 - 3| \ \square \ |-9| + |3|$

In problems 25–32, evaluate each expression.

25. $-3^2 + 10 \div 2$ 26. $(-3)^2 + 10 \cdot 2$

27. $\dfrac{4 + 2^2}{2}$ 28. $\dfrac{(4 + 2)^2}{2}$

29. $\dfrac{|5 - 2| - |-7|}{|5 - 2|}$

30. $\dfrac{\big|3 - |4 - 11|\big|}{-|5^2 - 3^2|}$

31. $\dfrac{(-3)^2 - 2 \cdot 3 + 6}{4 - 2^2 + 3}$

32. $\dfrac{6^2 - 4(-3)(-2)}{6 - 6^2 \div 4}$

33. What part of the real number line corresponds to the interval $(-\infty, \infty)$?

34. Write the interval corresponding to $x \geq 0$.

In problems 35–38, express each inequality or graph using interval notation.

35. $1 < x \leq 3$

36. $-4 \leq x \leq 3$

37.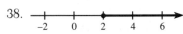

38.

In problems 39–42, write an inequality that describes each interval or graph.

39. $(-\infty, 5]$

40. $(-2, \infty)$

41.

42.

In problems 43–50, graph the subset of the real numbers that is represented by each of the following and write your answer in interval notation.

43. $(-\infty, 4) \cap (-3, \infty)$

44. $[-4, 17) \cap [-20, 10]$

45. $x > 4$ and $x \geq 0$

46. $x < 10$ and $x < -1$

47. $[0, \infty) \cup [-1, 5]$

48. $(-\infty, 4) \cup (0, 2)$

49. $x > 7$ or $x < 0$

50. $x > 4$ and $x < 0$

In problems 51–56, use your calculator to evaluate each of the following. List all the digits on your display in the answer.

51. $\dfrac{-1}{25916.8}$

52. $\dfrac{51.412}{127.01}$

53. $(3.679)^7$

54. $(1.28)^{10}$

55. $\dfrac{-1}{(-0.3019)^5}$

56. $\dfrac{-1}{(-3.8)^{12}}$

0.2 | INTEGRAL EXPONENTS

If \$1000 is placed in a 5-year savings certificate that pays an interest rate of 10% per year, compounded annually, then the amount returned after 5 years is given by

$$1000(1.1)^5.$$

The 5 in this expression is an **exponent.** Exponents provide an easier way to denote certain multiplications. For example

$$(1.1)^5 = (1.1)(1.1)(1.1)(1.1)(1.1).$$

An understanding of the properties of exponents is fundamental to the algebra needed to study functions and solve equations. Furthermore, the definition of exponential and logarithmic functions and many of the techniques in calculus also require an understanding of the properties of exponents.

For any real number a,

$$a^2 = a \cdot a \quad a^3 = a \cdot a \cdot a \quad \text{and} \quad a^n = a \cdot a \cdot a \cdot \ldots \cdot a \quad (n \text{ factors})$$

for any positive integer n. The positive integer n is called the **exponent,** the number a is called the **base,** and a^n is read "a to the nth power."

Note that $4a^n$ means $4(a^n)$, which is different from $(4a)^n$. The 4 is the coefficient of a^n in $4a^n$. Note also that $-x^n$ is not equivalent to $(-x)^n$ when n is even. For example, $-3^4 = -81$, but $(-3)^4 = 81$.

Some of the rules of exponents follow.

Positive Integer Exponents

For any real numbers a and b and positive integers m and n,

1. $a^m \cdot a^n = a^{m+n}$

2. For $a \neq 0$, $\quad \dfrac{a^m}{a^n} = \begin{cases} a^{m-n} & \text{if } m > n \\ 1 & \text{if } m = n \\ 1/a^{n-m} & \text{if } m < n \end{cases}$

3. $(ab)^m = a^m b^m$

4. $\left(\dfrac{a}{b}\right)^m = \dfrac{a^m}{b^m} \quad (b \neq 0)$

5. $(a^m)^n = a^{mn}$

EXAMPLE 1

Use properties of positive integer exponents to rewrite each of the following. Assume all denominators are nonzero.

(a) $\dfrac{5^6}{5^4}$ (b) $\dfrac{x^2}{x^5}$ (c) $\left(\dfrac{x}{y}\right)^4$ (d) $(3x^2 y^3)^4$ (e) $3^3 \cdot 3^2$

Solution

(a) $\dfrac{5^6}{5^4} = 5^{6-4} = 5^2$ (b) $\dfrac{x^2}{x^5} = \dfrac{1}{x^{5-2}} = \dfrac{1}{x^3}$ (c) $\left(\dfrac{x}{y}\right)^4 = \dfrac{x^4}{y^4}$

(d) $(3x^2 y^3)^4 = 3^4 (x^2)^4 (y^3)^4 = 81x^8 y^{12}$ (e) $3^3 \cdot 3^2 = 3^{3+2} = 3^5$

For certain calculus operations, use of negative exponents is necessary in order to write problems in the proper form. We can extend the rules for positive integer exponents to all integers by defining a^0 and a^{-n}. Clearly $a^m \cdot a^0$ should equal $a^{m+0} = a^m$, and it will if $a^0 = 1$.

Zero Exponent

For any nonzero real number a, we define $a^0 = 1$. We leave 0^0 undefined.

In Section 0.1, we defined a^{-1} as $1/a$ for $a \neq 0$, so we define a^{-n} as $(a^{-1})^n$.

Negative Exponents	$a^{-n} = (a^{-1})^n = \left(\dfrac{1}{a}\right)^n = \dfrac{1}{a^n} \qquad (a \neq 0)$
	$\left(\dfrac{a}{b}\right)^{-n} = \left[\left(\dfrac{a}{b}\right)^{-1}\right]^n = \left(\dfrac{b}{a}\right)^n \qquad (a \neq 0, b \neq 0)$

EXAMPLE 2

Write each of the following without exponents:

(a) $6 \cdot 3^0$ (b) 6^{-2} (c) $\left(\dfrac{1}{3}\right)^{-1}$ (d) $-\left(\dfrac{2}{3}\right)^{-4}$ (e) $(-4)^{-2}$

Solution

(a) $6 \cdot 3^0 = 6 \cdot 1 = 6$ (b) $6^{-2} = \dfrac{1}{6^2} = \dfrac{1}{36}$ (c) $\left(\dfrac{1}{3}\right)^{-1} = \dfrac{3}{1} = 3$

(d) $-\left(\dfrac{2}{3}\right)^{-4} = -\left(\dfrac{3}{2}\right)^4 = \dfrac{-81}{16}$ (e) $(-4)^{-2} = \dfrac{1}{(-4)^2} = \dfrac{1}{16}$

Using the definitions of zero and negative exponents enables us to extend the rules of exponents to all integers and to express them more simply.

Rules of Exponents	For real numbers a and b and *integers* m and n.
	1. $a^m \cdot a^n = a^{m+n}$ $\qquad\qquad$ 2. $a^m/a^n = a^{m-n} \qquad (a \neq 0)$
	3. $(ab)^m = a^m b^m$ $\qquad\qquad\quad$ 4. $(a^m)^n = a^{mn}$
	5. $(a/b)^m = a^m/b^m \quad (b \neq 0)$ $\quad$ 6. $a^0 = 1 \qquad (a \neq 0)$
	7. $a^{-n} = 1/a^n \quad (a \neq 0)$ $\qquad$ 8. $(a/b)^{-n} = (b/a)^n \quad (a, b \neq 0)$

Throughout the remainder of the text, we will assume all expressions are defined.

EXAMPLE 3

Use the rules of exponents and the definitions of a^0 and a^{-n} to simplify each of the following with positive exponents.

(a) $2(x^2)^{-2}$ (b) $x^{-2} \cdot x^{-5}$ (c) $\dfrac{x^{-8}}{x^{-4}}$ (d) $\left(\dfrac{2x^3}{3x^{-5}}\right)^{-2}$

Solution

(a) $2(x^2)^{-2} = 2x^{-4} = 2\left(\dfrac{1}{x^4}\right) = \dfrac{2}{x^4}$ (b) $x^{-2} \cdot x^{-5} = x^{-2-5} = x^{-7} = \dfrac{1}{x^7}$

(c) $\dfrac{x^{-8}}{x^{-4}} = x^{-8-(-4)} = x^{-4} = \dfrac{1}{x^4}$

(d) $\left(\dfrac{2x^3}{3x^{-5}}\right)^{-2} = \left(\dfrac{2x^8}{3}\right)^{-2} = \left(\dfrac{3}{2x^8}\right)^{2} = \dfrac{9}{4x^{16}}$

CHECKPOINT

1. Complete the following.

(a) $x^3 \cdot x^8 = x^?$ (b) $x \cdot x^4 \cdot x^{-3} = x^?$ (c) $\dfrac{1}{x^4} = x^?$

(d) $x^{24} \div x^{-3} = x^?$ (e) $(x^4)^2 = x^?$ (f) $(2x^4 y)^3 = ?$

2. True or false:

(a) $3x^{-2} = \dfrac{1}{9x^2}$ (b) $-x^{-4} = \dfrac{-1}{x^4}$ (c) $x^{-3} = -x^3$

3. Evaluate the following, if possible. For any that are meaningless, so state. Assume $x > 0$.

(a) 0^4 (b) 0^0 (c) x^0

(d) 0^x (e) 0^{-4} (f) -5^{-2}

EXAMPLE 4   Write $(x^2 y)/(9wz^3)$ with all factors in the numerator.

Solution

$\dfrac{x^2 y}{9wz^3} = x^2 y\left(\dfrac{1}{9wz^3}\right) = x^2 y\left(\dfrac{1}{9}\right)\left(\dfrac{1}{w}\right)\left(\dfrac{1}{z^3}\right) = x^2 y \cdot 9^{-1} w^{-1} z^{-3} = 9^{-1} x^2 y w^{-1} z^{-3}$

EXAMPLE 5   Simplify the following so all exponents are positive.

(a) $(2^3 x^{-4} y^5)^{-2}$ (b) $\dfrac{2x^4 (x^2 y)^0}{(4x^{-2} y)^2}$

Solution

(a) $(2^3 x^{-4} y^5)^{-2} = 2^{-6} x^8 y^{-10} = \dfrac{1}{2^6} \cdot x^8 \cdot \dfrac{1}{y^{10}} = \dfrac{x^8}{64 y^{10}}$

(b) $\dfrac{2x^4 (x^2 y)^0}{(4x^{-2} y)^2} = \dfrac{2x^4 \cdot 1}{4^2 x^{-4} y^2} = \dfrac{2}{4^2} \cdot \dfrac{x^4}{x^{-4}} \cdot \dfrac{1}{y^2} = \dfrac{2}{16} \cdot \dfrac{x^8}{1} \cdot \dfrac{1}{y^2} = \dfrac{x^8}{8y^2}$

CHECKPOINT
SOLUTIONS

1. (a) $x^3 \cdot x^8 = x^{3+8} = x^{11}$ (b) $x \cdot x^4 \cdot x^{-3} = x^{1+4+(-3)} = x^2$

(c) $\dfrac{1}{x^4} = x^{-4}$ (d) $x^{24} \div x^{-3} = x^{24-(-3)} = x^{27}$

(e) $(x^4)^2 = x^{(4)(2)} = x^8$

(f) $(2x^4y)^3 = 2^3(x^4)^3y^3 = 8x^{12}y^3$

2. (a) False. $3x^{-2} = 3\left(\dfrac{1}{x^2}\right) = \dfrac{3}{x^2}$

(b) True. $-x^{-4} = (-1)\left(\dfrac{1}{x^4}\right) = \dfrac{-1}{x^4}$

(c) False. $x^{-3} = \dfrac{1}{x^3}$

3. (a) $0^4 = 0$ (b) Meaningless. 0^0 is undefined.

(c) $x^0 = 1$ when $x \neq 0$

(d) $0^x = 0$ since $x > 0$

(e) Meaningless. 0^{-4} would be $\dfrac{1}{0^4}$, which is not defined.

(f) $-5^{-2} = (-1)\left(\dfrac{1}{5^2}\right) = \dfrac{-1}{25}$

EXERCISE 0.2

Compute problems 1–8. Write all answers without exponents.

1. $(-4)^3$

2. -5^3

3. -2^4

4. $(-2)^5$

5. 3^{-2}

6. 6^{-1}

7. $-\left(\dfrac{3}{2}\right)^2$

8. $\left(\dfrac{2}{3}\right)^3$

In problems 9–16, use rules of exponents to simplify the expressions. Express answers with positive exponents.

9. $6^5 \cdot 6^3$

10. $\dfrac{7^8}{7^3}$

11. $\dfrac{10^8}{10^9}$

12. $\dfrac{5^4}{(5^{-2} \cdot 5^3)}$

13. $(3^3)^3$

14. $(2^{-3})^{-2}$

15. $\left(\dfrac{2}{3}\right)^{-2}$

16. $\left(\dfrac{-2}{5}\right)^{-4}$

In problems 17–20, simplify by expressing answers with positive exponents.

17. $(x^2)^{-3}$

18. x^{-4}

19. $xy^{-2}z^0$

20. $(xy^{-2})^0$

In problems 21–36, use the rules of exponents to simplify.

21. $x^3 \cdot x^4$

22. $a^5 \cdot a$

23. $x^{-5} \cdot x^3$

24. $y^{-5} \cdot y^{-2}$

25. $2^{-3} \cdot 2^{-4}$

26. $a^3 \cdot a^2$

27. $\dfrac{x^8}{x^4}$

28. $\dfrac{a^5}{a^{-1}}$

29. $\dfrac{y^5}{y^{-7}}$

30. $\dfrac{y^{-3}}{y^{-4}}$

31. $(x^4)^3$

32. $(y^3)^{-2}$

33. $(xy)^2$

34. $(2m)^3$

35. $\left(\dfrac{2}{x}\right)^4$

36. $\left(\dfrac{8}{a^3}\right)^3$

In problems 37–46, compute and simplify so only positive exponents remain.

37. $(2x^{-2}y)^{-4}$

38. $(-32x^5)^{-3}$

39. $(-8a^{-3}b^2)(2a^5b^{-4})$

40. $(-3m^2y^{-1})(2m^{-3}y^{-1})$

41. $(2x^{-2}) \div (x^{-1}y^2)$

42. $(-8a^{-3}b^2c) \div (2a^5b^4)$

43. $\left(\dfrac{x^3}{y^{-2}}\right)^{-3}$

44. $\left(\dfrac{x^{-2}}{y}\right)^{-3}$

45. $\left(\dfrac{a^{-2}b^{-1}c^{-4}}{a^4b^{-3}c^0}\right)^{-3}$

46. $\left(\dfrac{4x^{-1}y^{-40}}{2^{-2}x^4y^{-10}}\right)^{-2}$

In calculus it is often necessary to write expressions in the form cx^n, where c is a constant. In problems 47–54, write the expressions in this form.

47. $\dfrac{1}{x}$

48. $\dfrac{1}{x^2}$

49. $(2x)^3$

50. $(3x)^2$

51. $\dfrac{1}{(4x^2)}$

52. $\dfrac{3}{(2x^4)}$

53. $\left(\dfrac{-x}{2}\right)^3$

54. $\left(\dfrac{-x}{3}\right)^2$

In problems 55–58, use a scientific calculator to evaluate the indicated powers.

55. 1.2^4

56. $(-3.7)^3$

57. $(-6)^5$

58. $(-.8)^{-9}$

APPLICATIONS

Compound interest If P is invested for n years at rate i (as a decimal), compounded annually, the compound amount that accrues is given by $A = P(1 + i)^n$, and the interest earned is $I = A - P$. In problems 59–62, find A and I for the given P, n, and i.

59. $1200 for 5 years at 12%

60. $1800 for 7 years at 10%

61. $5000 for 6 years at 11.5%

62. $800 for 20 years at 10.5%

0.3 | RADICALS AND RATIONAL EXPONENTS

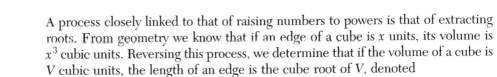

A process closely linked to that of raising numbers to powers is that of extracting roots. From geometry we know that if an edge of a cube is x units, its volume is x^3 cubic units. Reversing this process, we determine that if the volume of a cube is V cubic units, the length of an edge is the cube root of V, denoted

$$\sqrt[3]{V} \text{ units.}$$

When we seek the **cube root** of a number such as 8 (written $\sqrt[3]{8}$), we are looking for a real number whose cube equals 8. Since $2^3 = 8$, we know that $\sqrt[3]{8} = 2$. Similarly, $\sqrt[3]{-27} = -3$ since $(-3)^3 = -27$. The expression $\sqrt[n]{a}$ is called a **radical,** where $\sqrt{}$ is the **radical sign,** n the **index,** and a the **radicand.** When no index is indicated, the index is assumed to be 2 and the expression is called a **square root;** thus, $\sqrt{4}$ is the square root of 4 and represents the positive number whose square is 4.

Only one real number satisfies $\sqrt[n]{a}$ for a real number a and an odd number n; we call that number the **principal nth root**, or, more simply, the **nth root**.

For an even index n, there are two possible cases:

1. If a is negative, there is no real number equal to $\sqrt[n]{a}$. For example, there are no real numbers that equal $\sqrt{-4}$ or $\sqrt[4]{-16}$ because there is no real number b such that $b^2 = -4$ or $b^4 = -16$. In this case, we say $\sqrt[n]{a}$ is not a real number.

2. If a is positive, there are 2 real numbers whose nth power equals a. For example, $3^2 = 9$ and $(-3)^2 = 9$. In order to have a unique nth root, we define the (principal) nth root, $\sqrt[n]{a}$, as the *positive* number b satisfying $b^n = a$.

We summarize this discussion as follows.

nth Root of a

The **(principal) nth root** of a real number is defined as

$$\sqrt[n]{a} = b \quad \text{only if} \quad a = b^n$$

subject to the following conditions:

	$a = 0$	$a > 0$	$a < 0$
n even	$\sqrt[n]{a} = 0$	$\sqrt[n]{a} > 0$	$\sqrt[n]{a}$ not real
n odd	$\sqrt[n]{a} = 0$	$\sqrt[n]{a} > 0$	$\sqrt[n]{a} < 0$

When we are asked for the root of a number, we give the principal root.

EXAMPLE 1

Find the roots, if they are real numbers.

(a) $\sqrt[6]{64}$ (b) $-\sqrt{16}$ (c) $\sqrt[3]{-8}$ (d) $\sqrt{-16}$

Solution

(a) $\sqrt[6]{64} = 2$ because $2^6 = 64$

(b) $-\sqrt{16} = -(\sqrt{16}) = -4$

(c) $\sqrt[3]{-8} = -2$

(d) $\sqrt{-16}$ is not a real number because an even root of a negative number is not real.

To perform calculus operations on expressions involving radicals, it is sometimes necessary to rewrite the radicals in exponential form with fractional exponents.

We have stated that for $a \geq 0$ and $b \geq 0$.

$$\sqrt{a} = b \quad \text{only if} \quad a = b^2.$$

This means that $(\sqrt{a})^2 - b^2 = a$, or $(\sqrt{a})^2 = a$. In order to extend the properties of exponents to rational exponents, it is necessary to define

$$a^{1/2} = \sqrt{a}, \quad \text{so that} \quad (a^{1/2})^2 = a.$$

Exponent 1/n
For a positive integer n, we define

$$a^{1/n} = \sqrt[n]{a} \quad \text{if } \sqrt[n]{a} \text{ exists.}$$

Thus $(a^{1/n})^n = a^{(1/n)\cdot n} = a$.

Since we wish the properties established for integer exponents to extend to rational exponents, we make the following definitions.

Rational Exponents
For positive integer n and any integer m (with $a \neq 0$ when $m \leq 0$):

1. $a^{m/n} = (a^{1/n})^m = (\sqrt[n]{a})^m$.

2. $a^{m/n} = (a^m)^{1/n} = \sqrt[n]{a^m}$

if a is nonnegative when n is even.

Throughout the remaining discussion we assume all expressions are real.

EXAMPLE 2

Write the following in radical form and simplify.

(a) $16^{3/4}$ (b) $y^{-3/2}$ (c) $(6m)^{2/3}$

Solution

(a) $16^{3/4} = \sqrt[4]{16^3} = (\sqrt[4]{16})^3 = (2)^3 = 8$

(b) $y^{-3/2} = \dfrac{1}{y^{3/2}} = \dfrac{1}{\sqrt{y^3}}$

(c) $(6m)^{2/3} = \sqrt[3]{(6m)^2} = \sqrt[3]{36m^2}$

EXAMPLE 3

Write the following without radical signs.

(a) $\sqrt{x^3}$ (b) $\dfrac{1}{\sqrt[3]{b^2}}$ (c) $\sqrt[3]{(ab)^3}$

Solution

(a) $\sqrt{x^3} = x^{3/2}$ (b) $\dfrac{1}{\sqrt[3]{b^2}} = \dfrac{1}{b^{2/3}} = b^{-2/3}$ (c) $\sqrt[3]{(ab)^3} = (ab)^{3/3} = ab$

As noted, our definition of $a^{m/n}$ guarantees that the rules for exponents will apply to fractional exponents. Thus, we can perform operations with fractional exponents as we did with integer exponents.

EXAMPLE 4

Simplify the following expressions.

(a) $a^{1/2} \cdot a^{1/6}$ (b) $a^{3/4}/a^{1/3}$ (c) $(a^3b)^{2/3}$ (d) $(a^{3/2})^{1/2}$

(e) $a^{-1/2} \cdot a^{-3/2}$

Solution

(a) $a^{1/2} \cdot a^{1/6} = a^{1/2+1/6} = a^{3/6+1/6} = a^{4/6} = a^{2/3}$

(b) $a^{3/4}/a^{1/3} = a^{3/4-1/3} = a^{9/12-4/12} = a^{5/12}$

(c) $(a^3b)^{2/3} = (a^3)^{2/3}b^{2/3} = a^2b^{2/3}$

(d) $(a^{3/2})^{1/2} = a^{(3/2)(1/2)} = a^{3/4}$

(e) $a^{-1/2} \cdot a^{-3/2} = a^{-1/2-3/2} = a^{-2} = 1/a^2$

CHECKPOINT

1. Which of the following are *not* real numbers?

(a) $\sqrt[3]{-64}$ (b) $\sqrt{-64}$ (c) $\sqrt{0}$

(d) $\sqrt[4]{1}$ (e) $\sqrt[5]{-1}$ (f) $\sqrt[8]{-1}$

2. (a) Write as radicals: $x^{1/3}$, $x^{2/5}$, $x^{-3/2}$

    (b) Write with fractional exponents: $\sqrt[4]{x^3} = x^?$, $\dfrac{1}{\sqrt{x}} = \dfrac{1}{x^?} = x^?$

3. Evaluate the following.

(a) $8^{2/3}$ (b) $(-8)^{2/3}$ (c) $8^{-2/3}$ (d) $-8^{-2/3}$

4. Complete the following.

(a) $x \cdot x^{1/3} \cdot x^3 = x^?$ (b) $x^2 \div x^{1/2} = x^?$

(c) $(x^{-2/3})^{-3} = x^?$ (d) $x^{-3/2} \cdot x^{1/2} = x^?$

(e) $x^{-3/2} \cdot x = x^?$ (f) $\left(\dfrac{x^4}{y^2}\right)^{3/2} = ?$

5. True or false:

(a) $\dfrac{8x^{2/3}}{x^{-1/3}} = 4x$ (b) $(16x^8y)^{3/4} = 12x^6y^{3/4}$

(c) $\left(\dfrac{x^2}{y^3}\right)^{-1/3} = \left(\dfrac{y^3}{x^2}\right)^{1/3} = \dfrac{y}{x^{2/3}}$

We can perform operations with radicals by first rewriting in exponential form, performing the operations with exponents, and then converting the answer back to radical form. Another option is to apply directly the following rules for operations with radicals.

RULES FOR RADICALS	EXAMPLES
Given that $\sqrt[n]{a}$ and $\sqrt[n]{b}$ are real,*	
1. $\sqrt[n]{a^n} = (\sqrt[n]{a})^n = a$	1. $\sqrt[5]{6^5} = (\sqrt[5]{6})^5 = 6$
2. $\sqrt[n]{a} \cdot \sqrt[n]{b} = \sqrt[n]{ab}$	2. $\sqrt[3]{2} \sqrt[3]{4} = \sqrt[3]{8} = \sqrt[3]{2^3} = 2$
3. $\dfrac{\sqrt[n]{a}}{\sqrt[n]{b}} = \sqrt[n]{\dfrac{a}{b}} \quad (b \neq 0)$	3. $\dfrac{\sqrt{18}}{\sqrt{2}} = \sqrt{\dfrac{18}{2}} = \sqrt{9} = 3$

*Note that this means $a \geq 0$ and $b \geq 0$ if n is even.

Let us consider Rule 1 for radicals more carefully. Notice that if n is even and $a < 0$, then $\sqrt[n]{a}$ is not real, and Rule 1 does not apply. For example,

$$\sqrt{(-2)^2} \neq -2 \quad \text{since} \quad \sqrt{(-2)^2} = \sqrt{4} = 2 = -(-2).$$

We can generalize this observation as follows: If $a < 0$, then $\sqrt{a^2} = -a > 0$, so

$$\sqrt{a^2} = \begin{cases} a & \text{if } a \geq 0 \\ -a & \text{if } a < 0 \end{cases}$$

This means

$$\sqrt{a^2} = |a|$$

EXAMPLE 5

Simplify:

(a) $\sqrt[3]{8^3}$ (b) $\sqrt[5]{x^5}$ (c) $\sqrt{x^2}$

Solution

(a) $\sqrt[3]{8^3} = 8$ by Rule 1 for radicals   (b) $\sqrt[5]{x^5} = x$ (c) $\sqrt{x^2} = |x|$

Rule 2 for radicals $(\sqrt[n]{a} \cdot \sqrt[n]{b} = \sqrt[n]{ab})$ provides a procedure for simplifying radicals.

EXAMPLE 6

Simplify the following radicals, assuming the expressions are real.

(a) $\sqrt[3]{72a^3b^4}$ (b) $\sqrt{48x^5y^6} \quad (y \geq 0)$

Solution

(a) $\sqrt[3]{72a^3b^4} = \sqrt[3]{8 \cdot 9a^3b^3b} = \sqrt[3]{8} \cdot \sqrt[3]{a^3} \cdot \sqrt[3]{b^3} \cdot \sqrt[3]{9b} = 2ab\sqrt[3]{9b}$

(b) $\sqrt{48x^5y^6} = \sqrt{16 \cdot 3 \cdot x^4xy^6} = \sqrt{16} \sqrt{x^4} \sqrt{y^6} \sqrt{3x} = 4x^2y^3 \sqrt{3x}$

Rule 2 for radicals also provides a procedure for multiplying two roots with the same index.

EXAMPLE 7

Multiply the following and simplify the answers, assuming nonnegative variables.

(a) $\sqrt[3]{2xy} \cdot \sqrt[3]{4x^2y}$

(b) $\sqrt{8xy^3z} \sqrt{4x^2y^3z^2}$

Solution

(a) $\sqrt[3]{2xy} \cdot \sqrt[3]{4x^2y} = \sqrt[3]{2xy \cdot 4x^2y} = \sqrt[3]{8x^3y^2} = \sqrt[3]{8} \cdot \sqrt[3]{x^3} \cdot \sqrt[3]{y^2} = 2x\sqrt[3]{y^2}$

(b) $\sqrt{8xy^3z} \sqrt{4x^2y^3z^2} = \sqrt{32x^3y^6z^3} = \sqrt{16x^2y^6z^2} \sqrt{2xz} = 4xy^3z\sqrt{2xz}$

Rule 3 for radicals $(\sqrt[n]{a}/\sqrt[n]{b} = \sqrt[n]{a/b})$ indicates how to find the quotient of two roots with the same index.

EXAMPLE 8

Find the quotients and simplify the answers, assuming nonnegative variables.

(a) $\dfrac{\sqrt[3]{32}}{\sqrt[3]{4}}$

(b) $\dfrac{\sqrt{16a^3x}}{\sqrt{2ax}}$

Solution

(a) $\dfrac{\sqrt[3]{32}}{\sqrt[3]{4}} = \sqrt[3]{\dfrac{32}{4}} = \sqrt[3]{8} = 2$

(b) $\dfrac{\sqrt{16a^3x}}{\sqrt{2ax}} = \sqrt{\dfrac{16a^3x}{2ax}} = \sqrt{8a^2} = 2a\sqrt{2}$

Occasionally, we wish to express a fraction containing radicals in an equivalent form that contains no radicals in the denominator. This is accomplished by multiplying the numerator *and* denominator by the expression that will remove the radical. This process is called **rationalizing the denominator.**

EXAMPLE 9

Express each of the following with no radicals in the denominator. (Rationalize each denominator.)

(a) $\dfrac{15}{\sqrt{x}}$

(b) $\dfrac{2x}{\sqrt{18xy}}$ $(x, y > 0)$

(c) $\dfrac{3x}{\sqrt[3]{2x^2}}$

Solution

(a) We wish to create a perfect square under the radical in the denominator.

$$\frac{15}{\sqrt{x}} \cdot \frac{\sqrt{x}}{\sqrt{x}} = \frac{15\sqrt{x}}{x}$$

(b) $\dfrac{2x}{\sqrt{18xy}} \cdot \dfrac{\sqrt{2xy}}{\sqrt{2xy}} = \dfrac{2x\sqrt{2xy}}{\sqrt{36x^2y^2}} = \dfrac{2x\sqrt{2xy}}{6xy} = \dfrac{\sqrt{2xy}}{3y}$

(c) We wish to create a perfect cube under the radical in the denominator.

$$\frac{3x}{\sqrt[3]{2x^2}} \cdot \frac{\sqrt[3]{4x}}{\sqrt[3]{4x}} = \frac{3x\sqrt[3]{4x}}{\sqrt[3]{8x^3}} = \frac{3x\sqrt[3]{4x}}{2x} = \frac{3\sqrt[3]{4x}}{2}$$

CHECKPOINT

6. Simplify:

(a) $\sqrt[7]{x^7}$ (b) $[\sqrt[5]{(x^2 + 1)^2}]^5$ (c) $\sqrt{12xy^2} \cdot \sqrt{3x^2y}$

7. Rationalize the denominator of $\dfrac{x}{\sqrt{5x}}$.

It is also sometimes useful, especially in calculus, to *rationalize the numerator* of a fraction. For example, we can rationalize the numerator of

$$\frac{\sqrt[3]{4x^2}}{3x}$$

by multiplying the numerator and denominator by $\sqrt[3]{2x}$, which creates a perfect cube under the radical:

$$\frac{\sqrt[3]{4x^2}}{3x} \cdot \frac{\sqrt[3]{2x}}{\sqrt[3]{2x}} = \frac{\sqrt[3]{8x^3}}{3x\sqrt[3]{2x}} = \frac{2x}{3x\sqrt[3]{2x}} = \frac{2}{3\sqrt[3]{2x}}.$$

CHECKPOINT
SOLUTIONS

1. Only *even* roots of negatives are not real numbers. Thus $\sqrt{-64}$ and $\sqrt[8]{-1}$ are not real numbers.

2. (a) $x^{1/3} = \sqrt[3]{x}$, $x^{2/5} = \sqrt[5]{x^2}$, $x^{-3/2} = \dfrac{1}{x^{3/2}} = \dfrac{1}{\sqrt{x^3}}$

   (b) $\sqrt[4]{x^3} = x^{3/4}$, $\dfrac{1}{\sqrt{x}} = \dfrac{1}{x^{1/2}} = x^{-1/2}$

3. (a) $8^{2/3} = (\sqrt[3]{8})^2 = 2^2 = 4$

   (b) $(-8)^{2/3} = (\sqrt[3]{-8})^2 = (-2)^2 = 4$

   (c) $8^{-2/3} = \dfrac{1}{8^{2/3}} = \dfrac{1}{4}$

   (d) $-8^{-2/3} = -\left(\dfrac{1}{8^{2/3}}\right) = -\dfrac{1}{4}$

4. (a) $x \cdot x^{1/3} \cdot x^3 = x^{1 + 1/3 + 3} = x^{13/3}$

   (b) $x^2 \div x^{1/2} = x^{2 - 1/2} = x^{3/2}$

   (c) $(x^{-2/3})^{-3} = x^{(-2/3)(-3)} = x^2$

   (d) $x^{-3/2} \cdot x^{1/2} = x^{-3/2 + 1/2} = x^{-1}$

   (e) $x^{-3/2} \cdot x = x^{-3/2 + 1} = x^{-1/2}$

   (f) $\left(\dfrac{x^4}{y^2}\right)^{3/2} = \dfrac{(x^4)^{3/2}}{(y^2)^{3/2}} = \dfrac{x^6}{y^3}$

5. (a) False. $\dfrac{8x^{2/3}}{x^{-1/3}} = 8x^{2/3} \cdot x^{1/3} = 8x^{2/3+1/3} = 8x$

   (b) False. $(16x^8y)^{3/4} = 16^{3/4}(x^8)^{3/4}y^{3/4}$
   $$= (\sqrt[4]{16})^3 x^6 y^{3/4} = 8x^6 y^{3/4}$$

   (c) True.

6. (a) $\sqrt[7]{x^7} = x$ $\qquad$ (b) $[\sqrt[5]{(x^2+1)^2}]^5 = (x^2+1)^2$

   (c) $\sqrt{12xy^2} \cdot \sqrt{3x^2y} = \sqrt{36x^3y^3} = \sqrt{36x^2y^2 \cdot xy}$
   $$= \sqrt{36x^2y^2}\,\sqrt{xy} = 6xy\sqrt{xy}$$

7. $\dfrac{x}{\sqrt{5x}} = \dfrac{x}{\sqrt{5x}} \cdot \dfrac{\sqrt{5x}}{\sqrt{5x}} = \dfrac{x\sqrt{5x}}{5x} = \dfrac{\sqrt{5x}}{5}$.

EXERCISE 0.3

Unless stated otherwise, assume all variables are nonnegative and all denominators are nonzero.

In problems 1–12, find the powers and roots, if they are real numbers.

1. $\sqrt{256/9}$
2. $\sqrt{1.44}$
3. $\sqrt[5]{-32^3}$
4. $\sqrt[4]{-16^5}$
5. $-8^{1/3}$
6. $(-8)^{1/3}$
7. $16^{3/4}$
8. $32^{3/5}$
9. $-27^{-1/3}$
10. $-(16)^{-3/2}$
11. $\left(\dfrac{-8}{27}\right)^{-2/3}$
12. $\left(\dfrac{4}{9}\right)^{-3/2}$

In problems 13–16, replace each radical with a fractional exponent. Do not simplify.

13. $\sqrt{m^3}$
14. $\sqrt[3]{x^5}$
15. $\sqrt[4]{m^2n^5}$
16. $\sqrt[5]{x^3}$

In problems 17–20, write in radical form. Do not simplify.

17. $x^{7/4}$
18. $y^{11/5}$
19. $-(1/4)x^{-5/4}$
20. $-x^{-5/3}$

In problems 21–34, use the properties of exponents to simplify each expression so only positive exponents remain.

21. $y^{1/4} \cdot y^{1/2}$
22. $x^{2/3} \cdot x^{1/5}$
23. $z^{3/4} \cdot z^4$
24. $x^{-2/3} \cdot x^2$
25. $y^{-3/2} \cdot y^{-1}$
26. $z^{-2} \cdot z^{5/3}$
27. $x^{1/3}/x^{-2/3}$
28. $x^{-1/2}/x^{-3/2}$
29. $y^{-5/2}/y^{-2/5}$
30. $x^{4/9}/x^{1/12}$
31. $(x^{2/3})^{3/4}$
32. $(x^{4/5})^3$
33. $(x^{-1/2})^2$
34. $(x^{-2/3})^{-2/5}$

In problems 35–40, simplify each expression by using the properties of radicals. Assume nonnegative variables.

35. $\sqrt{64x^4}$
36. $\sqrt[3]{-64x^6y^3}$
37. $\sqrt{128x^4y^5}$
38. $\sqrt[3]{54x^5z^8}$
39. $\sqrt[3]{40x^8y^5}$
40. $\sqrt{32x^5y}$

In problems 41–48, perform the indicated operations and simplify.

41. $\sqrt{12x^3y} \cdot \sqrt{3x^2y}$
42. $\sqrt[3]{16x^2y} \cdot \sqrt[3]{3x^2y}$

43. $\sqrt{63x^5y^3} \cdot \sqrt{28x^2y}$

44. $\sqrt{10xz^{10}} \cdot \sqrt{30x^{17}z}$

45. $\dfrac{\sqrt{12x^3y^{12}}}{\sqrt{27xy^2}}$

46. $\dfrac{\sqrt{250xy^7z^4}}{\sqrt{18x^{17}y^2}}$

47. $\dfrac{\sqrt[4]{32a^9b^5}}{\sqrt[4]{162a^{17}}}$

48. $\dfrac{\sqrt[3]{-16x^3y^4}}{\sqrt[3]{128y^2}}$

In problems 49–54, rationalize each denominator and simplify.

49. $\sqrt{2/3}$

50. $\sqrt{5/8}$

51. $\dfrac{\sqrt{m^2x}}{\sqrt{mx^2}}$

52. $\dfrac{5x^3w}{\sqrt{4xw^2}}$

53. $\dfrac{\sqrt[3]{m^2x}}{\sqrt[3]{mx^5}}$

54. $\dfrac{\sqrt[4]{mx^3}}{\sqrt[4]{y^2z^5}}$

In calculus it is frequently important to write an expression in the form cx^n, where c is a constant. In problems 55–58, write each expression in this form.

55. $\dfrac{-2}{3\sqrt[3]{x^2}}$

56. $\dfrac{-2}{3\sqrt[4]{x^3}}$

57. $3x\sqrt{x}$

58. $\sqrt{x} \cdot \sqrt[3]{x}$

In calculus problems, the answers are frequently expected to be in a simple form with a radical instead of an exponent. In problems 59–62, write each expression with radicals.

59. $\dfrac{3}{2}x^{1/2}$

60. $\dfrac{4}{3}x^{1/3}$

61. $\dfrac{1}{2}x^{-1/2}$

62. $\dfrac{-1}{2}x^{-3/2}$

APPLICATIONS

Half-life In problems 63 and 64, use the fact that the quantity of a radioactive substance after t years is given by $q = q_0(2^{-t/k})$, where q_0 is the original amount of radioactive material and k is its **half-life** (the number of years for half the radioactive substance to decay).

63. The half-life of strontium-90 is 25 years. Find the amount of strontium-90 remaining after 10 years if $q_0 = 98$ kg.

64. The half-life of carbon-14 is 5600 years. Find the amount of carbon-14 remaining after 10,000 years if $q_0 = 40.0$ g.

65. **Population growth** Suppose the formula for the growth of the population of a city for the next 10 years is given by

$$P = P_0 (2.5)^{ht},$$

where P_0 is the population of the city at the present time and P is the population t years from now. If $h = 0.03$ and $P_0 = 30{,}000$, find P when $t = 10$.

66. **Advertising and sales** Suppose it has been determined that the sales at Ewing Gallery decline after the end of an advertising campaign, with daily sales given by

$$S = 2000(2^{-0.1x}),$$

where S is in dollars and x is the number of days after the campaign ends. What is the daily sales 10 days after the end of the campaign?

67. **Company growth** The growth of a company can be described by the equation

$$N = 500(0.02)^{0.7^t},$$

where t is the number of years the company has been in existence and N is the number of employees. What is the number of employees when $t = 0$? (This is the number of employees the company has when it starts.)

68. **Company growth** For the company in problem 67, what is the number of employees when $t = 5$?

0.4 | OPERATIONS WITH ALGEBRAIC EXPRESSIONS

In algebra we are usually dealing with combinations of real numbers (such as 3, $6/7$, $-\sqrt{2}$) and letters (such as x, a, m). Unless otherwise specified, the letters are symbols used to represent real numbers and are sometimes called **variables.** An expression obtained by performing additions, subtractions, multiplications, divisions, or extraction of roots with one or more real numbers or variables is called an **algebraic expression.** Unless otherwise specified, the variables represent all real numbers for which the algebraic expression is a real number. Examples of algebraic expressions are

$$3x + 2y, \quad \frac{x^3y + y}{x - 1}, \quad \text{and} \quad \sqrt{x} - 3.$$

Note that the variable x cannot be negative in the expression $\sqrt{x} - 3$, and that $(x^3y + y)/(x - 1)$ is not a real number when $x = 1$, because division by 0 is undefined.

Any product of a real number (called the **coefficient**) and one or more variables to powers is called a **term.** The sum of a finite number of terms with nonnegative integer powers on the variables is called a **polynomial.** If a polynomial contains only one variable x, then it is called a polynomial in x.

Polynomial in x   The general form of a **polynomial in x** is

$$a_nx^n + a_{n-1}x^{n-1} + \cdots + a_1x + a_0,$$

where each coefficient a_i is a real number and where $i = 0, 1, 2, \ldots, n$. If $a_n \neq 0$, the **degree** of the polynomial is n, and a_n is called the **leading coefficient.** The term a_0 is called the **constant term.**

Thus $4x^3 - 2x + 3$ is a third-degree polynomial in x with leading coefficient 4. If two or more variables are in a term, the degree of the term is the sum of the exponents of the variables. The degree of a nonzero constant term is zero. Thus, the degree of $4x^2y$ is $2 + 1 = 3$, the degree of $6xy$ is $1 + 1 = 2$, and the degree of 3 is 0. The **degree of a polynomial** containing one or more variables is the degree of the term in the polynomial having the highest degree. Therefore $2xy - 4x + 6$ is a second-degree polynomial.

A polynomial containing two terms is called a **binomial,** and one containing three terms is called a **trinomial.** A single-term polynomial is a **monomial.**

Since monomials and polynomials represent real numbers, the properties of real numbers can be used to add, subtract, multiply, divide, and simplify polynomials. For example, we can use the distributive law to add $3x$ and $2x$.

$$3x + 2x = (3 + 2)x = 5x$$

Similarly, $9xy - 3xy = (9 - 3)xy = 6xy$.

Terms with exactly the same variable factors are called **like terms.** We can add or subtract like terms by adding or subtracting the coefficients of the variables.

EXAMPLE 1

Compute $(4xy + 3x) + (5xy - 2x)$.

Solution

$$(4xy + 3x) + (5xy - 2x) = 4xy + 3x + 5xy - 2x$$
$$= 9xy + x$$

Subtraction of polynomials uses the Distributive Law to remove the parentheses.

EXAMPLE 2

Compute $(3x^2 + 4xy + 5y^2 + 1) - (6x^2 - 2xy + 4)$.

Solution Removing the parentheses gives

$$3x^2 + 4xy + 5y^2 + 1 - 6x^2 + 2xy - 4,$$

which simplifies to

$$-3x^2 + 6xy + 5y^2 - 3.$$

Using the rules of exponents and the commutative and associative laws for multiplication, we can multiply and divide monomials, as the following example shows.

EXAMPLE 3

Perform the indicated operations.

(a) $(8xy^3)(2x^3y)(-3xy^2)$

(b) $-15x^2y^3 \div (3xy^5)$

Solution

(a) $8 \cdot 2 \cdot (-3) \cdot x \cdot x^3 \cdot x \cdot y^3 \cdot y \cdot y^2 = -48x^5y^6$

(b) $\dfrac{-15x^2y^3}{3xy^5} = -\dfrac{15}{3} \cdot \dfrac{x^2}{x} \cdot \dfrac{y^3}{y^5} = -5 \cdot x \cdot \dfrac{1}{y^2} = -\dfrac{5x}{y^2}$

Symbols of grouping are used in algebra in the same way that they are in the arithmetic of real numbers. We have removed parentheses in the process of adding and subtracting polynomials. Other symbols of grouping, such as brackets, [ ], are treated the same as parentheses.

When there are two or more symbols of grouping involved, we may begin with the innermost and work outward.

EXAMPLE 4

Simplify $3x^2 - [2x - (3x^2 - 2x)]$.

Solution

$$3x^2 - [2x - (3x^2 - 2x)] = 3x^2 - [2x - 3x^2 + 2x]$$
$$= 3x^2 - [4x - 3x^2]$$
$$= 3x^2 - 4x + 3x^2$$
$$= 6x^2 - 4x$$

By the use of the Distributive Law, we can multiply a binomial by a monomial. For example,

$$x(2x + 3) = x \cdot 2x + x \cdot 3 = 2x^2 + 3x.$$

We can extend the Distributive Law to multiply polynomials with more than two terms. For example,

$$5(x + y + 2) = 5x + 5y + 10.$$

EXAMPLE 5

Find the following products.
(a) $-4ab(3a^2b + 4ab^2 - 1)$
(b) $(4a + 5b + c)ac$

Solution
(a) $-4ab(3a^2b + 4ab^2 - 1) = -12a^3b^2 - 16a^2b^3 + 4ab$
(b) $(4a + 5b + c)ac = 4a \cdot ac + 5b \cdot ac + c \cdot ac = 4a^2c + 5abc + ac^2$

The Distributive Law can be used to show us how to multiply two polynomials. Consider the indicated multiplication $(a + b)(c + d)$. If we first treat the sum $(a + b)$ as a single quantity, then two successive applications of the Distributive Law give

$$(a + b)(c + d) = (a + b) \cdot c + (a + b) \cdot d = ac + bc + ad + bd.$$

Thus we see that the product can be found by multiplying $(a + b)$ by c, multiplying $(a + b)$ by d, and then adding the products. This is frequently set up as follows.

PRODUCT OF TWO POLYNOMIALS

PROCEDURE	EXAMPLE
To multiply two polynomials:	Multiply $(3x + 4xy + 3y)$ by $(x - 2y)$.
1. Write one of the polynomials above the other.	1. $3x + 4xy + 3y$ $\underline{x - 2y}$
2. Multiply each term of the top polynomial by each term of the bottom one, and write the similar terms of the product under one another.	2. $3x^2 + 4x^2y + 3xy$ $\underline{\qquad\quad - 6xy - 8xy^2 - 6y^2}$
3. Add like terms to simplify the product.	3. $3x^2 + 4x^2y - 3xy - 8xy^2 - 6y^2$

EXAMPLE 6   Multiply $(4x^2 + 3xy + 4x)$ by $(2x - 3y)$.

Solution

$$4x^2 + 3xy + 4x$$
$$\underline{2x - 3y}$$
$$8x^3 + \ \ 6x^2y + 8x^2$$
$$\underline{\qquad - 12x^2y \qquad\quad - 9xy^2 - 12xy}$$
$$8x^3 - \ \ 6x^2y + 8x^2 - 9xy^2 - 12xy$$

Since the multiplications we must perform often involve binomials, the following special products are worth remembering.

Special Products   A. $(x + a)(x + b) = x^2 + (a + b)x + ab$

B. $(ax + b)(cx + d) = acx^2 + (ad + bc)x + bd$

It is easier to remember these two special products if we note the structure of the result and realize that we can obtain this result by finding the products of the First terms, Outside terms, Inside terms, and Last terms, and adding the results. This is called the FOIL method of multiplying two binomials.

EXAMPLE 7   Multiply the following.

(a) $(x - 4)(x + 3)$ (b) $(3x + 2)(2x + 5)$

Solution

$$\underset{\text{First}}{} \quad \underset{\text{Outside}}{} \quad \underset{\text{Inside}}{} \quad \underset{\text{Last}}{}$$

(a) $(x - 4)(x + 3) = (x^2) + (3x) + (-4x) + (-12) = x^2 - x - 12$

(b) $(3x + 2)(2x + 5) = (6x^2) + (15x) + (4x) + (10) = 6x^2 + 19x + 10$

Additional special products are as follows:

Additional Special Products

C. $(x + a)^2 = x^2 + 2ax + a^2$ (binomial squared)

D. $(x - a)^2 = x^2 - 2ax + a^2$ (binomial squared)

E. $(x + a)(x - a) = x^2 - a^2$ (difference of two squares)

F. $(x + a)^3 = x^3 + 3ax^2 + 3a^2x + a^3$ (binomial cubed)

G. $(x - a)^3 = x^3 - 3ax^2 + 3a^2x - a^3$ (binomial cubed)

EXAMPLE 8

Multiply the following.

(a) $(x + 5)^2$ (b) $(3x - 4y)^2$ (c) $(x - 2)(x + 2)$

(d) $(x^2 - y^3)^2$ (e) $(x + 4)^3$

Solution

(a) $(x + 5)^2 = x^2 + 2(5)x + 25 = x^2 + 10x + 25$

(b) $(3x - 4y)^2 = (3x)^2 - 2(3x)(4y) + (4y)^2 = 9x^2 - 24xy + 16y^2$

(c) $(x - 2)(x + 2) = x^2 - 4$

(d) $(x^2 - y^3)^2 = (x^2)^2 - 2(x^2)(y^3) + (y^3)^2 = x^4 - 2x^2y^3 + y^6$

(e) $(x + 4)^3 = x^3 + 3(4)(x^2) + 3(4^2)(x) + 4^3 = x^3 + 12x^2 + 48x + 64$

CHECKPOINT

1. Remove parentheses and combine like terms.

   $9x - 5x(x + 2) + 4x^2$

2. Find the following products.

   (a) $(2x + 1)(4x^2 - 2x + 1)$

   (b) $(x + 3)^2$

   (c) $(3x + 2)(x - 5)$

   (d) $(1 - 4x)(1 + 4x)$

All algebraic expressions can represent real numbers, so the techniques used to perform operations on polynomials and to simplify polynomials also apply to other algebraic expressions.

EXAMPLE 9

Perform the indicated operations.

(a) $3\sqrt{3} + 4x\sqrt{y} - 5\sqrt{3} - 11x\sqrt{y} - (\sqrt{3} - x\sqrt{y})$

(b) $x^{3/2}(x^{1/2} - x^{-1/2})$ (c) $(x^{1/2} - x^{1/3})^2$ (d) $(\sqrt{x} + 2)(\sqrt{x} - 2)$

Solution

(a) We remove parentheses, then combine the terms containing $\sqrt{3}$ and the terms containing $x\sqrt{y}$.

$$(3 - 5 - 1)\sqrt{3} + (4 - 11 + 1)x\sqrt{y} = -3\sqrt{3} - 6x\sqrt{y}$$

(b) $x^{3/2}(x^{1/2} - x^{-1/2}) = x^{3/2} \cdot x^{1/2} - x^{3/2} \cdot x^{-1/2} = x^2 - x$

(c) $(x^{1/2} - x^{1/3})^2 = (x^{1/2})^2 - 2x^{1/2}x^{1/3} + (x^{1/3})^2 = x - 2x^{5/6} + x^{2/3}$

(d) $(\sqrt{x} + 2)(\sqrt{x} - 2) = (\sqrt{x})^2 - (2)^2 = x - 4$

In later chapters we will need to write problems in a simplified form so that we can perform certain operations on them. We can often use division of one polynomial by another to obtain the simplification. The procedure for dividing one polynomial by another follows.

DIVISION OF POLYNOMIALS

PROCEDURE	EXAMPLE
To divide one polynomial by another:	Divide $4x^3 + 4x^2 + 5$ by $2x^2 + 1$.
1. Write with both polynomials in descending powers of a variable. Include missing terms with coefficient 0 in the dividend.	1. $2x^2 + 1 \overline{)4x^3 + 4x^2 + 0x + 5}$
2. (a) Divide the highest power of the divisor into the highest power of the dividend, and write this partial quotient above the dividend. Multiply the partial quotient times the divisor, write the product under the dividend, and subtract, getting a new dividend.	2. (a) $\begin{array}{r} 2x \\ 2x^2 + 1 \overline{)4x^3 + 4x^2 + 0x + 5} \\ \underline{4x^3 + 2x } \\ 4x^2 - 2x + 5 \end{array}$
(b) Repeat until the degree of the new dividend is less than the degree of the divisor. Any remainder is written over the divisor and added to the quotient.	(b) $\begin{array}{r} 2x + 2 \\ 2x^2 + 1 \overline{)4x^3 + 4x^2 + 0x + 5} \\ \underline{4x^3 + 2x } \\ 4x^2 - 2x + 5 \\ \underline{4x^2 + 2} \\ - 2x + 3 \end{array}$ Degree $(-2x + 3) <$ degree $(2x^2 + 1)$ Quotient: $2x + 2 + \dfrac{-2x + 3}{2x^2 + 1}$

EXAMPLE 10

Divide $(4x^3 - 13x - 22)$ by $(x - 3)$, $\quad x \neq 3$.

Solution

$$
\begin{array}{r}
4x^2 + 12x + 23 \\
x - 3 \overline{)4x^3 + 0x^2 - 13x - 22} \\
\underline{4x^3 - 12x^2} \\
12x^2 - 13x - 22 \\
\underline{12x^2 - 36x} \\
23x - 22 \\
\underline{23x - 69} \\
47
\end{array}
$$

($0x^2$ is inserted so that each power of x is present.)

The quotient is $4x^2 + 12x + 23$, with remainder 47, or

$$4x^2 + 12x + 23 + \frac{47}{x - 3}$$

CHECKPOINT

3. Use long division to find $(x^3 + 2x + 7) \div (x - 4)$.

CHECKPOINT
SOLUTIONS

1. $9x - 5x(x + 2) + 4x^2 = 9x - 5x^2 - 10x + 4x^2$

$$= -x^2 - x$$

Note that without parentheses around $9x - 5x$, multiplication has priority over subtraction.

2. (a) $\begin{array}{r}
4x^2 - 2x + 1 \\
2x + 1 \\
\hline
8x^3 - 4x^2 + 2x \\
4x^2 - 2x + 1 \\
\hline
8x^3 \qquad\quad + 1
\end{array}$

(b) $(x + 3)^2 = x^2 + 2(3x) + 3^2 = x^2 + 6x + 9$

(c) $(3x + 2)(x - 5) = 3x^2 - 15x + 2x - 10 = 3x^2 - 13x - 10$

(d) $(1 - 4x)(1 + 4x) = 1 - 16x^2$ (Note that this is different from $16x^2 - 1$.)

3. $\begin{array}{r}
x^2 + 4x + 18 \\
x - 4 \overline{)x^3 + 0x^2 + 2x + 7} \\
\underline{x^3 - 4x^2} \\
4x^2 + 2x + 7 \\
\underline{4x^2 - 16x} \\
18x + 7 \\
\underline{18x - 72} \\
79
\end{array}$ $\quad \left(\text{The answer is } x^2 + 4x + 18 + \dfrac{79}{x - 4}.\right)$

EXERCISE 0.4

For each polynomial in problems 1–4, (a) give the degree of the polynomial, (b) give the coefficient (numerical) of the highest degree term, (c) give the constant term, and (d) decide whether it is a polynomial of one or several variables.

1. $10 - 3x - x^2$
2. $5x^4 - 2x^9 + 7$
3. $7x^2y - 14xy^3z$
4. $2x^5 + 7x^2y^3 - 5y^6$

In problems 5–14, simplify by combining like terms.

5. $7x^2 + 8x + 4x^2 + 11x - 6$
6. $(16pq - 7p^2) + (5pq + 5p^2)$
7. $(3x^3 + 4x^2y^2) + (3x^2y^2 - 7x^3)$
8. $(4m^2 - 3n^2 + 5) - (3m^2 + 4n^2 + 8)$
9. $(4a + 2b) - (3a + 3c) + (6b + 2c)$
10. $(4rs - 2r^2s - 11rs^2) - (11rs^2 - 2rs + 4r^2s)$
11. $[8 - 4 - (q + 5)]$
12. $x^3 + [3x - (x^3 - 3x)]$
13. $x^2 - [x - (x^2 - 1) + 1 - (1 - x^2)] + x$
14. $y^3 - [y^2 - (y^3 + y^2)] - [y^3 + (1 - y^2)]$

In problems 15–60, perform the indicated operations and simplify.

15. $(5x^3)(7x^2)$
16. $(-3x^2y)(2xy^3)(4x^2y^2)$
17. $(39r^3s^2) \div (13r^2s)$
18. $(-15m^3n) \div (5mn^4)$
19. $(3mx)(2mx^2) - (4m^2x)x^2$
20. $\dfrac{15y^3z^2}{yz^2} - \dfrac{8y^4z}{y^2z}$
21. $ax^2(2x^2 + ax + ab)$
22. $-3(3 - x^2)$
23. $(3y + 4)(2y - 3)$
24. $(4x - 1)(x - 3)$
25. $(1 - 2x^2)(2 - x^2)$
26. $(x^3 + 3)(2x^3 - 5)$
27. $(4x + 3)^2$
28. $(2y + 5)^2$
29. $\left(x^2 - \dfrac{1}{2}\right)^2$
30. $(x^3y^3 - 0.3)^2$
31. $(2x + 1)(2x - 1)$
32. $(5y + 2)(5y - 2)$
33. $(0.1 - 4x)(0.1 + 4x)$
34. $\left(\dfrac{2}{3} + x\right)\left(\dfrac{2}{3} - x\right)$
35. $(x - 2)(x^2 + 2x + 4)$
36. $(a + b)(a^2 - ab + b^2)$
37. $(x^3 + 5x)(x^5 - 2x^3 + 5)$
38. $(x^3 - 1)(x^7 - 2x^4 - 5x^2 + 5)$
39. $(18m^2n + 6m^3n + 12m^4n^2) \div (6m^2n)$
40. $(16x^2 + 4xy^2 + 8x) \div (4xy)$
41. $(24x^8y^4 + 15x^5y - 6x^7y) \div (9x^5y^2)$
42. $(27x^2y^2 - 18xy + 9xy^2) \div (6xy)$
43. $(x + 1)^3$
44. $(x - 3)^3$
45. $(2x - 3)^3$
46. $(3x + 4)^3$
47. $(0.1x - 2)(x + 0.05)$
48. $(6.2x + 4.1)(6.2x - 4.1)$
49. $(x^3 + x - 1) \div (x + 2)$
50. $(x^5 + 5x - 7) \div (x + 1)$
51. $(x^4 + 3x^3 - x + 1) \div (x^2 + 1)$
52. $(x^3 + 5x^2 - 6) \div (x^2 - 2)$
53. $x^{1/2}(x^{1/2} + 2x^{3/2})$
54. $x^{-2/3}(x^{5/3} - x^{-1/3})$
55. $(x^{1/2} + 1)(x^{1/2} - 2)$
56. $(x^{1/3} - x^{1/2})(4x^{2/3} - 3x^{3/2})$
57. $(\sqrt{x} + 3)(\sqrt{x} - 3)$
58. $(x^{1/5} + x^{1/2})(x^{1/5} - x^{1/2})$
59. $(2x + 1)^{1/2}[(2x + 1)^{3/2} - (2x + 1)^{-1/2}]$
60. $(4x - 3)^{-5/3}[(4x - 3)^{8/3} + 3(4x - 3)^{5/3}]$

APPLICATIONS

61. **Package design** The volume of a rectangular box is given by V = (length)(width)(height). If a rectangular piece of cardboard that is 10 in. by 15 in. has a square with sides of length x cut from each corner (see Figure 0.8 below), and if the sides are folded up along the dotted lines to form a box, what expression of x would represent the volume?

FIGURE 0.8

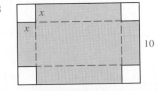

62. ***Investments*** Suppose that you have $4000 to invest, and you invest x dollars at 10% and the remainder at 8%. Write an expression that represents the
    (a) amount invested at 8%.
    (b) interest earned on the x dollars at 10%.
    (c) interest earned on the money invested at 8%.
    (d) total interest earned.

63. ***Medications*** Suppose that a nurse needs 10 cc of a 15.5% solution (that is, a solution that is 15.5% ingredient) of a certain medication, which must be obtained by mixing x cc of a 20% solution and y cc of a 5% solution. Write expressions involving x for
    (a) y, the amount of 5% solution.
    (b) the amount of ingredient in the x cc of 20% solution.
    (c) the amount of ingredient in the 5% solution.
    (d) the total amount of ingredient in the mixture.

0.5 | FACTORING

We can factor monomial factors out of a polynomial by using the Distributive Law in reverse; $ab + ac = a(b + c)$ is an example showing that a is a monomial factor of the polynomial $ab + ac$. But it is also a statement of the Distributive Law (with the sides of the equation interchanged). The monomial factor of a polynomial must be a factor of each term of the polynomial, so it is frequently called a **common monomial factor.**

EXAMPLE 1 | Factor $-3x^2t - 3x + 9xt^2$.

Solution

1. We can either factor out $3x$ and obtain
$$-3x^2t - 3x + 9xt^2 = 3x(-xt - 1 + 3t^2)$$

2. or we can factor out $-3x$ (factoring out the negative will make the first term of the polynomial positive) and obtain
$$-3x^2t - 3x + 9xt^2 = -3x(xt + 1 - 3t^2).$$

If a factor is common to each term of a polynomial, we can use the above procedure to factor it out, even if it is not a monomial. For example, we can factor

$(a + b)$ out of the polynomial $2x(a + b) - 3y(a + b)$. If we factor $(a + b)$ from both terms, we get $(a + b)(2x - 3y)$. The following example demonstrates the **factoring by grouping** technique.

EXAMPLE 2

Factor $5x - 5y + bx - by$.

Solution We can factor this polynomial by the use of grouping. The grouping is done so that common factors (frequently binomial factors) can be removed. We see that we can factor 5 from the first two terms and b from the last two, giving

$$5(x - y) + b(x - y).$$

This gives two terms with the common factor $x - y$, so we get

$$(x - y)(5 + b).$$

We can use the formula for multiplying two binomials to factor certain trinomials. The formula

$$(x + a)(x + b) = x^2 + (a + b)x + ab$$

can be used to factor trinomials such as

$$x^2 - 7x + 6.$$

EXAMPLE 3

Factor $x^2 - 7x + 6$.

Solution If this trinomial can be factored into an expression of the form

$$(x + a)(x + b)$$

then we need to find a and b such that

$$x^2 - 7x + 6 = x^2 + (a + b)x + ab$$

That is, we need to find a and b such that $a + b = -7$ and $ab = 6$. The two numbers whose sum is -7 and whose product is 6 are -1 and -6. Thus

$$x^2 - 7x + 6 = (x - 1)(x - 6).$$

A similar method can be used to factor trinomials such as $9x^2 - 31x + 12$. Finding the proper factors for this type of trinomial may involve a fair amount of trial and error because we must find factors a, b, c, and d such that

$$(ax + b)(cx + d) = acx^2 + (ad + bc)x + bd.$$

Another technique of factoring can be used to factor trinomials such as those we have been discussing. It is especially useful in factoring more complicated trinomials, such as $9x^2 - 31x + 12$. This procedure for factoring second-degree trinomials follows.

FACTORING A TRINOMIAL

PROCEDURE	EXAMPLE
To factor a trinomial into the product of its binomial factors:	Factor $9x^2 - 31x + 12$.
1. Form the product of the second-degree term and the constant term.	1. $9x^2 \cdot 12 = 108x^2$
2. Determine if there are any factors of the product of step 1 that will sum to the middle term of the trinomial. (If the answer is no, the trinomial will not factor into two binomials.)	2. The factors $-27x$ and $-4x$ give a sum of $-31x$.
3. Use the sum of these two factors to replace the middle term of the trinomial.	3. $9x^2 - 31x + 12 = 9x^2 - 27x - 4x + 12$
4. Factor this four-term expression by grouping.	4. $9x^2 - 31x + 12 = (9x^2 - 27x) + (-4x + 12)$ $\qquad = 9x(x - 3) - 4(x - 3)$ $\qquad = (x - 3)(9x - 4)$

In the example just completed, note that writing the middle term $(-31x)$ as $-4x - 27x$ rather than as $-27x - 4x$ (as we did) will also result in the correct factorization. (Try it.)

EXAMPLE 4

Factor $9x^2 - 9x - 10$.

Solution The product of the second-degree term and the constant is $-90x^2$. Factors of $-90x^2$ that sum to $-9x$ are $-15x$ and $6x$. Thus

$$9x^2 - 9x - 10 = 9x^2 - 15x + 6x - 10$$
$$= (9x^2 - 15x) + (6x - 10)$$
$$= 3x(3x - 5) + 2(3x - 5)$$
$$= (3x - 5)(3x + 2).$$

We can check this factorization by multiplying.

$$(3x - 5)(3x + 2) = 9x^2 + 6x - 15x - 10$$
$$= 9x^2 - 9x - 10.$$

Some special products that make factoring easier are the following.

Special Factorizations	The perfect-square trinomials: $$x^2 + 2ax + a^2 = (x + a)^2$$ $$x^2 - 2ax + a^2 = (x - a)^2$$ The difference of two squares: $$x^2 - a^2 = (x + a)(x - a)$$

EXAMPLE 5

Factor $25x^2 - 36y^2$.

Solution Since the binomial $25x^2 - 36y^2$ is the difference of two squares, we get

$$25x^2 - 36y^2 = (5x - 6y)(5x + 6y).$$

These two factors are called binomial **conjugates** because they differ in only one sign.

EXAMPLE 6

Factor $4x^2 + 12x + 9$.

Solution Although we can use the technique we have learned to factor trinomials, the factors come quickly if we recognize that this trinomial is a perfect square. It has two square terms, and the remaining term $(12x)$ is twice the product of the square roots of the squares ($12x = 2 \cdot 2x \cdot 3$). Thus

$$4x^2 + 12x + 9 = (2x + 3)^2.$$

Most of the polynomials we have factored have been second-degree polynomials, or **quadratic polynomials.** Some polynomials that are not quadratic are in a form that can be factored in the same manner as quadratics. For example, the polynomial $x^4 + 4x^2 + 4$ can be written as $a^2 + 4a + 4$, where $a = x^2$.

EXAMPLE 7

Factor $x^4 + 4x^2 + 4$ completely.

Solution Since the trinomial is in the form of a perfect square, letting $a = x^2$ will give us

$$x^4 + 4x^2 + 4 = a^2 + 4a + 4 = (a + 2)^2.$$

Thus

$$x^4 + 4x^2 + 4 = (x^2 + 2)^2.$$

EXAMPLE 8

Factor $x^4 - 16$ completely.

Solution The binomial $x^4 - 16$ can be treated as the difference of two squares, $(x^2)^2 - 4^2$, so

$$x^4 - 16 = (x^2 - 4)(x^2 + 4).$$

But $x^2 - 4$ can be factored into $(x - 2)(x + 2)$, so

$$x^4 - 16 = (x - 2)(x + 2)(x^2 + 4).$$

CHECKPOINT

1. Factor the following.
   (a) $8x^3 - 12x$ (b) $3x(x^2 + 5) - 5(x^2 + 5)$ (c) $x^2 - 10x - 24$
   (d) $x^2 - 5x + 6$ (e) $4x^2 - 20x + 25$ (f) $100 - 49x^2$

2. Consider $10x^2 - 17x - 20$ and observe that $(10x^2)(-20) = -200x^2$.
   (a) Find two numbers whose product is $-200x^2$ and whose sum is $-17x$.
   (b) Replace $-17x$ in $10x^2 - 17x - 20$ with the two numbers in (a).
   (c) Factor (b) by grouping.

3. True or false:
   (a) $4x^2 + 9 = (2x + 3)^2$
   (b) $x^2 - x + 12 = (x - 4)(x + 3)$
   (c) $5x^5 - 20x^3 = 5x^3(x^2 - 4) = 5x^3(x + 2)(x - 2)$ ■

A polynomial is said to be factored completely if all possible factorizations have been completed. For example, $(2x - 4)(x + 3)$ is not factored completely because a 2 can still be factored out of $2x - 4$. Confining our attention to factors with integer coefficients, we can factor a number of polynomials completely by using the following guidelines.

Guidelines for Factoring Completely	Look for:	Monomials first.
	Then for:	Difference of two squares.
	Then for:	Trinomial squares.
	Then for:	Other methods of factoring trinomials.

EXAMPLE 9

Factor completely $12x^2 - 36x + 27$.

Solution

$$12x^2 - 36x + 27 = 3(4x^2 - 12x + 9) \qquad \text{(Monomial)}$$
$$= 3(2x - 3)^2 \qquad \text{(Perfect square)}$$

EXAMPLE 10

Factor completely $16x^2 - 64y^2$.

Solution

$$16x^2 - 64y^2 = 16(x^2 - 4y^2)$$
$$= 16(x + 2y)(x - 2y)$$

Note that factoring the difference of two squares immediately would give $(4x + 8y)(4x - 8y)$, which is not factored completely (since we could still factor 4 from $4x + 8y$ and 4 from $4x - 8y$).

CHECKPOINT
SOLUTIONS

1. (a) $8x^3 - 12x = 4x(2x^2 - 3)$

(b) $3x(x^2 + 5) - 5(x^2 + 5) = (x^2 + 5)(3x - 5)$

(c) $x^2 - 10x - 24 = (x - 12)(x + 2)$

(d) $x^2 - 5x + 6 = (x - 3)(x - 2)$

(e) $4x^2 - 20x + 25 = (2x - 5)^2$

(f) $100 - 49x^2 = (10 + 7x)(10 - 7x)$

2. (a) $(-25x)(+8x) = -200x^2$ and $-25x + 8x = -17x$

(b) $10x^2 - 17x - 20 = 10x^2 - 25x + 8x - 20$

(c) $\qquad = (10x^2 - 25x) + (8x - 20)$
$\qquad = 5x(2x - 5) + 4(2x - 5)$
$\qquad = (2x - 5)(5x + 4)$

3. (a) False. $4x^2 + 9$ cannot be factored. In fact, sums of squares cannot be factored.

(b) False. $x^2 - x + 12$ cannot be factored. We cannot find two numbers whose product is $+12$ and whose sum is -1.

(c) True.

EXERCISE 0.5

Factor the following completely.

1. $9ab - 12a^2b + 18b^2$

2. $8a^2b - 160x + 4bx^2$

3. $4x^2 + 8xy^2 + 2xy^3$

4. $12y^3z + 4yz^2 - 8y^2z^3$

5. $5(y - 4) - x^2(y - 4)$

6. $2(x + 1) - 5x(x + 1)$

7. $6x - 6m + xy - my$

8. $x^3 - x^2 - 5x + 5$

9. $x^2 + 8x + 12$

10. $x^2 + 6x + 8$

11. $x^2 - x - 6$

12. $x^2 - 2x - 8$

13. $2x^2 - 8x - 42$

14. $3x^2 - 21x + 36$

15. $7x^2 - 10x - 8$

16. $12x^2 + 11x + 2$

17. $x^2 - 10x + 25$

18. $4y^2 + 12y + 9$

19. $49a^2 - 144b^2$

20. $16x^2 - 25y^2$

21. $2x^3 - 8x^2 + 8x$

22. $x^3 + 16x^2 + 64x$

23. $2x^2 + x - 6$

24. $2x^2 + 13x + 6$

25. $3x^2 + 3x - 36$

26. $4x^2 - 8x - 60$

27. $2x^3 - 8x$

28. $16z^2 - 81w^2$

29. $10x^2 + 19x + 6$

30. $6x^2 + 67x - 35$

31. $9 - 47x + 10x^2$

32. $10x^2 + 21x - 10$

33. $9x^2 + 21x - 8$

34. $9x^2 + 22x + 8$

35. $y^4 - 16x^4$

36. $x^8 - 81$

37. $x^4 - 8x^2 + 16$

38. $81 - 18x^2 + x^4$

39. $4x^4 - 5x^2 + 1$

40. $x^4 - 3x^2 - 4$

The following factorization formulas involving cubes can be verified by multiplication.

Factorizations with cubes

Perfect cube
$$a^3 + 3a^2b + 3ab^2 + b^3 = (a + b)^3$$
Perfect cube
$$a^3 - 3a^2b + 3ab^2 - b^3 = (a - b)^3$$
Difference of two cubes
$$a^3 - b^3 = (a - b)(a^2 + ab + b^2)$$
Sum of two cubes
$$a^3 + b^3 = (a + b)(a^2 - ab + b^2)$$

In problems 41–48, use these cube formulas to factor each expression.

41. $x^3 + 3x^2 + 3x + 1$

42. $x^3 + 6x^2 + 12x + 8$

43. $x^3 - 12x^2 + 48x - 64$

44. $y^3 - 9y^2 + 27y - 27$

45. $x^3 - 64$ 46. $8x^3 - 1$

47. $27 + 8x^3$ 48. $a^3 + 216$

In problems 49–54, determine the missing factor.

49. $x^{3/2} + x^{1/2} = x^{1/2}(?)$

50. $2x^{1/4} + 4x^{3/4} = 2x^{1/4}(?)$

51. $x^{-3} + x^{-2} = x^{-3}(?)$

52. $x^{-1} - x = x^{-1}(?)$

53. $(-x^3 + x)(3 - x^2)^{-1/2} + 2x(3 - x^2)^{1/2}$
$$= (3 - x^2)^{-1/2}(?)$$

54. $4x(4x + 1)^{-1/3} - (4x + 1)^{2/3}$
$$= (4x + 1)^{-1/3}(?)$$

APPLICATIONS

55. **Volume** Suppose that squares of side x are cut from four corners of an 8- × 8-inch piece of cardboard, and an open-top box is formed (see Figure 0.9). The volume of the box is given by $64x - 32x^2 + 4x^3$. Factor this expression.

FIGURE 0.9

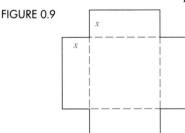

56. **Power in a Circuit** Factor the following expression for the maximum power in a certain electrical circuit.

$$(R + r)^2 - 2r(R + r)$$

0.6 | ALGEBRAIC FRACTIONS

Evaluating certain limits and graphing rational functions require an understanding of algebraic fractions. The fraction 6/8 can be reduced to 3/4 by dividing both the numerator and denominator by 2. In the same manner, the algebraic fraction

$$\frac{(x + 2)(x + 1)}{(x + 1)(x + 3)}$$

can be reduced to

$$\frac{x + 2}{x + 3}$$

by dividing both the numerator and denominator by $x + 1$, if $x \neq -1$.

Simplifying Fractions

We *simplify* algebraic fractions by factoring the numerator and denominator and then dividing both the numerator and denominator by any common factors.*

*We assume all fractions are defined.

EXAMPLE 1

Simplify $\dfrac{3x^2 - 14x + 8}{x^2 - 16}$, $\quad x^2 \neq 16$.

Solution

$$\frac{3x^2 - 14x + 8}{x^2 - 16} = \frac{(3x - 2)(x - 4)}{(x - 4)(x + 4)}$$

$$= \frac{(3x - 2)\overset{1}{\cancel{(x - 4)}}}{\underset{1}{\cancel{(x - 4)}}(x + 4)}$$

$$= \frac{3x - 2}{x + 4}$$

We can multiply fractions by writing the product as the product of the numerators divided by the product of the denominators. For example,

$$\frac{4}{5} \cdot \frac{10}{12} \cdot \frac{2}{5} = \frac{80}{300},$$

which reduces to $\frac{4}{15}$.

We can also find the product by reducing the fractions before we indicate the multiplication in the numerator and denominator. For example, in

$$\frac{4}{5} \cdot \frac{10}{12} \cdot \frac{2}{5},$$

we can divide the numerator and denominator by 5 and then by 4, giving

$$\overset{1}{\underset{1}{\cancel{4}}} \cdot \frac{\overset{2}{\cancel{10}}}{\underset{3}{\cancel{12}}} \cdot \frac{2}{5} = \frac{1}{1} \cdot \frac{2}{3} \cdot \frac{2}{5} = \frac{4}{15}.$$

Product of Fractions   We *multiply* algebraic fractions by writing the product of the numerators divided by the product of the denominators, and then reduce to lowest terms. We may also reduce prior to finding the product.

EXAMPLE 2   Multiply: (a) $\dfrac{4x^2}{5y} \cdot \dfrac{10x}{y^2} \cdot \dfrac{y}{8x^2}$ (b) $\dfrac{-4x + 8}{3x + 6} \cdot \dfrac{2x + 4}{4x + 12}$

Solution

(a) $\dfrac{4x^2}{5y} \cdot \dfrac{10x}{y^2} \cdot \dfrac{y}{8x^2} = \dfrac{\overset{1}{\cancel{4x^2}}}{\underset{1 \cdot 1}{\cancel{5y}}} \cdot \dfrac{\overset{2}{\cancel{10x}}}{y^2} \cdot \dfrac{\overset{1}{\cancel{y}}}{\underset{2}{\cancel{8x^2}}}$

$$= \frac{1}{1} \cdot \frac{\overset{1}{\cancel{2}}x}{y^2} \cdot \frac{1}{\underset{1}{\cancel{2}}} = \frac{x}{y^2}$$

(b) $\dfrac{-4x + 8}{3x + 6} \cdot \dfrac{2x + 4}{4x + 12} = \dfrac{-4(x - 2)}{3(x + 2)} \cdot \dfrac{2(x + 2)}{4(x + 3)}$

$$= \frac{\overset{-1}{\cancel{-4}}(x - 2)}{3\cancel{(x + 2)}} \cdot \frac{2\cancel{(x + 2)}}{\underset{1}{\cancel{4}}(x + 3)}$$

$$= \frac{-2(x - 2)}{3(x + 3)}$$

In arithmetic we learned to divide one fraction by another by inverting the divisor and multiplying. The same rule applies to division of algebraic fractions.

EXAMPLE 3

(a) Divide $\dfrac{a^2b}{c}$ by $\dfrac{ab}{c^2}$

(b) $\dfrac{6x^2 - 6}{x^2 + 3x + 2} \div \dfrac{x - 1}{x^2 + 4x + 4}$

Solution

(a) $\dfrac{a^2b}{c} \div \dfrac{ab}{c^2} = \dfrac{a^2b}{c} \cdot \dfrac{c^2}{ab} = \dfrac{\overset{a \cdot 1}{\cancel{a^2b}}}{\cancel{c}} \cdot \dfrac{\overset{c}{\cancel{c^2}}}{\cancel{ab}} = \dfrac{ac}{1} = ac$

(b) $\dfrac{6x^2 - 6}{x^2 + 3x + 2} \div \dfrac{x - 1}{x^2 + 4x + 4} = \dfrac{6x^2 - 6}{x^2 + 3x + 2} \cdot \dfrac{x^2 + 4x + 4}{x - 1}$

$= \dfrac{6(x - 1)(x + 1)}{(x + 2)(x + 1)} \cdot \dfrac{(x + 2)(x + 2)}{x - 1}$

$= 6(x + 2)$

CHECKPOINT

1. Reduce $\dfrac{2x^2 - 4x}{2x}$.

2. Multiply: $\dfrac{x^2}{x^2 - 9} \cdot \dfrac{x + 3}{3x}$.

3. Divide: $\dfrac{5x^2(x - 1)}{2(x + 1)} \div \dfrac{10x^2}{(x + 1)(x - 1)}$.

If two fractions are to be added, it is convenient that each be expressed with the same denominator. If the denominators are not the same, we can write the equivalents of each of the fractions with a common denominator. We usually use the lowest common denominator (LCD) when we write the equivalent fractions. The **lowest common denominator** is the lowest-degree variable expression into which all denominators will divide. If the denominators are polynomials, then the LCD is the lowest-degree polynomial into which all denominators will divide. We can find the lowest common denominator as follows.

FINDING THE LOWEST COMMON DENOMINATOR

PROCEDURE	EXAMPLE
To find the lowest common denominator of a set of fractions:	Find the LCD of $\dfrac{1}{x^2 - x}, \dfrac{1}{x^2 - 1}, \dfrac{1}{x^2}$.
1. Completely factor each denominator.	1. The factored denominators are $x(x - 1), (x + 1)(x - 1), x \cdot x$.
2. Write the LCD as the product of each of these factors used the maximum number of times it occurs in any one denominator.	2. x occurs a maximum of 2 times in one denominator, $x - 1$ occurs once, and $x + 1$ occurs once. Thus the LCD is $x \cdot x(x - 1)(x + 1) = x^2(x - 1)(x + 1)$.

The procedure for combining (adding or subtracting) two or more fractions is as follows.

ADDING OR SUBTRACTING FRACTIONS

PROCEDURE	EXAMPLE
To combine fractions:	Combine $\dfrac{y-3}{y-5} + \dfrac{y-23}{y^2-y-20}$.
1. Find the LCD of the fractions.	1. $y^2 - y - 20 = (y-5)(y+4)$, so the LCD is $(y-5)(y+4)$.
2. Write the equivalent of each fraction with the LCD as its denominator.	2. The sum is $\dfrac{(y-3)(y+4)}{(y-5)(y+4)} + \dfrac{y-23}{(y-5)(y+4)}$.
3. Add or subtract as indicated by combining like terms in the numerator over the LCD.	3. $= \dfrac{y^2+y-12+y-23}{(y-5)(y+4)}$ $= \dfrac{y^2+2y-35}{(y-5)(y+4)}$
4. Reduce the fraction, if possible.	4. $y-5$ is a factor of the numerator, so the sum is $\dfrac{y+7}{y+4}$, if $y \neq 5$.

EXAMPLE 4 | Add $\dfrac{3x}{a^2} + \dfrac{4}{ax}$.

Solution

1. The LCD is a^2x.

2. $\dfrac{3x}{a^2} + \dfrac{4}{ax} = \dfrac{3x}{a^2} \cdot \dfrac{x}{x} + \dfrac{4}{ax} \cdot \dfrac{a}{a} = \dfrac{3x^2}{a^2x} + \dfrac{4a}{a^2x}$

3. $\dfrac{3x^2}{a^2x} + \dfrac{4a}{a^2x} = \dfrac{3x^2+4a}{a^2x}$

4. The sum is in lowest terms.

EXAMPLE 5 | Combine $\dfrac{y-3}{(y-5)^2} + \dfrac{y-2}{y^2-y-20}$.

Solution $y^2 - y - 20 = (y-5)(y+4)$, so the LCD is $(y-5)^2(y+4)$. Writing the equivalent fractions, then combining them gives

$$\dfrac{y-3}{(y-5)^2} + \dfrac{y-2}{(y-5)(y+4)} = \dfrac{(y-3)(y+4)}{(y-5)^2(y+4)} + \dfrac{(y-2)(y-5)}{(y-5)(y+4)(y-5)}$$

$$= \frac{(y^2 + y - 12) + (y^2 - 7y + 10)}{(y - 5)^2(y + 4)}$$

$$= \frac{2y^2 - 6y - 2}{(y - 5)^2(y + 4)}.$$

A fractional expression that contains one or more fractions in its numerator or denominator is called a **complex fraction.** An example of a complex fraction is

$$\frac{\dfrac{1}{3} + \dfrac{4}{x}}{3 - \dfrac{1}{xy}}.$$

We can simplify fractions of this type using the property $\dfrac{a}{b} = \dfrac{ac}{bc}$, with c equal to the LCD of *all* the fractions contained in the numerator and denominator of the complex fraction.

For example, all fractions contained in

$$\frac{\dfrac{1}{3} + \dfrac{4}{x}}{3 - \dfrac{1}{xy}} \qquad \text{have LCD } 3xy.$$

We simplify this complex fraction by multiplying the numerator and denominator as follows:

$$\frac{3xy\left(\dfrac{1}{3} + \dfrac{4}{x}\right)}{3xy\left(3 - \dfrac{1}{xy}\right)} = \frac{3xy\left(\dfrac{1}{3}\right) + 3xy\left(\dfrac{4}{x}\right)}{3xy(3) - 3xy\left(\dfrac{1}{xy}\right)} = \frac{xy + 12y}{9xy - 3}.$$

EXAMPLE 6

Simplify $\dfrac{x^{-3} + x^2y^{-3}}{(xy)^{-2}}$ so that positive exponents remain.

Solution

$$\frac{x^{-3} + x^2y^{-3}}{(xy)^{-2}} = \frac{\dfrac{1}{x^3} + \dfrac{x^2}{y^3}}{\dfrac{1}{(xy)^2}}, \qquad \text{LCD} = x^3y^3$$

$$= \frac{x^3y^3\left(\dfrac{1}{x^3} + \dfrac{x^2}{y^3}\right)}{x^3y^3\left(\dfrac{1}{x^2y^2}\right)} = \frac{y^3 + x^5}{xy}$$

CHECKPOINT

4. Add or subtract:

(a) $\dfrac{5x - 1}{2x - 5} - \dfrac{x + 9}{2x - 5}$

(b) $\dfrac{x + 1}{x} + \dfrac{x}{x - 1}$

5. Simplify $\dfrac{\dfrac{y}{x} - 1}{\dfrac{y}{x} - \dfrac{x}{y}}$.

We can simplify algebraic fractions whose denominators contain sums and differences involving square roots by rationalizing the denominators. Using the fact that $(x + y)(x - y) = x^2 - y^2$, we multiply the numerator and denominator of an algebraic fraction of this type by the conjugate of the denominator to simplify the fraction.

EXAMPLE 7

Rationalize the denominators.

(a) $\dfrac{1}{\sqrt{x} - 2}$

(b) $\dfrac{3 + \sqrt{x}}{\sqrt{x} + \sqrt{5}}$

Solution Multiplying $\sqrt{x} - 2$ by $\sqrt{x} + 2$, its conjugate, gives the difference of two squares and removes the radical from the denominator in (a). We also use the conjugate in (b).

(a) $\dfrac{1}{\sqrt{x} - 2} \cdot \dfrac{\sqrt{x} + 2}{\sqrt{x} + 2} = \dfrac{\sqrt{x} + 2}{(\sqrt{x})^2 - (2)^2} = \dfrac{\sqrt{x} + 2}{x - 4}$

(b) $\dfrac{3 + \sqrt{x}}{\sqrt{x} + \sqrt{5}} \cdot \dfrac{\sqrt{x} - \sqrt{5}}{\sqrt{x} - \sqrt{5}} = \dfrac{3\sqrt{x} - 3\sqrt{5} + x - \sqrt{5x}}{x - 5}$

CHECKPOINT

6. Rationalize the denominator $\dfrac{\sqrt{x}}{2\sqrt{x} - 3}$.

CHECKPOINT
SOLUTIONS

1. $\dfrac{2x^2 - 4x}{2x} = \dfrac{2x(x - 2)}{2x} = x - 2$

2. $\dfrac{x^2}{x^2 - 9} \cdot \dfrac{x + 3}{3x} = \dfrac{x^2 \cdot (x + 3)}{(x + 3)(x - 3) \cdot 3x} = \dfrac{x}{3(x - 3)} = \dfrac{x}{3x - 9}$

3. $\dfrac{5x^2(x - 1)}{2(x + 1)} \div \dfrac{10x^2}{(x + 1)(x - 1)} = \dfrac{5x^2(x - 1)}{2(x + 1)} \cdot \dfrac{(x + 1)(x - 1)}{10x^2}$

$= \dfrac{(x - 1)^2}{4}$

4. (a) $\dfrac{5x-1}{2x-5} - \dfrac{x+9}{2x-5} = \dfrac{(5x-1)-(x+9)}{2x-5}$

$= \dfrac{5x-1-x-9}{2x-5}$

$= \dfrac{4x-10}{2x-5} = \dfrac{2(2x-5)}{2x-5} = 2$

(b) $\dfrac{x+1}{x} + \dfrac{x}{x-1}$ has LCD $= x(x-1)$

$\dfrac{x+1}{x} + \dfrac{x}{x-1} = \dfrac{x+1}{x} \cdot \dfrac{(x-1)}{(x-1)} + \dfrac{x}{x-1} \cdot \dfrac{x}{x}$

$= \dfrac{x^2-1}{x(x-1)} + \dfrac{x^2}{x(x-1)} = \dfrac{x^2-1+x^2}{x(x-1)}$

$= \dfrac{2x^2-1}{x(x-1)}$

5. $\dfrac{\dfrac{y}{x}-1}{\dfrac{y}{x}-\dfrac{x}{y}} = \dfrac{\left(\dfrac{y}{x}-1\right)}{\left(\dfrac{y}{x}-\dfrac{x}{y}\right)} \cdot \dfrac{xy}{xy}$

$= \dfrac{\dfrac{y}{x}\cdot xy - 1 \cdot xy}{\dfrac{y}{x}\cdot xy - \dfrac{x}{y}\cdot xy}$

$= \dfrac{y^2-xy}{y^2-x^2}$

$= \dfrac{y(y-x)}{(y+x)(y-x)} = \dfrac{y}{y+x}$

6. $\dfrac{\sqrt{x}}{2\sqrt{x}-3} = \dfrac{\sqrt{x}}{2\sqrt{x}-3} \cdot \dfrac{2\sqrt{x}+3}{2\sqrt{x}+3}$

$= \dfrac{2x+3\sqrt{x}}{4x-9}$

EXERCISE 0.6

Simplify the following fractions.

1. $\dfrac{18x^3y^3}{9x^3z}$

2. $\dfrac{15a^4b^5}{30a^3b}$

3. $\dfrac{x-3y}{3x-9y}$

4. $\dfrac{x^2-6x+8}{x^2-16}$

5. $\dfrac{x^2-2x+1}{x^2-4x+3}$

6. $\dfrac{x^2-5x+6}{9-x^2}$

7. $\dfrac{6x^3y^3-15x^2y}{3x^2y^2+9x^2y}$

8. $\dfrac{x^2y^2-4x^3y}{x^2y-2x^2y^2}$

In problems 9–38, perform the indicated operations and simplify.

9. $\dfrac{6x^3}{8y^3} \cdot \dfrac{16x}{9y^2} \cdot \dfrac{15y^4}{x^3}$

10. $\dfrac{25ac^2}{15a^2c} \cdot \dfrac{4ad^4}{15abc^3}$

11. $\dfrac{8x - 16}{x - 3} \cdot \dfrac{4x - 12}{3x - 6}$

12. $\dfrac{x^2 + 7x + 12}{3x^2 + 13x + 4} \cdot \dfrac{3x + 1}{x + 3}$

13. $(x^2 - 4) \cdot \dfrac{2x - 3}{x + 2}$

14. $\dfrac{4x + 4}{x - 4} \cdot \dfrac{x^2 - 6x + 8}{8x^2 + 8x}$

15. $\dfrac{x^2 - x - 2}{2x^2 - 8} \cdot \dfrac{18 - 2x^2}{x^2 - 5x + 4} \cdot \dfrac{x^2 - 2x - 8}{x^2 - 6x + 9}$

16. $\dfrac{x^2 - 5x - 6}{x^2 - 5x + 4} \cdot \dfrac{x^2 - x - 12}{x^3 - 6x^2} \cdot \dfrac{x - x^3}{x^2 - 2x + 1}$

17. $\dfrac{15ac^2}{7bd} \div \dfrac{4a}{14b^2d}$

18. $\dfrac{16}{x - 2} \div \dfrac{4}{3x - 6}$

19. $\dfrac{y^2 - 2y + 1}{7y^2 - 7y} \div \dfrac{y^2 - 4y + 3}{35y^2}$

20. $\dfrac{6x^2}{4x^2y - 12xy} \div \dfrac{3x^2 + 12x}{x^2 + x - 12}$

21. $(x^2 - x - 6) \div \dfrac{9 - x^2}{x^2 - 3x}$

22. $\dfrac{2x^2 + 7x + 3}{4x^2 - 1} \div (x + 3)$

23. $\dfrac{a}{a - 2} - \dfrac{a - 2}{a}$

24. $x - \dfrac{2}{x - 1}$

25. $\dfrac{x}{x + 1} + x + 1$

26. $\dfrac{x - 1}{x + 1} - \dfrac{2}{x^2 + x}$

27. $\dfrac{4a}{3x + 6} + \dfrac{5a^2}{4x + 8}$

28. $\dfrac{b - 1}{b^2 + 2b} + \dfrac{b}{3b + 6}$

29. $\dfrac{x - 7}{x^2 - 9x + 20} - \dfrac{x + 2}{x^2 - 5x + 4}$

30. $\dfrac{x + 1}{x^2 + x - 6} - \dfrac{2x - 1}{2 - x}$

31. $\dfrac{3x - 1}{2x - 4} + \dfrac{4x}{3x - 6} - \dfrac{x - 4}{5x - 10}$

32. $\dfrac{2x + 1}{4x - 2} + \dfrac{5}{2x} - \dfrac{x + 4}{2x^2 - x}$

33. $\dfrac{1}{x^2 - 4y^2} - \dfrac{1}{x^2 - 4xy + 4y^2}$

34. $\dfrac{3x^2}{x^2 - 4} + \dfrac{2}{x^2 - 4x + 4} - 3$

35. $\dfrac{x}{x^2 - 4} + \dfrac{4}{x^2 - x - 2} - \dfrac{x - 2}{x^2 + 3x + 2}$

36. $\dfrac{1}{y^2 + 2y - 35} - \dfrac{y - 1}{y^2 - 4y - 5} + \dfrac{2}{y^2 + 8y + 7}$

37. $\dfrac{-x^3 + x}{\sqrt{3 - x^2}} + 2x\sqrt{3 - x^2}$

38. $\dfrac{3x^2(x + 1)}{\sqrt{x^3 + 1}} + \sqrt{x^3 + 1}$

In problems 39–48, simplify each complex fraction.

39. $\dfrac{3 - \dfrac{2}{3}}{14}$

40. $\dfrac{4 - \dfrac{3}{4}}{26}$

41. $\dfrac{\dfrac{1}{x} + \dfrac{1}{y}}{\dfrac{1}{x} - \dfrac{1}{y}}$

42. $\dfrac{\dfrac{5}{2y} + \dfrac{3}{y}}{\dfrac{1}{4} + \dfrac{1}{3y}}$

43. $\dfrac{2 - \dfrac{1}{x}}{2x - \dfrac{3x}{x + 1}}$

44. $\dfrac{1 - \dfrac{2}{x - 2}}{x - 6 + \dfrac{10}{x + 1}}$

45. $\dfrac{\sqrt{a} - \dfrac{b}{\sqrt{a}}}{a - b}$

46. $\dfrac{\sqrt{x - 1} + \dfrac{1}{\sqrt{x - 1}}}{x}$

47. $\dfrac{\sqrt{x^2 + 9} - \dfrac{13}{\sqrt{x^2 + 9}}}{x^2 - x - 6}$

48. $\dfrac{\sqrt{x^2 + 3} - \dfrac{x + 5}{\sqrt{x^2 + 3}}}{x^2 + 5x + 4}$

In problems 49–52, rewrite each fraction so only positive exponents remain, and simplify.

49. $\dfrac{2a^{-1} - b^{-1}}{(ab)^{-1}}$

50. $\dfrac{x^{-2} + y^{-2}}{x^{-2} - y^{-2}}$

51. $\dfrac{xy^{-2} + x^{-2}y}{x + y}$

52. $\dfrac{x^{-2} + xy^{-2}}{(x^2y)^{-2}}$

In problems 53–56, rationalize the denominator of each fraction and simplify.

53. $\dfrac{1}{\sqrt{5} - 3}$

54. $\dfrac{3}{\sqrt{7} + 4}$

55. $\dfrac{1 - \sqrt{x}}{1 + \sqrt{x}}$

56. $\dfrac{x - 3}{x - \sqrt{3}}$

In problems 57 and 58, rationalize the numerator of each fraction and simplify.

57. $\dfrac{\sqrt{x + h} - \sqrt{x}}{h}$

58. $\dfrac{\sqrt{9 + 2h} - 3}{h}$

APPLICATIONS

59. **Time study** Workers A, B, and C can complete a job in a, b, and c hours, respectively. Working together they can complete

$$\frac{1}{a} + \frac{1}{b} + \frac{1}{c}$$

of the job in one hour. Add these fractions to obtain an expression for what they can do in one hour working together.

60. **Focal length** Two thin lenses with focal lengths p and q and separated by a distance d have their combined focal length given by the reciprocal of

$$\frac{1}{p} + \frac{1}{q} - \frac{d}{pq}.$$

(a) Combine these fractions.

(b) Use the reciprocal of your answer in (a) to find the combined focal length.

0.7 | LINEAR EQUATIONS AND INEQUALITIES

A firm is said to break even if its total revenue *equals* its total cost. If we have an expression representing total revenue and an expression representing total cost for a product, these expressions are *equal* when the firm breaks even. An **equation** is a statement that two quantities or algebraic expressions are equal. The two quantities on either side of the equal sign are called **members** of the equation. For example, $2 + 2 = 4$ is an equation with members $2 + 2$ and 4; $3x - 2 = 7$ is an equation with $3x - 2$ as its left member and 7 as its right member. Note that the equation $7 = 3x - 2$ is the same statement as $3x - 2 = 7$. An equation with one literal number, such as $3x - 2 = 7$, is known as an equation in one variable. The literal number (x in this case) is called a **variable** because the value of the literal number determines whether the equation is true or not. For example, $3x - 2 = 7$ is true only for $x = 3$. Finding the value(s) of the variable(s) that make the equation true is called **solving the equation.** The set of solutions of an equation is called a **solution set** of the equation. The variable in an equation is sometimes called the **unknown.**

Some equations involving variables are true only for certain values of the variables, while others are true for all values of the variables. Equations that are true for all values of the variables are called **identities.** The equation $2(x - 1) = 2x - 2$ is an example of an identity. Equations that are true only for certain values of the variables are called **conditional equations** or simply **equations.** The values of the variables for which the equations are true are called the **solutions** of the equations.

Two equations are said to be **equivalent** if they have exactly the same solution set. For example,

$$4x - 12 = 16$$
$$4x = 28$$
$$x = 7$$

are equivalent equations because they all have the same solution, namely 7. We can often solve a complicated linear equation by finding an equivalent equation whose solution is easily found. We use the following properties of equality to reduce an equation to a simple equivalent equation.

PROPERTIES OF EQUALITY	EXAMPLES
Substitution Property The equation formed by substituting one expression for an equal expression is equivalent to the original equation.	$3(x - 3) - \frac{1}{2}(4x - 18) = 4$ is equivalent to $3x - 9 - 2x + 9 = 4$ and to $x = 4$. We say the solution set is $\{4\}$, or the solution is 4.
Addition Property The equation formed by adding the same quantity to both sides of an equation is equivalent to the original equation.	$x - 4 = 6$ is equivalent to $x = 10$. $x + 5 = 12$ is equivalent to $x = 7$. (Subtracting 5 from both sides is equivalent to adding -5 to both sides.)
Multiplication Property The equation formed by multiplying both sides of an equation by the same nonzero quantity is equivalent to the original equation.	$\frac{1}{3}x = 6$ is equivalent to $x = 18$, and $5x = 20$ is equivalent to $x = 4$. (Dividing both sides by 5 is equivalent to multiplying both sides by $\frac{1}{5}$.)

If an equation contains one variable and if the variable occurs to the first degree, the equation is called a **linear equation in one variable.** The three properties above permit us to reduce any linear equation in one unknown to an equivalent equation whose solution is obvious. We may solve linear equations in one unknown by using the following procedure:

SOLVING A LINEAR EQUATION

PROCEDURE	EXAMPLE
To solve a linear equation in one unknown:	Solve $\dfrac{3x}{4} + 3 = \dfrac{2(x-1)}{6}$.
1. If the equation contains fractions, multiply both sides by the least common denominator (LCD) of the fractions.	1. LCD is 12. $12\left(\dfrac{3x}{4} + 3\right) = 12\left(\dfrac{2(x-1)}{6}\right)$
2. Remove any parentheses in the equation.	2. $\qquad 9x + 36 = 4x - 4$
3. Perform any additions or subtractions to get all terms containing the variable on one side and all other terms on the other side.	3. $9x + 36 - 4x = 4x - 4 - 4x$ $\qquad 5x + 36 = -4$ $\quad 5x + 36 - 36 = -4 - 36$ $\qquad\qquad 5x = -40$
4. Divide both sides of the equation by the coefficient of the variable.	4. $\dfrac{5x}{5} = \dfrac{-40}{5}$ $\quad x = -8$
5. Check the solution by substitution in the original equation.	5. $\dfrac{3(-8)}{4} + 3 = -\dfrac{18}{6}$ ✓

EXAMPLE 1 | Solve $2(3y - 1) = 4(y - 5)$ for y.

Solution

1. No fractions are involved.

2. $6y - 2 = 4y - 20$ (Removing parentheses)

3. $2y - 2 = -20$ (Subtracting $4y$ from both sides)
   $2y = -18$ (Adding 2 to both sides)

4. $y = -9$ (Dividing both sides by 2)

5. $2(-28) = 4(-14)$ (Checking)

EXAMPLE 2 | The relation between degrees Celsius and degrees Fahrenheit is given by

$$F = \frac{9}{5}C + 32.$$

What Celsius temperature is equivalent to 176°F?

Solution If $F = 176$, the equation is $176 = \frac{9}{5}C + 32$. Solving for C gives

$$880 = 9C + 160$$
$$720 = 9C$$
$$80 = C.$$

Thus $80°C$ is equivalent to $176°F$.

CHECKPOINT

1. Solve for x.

  (a) $x + 9 = -2$ (b) $4x = 7$ (c) $-\frac{1}{3}x = 15$

  (d) $3(x - 7) = 19 - x$ (e) $4 - 5x = 4 + x$

2. Let $\dfrac{5(x - 3)}{6} - x = 1 - \dfrac{x}{9}$.

  (a) Find the LCD of the denominators.
  (b) Multiply both sides of the equation by the LCD.
  (c) Complete the solution.

EXAMPLE 3

Suppose that the relationship between a firm's profit P and the number x of items sold can be described by the equation

$$5x - 4P = 1200.$$

(a) How many units must be produced and sold for the firm to make a profit of $150?
(b) Solve this equation for P in terms of x.
(c) Find the profit when 240 units are sold.

Solution

(a) $5x - 4(150) = 1200$ (b) $5x - 1200 = 4P$
$\qquad\ 5x - 600 = 1200$ $\qquad\qquad P = \dfrac{5}{4}x - 300$
$\qquad\qquad\ \ 5x = 1800$
$\qquad\qquad\quad x = 360$ units

(c) $P = \dfrac{5}{4}x - 300$

$\quad\ P = \dfrac{5}{4}(240) - 300 = 0$

We say that the firm breaks even (profit $P = 0$) when $x = 240$ units.

EXAMPLE 4   A bicycle costs the wholesaler $28.00. What will the retailer sell it for if the wholesaler's markup is 20% of the wholesale selling price and the retailer's markup is 30% of the retail selling price?

Solution The wholesaler's markup of 20% means his or her cost ($28.00) plus 20% of the wholesale selling price gives the wholesale selling price.

$$\$28.00 + 0.20S_w = S_w$$
$$\$28.00 = 0.80S_w$$
$$\$35.00 = S_w \qquad \text{(See Figure 0.10.)}$$

The wholesaler's selling price is $35.00, so the retailer's cost is $35.00. The retailer's markup is 30%, so the retail cost ($35.00) plus 30% of the retail selling price is the retail selling price.

$$\$35.00 + 0.30S_r = S_r$$
$$\$35.00 = 0.70S_r$$
$$\$50.00 = S_r$$

The retailer will sell the bicycle for $50.00.

FIGURE 0.10

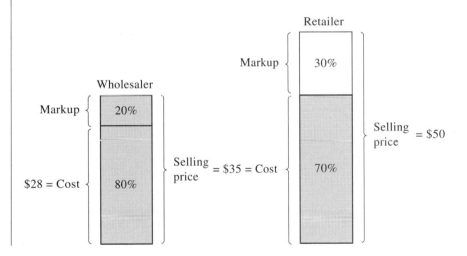

In calculus we sometimes need to solve inequalities. The **solution set** of an inequality contains the values of the variable that satisfy the inequality. Two inequalities are **equivalent** if they have the same solution set. We use properties of inequalities to reduce an inequality to an equivalent inequality whose solution can be easily found.

PROPERTIES THAT GIVE EQUIVALENT INEQUALITIES	EXAMPLES
Substitution Property Substituting one expression for an equal expression	$5x - 4x < 6$ is equivalent to $x < 6$.
Addition Property Adding the same quantity to both sides of an inequality	$x - 4 > 6$ is equivalent to $x > 10$. $x + 5 < 12$ is equivalent to $x < 7$.
Multiplication Property I Multiplying both sides of an inequality by the same *positive* quantity	$\frac{1}{2}x > 8$ is equivalent to $x > 16$. $3x < 6$ is equivalent to $x < 2$.
Multiplication Property II Multiplying both sides of an inequality by a *negative* number and reversing the sense of the inequality	$\dfrac{x}{-3} < 4$ is equivalent to $x > -12$. $-3x > -27$ is equivalent to $x < 9$.

EXAMPLE 5   Solve the following inequality and graph the solution set.

$$\frac{s}{-2} < -4$$

Solution

$$\frac{s}{-2} < -4$$

$$\frac{s}{-2}(-2) > -4(-2)$$

$$s > 8$$

The solution set is $(8, \infty)$. The graph of the solution set is shown in Figure 0.11.

FIGURE 0.11

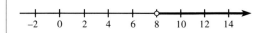

Solving some inequalities will require several operations. In this case, the order in which the operations are performed is the same as that used in solving linear equations.

EXAMPLE 6 | Solve the inequality $2(x - 4) \leq \dfrac{x - 3}{3}$

Solution

$$6(x - 4) \leq x - 3 \qquad \text{(Multiplying both sides by 3)}$$

$$6x - 24 \leq x - 3 \qquad \text{(Removing parentheses)}$$

$$5x \leq 21 \qquad \text{(Performing additions and subtractions)}$$

$$x \leq \tfrac{21}{5} \qquad \text{(Dividing)}$$

The solution set is $(-\infty, \tfrac{21}{5}]$. See Figure 0.12.

FIGURE 0.12

CHECKPOINT

Solve each inequality and give the solution in interval notation.

3. $-5x > 10$ \qquad\qquad 4. $8x - 3 \geq 3(x - 6)$

A **compound inequality** can be solved by decomposing it into two inequalities.

EXAMPLE 7 | Solve the compound inequality $4x - 4 < 3x - 2 < 7x$.

Solution The values of x that satisfy $4x - 4 < 3x - 2 < 7x$ satisfy *both* of the inequalities

$4x - 4 < 3x - 2$	and	$3x - 2 < 7x$
$x - 4 < -2$		$-2 < 4x$
$x < 2$		$-\tfrac{1}{2} < x$

Thus the given inequality is true if and only if $x < 2$ *and* $-\tfrac{1}{2} < x$; or equivalently

$$-\tfrac{1}{2} < x < 2$$

The solution set is $(-\tfrac{1}{2}, 2)$. The graph is shown in Figure 0.13.

FIGURE 0.13

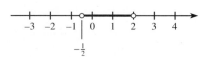

CHECKPOINT
SOLUTIONS

1. (a) $x + 9 = -2$

$x = -2 - 9$

$= -11$

(b) $4x = 7$

$x = \dfrac{7}{4}$

(c) $-\dfrac{1}{3}x = 15$

$x = (15)(-3)$

$= -45$

(d) $3(x - 7) = 19 - x$

$3x - 21 = 19 - x$

$4x = 40$

$x = 10$

(e) $4 - 5x = 4 + x$

$-5x = x$

$0 = 6x$

$\dfrac{0}{6} = x$

$x = 0$

2. $\dfrac{5(x - 3)}{6} - x = 1 - \dfrac{x}{9}$

(a) LCD of 6 and 9 is 18.

(b) $18\left(\dfrac{5x - 15}{6}\right) - 18(x) = 18(1) - 18\left(\dfrac{x}{9}\right)$

(c) $3(5x - 15) - 18x = 18 - 2x$
$15x - 45 - 18x = 18 - 2x$
$-45 - 3x = 18 - 2x$
$-63 = x$

3. $-5x > 10$

$-\left(\dfrac{1}{5}\right)(-5x) < \left(-\dfrac{1}{5}\right)(10)$ $\begin{cases} \text{Multiply both sides} \\ \text{by } -\frac{1}{5} \text{ and reverse} \\ \text{the inequality sign.} \end{cases}$

$x < -2$ The solution set is $(-\infty, -2)$.

4. $8x - 3 \geq 3(x - 6)$
$8x - 3 \geq 3x - 18$
$5x \geq -15$
$x \geq -3$ The solution set is $[-3, \infty)$.

EXERCISE 0.7

In problems 1–20, solve each equation.

1. $4x + 4 = 4$

2. $x = 3x$

3. $4x - 7 = 8x - 2$

4. $3x + 2 = 7x + 2$

5. $15 + x = 3(x - 1)$

6. $4x - 1 = 3(x - 1)$

7. $3x + \dfrac{1}{2} = 8$

8. $\dfrac{x}{2} + 4 = \dfrac{1}{3}$

9. $\dfrac{5x}{2} - 4 = \dfrac{2x - 7}{6}$

10. $\dfrac{2x}{3} - 1 = \dfrac{x - 2}{2}$

11. $\dfrac{5x - 1}{9} = \dfrac{5(x - 1)}{6}$

12. $\dfrac{6x + 5}{2} = \dfrac{5(2 - x)}{3}$

13. $0.4x = 16$

14. $0.4x + 5 = 9$

15. $2(x - 7) = 5(x + 3) - x$

16. $3(x - 4) = 4 - 2(x + 2)$

17. $\dfrac{x+3}{2x-1}=4$ 18. $\dfrac{x-2}{3x+2}=2$

19. $\dfrac{1}{x+2}-\dfrac{1}{2}=\dfrac{x}{x+2}$ 20. $\dfrac{1}{4x}+\dfrac{2}{x}=\dfrac{5}{12}$

⊞ In problems 21–22, use a calculator to solve each equation. Round your answer to three decimal places.

21. $3.259x-8.638=-3.8(8.625x+4.917)$

22. $3.319(14.1x-5)=9.95-4.6x$

In problems 23–26, solve each equation for y in terms of x.

23. $3x+2y=40$ 24. $4x-3y+18=0$

25. $5(x-y-1)=6(y-x+1)$

26. $4(x+y)=3(x-1)+2(y-1)$

In problems 27–38, solve each inequality and then graph the solution and express it in interval notation.

27. $x-3\geq 2x+1$ 28. $2x-1\leq 3x+4$

29. $3(x-1)<2x-1$ 30. $2(x+1)>x-1$

31. $\dfrac{x}{3}>x-1$ 32. $\dfrac{x-3}{4}\geq 2x$

33. $-\dfrac{x}{4}\leq 4$ 34. $1-5x<21$

35. $-1<\dfrac{3x+1}{2}<1$ 36. $-3<\dfrac{1-2x}{4}<3$

37. $2x+1\leq x-3\leq 3x+6$

38. $4x-1<4-x\leq x+2$

APPLICATIONS

39. **Wildlife management** In wildlife management, the capture-mark-recapture technique is used to estimate the populations of fish or birds in an area or to measure the infestation of insects such as Japanese beetles. Suppose 100 individuals of the species being studied are caught, marked, and released, and one week later 100 more are caught. To estimate the total number of individuals, the following relationship is used:

$$\frac{\text{Total marked found in 2nd capture}}{\text{Total in 2nd capture}}=\frac{\text{Total number marked}}{\text{Total population}}.$$

(a) If in the second capture of 100, it is found that 3 are marked, what is the total population estimate?

(b) Suppose that 1000 beetles are captured, marked, and released. Suppose further that in the second capture of 1000 it is found that 63 are marked. What is the population estimate?

40. **Simple interest** Joe bought a radio for $99.95. He paid $19.95 down and agreed to pay the balance plus a finance charge of $2.00 in three months. What rate of simple interest did he pay? (Use the formula: interest = principal × rate × time.)

41. **Height-weight relationships** It has been noted that for adults over 5 feet tall in the northeast United States, their ideal weight is related to their height according to

$$3w+110=11(h-20)$$

where w is measured in pounds and h is measured in inches. Use the formula above to answer the following.

(a) Find the ideal weight of an adult whose height is 5 feet, 6 inches.

(b) What should be the height of adults weighing 160 pounds.

42. **Manufacturing** A firm produces two types of widgets, A and B. Each unit of A requires 3 work-hours and each unit of B requires 4 work-hours. If there are 430 work-hours available each week, how many units of A can be produced if 40 units of B are produced?

43. **Organizational impact** The Hillcrest Youth Organization determines the number of youths it has served by adding its active registrations and the number of dropouts. If the drop-out rate is one-third of the total served, find the total number of youths served when there are 6000 youths actively registered.

44. **Population** A city has a population P at the beginning of a year. The birth rate during the year was 10 per thousand and the death rate was 12 per thousand (of the year's original population). During the year, 360 people moved into the city and 190 moved away. If the population at the end of the year is 30,110, what was the population at the beginning of the year?

45. **Insect behavior** The number of times n per minute that a cricket chirps is related to the Fahrenheit temperature T. This relationship can be approximated by

$$7n - 12T = 52.$$

(a) Solve this equation for T.
(b) If you count 28 chirps in 15 seconds, find the approximate temperature.

46. **Seawater pressure** In seawater, the pressure p is related to the depth d according to

$$33p - 18d = 495,$$

where d is in feet and p is in pounds per square inch.
(a) Solve this equation for p in terms of d.
(b) The *Titanic* was discovered at a depth of 12,460 ft. Find the pressure at this depth.

47. **Investments** The total amount of a simple interest investment is given by

$$A = P + Prt.$$

What principal P must be invested for $t = 5$ years at the simple interest rate $r = 10\%$ so that the amount A grows to $6,000?

48. **Sales tax** The total price of a new car (including 6% sales tax) is $10,033. How much of this is tax?

49. **Markup** A retailer wants a 30% markup on the selling price of an item that costs him $214.90. What selling price should he charge?

50. **Markup** A toaster costs the Ace Department Store $22.74. If the store marks the toaster up by 40% of the selling price, what is the selling price?

51. **Markup** A room air conditioner costs the wholesaler $154.98. If the wholesaler's markup is 10% of the wholesale selling price and if the retailer's markup is 30% of the retail selling price, for what does the retailer sell the air conditioner?

52. **Markup** An electric mixer retails for $48.54, which includes a markup of 40% for the retailer and a markup of 20% for the wholesaler. If these markups are based on selling price, what did the mixer cost the (a) retailer? (b) wholesaler?

53. **Markup** A dinette set costs a wholesaler $189 and her markup is 10% of her selling price. If the retailer's markup is 30% of his selling price for the item, what is the retailer's selling price?

54. **Markup** A wholesaler wants to establish a list price for an item so that his selling price gives a trade discount of 10% of the list price. If he makes a markup of 20% of this selling price, and if his cost is $160, what list price should he establish?

55. **Profit** A car dealer purchases 20 new automobiles for $8000 each. If he sells 16 of them at a profit of 20%, for how much must he sell the remaining 4 to obtain an average profit of 18%?

56. **Investment mix** A woman has $90,000 to invest. She has chosen one relatively safe investment fund that has an annual yield of 10% and another riskier one that has a 15% annual yield. How much should she invest in each fund if she would like to earn $10,000 per year from her investments?

57. **Profit** Suppose that when a company produces and sells x units of its product, the total cost is $C = 27.5x + 13,750$ and the revenue (income) is given by $R = 40x$. Find x so that revenue is greater than total cost (that is, so that a profit is made).

58. **Commission** A salesperson has monthly income I given by $I = 1000 + 0.062S$, where S is the monthly sales volume. How much must she sell to make at least $3500 in a month?

59. ***Federal income taxes*** The 1991 tax brackets for a single person claiming one personal exemption are given in the following table.

Taxable income I	Tax T
$0–$20,350	15% I
$20,350–$49,300	28% (I − 20,350) + 3052.50
> $49,300	31% (I − 49,300) + 11,158.50

(a) Write the income ranges in the table as inequalities.
(b) For each income bracket, write the inequality that represents the amount of tax owed.

60. ***Age-height norms for boys*** From data adapted from the National Center for Health Statistics, the height H in inches and age A in years for boys between 4 and 16 years of age are related according to

$$H = 2.31A + 31.26.$$

To account for normal variability among boys, normal height for a given age is ±5% of the height obtained from the equation. Find the normal height range for a boy that is
(a) 10.5 years old, and write it as an inequality.
(b) 5.75 years old, and write it as an inequality.

KEY TERMS & FORMULAS

SECTION	KEY TERM	FORMULA
0.1	Sets and set membership	
	Natural numbers	$\{1, 2, 3, 4, \ldots\}$
	Empty set	$\varnothing$
	Set equality	
	Subset	$A \subseteq B$
	Universal set	U
	Venn diagrams	
	Set intersection	$A \cap B$
	Disjoint sets	$A \cap B = \varnothing$
	Set union	$A \cup B$
	Set complement	A'
	Real numbers	
	Subsets and properties	
	Real number line	
	Inequalities	
	Intervals and interval notation	
	Absolute value	
	Order of operations	

SECTION	KEY TERM	FORMULA
0.2	Exponent and base	a^n has base a, exponent n
	Zero exponent	$a^0 = 1, a \neq 0$
	Negative exponent	$a^{-n} = \dfrac{1}{a^n}$
	Rules of exponents	
0.3	Radical	$\sqrt[n]{a}$
	Radicand, index	radicand $= a$; index $= n$
	Principal nth root	$\sqrt[n]{a} = b$ only if $b^n = a$ and $a \geq 0$ when n is even
	Fractional exponents	$a^{1/n} = \sqrt[n]{a}$ $a^{m/n} = \sqrt[n]{a^m} = (\sqrt[n]{a})^m$
	Properties of radicals	
	Rationalizing the denominator	
0.4	Algebraic expression	
	Variable	
	Constant term	
	Coefficient; leading coefficient	
	Term	
	Polynomial	$a_n x^n + \cdots + a_1 x + a_0$
	Degree	
	Monomial	
	Binomial	
	Trinomial	
	Like terms	
	Distributive Law	$a(b + c) = ab + ac$
	Binomial products	
	Division of polynomials	
0.5	Factor	
	Common factor	
	Factoring by grouping	
	Special factorizations	
	Conjugates	$a + b; a - b$
	Quadratic polynomials	$ax^2 + bx + c$
	Factoring completely	

SECTION	KEY TERM	FORMULA
0.6	Algebraic fractions	
	Numerator	
	Denominator	
	Reduce	
	Product of fractions	
	Quotient of fractions	
	Common denominator	
	Lowest common denominator (LCD)	
	Addition and subtraction of fractions	
	Complex fraction	
	Rationalize the denominator	
0.7	Equation; members; variable	
	Identities	
	Conditional equations	
	Properties of equality	
	Linear equation in one variable	
	Inequality	
	Solution set	
	Equivalent inequalities	
	Properties that give	
	Solution of inequalities in one variable	
	Compound inequality	

REVIEW
EXERCISES

0.1

1. Is $A \subseteq B$, if $A = \{1, 2, 5, 7\}$ and $B = \{x: x \text{ is a positive integer}, x < 8\}$?
2. Is it true that $3 \in \{x: x > 3\}$?
3. Are $A = \{1, 2, 3, 4\}$ and $B = \{x: x \leq 1\}$ disjoint?

In problems 4–6, use the sets $A = \{1, 2, 3, 9\}$, $B = \{1, 3, 5, 6, 7, 8, 10\}$, and $U = \{1, 2, 3, 4, 5, 6, 7, 8, 9, 10\}$ to find the elements of the sets described.

4. $A \cup B$ 5. $A \cap B$ 6. A'

7. Indicate whether the given expression is one or more of the following: rational, irrational, integer, natural, or meaningless.

   (a) π (b) 0/6   (c) 6/0

8. Insert the proper sign $<$, $=$, or $>$ to replace each $\square$.

(a) $\pi \square 3.14$ 　　　　(b) $-100 \square 0.1$ 　　　　(c) $-3 \square -12$

⊞ For problems 9–14, evaluate each expression. Use a calculator when necessary.

9. $|5 - 11|$

10. $44 \div 2 \cdot 11 - 10^2$

11. $\dfrac{4 + 3^2}{4}$

12. $\dfrac{(3)(2)(15) - (5)(8)}{(4)(10)}$

13. $2 - [3 - (2 - |-3|)] + 11$

14. $-4^2 - (-4)^2 + 3$

15. Write each inequality in interval notation, name the type of interval, and graph it on a real number line.

(a) $0 \le x \le 5$ 　　　　(b) $x \ge -3$ and $x < 7$ 　　　　(c) $(-4, \infty) \cap (-\infty, 0)$

16. Write an inequality that represents each of the following.

(a) $(-1, 16)$ 　　　　(b) $[-12, 8]$ 　　　　(c)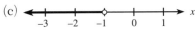

0.2

17. Evaluate each of the following without a calculator.

(a) $\left(\dfrac{3}{8}\right)^0$ 　　　　(b) $2^3 \cdot 2^4$ 　　　　(c) $\dfrac{4^9}{4^3}$ 　　　　(d) $\left(\dfrac{1}{7}\right)^3 \left(\dfrac{1}{7}\right)^{-4}$

18. Use the rules of exponents to simplify each of the following with positive exponents. Assume all variables are nonzero.

(a) $x^5 \cdot x^{-7}$ 　　　(b) x^8/x^{-2} 　　　(c) $(x^3)^3$ 　　　(d) $(y^4)^{-2}$ 　　　(e) $(-y^{-3})^{-2}$

For problems 19–22, rewrite each expression so only positive exponents remain. Assume all variables are nonzero.

19. $\left(\dfrac{2}{3}x^2 y^{-4}\right)^{-2}$ 　　　20. $\left(\dfrac{x^{-2}}{2y^{-1}}\right)^2$ 　　　21. $\dfrac{(-x^4 y^{-2} z^2)^0}{-(x^4 y^{-2} z^2)^{-2}}$ 　　　22. $\left(\dfrac{x^{-3} y^4 z^{-2}}{3x^{-2} y^{-3} z^{-3}}\right)^{-1}$

0.3

23. Find the following roots.

(a) $-\sqrt[3]{-64}$ 　　　　(b) $\sqrt{4/49}$

24. Write each of the following with an exponent and with the variable in the numerator.

(a) $\sqrt{x}$ 　　　　(b) $\sqrt[3]{x^2}$ 　　　　(c) $1/\sqrt[4]{x}$

25. Write each of the following in radical form.

(a) $x^{2/3}$ 　　　　(b) $x^{-1/2}$ 　　　　(c) $-x^{3/2}$

26. Rationalize each of the following denominators and simplify.

(a) $\dfrac{5xy}{\sqrt{2x}}$ 　　　　(b) $\dfrac{y}{x\sqrt[3]{xy^2}}$

In problems 27–32, use the properties of exponents to simplify, so only positive exponents remain. Assume all variables are positive.

27. $x^{1/2} \cdot x^{1/3}$ 　　　28. $y^{-3/4}/y^{-7/4}$ 　　　29. $x^4 \cdot x^{1/4}$

30. $1/(x^{-4/3} \cdot x^{-7/3})$ 31. $(x^{4/5})^{1/2}$ 32. $(x^{1/2}y^2)^4$

In problems 33–38, simplify each expression. Assume all variables are positive.

33. $\sqrt{12x^3y^5}$ 34. $\sqrt{1250x^6y^9}$ 35. $\sqrt[3]{24x^4y^4} \cdot \sqrt[3]{45x^4y^{10}}$

36. $\sqrt{16a^2b^3} \cdot \sqrt{8a^3b^5}$ 37. $\dfrac{\sqrt{52x^3y^6}}{\sqrt{13xy^4}}$ 38. $\dfrac{\sqrt{32x^4y^3}}{\sqrt{6xy^{10}}}$

0.4   In problems 39–56, perform the indicated operations and simplify.

39. $(3x + 5) - (4x + 7)$ 40. $x(1 - x) + x[x - (2 + x)]$

41. $(3x^3 - 4xy - 3) + (5xy + x^3 + 4y - 1)$ 42. $(4xy^3)(6x^4y^2)$

43. $(3x - 4)(x - 1)$ 44. $(3x - 1)(x + 2)$

45. $(4x + 1)(x - 2)$ 46. $(3x - 7)(2x + 1)$

47. $(2x - 3)^2$ 48. $(4x + 3)(4x - 3)$

49. $(2x^2 + 1)(x^2 + x - 3)$ 50. $(2x - 1)^3$

51. $(x - y)(x^2 + xy + y^2)$ 52. $\dfrac{4x^2y - 3x^3y^3 - 6x^4y^2}{2x^2y^2}$

53. $(3x^4 + 2x^3 - x + 4) \div (x^2 + 1)$ 54. $(x^4 - 4x^3 + 5x^2 + x) \div (x - 3)$

55. $x^{4/3}(x^{2/3} - x^{-1/3})$ 56. $(\sqrt{x} + \sqrt{a - x})(\sqrt{x} - \sqrt{a - x})$

0.5   In problems 57–65, factor each expression completely.

57. $2x^4 - x^3$ 58. $4(x^2 + 1)^2 - 2(x^2 + 1)^3$ 59. $4x^2 - 4x + 1$

60. $16 - 9x^2$ 61. $2x^4 - 8x^2$ 62. $x^2 - 4x - 21$

63. $3x^2 - x - 2$ 64. $12x^2 - 23x - 24$ 65. $16x^4 - 72x^2 + 81$

66. Factor as indicated: $x^{-2/3} + x^{-4/3} = x^{-4/3}(?)$

0.6   67. Reduce each of the following to lowest terms:

(a) $\dfrac{2x}{2x + 4}$ (b) $\dfrac{4x^2y^3 - 6x^3y^4}{2x^2y^2 - 3xy^3}$

In problems 68–74, perform the indicated operations and simplify.

68. $\dfrac{x^2 - 4x}{x^2 + 4} \cdot \dfrac{x^4 - 16}{x^4 - 16x^2}$ 69. $\dfrac{x^2 + 6x + 9}{x^2 - 7x + 12} \div \dfrac{x^2 + 4x + 3}{x^2 - 3x - 4}$

70. $\dfrac{x^4 - 2x^3}{3x^2 - x - 2} \div \dfrac{x^3 - 4x}{9x^2 - 4}$ 71. $1 + \dfrac{3}{2x} - \dfrac{1}{6x^2}$

72. $\dfrac{1}{x - 2} - \dfrac{x - 2}{4}$ 73. $\dfrac{x + 2}{x^2 - x} - \dfrac{x^2 + 4}{x^2 - 2x + 1} + 1$

74. $\dfrac{x - 1}{x^2 - x - 2} - \dfrac{x}{x^2 - 2x - 3} + \dfrac{1}{x - 2}$

In problems 75 and 76, simplify each complex fraction.

75. $\dfrac{x - 1 - \dfrac{x - 1}{x}}{\dfrac{1}{x - 1} + 1}$

76. $\dfrac{x^{-2} - x^{-1}}{x^{-2} + x^{-1}}$

77. Rationalize the denominator of $\dfrac{3x - 3}{\sqrt{x} - 1}$ and simplify.

78. Rationalize the numerator of $\dfrac{\sqrt{x} - \sqrt{x - 4}}{2}$ and simplify.

0.7

Solve the equations in problems 79–86.

79. $x + 7 = 14$

80. $3x - 8 = 23$

81. $2(x - 4) = 3x + 5$

82. $\dfrac{6x + 3}{6} = \dfrac{5(x - 2)}{9}$

83. $2x + \dfrac{1}{2} = \dfrac{x}{2} + \dfrac{1}{3}$

84. $0.6x + 4 = x - 0.02$

85. $\dfrac{3}{x} - 2 = 3 + \dfrac{1}{x}$

86. $2.81(3.62x - 4.02) = \dfrac{0.061x - 3.82}{412}$

In problems 87–90, solve each inequality. Express the solution in interval notation and graph it.

87. $3x - 9 \le 4(3 - x)$

88. $-\dfrac{2}{5}x \le 10$

89. $\dfrac{4(x - 2)}{3} \ge 3x - \dfrac{1}{6}$

90. $-1 < \dfrac{x - 2}{3} < 1$

APPLICATIONS

91. **Cost analysis** The owner of a small construction business needs a new truck. He can buy a diesel truck for $18,000 and it will cost him $0.16 per mile to operate. He can buy a gas engine truck for $16,000 and it will cost him $0.21 per mile to operate. Find the number of miles he must drive before the costs are equal. If he normally keeps a truck for 5 years, which is the better buy?

92. **Profit** A company's income is given by $I = 38x$, and their expenses are given by $E = 13x + 8500$, where x is the number of units produced and sold.
    (a) Determine x so that the company's income exceeds expenses (that is, so the company makes a profit).
    (b) Determine x so that the company's income exactly meets expenses (that is, so the company breaks even).

CAMPAIGN MANAGEMENT

A politician is trying to win election to the city council, and as his campaign manager, you need to decide how to promote the candidate. There are three ways you can do so: you can send glossy, full-color pamphlets to registered voters of the city, you can run a commercial during the television news on a local cable network, and/or you can buy a full-page ad in the newspaper.

Two hundred fifty thousand voters live in the city, and 36% of them read the newspaper. Fifty thousand voters watch the local cable network news, and 30% of them also read the newspaper.

You also know that the television commercial would cost $40,000, the newspaper ad, $27,000, and the pamphlets mailed to voters, 90 cents each, including printing and bulk-rate postage.

Suppose the success of the candidate depends on your campaign reaching at least 125,000 voters, and because your budget is limited, you must achieve this goal at a minimum cost. What would your plan and the cost of that plan be?

If you need help devising a method of solution for this problem, try answering the following questions first.

1. How many voters in the city read the newspaper but do not watch the local cable television news?

2. How many voters read the newspaper or watch the local cable television news or both?

3. Complete the following chart indicating the number of voters reached by each promotional option, the total cost, and the cost per voter reached.

	Number of voters reached	Total cost	Cost per voter reached
Pamphlet			
Television			
Newspaper			

4. Now, explain your plan and the cost of that plan.

PREREQUISITE PROBLEM TYPE	REVIEW SECTION/ANSWER
Sections 1.1, 1.2, 1.3, 1.4, 1.5, 1.6	Section 0.1, Real numbers
Evaluate:	
(a) $2(3)^3 - 3(3)^2 + 1$ (b) $\dfrac{-1-3}{-2-4}$	(a) 28 (b) $\frac{2}{3}$
(c) $\dfrac{19-11}{6-3.5}$ (d) $\dfrac{-(40)}{2(-0.4)}$	(c) 3.2 (d) 50
(e) $b^2 - 4ac$ if $a=4, b=-15, c=-8$	(e) 353
Sections 1.2, 1.4	Section 0.4, Algebraic expressions
Identify the coefficient of x (and/or of x^2) and the constant term in each expression.	
(a) $-\frac{1}{2}x + 4$ (b) $\frac{1}{4}x$	(a) $-\frac{1}{2}$; 4 (b) $\frac{1}{4}$; 0
(c) $-0.4x^2 - 4x + 4$ (d) $4x^2 - 15x - 8$	(c) -0.4; -4; 4 (d) 4; -15; -8
Section 1.1	Section 0.4, Algebraic expressions
Simplify $\dfrac{[3(x+h)-1]-(3x-1)}{h}$.	3
Sections 1.1, 1.5	Section 0.1, Section 0.3, Real numbers Radicals
(a) $1/x$ is undefined for which real numbers?	(a) 0 (b) $x \le 4$
(b) $\sqrt{4-x}$ is a real number for which values of x?	
Sections 1.1, 1.2, 1.3, 1.4, 1.5, 1.6	Section 0.1, Real number line
Locate 2, 1, $\frac{1}{2}$, 0, $-\frac{1}{2}$, -1 on a number line	
Sections 1.4, 1.5, 1.6	Section 0.5, Factoring
Factor completely.	
(a) $4x^2 - 400x + 3600$ (b) $q^2 + 20q - 2400$	(a) $4(x-10)(x-90)$ (b) $(q+60)(q-40)$
Sections 1.2, 1.3, 1.4, 1.6	Section 0.7, Linear equations
Solve:	
(a) $10x = 2.5x + 1200$ (b) $-3q + 26 = 4q - 9$	(a) $x = 160$ (b) $q = 5$
(c) $2x + 3y = 5$ for y	(c) $y = -\frac{2}{3}x + \frac{5}{3}$

WARM UP

1 | FUNCTIONS

In this chapter, we introduce the concept of a function and consider some special mathematical functions: linear, quadratic, polynomial, and rational functions. We examine the algebraic structure of the formulas that define these functions, and we consider the characteristics of the graphs of each type of function.

A variety of applications that use each type of function are considered. Special attention is given to the functions that model a company's total costs, total revenue, and profit and that model supply and demand in the marketplace. These important business application functions are carefully developed because, in later chapters, we expand our study of them as we expand our mathematical skills.

1.1 | FUNCTIONS AND GRAPHS

It is reasonable to assume that a relation exists between the number of items a firm sells and its total revenue (the money brought into the firm by the sale of its product). It is frequently possible to express this relation by means of an equation. For example, if a firm sells its product for $35 per unit, then the total revenue for a period of time could be expressed by the equation

$$R = 35x$$

where x represents the quantity sold by the firm during that period.

An equation containing two variables expresses a **relation** between those two variables. For example, the equation $R = 35x$ expresses a relation between the two variables x and R, and the equation $y = 4x - 3$ expresses a relation between the two variables x and y.

In addition to defining a relation by an equation or rule of correspondence, we may also define it as any set of **ordered pairs** of real numbers (a, b). For example, the solutions to $y = 4x - 3$ are pairs of numbers (one for x and one for y). We write the pairs (x, y) so that the first number is the x-value and the second is the y-value, and these ordered pairs define the relation between x and y.

Relation	A **relation** is defined by a set of ordered pairs or by a rule that determines how the ordered pairs are found.

For example,

$$\{(1, 3), (2, 6), (3, 9), (4, 12)\}$$

expresses a relation between the set of first components, $\{1, 2, 3, 4\}$, and the set of second components, $\{3, 6, 9, 12\}$. The set of first components is called the **domain** of the relation, and the set of second components is called the **range** of the relation. Figure 1.1 uses arrows to indicate how the inputs from the domain (the first components) are associated with the outputs in the range (the second components).

FIGURE 1.1

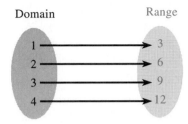

Domain   Range

An equation frequently expresses how the second component (the output) is obtained from the first component (the input). For example, the equation

$$y = 4x - 3$$

expresses how the output y results from the input x. This equation expresses a special relation between x and y, because each value of x that is substituted into the equation results in only one value for y. If each value of x put into an equation results in one value of y, we say that the equation expresses y as a **function** of x.

Definition of a Function	In general, a **function** is a relation between two sets such that to each element of the domain (input) there corresponds exactly one element of the range (output).

When a function is defined by an equation, the variable that represents the numbers in the domain (input) is called the **independent variable** of the function, and the variable that represents the numbers in the range (output) is called the **dependent variable** (because its values depend on the values of the independent variable). When we say "the equation $y = 4x - 3$ defines y as a function of x," we are saying that the equation defines a function with independent variable x and dependent variable y.

The equation

$$y = 4x^2$$

defines y as a function of x, because only one value of y will result from each value of x that is substituted into the equation. Thus x is the independent variable and y is the dependent variable.

EXAMPLE 1

Does $y^2 = 2x$ express y as a function of x?

Solution No, because for some values of x there is more than one value for y. In fact, there are two y-values for each $x > 0$. For example, if $x = 8$, $y = \pm 4$. The equation $y^2 = 2x$ expresses a relation between x and y, but y is not a function of x.

It is possible to picture geometrically the relations and functions that we have been discussing by sketching their graphs on a rectangular coordinate system. We construct a rectangular coordinate system by drawing two real number lines (called **coordinate axes**) perpendicular to each other and intersecting at their origins (called the **origin** of the system).

Any point P plotted a units from the y-axis (right or left, depending on whether a is positive or negative) and b units from the x-axis (up or down, depending on whether b is positive or negative) is denoted by the ordered pair (a, b). See Figure 1.2.

FIGURE 1.2

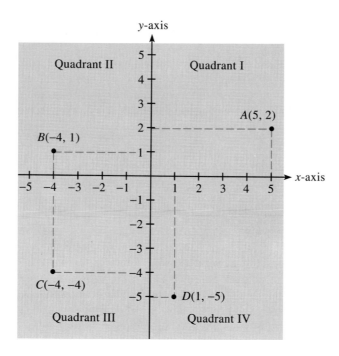

The values a and b in the ordered pair associated with the point P are called the **rectangular** (or **Cartesian**) **coordinates** of the point, where a is the **x-coordinate** (or **abscissa**), and b is the **y-coordinate** (or **ordinate**). The ordered pairs (a, b) and (c, d) are equal if and only if $a = c$ and $b = d$.

We can sketch the graph of an equation that defines a function (or relation) by plotting a limited number of points whose coordinates (x, y) satisfy the equation. When enough points have been plotted to suggest the shape of the graph, we draw a smooth curve through the points.

EXAMPLE 2

(a) Graph the function $y = 4x^2$.

(b) Graph the relation $y^2 = 2x$.

Solution

(a) We choose some sample values of x and find the corresponding values of y. Placing these in a table, we have sample points to plot. When we have enough to determine the shape of the graph, we connect the points to complete the graph. The table and graph are shown in Figure 1.3(a).

(b) Sample points of the relation are given in the table of values. Note that no negative values are in the domain of the relation. Choosing points that can be easily graphed and completing the curve gives the graph in Figure 1.3(b).

FIGURE 1.3

x	y
-1	4
$-\frac{1}{2}$	1
0	0
$\frac{1}{2}$	1
1	4
2	16

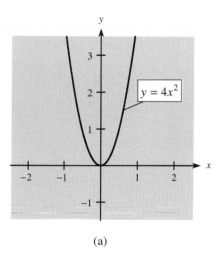

(a)

x	y
-3	—
-2	—
-1	—
0	0
1	$\pm\sqrt{2}$
2	± 2
3	$\pm\sqrt{6}$
4	$\pm 2\sqrt{2}$
5	$\pm\sqrt{10}$
6	$\pm 2\sqrt{3}$
7	$\pm\sqrt{14}$
8	± 4

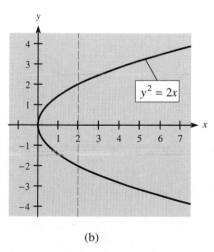

(b)

We can determine whether a relation is a function by inspecting its graph. If the relation is a function, no two points on the graph will have the same first coordinate (component). Thus no two points of the graph will lie on the same vertical line.

Vertical Line Test   If no vertical line exists that intersects the graph of a relation in more than one point, then the graph is the graph of a function.

Performing this test on the graph of $y = 4x^2$ [Figure 1.3(a)], we easily see that this equation describes a function. The vertical line test indicates, however, that the equation $y^2 = 2x$ [which is graphed in Figure 1.3(b)] is not a function. For example, a vertical line at $x = 2$ intersects the curve at $(2, 2)$ and $(2, -2)$.

We can use functional notation to indicate that y is a function of x. The function is denoted by f, and we write $y = f(x)$. This is read "y is a function of x" or "y equals f of x." For specific values of x, $f(x)$ represents the values of the function (that is, outputs or y-values) at those x-values. Thus if

$$f(x) = 3x^2 + 2x + 1,$$
then
$$f(2) = 3(2)^2 + 2(2) + 1 = 17$$
and
$$f(-3) = 3(-3)^2 + 2(-3) + 1 = 22.$$

Figure 1.4 represents this functional notation as (a) an operator on x and as (b) a y-coordinate for a given x-value.

FIGURE 1.4

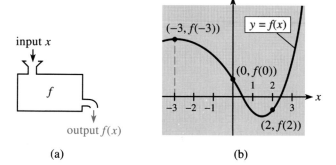

(a)

(b)

Letters other than f may also be used to denote functions. For example, $y = g(x)$ or $y = h(x)$ may be used.

EXAMPLE 3

If $y = f(x) = 2x^3 - 3x^2 + 1$, find the following.

(a) $f(0)$ (b) $f(3)$ (c) $f(-1)$

Solution

(a) $f(0) = 2(0)^3 - 3(0)^2 + 1 = 1$
   Thus $y = 1$ when $x = 0$.

(b) $f(3) = 2(3)^3 - 3(3)^2 + 1 = 2(27) - 3(9) + 1 = 28$
   Thus $y = 28$ when $x = 3$.

(c) $f(-1) = 2(-1)^3 - 3(-1)^2 + 1 = 2(-1) - 3(1) + 1 = -4$
Thus $y = -4$ when $x = -1$.

EXAMPLE 4   If $g(x) = 4x^2 - 3x + 1$, find the following.

(a) $g(a)$ (b) $g(-a)$ (c) $g(b)$ (d) $g(a + b)$

Solution

(a) $g(a) = 4(a)^2 - 3(a) + 1 = 4a^2 - 3a + 1$
(b) $g(-a) = 4(-a)^2 - 3(-a) + 1 = 4a^2 + 3a + 1$
(c) $g(b) = 4(b)^2 - 3(b) + 1 = 4b^2 - 3b + 1$
(d) $g(a + b) = 4(a + b)^2 - 3(a + b) + 1$

EXAMPLE 5   Given $f(x) = 3x - 1$, find the following.

(a) $f(4)$ (b) $f(\lambda)$ (c) $\dfrac{f(x + h) - f(x)}{h}$, if $h \neq 0$

Solution

(a) $f(4) = 3(4) - 1 = 11$ (b) $f(\lambda) = 3(\lambda) - 1 = 3\lambda - 1$

(c) $\dfrac{f(x + h) - f(x)}{h} = \dfrac{[3(x + h) - 1] - (3x - 1)}{h}$

$$= \frac{3x + 3h - 1 - 3x + 1}{h} = \frac{3h}{h} = 3$$

We will limit our discussion in this text to **real functions,** which are functions whose domains and ranges contain only real numbers. If the domain and range of a function are not specified, it is assumed that the domain consists of all real numbers that result in real numbers in the range, and that the range is a subset of the real numbers.

In general, if the domain of a function is unspecified, it will include all real numbers except:

1. values that result in a denominator of 0, and

2. values that result in an even root of a negative number.

EXAMPLE 6   Find the domain of each of the following functions; find the range for the functions in (a) and (b).

(a) $y = 4x^2$ (b) $y = \sqrt{4 - x}$ (c) $y = 1 + 1/x$

Solution

(a) There are no restrictions on the numbers substituted for x, so the domain consists of all real numbers. Since the square of any real number is nonnegative, $4x^2$ must be nonnegative. Thus the range is $y \geq 0$.

(b) We note the restriction that $4 - x$ cannot be negative. Thus the domain consists of only numbers less than or equal to 4. That is, the domain is the set of real numbers satisfying $x \leq 4$. Since $\sqrt{4 - x}$ is always nonnegative, the range is all $y \geq 0$.

(c) $1 + 1/x$ is undefined at $x = 0$ since $1/0$ is undefined. Hence, the domain consists of all real numbers except 0.

CHECKPOINT

1. If $y = f(x)$, the independent variable is _____ and the dependent variable is _____.

2. If $(1, 3)$ is on the graph of $y = f(x)$, then $f(1) = $?

3. If $f(x) = 1 - x^3$, find $f(-2)$.

4. If $f(x) = 2x^2$, find $f(x + h)$.

5. If $f(x) = \dfrac{1}{x + 1}$, what is the domain of $f(x)$?

We can form new functions by performing algebraic operations with two or more functions. We define new functions that are the sum, difference, product, and quotient of two functions as follows.

Operations with Functions

Let f and g be functions of x, and define the following.

Sum $\qquad (f + g)(x) = f(x) + g(x)$

Difference $\qquad (f - g)(x) = f(x) - g(x)$

Product $\qquad (f \cdot g)(x) = f(x) \cdot g(x)$

Quotient $\qquad \left(\dfrac{f}{g}\right)(x) = \dfrac{f(x)}{g(x)}$ if $g(x) \neq 0$

EXAMPLE 7

If $f(x) = 3x + 2$ and $g(x) = x^2 - 3$, find the following functions.

(a) $(f + g)(x)$ (b) $(f - g)(x)$

(c) $(f \cdot g)(x)$ (d) $\left(\dfrac{f}{g}\right)(x)$

Solution

(a) $(f + g)(x) = f(x) + g(x) = (3x + 2) + (x^2 - 3) = x^2 + 3x - 1$

(b) $(f - g)(x) = f(x) - g(x) = (3x + 2) - (x^2 - 3) = -x^2 + 3x + 5$

(c) $(f \cdot g)(x) = f(x) \cdot g(x) = (3x + 2)(x^2 - 3) = 3x^3 + 2x^2 - 9x - 6$

(d) $\left(\dfrac{f}{g}\right)(x) = \dfrac{f(x)}{g(x)} = \dfrac{3x + 2}{x^2 - 3}, \quad x^2 - 3 \neq 0$

We now consider a new way to combine two functions. Just as we can substitute a number for the independent variable in a function, we can substitute a second function for the variable. This creates a new function, called a **composite function.**

Composite Functions

Let f and g be functions. Then the **composite functions** g of f (denoted $g \circ f$) and f of g (denoted $f \circ g$) are defined as follows:

$$(g \circ f)(x) = g(f(x))$$
$$(f \circ g)(x) = f(g(x))$$

Note that the domain of $g \circ f$ is the subset of the domain of f for which $g \circ f$ is defined. Similarly, the domain of $f \circ g$ is the subset of the domain of g for which $f \circ g$ is defined.

EXAMPLE 8

If $f(x) = 2x^3 + 1$ and $g(x) = x^2$, find

(a) $(g \circ f)(x)$ (b) $(f \circ g)(x)$.

Solution

(a) $(g \circ f)(x) = g(f(x))$
$\qquad\qquad = g(2x^3 + 1)$
$\qquad\qquad = (2x^3 + 1)^2 = 4x^6 + 4x^3 + 1$

(b) $(f \circ g)(x) = f(g(x))$
$\qquad\qquad = f(x^2)$
$\qquad\qquad = 2(x^2)^3 + 1$
$\qquad\qquad = 2x^6 + 1$

Figure 1.5 illustrates both composite functions found in Example 8.

FIGURE 1.5

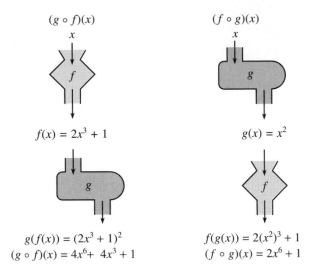

$(g \circ f)(x)$

$f(x) = 2x^3 + 1$

$g(f(x)) = (2x^3 + 1)^2$

$(g \circ f)(x) = 4x^6 + 4x^3 + 1$

$(f \circ g)(x)$

$g(x) = x^2$

$f(g(x)) = 2(x^2)^3 + 1$

$(f \circ g)(x) = 2x^6 + 1$

EXAMPLE 9

Suppose that a woman's ability to buy a house by borrowing y dollars is related to her ability to make a monthly payment x, according to

$$y = 100x,$$

and that her ability to make monthly payment x is related to her monthly income z by

$$x = 0.20z.$$

(a) Write a function in terms of her monthly income that describes her ability to buy a house by borrowing y dollars.

(b) If her monthly income is $3000, how much could she borrow in order to buy a house?

Solution

(a) Her ability to buy a house by borrowing y dollars is

$$y = f(x), \text{ where } x = g(z).$$

Thus

$$y = f(g(z)) = f(0.20z) = 100(0.20z)$$

or

$$y = 20z$$

gives y as a function of z, her monthly income.

(b) If her monthly income is $3000, then the amount she could borrow to buy a house is

$$y = f(g(3000)) = 20(3000) = 60,000 \quad \text{(dollars)}.$$

TECHNOLOGY CORNER

Graphics calculators and computers can be used to graph functions easily. In order to make the best use of these tools, however, we need to know how to enter information into them and how to judge their outputs.

1. Graph the function $y = x^3 + 3x^2 + 3$ over the following intervals.
   (a) $-50 \leq x \leq 50$ and $-120{,}000 \leq y \leq 120{,}000$
   (b) $-10 \leq x \leq 10$ and $-700 \leq y \leq 1300$
   (c) $-4 \leq x \leq 2$ and $-20 \leq y \leq 20$

2. Are there any features on one of the graphs in (1) that are not distinguishable on another? Explain.

3. Which of the graphs in (1) most accurately reflects the shape and subtleties of the true graph of this function? Explain your choice.

4. If we want to graph $y = x^{2/3}$, there are three ways we might enter this function into a calculator or computer: (i) $x \wedge 2 \div 3$, (ii) $x \wedge (2 \div 3)$, and (iii) $(x \wedge 2) \wedge (1 \div 3)$.
   (a) Graph $y = x^{2/3}$ by methods (i), (ii), and (iii).
   (b) Are the three graphs the same?
   (c) Which one (or ones) represents the correct graph of $y = x^{2/3}$? Explain how you know.
   (d) What functions are represented by the graphs that do not represent $y = x^{2/3}$?

5. (a) Graph $f(x) = \sqrt{x^2 - 2x - 3}$.
   (b) Use the graph to determine this function's domain and range.
   (c) Where does $f(x) = 0$?

6. (a) Graph $f(x) = 5 - \sqrt{169 - (x + 1)^2}$
   (b) Use the graph to determine this function's domain and range.
   (c) For what values of x does $f(x) = 0$? Over what intervals for x is $f(x) > 0$? Over what intervals for x is $f(x) < 0$?

1. Independent variable is x; dependent variable is y.

2. $f(1) = 3$

3. $f(-2) = 1 - (-2)^3 = 1 - (-8) = 9$

4. $f(x + h) = 2(x + h)^2 = 2(x^2 + 2xh + h^2)$
   $$= 2x^2 + 4xh + 2h^2$$

5. The domain is all real numbers *except* $x = -1$, because $f(x)$ is undefined when $x = -1$.

EXERCISE 1.1

1. If $y = 3x^3$, is y a function of x?

2. If $y = 6x^2$, is y a function of x?

3. If $y^2 = 3x$, is y a function of x?

4. If $y^2 = 10x^2$, is y a function of x?

5. If $p = 2q$, is p a function of q?

6. If $y = \sqrt{4x}$, is y a function of x?

7. If $p = \pm\sqrt{2q}$, is p a function of q?

8. If $R = \sqrt[3]{x}$, is R a function of x?

9. If $R(x) = 8x - 10$, find the following.
   (a) $R(0)$ (b) $R(2)$
   (c) $R(-3)$ (d) $R(1.6)$

10. If $h(x) = 3x^2 - 2x$, find the following.
    (a) $h(3)$ (b) $h(-3)$
    (c) $h(2)$ (d) $h(\frac{1}{6})$

11. If $C(x) = 4x^2 - 3$, find the following.
    (a) $C(0)$ (b) $C(-1)$
    (c) $C(-2)$ (d) $C(-\frac{3}{2})$

12. If $R(x) = 100x - x^3$, find the following.
    (a) $R(1)$ (b) $R(10)$
    (c) $R(2)$ (d) $R(-10)$

13. If $f(x) = x^3 - 4/x$, find the following.
    (a) $f(-\frac{1}{2})$ (b) $f(2)$ (c) $f(-2)$

14. If $C(x) = (x^2 - 1)/x$, find the following.
    (a) $C(1)$ (b) $C(\frac{1}{2})$ (c) $C(-2)$

15. If $f(x) = 1 + x + x^2$, find the following.
    (a) $f(2 + 1)$ (b) $f(x + 1)$ (c) $f(x + h)$

16. If $f(x) = 3x^2 - 6x$, find the following.
    (a) $f(3 + 2)$ (b) $f(x + 2)$ (c) $f(x + h)$

17. If $f(x) = x - 2x^2$, find the following.
    (a) $f(x + h)$ (b) $f(x + h) - f(x)$
    (c) $\dfrac{f(x + h) - f(x)}{h}$

18. If $f(x) = 2x^2 - x + 3$, find the following.
    (a) $f(x + h)$ (b) $f(x + h) - f(x)$
    (c) $\dfrac{f(x + h) - f(x)}{h}$

19. Does Figure 1.6 below represent y as a function of x?

FIGURE 1.6

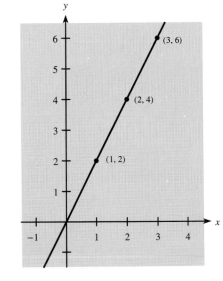

20. Does Figure 1.7 represent s as a function of t?

FIGURE 1.7

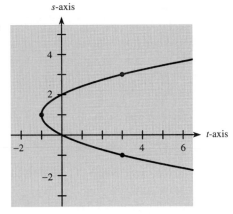

21. Does Figure 1.8 below represent y as a function of x?

FIGURE 1.8

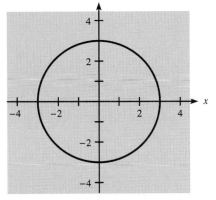

22. Does Figure 1.9 below represent y as a function of x?

FIGURE 1.9

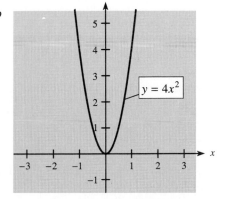

23. If $y = f(x)$ in Figure 1.6, what is $f(1)$?

24. If $y = f(x)$ in Figure 1.6, what is $f(2)$?

25. If $y = g(x)$ in Figure 1.9, what is $g(0)$?

26. Is there a value of x in the domain of the function represented by Figure 1.9 such that $g(x) = 0$?

27. The graph of $y = x^2 - 4x$ is shown in Figure 1.10.
    (a) If the coordinates of the point P on the graph are (a, b), how are a and b related?
    (b) What are the coordinates of the point Q? Do they satisfy the equation?
    (c) What are the coordinates of R? Do they satisfy the equation?
    (d) What are the x-values of the points on the graph whose y-coordinates are 0? Are these x-values solutions to the equation $x^2 - 4x = 0$?

FIGURE 1.10

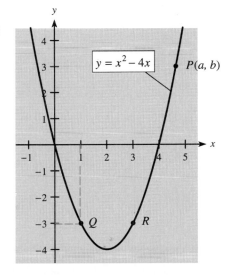

28. The graph of $y = 2x^2$ is shown in Figure 1.11.
    (a) If the point P, with coordinates (a, b), is on the graph, how are a and b related?
    (b) Does the point $(1, 1)$ lie on the graph? Do the coordinates satisfy the equation?
    (c) What are the coordinates of point R? Do they satisfy the equation?
    (d) What is the x-value of the point whose y-coordinate is 0? Does this value of x satisfy the equation $0 = 2x^2$?

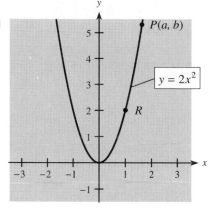

FIGURE 1.11

For $f(x)$ and $g(x)$ given in problems 29–32, find
(a) $(f + g)(x)$ (b) $(f - g)(x)$
(c) $(f \cdot g)(x)$ (d) $(f/g)(x)$.

29. $f(x) = 3x, \quad g(x) = x^3$
30. $f(x) = \sqrt{x}, \quad g(x) = 1/x$
31. $f(x) = \sqrt{2x}, \quad g(x) = x^2$
32. $f(x) = (x - 1)^2, \quad g(x) = 1 - 2x$

For $f(x)$ and $g(x)$ given in problems 33–36, find
(a) $(f \circ g)(x)$ (b) $(g \circ f)(x)$
(c) $f(f(x))$ (d) $f^2(x) = (f \cdot f)(x)$

33. $f(x) = (x - 1)^3, \quad g(x) = 1 - 2x$
34. $f(x) = 3x, \quad g(x) = x^3 - 1$
35. $f(x) = 2\sqrt{x}, \quad g(x) = x^4 + 5$
36. $f(x) = \dfrac{1}{x^3}, \quad g(x) = 4x + 1$

State the domain and range of each of the following functions.

37. $y = x^2 + 4$ 38. $y = x^2 - 1$
39. $y = \sqrt{x - 1}$ 40. $y = \sqrt{x^2 + 1}$

State the domain of each of the following functions.

41. $y = \dfrac{1}{x}$ 42. $R = \dfrac{3}{x + 3}$

43. $y = \dfrac{\sqrt{x - 1}}{x - 2}$ 44. $y = \dfrac{\sqrt{x^2 + 1}}{x}$

APPLICATIONS

45. **Body-heat loss** The description of body-heat loss due to convection involves a coefficient of convection K_c, which depends on wind speed v according to the equation
$$K_c = 4\sqrt{4v + 1}.$$
(a) Is K_c a function of v?
(b) What is the domain?
(c) What restrictions do nature and common sense put on v?

46. **Efficiency of a muscle** The efficiency E of a muscle performing a maximal contraction is related to the time t that the muscle is contracted according to
$$E = \frac{1 - 0.24t}{2 + t}.$$
(a) Is E a function of t?
(b) What is the domain?
(c) What restrictions do nature and common sense put on the domain?

47. **Fahrenheit-Celsius** The equation
$$C = \tfrac{5}{9}F - \tfrac{160}{9}$$
gives the relation between temperature readings in Celsius and Fahrenheit.
(a) Is C a function of F?
(b) What is the domain?
(c) If we consider this equation as relating temperatures of water in its liquid state, what are the domain and range?
(d) What is C when $F = 40°$?

48. **Pressure of a gas** The pressure P of a certain gas is related to volume V according to
$$P = \frac{100}{V}.$$
(a) Is 0 in the domain of this function?
(b) What is $P(100)$?
(c) What is $P(50)$?
(d) As volume decreases, what happens to pressure?

49. ***Population of organisms*** The population size y of a certain organism at time t is given by

$$y = f(t) = 4t^2 + 2t.$$

What is
(a) $f(1)$?   (b) $f(2)$?   (c) $f(3)$?

50. ***Drug reaction*** The reaction R to an injection of a drug is related to the dosage x according to

$$R(x) = x^2\left(500 - \frac{x}{3}\right),$$

where 1000 mg is the maximum dosage. What is $R(100)$?

51. ***Nerve response*** The number of action potentials produced by a nerve t seconds after a stimulus may be described by

$$N(t) = 25t + \frac{4}{t^2 + 2} - 2.$$

What is
(a) $N(2)$?   (b) $N(10)$?

52. ***Cost*** The total cost of producing a product is given by

$$C = 300x + 0.1x^2 + 1200,$$

where x represents the number of units produced. What is the
(a) total cost of producing 10 units?
(b) average cost per unit when 10 units are produced?

53. ***Cost-benefit*** Suppose that the cost C (in dollars) of removing p percent of the particulate pollution from the smokestacks of an industrial plant is given by

$$C(p) = \frac{7300p}{100 - p}.$$

(a) Find the domain of this function. Recall that p represents the percentage of pollution that is removed.
(b) Find $C(45)$.   (c) Find $C(90)$.
(d) Find $C(99)$.   (e) Find $C(99.6)$.

54. ***Test reliability*** If a test having reliability r is lengthened by a factor n ($n \geq 1$), the reliability

R of the new test is given by

$$R(n) = \frac{nr}{1 + (n-1)r} \qquad 0 < r \leq 1.$$

If the reliability is $r = 0.6$, the equation becomes

$$R(n) = \frac{0.6n}{0.4 + 0.6n}.$$

(a) Find $R(1)$.
(b) Find $R(2)$; that is, find R when the test length is doubled.
(c) What percentage improvement is there in the reliability when the test length is doubled?

55. ***Area*** If 100 feet of fence is to be used to fence in a rectangular yard, then the resulting area of the fenced yard is given by

$$A = x(50 - x),$$

where x is the width of the rectangle.
(a) Is A a function of x?
(b) If $A = A(x)$, find $A(2)$ and $A(30)$.
(c) What restrictions must be placed on x (the domain) so that the problem makes physical sense?

56. ***Postal restrictions*** If a box with square cross section is to be sent by the postal service, there are restrictions on its size such that its volume is given by $V = x^2(108 - 4x)$, where x is the length of each side of the cross section (in inches).
(a) Is V a function of x?
(b) If $V = V(x)$, find $V(10)$ and $V(20)$.
(c) What restrictions must be placed on x (the domain) so that the problem makes physical sense?

57. ***Profit*** Suppose that the profit from the production and sale of x units of a product is given by

$$P(x) = 180x - \frac{x^2}{100} - 200.$$

In addition, suppose that for a certain month the number of units produced on day t of the

month is

$$x = q(t) = 1000 + 10t.$$

(a) Find $(P \circ q)(t)$ to express the profit as a function of the day of the month.
(b) On the fifteenth day of the month, find the number of units produced, and find the profit.

58. **Fish species growth** For many species of fish, the weight W is a function of the length L that can be expressed by

$$W = W(L) = kL^3 \qquad k = \text{constant}.$$

Suppose that for a particular species $k = 0.02$, and that for this species the length (in cm) is a function of the number of years t that the fish has been alive that is given by

$$L = L(t) = 50 - \frac{(t - 20)^2}{10} \qquad 0 \le t \le 20.$$

Find $(W \circ L)(t)$ in order to express W as a function of the age t of the fish.

59. **Fencing a lot** A farmer wishes to fence the perimeter of a rectangular lot with an area of 1600 square feet. If the lot is x feet long, express the amount L of fence needed as a function of x.

60. **Cost** A shipping crate has a square base with sides of length x feet, and it is half as tall as it is wide. If the material for the bottom and sides of the box costs \$2.00 per square foot and the material for the top costs \$1.50 per square foot, express the total cost of material for the box as a function of x.

61. **Revenue** An agency charges \$10 per person for a trip to a concert if 30 people travel in a group. But for each person above the 30, the charge will be reduced by \$0.20. If x represents the number of people above the 30, write the agency's revenue R as a function of x.

62. **Revenue** A company handles an apartment building with 50 units. Experience has shown that if the rent for each of the units is \$360 per month, all of the units will be filled, but one unit will become vacant for each \$10 increase in the monthly rate. If x represents the number of \$10 increases, write the revenue R from the building as a function of x.

1.2 LINEAR FUNCTIONS

OBJECTIVES

- To graph linear functions
- To find slopes of lines
- To find slopes of parallel and perpendicular lines
- To write equations of lines

One very special function is the **linear function.**

Linear Functions   A **linear function** is a function of the form

$$f(x) = ax + b \qquad \text{or} \qquad y = ax + b$$

where a and b are constants.

Since the graph of a linear function is always a straight line, only two points are required to determine its graph. However, we often use a third point as a check that we have drawn the line accurately.

EXAMPLE 1 Graph the equation $3x + y = 9$.

Solution Plot any two points that satisfy the equation. We arbitrarily choose $x = 0$ and $x = 5$, and find the corresponding y values.

If $x = 0$, then $y = 9$, so $(0, 9)$ is one point.
If $x = 5$, then $y = -6$, so $(5, -6)$ is another point.

Draw a straight line through the points. (See Figure 1.12.) A third point can be used as a check. If $x = 2$, then $y = 3$, so $(2, 3)$ should be on the line.

FIGURE 1.12

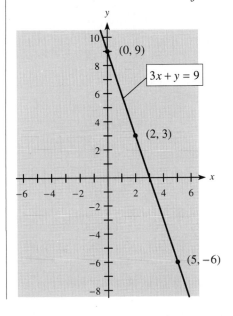

The points where $y = 0$ are points at which a graph intersects the x-axis, and are called the **x-intercepts** of the graph; **y-intercepts** are points where the graph intersects the y-axis.

Intercepts   (a) To find the y-intercept(s) of the graph of an equation, set $x = 0$ in the equation and solve for y.
(b) To find the x-intercept(s), set $y = 0$ and solve for x.

The x- and y-intercepts can frequently be used to determine the graph of a linear equation because they are usually easy to find. For example, the graph of $3x + y = 9$ (Figure 1.12) has x-intercept $(3, 0)$ and y-intercept $(0, 9)$.

Despite the ease of using intercepts, this method is not always the best. For example, vertical lines, horizontal lines, or lines that pass through the origin may have a single intercept, and if a line has both intercepts very close to the origin, the intercepts may lead to an inaccurate graph.

Note in Figure 1.12 that the y-value on the line changes -9 units (from 9 to 0) while the x-value changes $+3$ units (from 0 to 3). The ratio of this change in y to the corresponding change in x is called the **slope** of the line. The slope of any nonvertical line can be found by using any two points on the line as follows.

Slope of a Line

If a nonvertical line passes through the points $P_1(x_1, y_1)$ and $P_2(x_2, y_2)$, its **slope** m is found by using either

$$m = \frac{y_2 - y_1}{x_2 - x_1} \quad \text{or} \quad m = \frac{y_1 - y_2}{x_1 - x_2}.$$

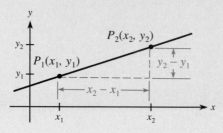

Note that for a given line, the slope is the same regardless of which two points are used in the calculation; this is because corresponding sides of similar triangles are in proportion.

We may also write the slope by using the notation

$$m = \frac{\Delta y}{\Delta x} \quad (\Delta y = y_2 - y_1 \quad \text{and} \quad \Delta x = x_2 - x_1),$$

where Δy means "change in y" and Δx means "change in x."

EXAMPLE 2

Find the slope of:

(a) line ℓ_1, passing through $(-2, 1)$ and $(4, 3)$.

(b) line ℓ_2, passing through $(3, 0)$ and $(4, -3)$.

Solution

(a) $m = \dfrac{3 - 1}{4 - (-2)} = \dfrac{2}{6} = \dfrac{1}{3} \quad$ or $\quad m = \dfrac{1 - 3}{-2 - 4} = \dfrac{-2}{-6} = \dfrac{1}{3}$

This means that a point 3 units to the right and 1 unit up from any point on the line is also on the line. Line ℓ_1 is shown in Figure 1.13.

FIGURE 1.13

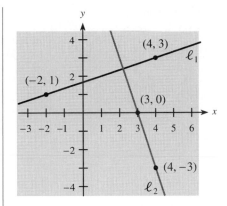

(b) $m = \dfrac{0 - (-3)}{3 - 4} = \dfrac{3}{-1} = -3$

This means that a point 1 unit to the right and 3 units down from any point on the line is also on the line. Line ℓ_2 is also shown in Figure 1.13.

From the previous discussion we see that the slope describes the direction of a line as follows:

Orientation of a line and its slope

1. The slope is *positive* if the line slopes upward toward the right.

    $$m = \frac{\Delta y}{\Delta x} > 0$$

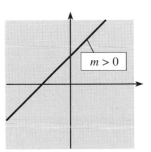

2. The slope is *negative* if the line slopes downward toward the right.

    $$m = \frac{\Delta y}{\Delta x} < 0$$

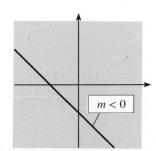

Two additional facts should be stated:

3. The slope of a *horizontal line* is 0, because the y-values are the same for any two points on the line ($y_2 - y_1 = 0$).

$$m = \frac{\Delta y}{\Delta x} = 0 \quad \text{since } \Delta y = 0$$

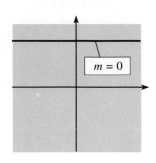

4. The slope of a *vertical line* is *undefined*, because $x_2 - x_1$ would equal 0, and division by 0 is undefined. (*Note:* Here y is not a function of x.)

$$m = \frac{\Delta y}{\Delta x} \text{ is undefined} \quad \text{since } \Delta x = 0$$

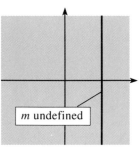

Clearly, two distinct nonvertical lines that have the same slope are parallel and, conversely, two parallel lines have the same slope.

Parallel Lines   Two distinct nonvertical lines are *parallel* if and only if their slopes are *equal*.

Because the slope of a vertical line is undefined, we cannot use slope in discussing parallel and perpendicular relations involving vertical lines. Two vertical lines are parallel, and any horizontal line is perpendicular to any vertical line.

EXAMPLE 3   Show that $ABCD$ is a parallelogram, where the vertices are $A\,(-2, 3)$, $B\,(3, 5)$, $C\,(5, 0)$, and $D\,(0, -2)$.

Solution $ABCD$ is a parallelogram if AB is parallel to CD and AD is parallel to BC.

$$m_{\overline{AB}} = \frac{5 - 3}{3 - (-2)} = \frac{2}{5} \qquad m_{\overline{CD}} = \frac{0 - (-2)}{5 - 0} = \frac{2}{5}$$

$$m_{\overline{AD}} = \frac{3 - (-2)}{-2 - 0} = \frac{5}{-2} \qquad m_{\overline{BC}} = \frac{5 - 0}{3 - 5} = \frac{5}{-2}$$

Segments AB and CD lie on parallel lines as do segments BC and AD, so $ABCD$ is a parallelogram.

Note that the lines ℓ_1 and ℓ_2 of Figure 1.13 on the previous page appear to be perpendicular and that the slope of ℓ_1, $\frac{1}{3}$, is the negative reciprocal of the slope of

ℓ_2, -3. In fact, any two nonvertical lines that are perpendicular have slopes that are negative reciprocals of each other.

Slopes of Perpendicular Lines	A line ℓ_1 with slope m, where $m \neq 0$, is *perpendicular* to line ℓ_2 if and only if the slope of ℓ_2 is $-1/m$. (The slopes are *negative reciprocals*.)

EXAMPLE 4

Show that the parallelogram $ABCD$ of Example 3 is a rectangle.

Solution From Example 3, we have $m_{\overline{AB}} = \frac{2}{5}$ and $m_{\overline{BC}} = -\frac{5}{2}$, so $\overline{AB}$ is perpendicular to $\overline{BC}$. Therefore, $ABCD$ is a rectangle.

If the slope of a line is m, then the slope between a fixed point (x_1, y_1) and any other point (x, y) on the line is also m. That is,

$$m = \frac{y - y_1}{x - x_1}.$$

Solving for $y - y_1$ gives the point-slope form of the equation of a line.

Point-Slope Form	The equation of the line passing through the point (x_1, y_1) and with slope m can be written in the **point-slope form** $$y - y_1 = m(x - x_1).$$

EXAMPLE 5

Write an equation for each line passing through $(1, -2)$ and having

(a) slope $\frac{2}{3}$.   (b) undefined slope.   (c) point $(2, 3)$ also on it.

Solution

(a) Here $m = \frac{2}{3}$, $x_1 = 1$, and $y_1 = -2$. An equation of the line is

$$y - (-2) = \frac{2}{3}(x - 1).$$

This may be written as $y = \frac{2}{3}x - \frac{8}{3}$ or in the **general form** as $2x - 3y - 8 = 0$.

(b) Because m is undefined, we cannot use the point-slope form. This line is vertical, so every point on it has x-coordinate 1. Thus, the equation is $x = 1$.

(c) First find

$$m = \frac{3 - (-2)}{2 - 1} = 5.$$

Using $m = 5$ and the point $(1, -2)$ [the other point could also be used] gives

$$y - (-2) = 5(x - 1) \quad \text{or} \quad y = 5x - 7.$$

The graph of $x = 1$ [from Example 5(b)] is a vertical line, as shown in Figure 1.14(a); the graph of $y = 1$ has slope 0, and its graph is a horizontal line, as shown in Figure 1.14(b).

FIGURE 1.14

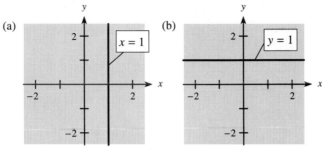

The point-slope form, with the intercept point $(0, b)$, can be used to derive the following special form for the equation of a line.

Slope-Intercept Form

The **slope-intercept form** of the equation of a line with slope m and y-intercept b is

$$y = mx + b.$$

EXAMPLE 6

(a) Find the slope and y-intercept of the line whose equation is $x + 2y = 8$.

(b) Use this information to graph the equation.

Solution

(a) To put the equation in slope-intercept form, we must solve it for y:

$$2y = -x + 8 \quad \text{or} \quad y = -\frac{1}{2}x + 4.$$

Thus the slope is $-\frac{1}{2}$ and the y-intercept is 4.

(b) First we plot the y-intercept, $(0, 4)$. The point $(2, 3)$ is on the line because it is 2 units to the right of and 1 unit below $(0, 4)$. A third point (for a check) is plotted at $(4, 2)$. The graph is shown in Figure 1.15.

FIGURE 1.15

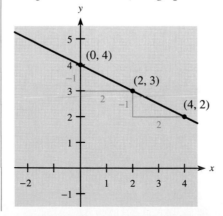

It is also possible to graph a straight line if we have its slope and any point that it passes through; we simply plot the point that is given, and then use the slope to plot other points.

The following summarizes the forms of equations of lines.

Forms of Linear Equations		
General form:	$ax + by + c = 0$
Point-slope form:	$y - y_1 = m(x - x_1)$
Slope-intercept form:	$y = mx + b$
Vertical line:	$x = a$
Horizontal line:	$y = b$

CHECKPOINT

1. Find the slope of the line through $(4, 6)$ and $(28, -6)$.

2. If a line has slope $m = 0$, then the line is _____. If a line has slope m undefined, then the line is _____.

3. Suppose that line 1 has slope $m_1 = 3$ and line 2 has slope m_2.
   (a) If line 1 is perpendicular to line 2, find m_2.
   (b) If line 1 is parallel to line 2, find m_2.

4. Write the point-slope form of the equation of the line that has slope $-\frac{3}{4}$ and passes through $(4, -6)$.

5. What are the slope and y-intercept of the graph of $x = -4y + 1$? ■

EXAMPLE 7

Write the equation of the line passing through $(2, -1)$ if it is
(a) parallel to $2x + 3y = 5$.
(b) perpendicular to $x = 4y$.

Solution

(a) The slope-intercept form of $2x + 3y = 5$ is

$$y = -\frac{2}{3}x + \frac{5}{3}.$$

Thus a line parallel to it has slope $-\frac{2}{3}$. Using $m = -\frac{2}{3}$ and $(2, -1)$, we have

$$y - (-1) = -\frac{2}{3}(x - 2).$$

A general form of this equation is $2x + 3y - 1 = 0$.

(b) The slope-intercept form of $x = 4y$ is $y = \frac{1}{4}x$.

Thus a line perpendicular to it has slope -4. Using $m = -4$ and $(2, -1)$, we have $y - (-1) = -4(x - 2)$ or $4x + y = 7$.

TECHNOLOGY CORNER

1. (a) Graph $y = mx$ for $m - \frac{1}{2}, -\frac{1}{2}, 5,$ and -5.
   (b) What is the x-intercept of each graph? What is the y-intercept?
   (c) Which lines rise from left to right? Which ones fall?

2. (a) For each choice of m in 1(a), graph $f(x) = mx + b$ for $b = -2, 1,$ and 5.
   (b) For a fixed m and different b's, what do you notice about the lines?

3. Consider the following linear functions.
   (a) $y = 3x + 2$ (b) $y = 3x - 2$ (c) $y = -3x + 2$
   (d) $y = -3x - 2$ (e) $y = 2$ (f) $x + y = 1$

   Try to match each of these equations with graphs A–F below. Then write a statement saying why you made each match.

   A 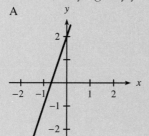   B 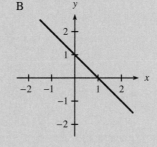   C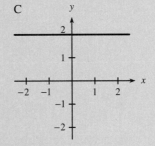

   D 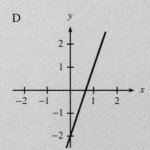   E 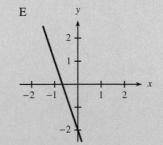   F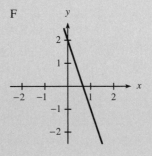

4. Graph each function in (3) to check your matches.

CHECKPOINT
SOLUTIONS

1. $m = \dfrac{y_2 - y_1}{x_2 - x_1} = \dfrac{-6 - (6)}{28 - (4)} = \dfrac{-12}{24} = -\dfrac{1}{2}$ or

   $m = \dfrac{y_1 - y_2}{x_1 - x_2} = \dfrac{6 - (-6)}{4 - (28)} = \dfrac{12}{-24} = -\dfrac{1}{2}$

2. If $m = 0$, then the line is horizontal. If m is undefined, then the line is vertical.

3. (a) $m_2 = \dfrac{-1}{m_1} = -\dfrac{1}{3}$ (b) $m_2 = m_1 = 3$

4. Use $y - y_1 = m(x - x_1)$. Hence, $y - (-6) = \dfrac{-3}{4}(x - 4)$,   or $3x + 4y = 12$.

5. If $x = -4y + 1$, then the slope-intercept form is $y = mx + b$ or $y = -\frac{1}{4}x + \frac{1}{4}$. Hence, $m = -\frac{1}{4}$ and the y-intercept is $(0, \frac{1}{4})$. ■

EXERCISE 1.2

In problems 1–12, graph the linear equations.

1. $y = \dfrac{5 - x}{2}$ 2. $y = \dfrac{7 - x}{3}$

3. $3x - y = 0$ 4. $5x - y = 0$

5. $y = 3$ 6. $y = -5$

7. $x = -4$ 8. $x = -2$

9. $\dfrac{x}{2} + \dfrac{y}{4} = 1$ 10. $\dfrac{x}{3} - \dfrac{y}{5} = 1$

11. $0.1x - 0.3y = 0.1$ 12. $0.5x + 0.2y = 0.6$

In problems 13–18, find the slope of the line passing through each pair of points.

13. $(1, 2)$ and $(2, 4)$ 14. $(2, 3)$ and $(3, 4)$

15. $(-1, 3)$ and $(0, 6)$

16. $(-1, 2)$ and $(2, -3)$

17. $(0.7, 3)$ and $(0.7, -3)$

18. $(10, 0.2)$ and $(2, 0.2)$

In problems 19–22 consider the four points $A (-3, 0)$, $B (3, 3)$, $C (2, 0)$, and $D (6, -3)$.

19. Is line AB parallel to line CD?

20. Is line AD parallel to line BC?

21. Is line AB perpendicular to line BD?

22. Is line BD perpendicular to line DC?

In problems 23–28, find the slope and y-intercept of each line whose equation is given.

23. $x = 4y + 3$ 24. $x = -\frac{5}{2}y$

25. $y = \frac{1}{2}x - \frac{2}{3}$ 26. $y = \frac{2}{3}x + \frac{1}{2}$

27. $2.61x + \pi y = 91.7$

28. $1.31x - 3.82y = 0.0213$

For each line described in problems 29–38, sketch the graph and write the equation.

29. slope $\frac{1}{2}$; y-intercept 3

30. slope $\frac{2}{3}$; y-intercept -1

31. slope -2; y-intercept $\frac{1}{2}$

32. slope -1; y-intercept $\frac{3}{2}$

33. passes through $(2, 0)$ with slope $\frac{1}{2}$

34. passes through $(3, 0)$ with slope 2

35. passes through $(-1, 3)$ with slope -2

36. passes through $(1, 1)$ with slope $-\frac{1}{3}$

37. passes through $(4, -1)$ with undefined slope

38. passes through $(4, -1)$ with slope 0

In problems 39–42, write the equations of the lines passing through the given points.

39. $(7, 3)$ and $(-6, 2)$ 40. $(10, 2)$ and $(5, 7)$

41. $(10, 2)$ and $(5, 2)$ 42. $(3, 6)$ and $(3, 8)$

For problems 43 and 44, consider the following three lines:

$$\ell_1: \quad 4x - 3y + 22 = 0$$
$$\ell_2: \quad 3x + 4y - 21 = 0$$
$$\ell_3: \quad 3x + 4y + 4 = 0$$

43. Which pair(s) of lines are parallel?

44. Which pair(s) of lines are perpendicular?

45. Find the equation of the x-axis.

46. Find the equation of the y-axis.

47. Write the equation of the line through $(-2, -7)$ that is parallel to $3x + 5y = 11$.

48. Write the equation of the line through $(6, -4)$ that is parallel to $4x - 5y = 6$.

49. Write the equation of the line through $(3, 1)$ that is perpendicular to $5x - 6y = 4$.

50. Write the equation of the line through $(-2, -8)$ that is perpendicular to $x = 4y + 3$.

51. Write the equation of the line that is perpendicular to and has the same x-intercept as $5x - 8y = 80$.

52. Do the equations $4x - y = 2$ and $8x - 2y = 4$ represent parallel lines or the same line?

APPLICATIONS

53. **Fahrenheit-Celsius** Write the equation of the linear relationship between temperature in Celsius (C) and in Fahrenheit (F). (Water freezes at $0°C$ and $32°F$ and boils at $100°C$ and $212°F$.)

54. **Pollution effects** Suppose that the fish population y in a certain river is related to the tons of pollutants x according to the equation $y = 100,000 - 1500x$. Sketch the graph of this equation.

55. **Chemical reactions** The activity of particles in a chemical reaction (such as digestion) or in the diffusion of a solution is related to the concentration of the particles, according to the formula $A = KC$, where A is the activity, C is the concentration, and K is the fraction of the concentration that is effective in determining the diffusion or the chemical reaction. Sketch the equation if $K = 0.7$, with the C-axis horizontal.

56. **Blood oxygenation** The rate of oxygen consumption of the blood, x, measures the cardiac output (blood flow through the lungs), y, by

$$y = x/(A - V) = [1/(A - V)]x,$$

where A is the arterial concentration of oxygen and V is the venous concentration of oxygen. Sketch the graph of the equation above if $1/(A - V) = 3/4$.

57. **Egg production in fish** Suppose that there is a linear relationship between the length (in centimeters) of a certain species of fish and the number of eggs its members lay. If it is known that a fish 100 cm long lays 20,000 eggs and a fish 50 cm long lays 6000 eggs, write an equation that gives the number of eggs as a function of the length of the fish.

58. **Investments** If $1000 is invested at 10% simple interest for t years, then the total amount A of the investment is given by

$$A = f(t) = 1000 + 100t.$$

(a) Find $f(5)$.
(b) Graph this function.
(c) Find how long it takes for this investment to double.

59. **Cholesterol and coronary heart disease risk** The Seven Countries Study, conducted by Ancel Keys, was a long-term study of the relationship of cholesterol to coronary heart disease (CHD) mortality in men. The relationship was approximated by the line shown in Figure 1.16. The line passes through the points $(200, 25)$ and $(250, 49)$, meaning that there were 25 CHD deaths among men with 200 mg/dl of cholesterol and 49 CHD deaths among men with 250 mg/dl of cholesterol. Using x to represent the cholesterol and y to represent CHD deaths, write the equation that represents this relationship.

FIGURE 1.16

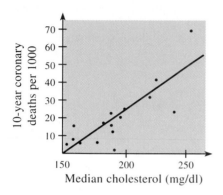

Units sold	Total revenue
3	14.94
5	24.90
8	39.84
11	54.78
15	74.70

60. **Home heating costs** Residential customers who heat their homes with natural gas have their monthly bills calculated by the addition of a base service charge of $5.19 per month and an energy charge of 51.91 cents per hundred cubic feet (CCF). Write an equation for the monthly charge y in terms of x, the number of CCF used.

61. **Age-sleep relationship** Each day, a young person should sleep 8 hours plus $\frac{1}{4}$ hour for each year that the person is under 18 years of age. Assuming that the relation is linear, write the equation relating hours of sleep y and age x.

62. **Pollution effects** It has been estimated that a certain stream can support 85,000 fish if it is pollution-free. It has further been estimated that for each ton of pollutants in the stream, 1700 fewer fish can be supported. Write the equation that gives the population of fish p in terms of the tons of pollutants x.

63. **Revenue** The following table gives the number of units of a product sold and the total revenue from the sale.
   (a) Plot the points and observe that they lie on a straight line.
   (b) Determine the equation of this line.
   (c) What domain is reasonable for this business application?

Church attendance The following table shows the percentages of adults and teens who attended church each year from 1980 to 1989. Assume that the percentage of adults who attended church during these years can be modeled with the function $a(x)$ and the percentage of teenagers who behaved similarly can be modeled with the function $t(x)$ where

$$a(x) = 29.73 + 0.13x \qquad t(x) = 24.33 + 0.33x,$$

and x denotes the number of years past 1900. The functions a and t and the data in the table are all graphed in the figure below. Use this information in problems 64 and 65.

Year	Percentage of adults	Percentage of teens
1980	41	50
1981	41	54
1982	41	50
1983	40	53
1984	40	52
1985	42	52
1986	40	54
1987	40	52
1988	42	51
1989	43	57

Source: *World Almanac*, 1991.

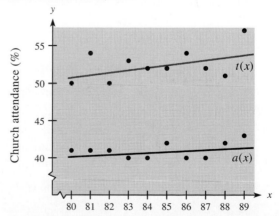

64. (a) Which equation appears to represent more accurately the percentage attending church?
    (b) For what year can you guarantee that $a(x)$ can no longer be used to model the percentage of adults attending church?

65. (a) Assuming that a and t are valid models, during what year will 50% of adults attend church?
    (b) In what year will 60% of teenagers attend church?

1.3 | APPLICATIONS OF LINEAR FUNCTIONS

OBJECTIVES

- To formulate, graph, and evaluate total cost, total revenue, and profit functions
- To find break-even points
- To evaluate and graph supply and demand functions
- To find market equilibrium
- To solve additional application problems

COST, REVENUE, AND PROFIT

The **profit** a firm makes on its product is the difference between the amount it receives from sales (its revenue) and its cost. If x units are produced and sold, we can write the following.

Profit

$$P(x) = R(x) - C(x)$$

where $P(x)$ = profit from sale of x units,
$R(x)$ = revenue from sale of x units, and
$C(x)$ = cost of production and sale of x units.

In general, **revenue** is found by using the equation

revenue = (price per unit)(number of units).

The **cost** is composed of two parts, fixed costs and variable costs. **Fixed costs** (*FC*), such as depreciation, rent, utilities, and so on, remain constant regardless of the number of units produced. **Variable costs** (*VC*) are those directly related to the number of units produced. Thus the cost is found by using the equation

cost = variable costs + fixed costs.

EXAMPLE 1

Suppose that a firm manufactures radios and sells them for $50 each. If the costs incurred in the production and sale of the radios are $200,000 plus $10 for each radio produced and sold, write the profit function for the production and sale of x radios.

Solution The profit function is given by $P(x) = R(x) - C(x)$, where $R(x) = 50x$ and $C(x) = 10x + 200,000$. Thus,

$$P(x) = 50x - (10x + 200,000)$$
$$P(x) = 40x - 200,000.$$

Figure 1.17 shows the graphs of $R(x)$, $C(x)$, and $P(x)$.

FIGURE 1.17

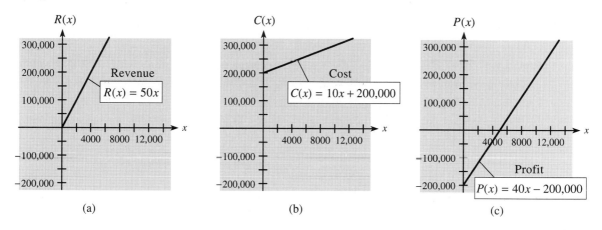

(a)　　　　　　　　　(b)　　　　　　　　　(c)

In Example 1, both the revenue function and the cost function are linear, so their difference, the profit function, is also linear. The slope of the profit function represents the rate of change in profit with respect to the number of units produced and sold. This is called the **marginal profit** $(\overline{MP})$ for the product. Thus the marginal profit for the radios of Example 1 is $40. Similarly, the **marginal cost** $(\overline{MC})$ for this product is $10 (the slope of the cost function), and the **marginal revenue** $(\overline{MR})$ is $50 (the slope of the revenue function).

EXAMPLE 2

Suppose that the cost (in dollars) for a product is

$$C = 21.75x + 4890.$$

(a) What is the slope of the graph of this linear function?

(b) What is the marginal cost for this product, and what does it mean?

Solution

(a) Since the equation has the form

$$C = mx + b,$$

the slope is 21.75.

(b) The marginal cost is the slope of this linear function. Thus it is

$$\overline{MC} = 21.75.$$

Since the marginal cost is the slope of the cost line, production of each additional unit will cost $21.75 more, at any level of production.

By observing the intercepts on the graphs in Figure 1.17, we note the following.

Revenue: 0 units produce 0 revenue.
Cost: 0 units' costs equal fixed costs = $200,000.
Profit: 0 units yield a loss equal to fixed costs = $200,000.
            5000 units result in a profit of $0 (no loss or gain).

The point at which the profit is 0 is called the **break-even point.**

EXAMPLE 3

Suppose that a manufacturer produces and sells a product with monthly revenue $R(x) = 10x$ and cost $C(x) = 2.50x + 1200$. How many units must be produced each month to break even?

Solution Using the fact that the profit function is found by subtracting the total cost function from the total revenue function, we can form the profit function.

$$P(x) = R(x) - C(x)$$
$$= 10x - (2.50x + 1200)$$
$$= 7.50x - 1200$$

We can find the point where the profit is zero (the break-even point) by setting $P(x) = 0$ and solving for x.

$$0 = 7.50x - 1200$$
$$1200 = 7.50x$$
$$x = 160$$

Thus the manufacturer will break even if 160 units per month are produced and sold. The manufacturer will make a profit if more than 160 units are produced. [See Figure 1.18(a).]

FIGURE 1.18

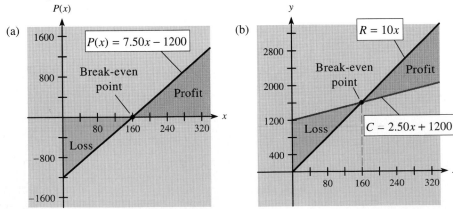

Figure 1.18(b) shows the graphs of cost and revenue functions for the product of Example 3. Clearly they intersect at the break-even point, where $x = 160$. This suggests a method of finding the break-even point without forming the profit function. By noting that $R = C$ at the break-even point, we can solve the two equations simultaneously to find the break-even quantity.

$$10x = 2.50x + 1200$$
$$7.5x = 1200$$
$$x = 160$$

1. Give the formula that expresses profit in terms of revenue and cost.

2. Identify two ways that break-even points can be found.

3. If $C(x)$, $R(x)$, and $P(x)$ are linear functions, how are their marginals found? ■

SUPPLY, DEMAND, AND MARKET EQUILIBRIUM

Economists and managers also use points of intersection to determine market equilibrium. **Market equilibrium** occurs when the quantity of commodity demanded is equal to the quantity supplied.

Demand by consumers for a commodity is related to the price of the commodity. The **law of demand** states that the quantity demanded will increase as price decreases, or that the quantity demanded will decrease as price increases. Figure 1.19 on the following page shows the graph of a typical linear demand function. Note that although quantity demanded is a function of price, economists have traditionally graphed the demand function with price on the vertical axis. Throughout this text, we will follow this tradition. Linear equations relating price and quantity demanded can be solved for either p or q, and we will have occasion to use the equations in both forms.

Just as a consumer's willingness to buy is related to price, a manufacturer's willingness to supply goods is also related to price. The **law of supply** states that the quantity supplied for sale will increase as the price of a product increases. Figure 1.20 shows the graph of a typical linear supply function. As with demand, price is placed on the vertical axis. Note that negative prices and quantities have no meaning, so supply and demand curves are restricted to the first quadrant.

FIGURE 1.19

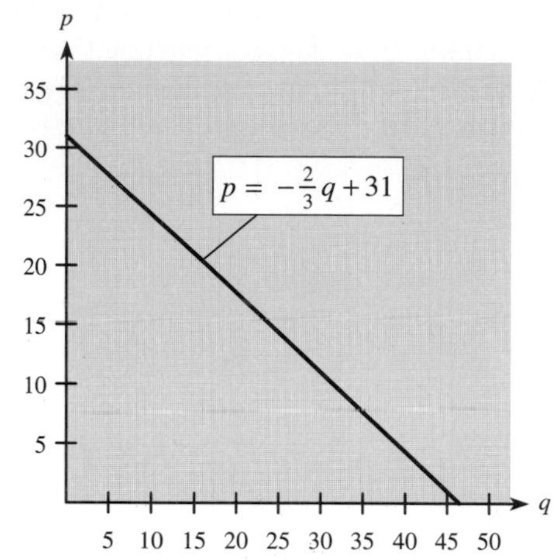

FIGURE 1.20

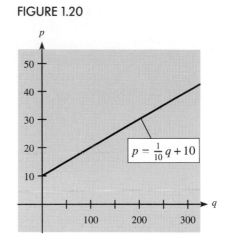

$$p = -\frac{2}{3}q + 31$$

$$p = \frac{1}{10}q + 10$$

If the supply and demand curves for a commodity are graphed on the same coordinate system, with the same units, market equilibrium occurs at the point where the curves intersect. The price at that point is the **equilibrium price,** and the quantity at that point is the **equilibrium quantity.**

For the supply and demand functions shown in Figure 1.21 we see that the curves intersect at the point (30, 11). This means that when the price is $11, consumers are willing to purchase the same number of units (30) that producers are willing to supply.

FIGURE 1.21

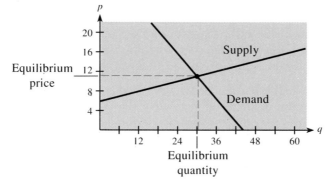

In general, the equilibrium price and the equilibrium quantity must both be positive for the market equilibrium to have meaning.

We can find the market equilibrium by graphing the supply and demand functions on the same coordinate system and observing their point of intersection. Finding the point(s) common to the graphs of two (or more) functions is called solving a

system of equations or **solving simultaneously.** This process generally can be accomplished more accurately by algebraic methods than by graphing. When we replace one expression in a system with an equivalent expression in order to solve the system algebraically, we are using the **substitution method** of solving a system of equations. This is illustrated in the following example.

EXAMPLE 4

Find the market equilibrium point for the following supply and demand functions.

Demand: $p = -3q + 36$
Supply: $\quad p = 4q + 1$

Solution At market equilibrium the demand price equals the supply price. Thus,

$$-3q + 36 = 4q + 1$$
$$35 = 7q$$
$$q = 5$$
$$p = 21.$$

The equilibrium point is (5, 21).

EXAMPLE 5

A group of wholesalers will buy 50 dryers per month if the price is \$200 and 30 per month if the price is \$300. The manufacturer is willing to supply 20 if the price is \$210 and 30 if the price is \$230. Assuming that the resulting supply and demand functions are linear, find the equilibrium point for the market.

Solution Demand function:

$$m = \frac{300 - 200}{30 - 50} = -5$$
$$p - 200 = -5(q - 50)$$
$$p = -5q + 450$$

Supply function:

$$m = \frac{230 - 210}{30 - 20} = 2$$
$$p - 230 = 2(q - 30)$$
$$p = 2q + 170$$

Since the prices are equal at market equilibrium, we have

$$-5q + 450 = 2q + 170$$
$$280 = 7q$$
$$q = 40$$
$$p = 250.$$

The equilibrium point is (40, 250). See Figure 1.22 on the following page for the graphs of these functions.

FIGURE 1.22

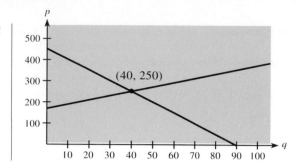

If a supplier is taxed $K per unit sold, then the tax is passed on to the consumer by adding $K to the selling price of the product. If the original supply function is $p = f(q)$, then passing the tax on gives a new supply function, $p = f(q) + K$. Because the value of the product is not changed by the tax, the demand function is unchanged. Figure 1.23 shows the effect that this has on market equilibrium.

FIGURE 1.23

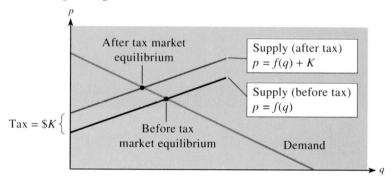

Notice that the new market equilibrium point is the point of intersection of the original demand function and the new (after taxes) supply function.

EXAMPLE 6

In Example 5 the supply and demand functions for dryers were given as follows.

Supply: $p = 2q + 170$
Demand: $p = -5q + 450$

The equilibrium point was $q = 40$, $p = \$250$. If the wholesaler is taxed $14 per unit sold, what is the new equilibrium point?

Solution The $14 tax per unit is passed on by the wholesaler, so the new supply function is

$$p = 2q + 170 + 14,$$

and the demand function is unchanged. Thus we solve the system

$$\begin{cases} p = 2q + 184 \\ p = -5q + 450. \end{cases}$$

$$2q + 184 = -5q + 450$$
$$7q = 266$$
$$q = 38$$
$$p = 2(38) + 184 = 260$$

The new equilibrium point is $q = 38$, $p = \$260$.

4. (a) Does a typical linear demand function have positive slope or negative slope? Why?

   (b) Does a typical linear supply function have positive slope or negative slope? Why?

5. (a) What do we call the point of intersection of a supply function and a demand function?

   (b) What algebraic technique is used to find the point named in part (a)? ■

OTHER LINEAR MODELS

Linear functions also can be used to model applications that occur outside the fields of business and economics.

Insulation is important for energy conservation in both warm and cold climates. The R-value of insulation is a measure of its ability to resist heat transfer, with higher R-values corresponding to greater insulation. Various materials are used for insulating walls and ceilings; two of the most common are fiberglass and cellulose fiber.

EXAMPLE 7

Use the data in the table below to solve the following problems.

(a) Write linear equations relating the R-value to the thickness in inches for fiberglass insulation and cellulose fiber.

(b) Use the costs per cubic foot to determine which product costs less and provides an R-value of 24.

	Thickness (in.)	R-value	Cost/cubic foot ($)
Fiberglass	3.5	11	2.50
	6	19	2.50
Cellulose	3.5	13	3.95
	6	22	3.95

Solution

(a) Using the two points given for each product, we can write these equations.

Fiberglass: (3.5, 11), (6, 19); Cellulose: (3.5, 13), (6, 22);

$$m = \frac{19 - 11}{6 - 3.5} = \frac{8}{2.5} = 3.2 \qquad\qquad m = \frac{22 - 13}{6 - 3.5} = \frac{9}{2.5} = 3.6$$

$$R - 19 = 3.2(t - 6) \qquad\qquad\qquad R - 22 = 3.6(t - 6)$$

$$R = 3.2t - 0.2 \qquad\qquad\qquad\qquad R = 3.6t + 0.4$$

(b) The thickness of fiberglass that gives R-24 is the solution to

$$24 = 3.2t - 0.2, \text{ or}$$
$$t = 7.5625 \text{ (inches)}.$$

The cost of a 12″ × 12″ piece of fiberglass of this thickness is

$$\frac{7.5625}{12} \cdot 2.50 \approx 1.58 \text{ (dollars)}.$$

The thickness of cellulose that gives R-24 is the solution to

$$24 = 3.6t + 0.4, \text{ or}$$
$$t = 6.5556 \text{ (inches)}.$$

The cost of a 12″ × 12″ piece of cellulose of this thickness is

$$\frac{6.5556}{12} \cdot 3.95 \approx 2.16 \text{ (dollars)}.$$

Thus the fiberglass insulation will be less expensive even though a greater thickness will be required.

The following table gives the recommended weight according to height for medium-framed adult women between the heights of 5 feet and 6 feet.

TABLE 1.1

Height in inches (with 1″ heels)	Weight in pounds (with 3 lb of clothing)
60	119
61	122
62	125
63	128
64	131
65	134
66	137
67	140
68	143
69	146
70	149
71	152
72	155

The points representing height and weight appear to lie on a straight line. (See Figure 1.24.)

FIGURE 1.24

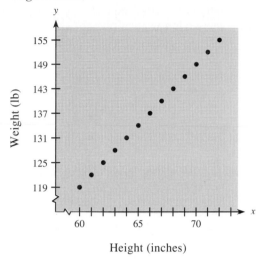

Height (inches)

EXAMPLE 8

(a) Using the fact that the data in Table 1.1 determine a linear relationship between height and recommended weight, write the linear equation relating recommended weight to height.

(b) Use the result of part (a) to find the recommended weight for someone who is 4'10", someone who is $63\frac{1}{2}''$, and someone who is 75".

Solution

(a) Since the points lie on a straight line, any two of them can be used to find the slope and write the equation. Using the first two points gives the following.

$$m = \frac{y_2 - y_1}{x_2 - x_1} = \frac{122 - 119}{61 - 60} = 3$$
$$y - 119 = 3(x - 60)$$
$$y = 3x \quad 180 + 119$$
$$y = 3x - 61$$

(b) Since 4'10" = 58", we use $x = 58''$.

$$y = 3(58) - 61 = 174 - 61 = 113 \text{ lb.}$$

For $x = 63.5''$ and $x = 75''$ we have

$$y = 3(63.5) - 61 = 190.5 - 61 = 129.5 \text{ lb.}$$
$$y = 3(75) - 61 = 225 - 61 = 164 \text{ lb.}$$

Insurance experts agree that weight measurements near the ones given in the previous example correspond to those of people who live longest. The Food and

Drug Administration states that a woman whose weight is 20 percent above that in the table can be considered obese and hence, less healthy. The "danger line" for obesity can be defined by the equation $y = 3x - 61 + 0.20(3x - 61)$, or $y = 3.6x - 73.2$, where x is a woman's height and y is her weight.

TECHNOLOGY CORNER

An electric utility company determines the monthly cost for residential customers by adding an energy charge of $0.0838 per kilowatt hour (kWh) to its base charge of $4.95 per month.

1. Which of the graphs below is the best match for the graph of this function? Explain your choice.

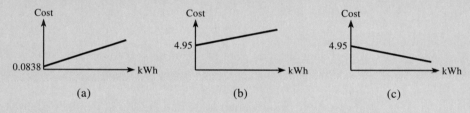

(a)   (b)   (c)

2. Write the equation for the monthly cost y in terms of x and graph this equation to verify your choice in (1).

3. What is the domain of the function you graphed in (2)? What is the domain for this application?

1. $P(x) = R(x) - C(x)$.

2. Break-even occurs at values of x where revenue equals cost $[R(x) = C(x)]$ or at x-values where profit is zero $[P(x) = 0]$.

3. For linear functions, the marginals are the slopes.

4. (a) Negative slope, because demand falls as price increases
   (b) Positive slope, because supply increases as price increases

5. (a) Market equilibrium point   (b) Solving simultaneously

EXERCISE 1.3

COST, REVENUE, AND PROFIT

1. A calculator has the following costs for a given period: fixed costs, $3400; variable costs, $17 for each item produced.
   (a) Write the equation that represents cost.
   (b) What will it cost to produce 200 units during the given period?

2. A stereo receiver has a fixed cost of $1650 and a variable cost of $105 for each item produced during a given month.
   (a) Write the equation that represents the cost.
   (b) What will it cost to produce 215 items during the month?

3. A calculator is sold for $34 per unit.
   (a) Write the equation that represents the revenue function.
   (b) What will the revenue be if 300 units are sold?

4. A stereo receiver is sold for $215 per item.
   (a) Write the equation that represents the revenue function.
   (b) What will the revenue be from the sale of 50 items?

5. Suppose that a calculator has cost function $C(x) = 17x + 3400$ and revenue function $R(x) = 34x$.
   (a) What is the equation of the profit function for this calculator?
   (b) What is the profit on 300 units?
   (c) How many units must be sold to ensure no money will be lost during the period?

6. Suppose that a stereo receiver has cost function $C(x) = 105x + 1650$ and revenue function $R(x) = 215x$.
   (a) What is the equation of the profit function for this commodity?
   (b) What is the profit on 50 items?
   (c) How many items must be sold in a month to avoid losing money?

7. A linear cost function is $C(x) = 5x + 250$.
   (a) What are the slope and C-intercept?

   (b) What is the marginal cost, and what does it mean?
   (c) What are the fixed costs?
   (d) How are your answers to parts (a), (b), and (c) related?
   (e) What is the cost of producing one more item if 50 are currently being produced? What is it if 100 are currently being produced?

8. A linear revenue function is $R = 27x$.
   (a) What is the slope?
   (b) What is the marginal revenue, and what does it mean?
   (c) What is the revenue received from selling one more item if 50 are currently being sold? if 100 are being sold?

9. A linear profit function is $P = 51x - 710$.
   (a) What are the slope and P-intercept of the profit function?
   (b) What is the marginal profit and what does it mean?
   (c) What is the significance of the P-intercept?
   (d) How much profit is expected if 20 items are produced and sold?
   (e) How much additional profit would be expected if production and sales increased from 20 to 21?

10. Let $C(x) = 5x + 250$ and $R(x) = 27x$.
    (a) Write the profit function $P(x)$.
    (b) What is the slope of the profit function?
    (c) What is the marginal profit?
    (d) Interpret the marginal profit. What does this tell the manager of the firm with this profit function if the objective is to make the most profit?

11. Given $C(x) = 21.95x + 1400$ and $R(x) = 10x$, find the profit function.
    (a) What is marginal profit, and what does it mean?
    (b) What should a firm with these cost, revenue, and profit functions do? (*Hint:* Graph the profit function and see where it goes.)

12. Suppose that the cost function for a radio is linear, that the marginal cost is $27, and that the fixed costs amount to $3000. Write the equation of this cost function and graph it.

13. Suppose that the production and sale of each additional unit of a stereo system result in an increase of $50 in profit, regardless of the level of production. If the sale of 1000 units gives a profit of $4000, write the equation of the profit function.

14. Suppose that the revenue function for the radio in problem 12 is linear and the marginal revenue is $30. Write the revenue function and the profit function.

15. Figure 1.25 shows graphs of the total cost function and the total revenue function for a commodity.
    (a) Label each function correctly.
    (b) Determine the fixed costs.
    (c) Locate the break-even point and determine the number of units that must be sold to break even.
    (d) Estimate the marginal cost and marginal revenue.

FIGURE 1.25

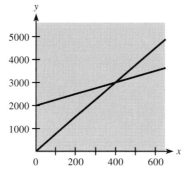

16. A manufacturer of tub faucets has a revenue function of $R(x) = 81.50x$ and a cost function of $C(x) = 63x + 1850$. Find the number of units that must be sold to break even.

17. A jewelry maker incurs costs for necklaces according to $C(x) = 35x + 1650$. If the revenue function for the necklaces is $R(x) = 85x$, how many necklaces must be sold to break even?

18. A small business recaps and sells tires. If a set of four tires has the revenue function $R(x) = 89x$ and the cost function $C(x) = 1400 + 75x$, find the number of sets of tires that must be sold to break even.

19. A manufacturer sells belts for $12 each. The fixed costs are $1600 per month, and the variable costs are $8 per unit.
    (a) Write the equations of the revenue and cost functions.
    (b) Find the break-even point.

20. A manufacturer sells watches for $50 each. The fixed costs related to this product are $10,000 per month, and the variable costs are $30 per watch.
    (a) Write the equations of the revenue and cost functions.
    (b) How many watches must be sold to break even?

21. (a) Write the profit function for problem 19.
    (b) Set profit equal to zero and solve for x. Compare this x-value with the break-even point from problem 19(b).

22. (a) Write the profit function for problem 20.
    (b) Set profit equal to zero and solve for x. Compare this x-value with the break-even point from problem 20(b).

23. Suppose that a firm will not begin production of a product unless it receives a 20% return on its investment for fixed costs. If the fixed costs are $50,000, the variable costs are $2 per unit, and the product sells for $5 per unit, how many units must be produced to break even (that is, make the required return)?

24. Suppose that a firm requires a 10% return on its investment for fixed costs to break even. If the product sells for $2 per unit, the variable costs are $.50 per unit, and the fixed costs are $30,000, how many units must be produced to break even?

SUPPLY, DEMAND, AND MARKET EQUILIBRIUM

Figure 1.26 is the graph of the demand function for a product, and Figure 1.27 is the graph of the supply function for the same product. Use these graphs to solve problems 25 and 26.

FIGURE 1.26

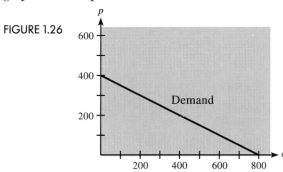

FIGURE 1.27

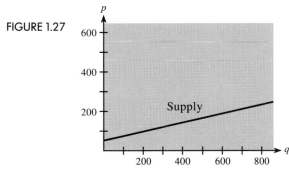

25. (a) How many units q are demanded when the price p is \$100?
    (b) How many units q are supplied when the price p is \$100?
    (c) Will there be a market surplus (more supplied) or shortage (more demanded) when $p = \$100$?

26. (a) How many units q are demanded when the price p is \$200?
    (b) How many units q are supplied when the price p is \$200?
    (c) Will there be a market surplus or shortage when the price p is \$200?

27. If the demand for a pair of shoes is given by $2p + 5q = 200$ and the supply function for it is $p - 2q = 10$, compare the quantities demanded and supplied when the price is \$60. Will there be a surplus or shortfall at this price?

28. If the demand and supply functions for Z-brand phones are $p + 2q = 100$ and $35p - 20q = 350$, respectively, compare the quantity demanded and the quantity supplied when $p = 14$. Are there surplus phones or not enough to meet demand?

29. Figure 1.28 shows a supply function and a demand function.

FIGURE 1.28

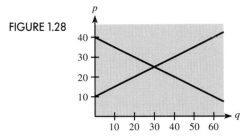

Label the equilibrium point and determine the price and quantity at which market equilibrium occurs.

30. (a) Will a price above the equilibrium price result in a market surplus or shortage?
    (b) Will a price below the equilibrium price result in a market surplus or shortage?

31. Suppose that the demand per month for a product is 5 if the price is \$310, 10 if the price is \$300, and 15 if the price is \$290. Assuming that the demand curve is linear,
    (a) graph the curve.
    (b) write its equation.

32. Suppose that the demand per month for a commodity is 24 if the price is \$16, 20 if the price is \$18, 16 if the price is \$20, and 12 if the price is \$22. Assuming that the demand curve is linear,
    (a) graph the curve.
    (b) write its equation.

33. A manufacturer will supply the product in problem 31 as follows:

    5 if the price is \$42,

10 if the price is $82,
15 if the price is $122.

Assuming that the supply curve is linear,
(a) graph it.   (b) write the equation.

34. A manufacturer will supply the commodity of problem 32 as follows:

8 if the price is $14,
14 if the price is $16,
20 if the price is $18,
26 if the price is $20.

Assuming that the supply curve is linear,
(a) graph the curve.   (b) write the equation.

35. Find the market equilibrium point for the following demand and supply functions (found in problems 31 and 33).

Demand: $p = -2q + 320$
Supply: $p = 8q + 2$

36. Find the market equilibrium point for the following demand and supply functions (found in problems 32 and 34).

Demand: $p = -2q + 56$
Supply: $3p - q = 34$

37. Find the equilibrium point for the following supply and demand functions.

Demand: $p = -4q + 220$
Supply: $p = 15q + 30$

38. Retailers will buy 45 Z-brand phones from a wholesaler if the price is $10 each and 20 if the price is $60 each. The wholesaler is willing to supply 35 phones at $30 each and 70 at $50 each. Assuming that the resulting supply and demand functions are linear, find market equilibrium.

39. A group of retailers will buy 80 televisions from a wholesaler if the price is $350 each and 120 if the price is $300 each. The wholesaler is willing to supply 60 if the price is $280 and 140 if the price is $370. Assuming that the resulting supply and demand functions are linear, find the equilibrium point for the market.

40. A shoestore owner will buy 10 pairs of a certain shoe if the price is $75 per pair, and 30 pairs if the price is $25 per pair. The supplier of the shoes is willing to provide 35 pairs if the price is $80 per pair, and 5 pairs if the price is $20 per pair. Assuming that the supply and demand functions for the shoes are linear, find the market equilibrium.

Problems 41–46 involve market equilibrium after taxation. Use Figure 1.29 to answer problems 41 and 42.

FIGURE 1.29

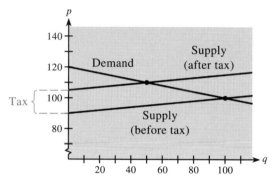

41. (a) What is the amount of the tax?
    (b) What are the original equilibrium price and quantity?
    (c) What are the new equilibrium price and quantity?
    (d) Does the supplier suffer from the tax even though it is passed on?

42. (a) If the tax is doubled, how many units will be sold?
    (b) Can a government lose money by increasing taxes?

43. Suppose that the following are the demand and supply functions for a product.

Demand: $p = -4q + 220$
Supply: $p = 15q + 30.$

If a $38 tax is placed on each unit of the product, what are the new equilibrium price and quantity?

44. Suppose that a product has the following demand and supply functions.

$$\text{Demand:} \quad p = 480 - 3q$$
$$\text{Supply:} \quad p = 17q + 80$$

If a $56 tax is placed on each unit of the product, what is the new equilibrium point?

45. Suppose that a certain product has the following demand and supply functions.

$$\text{Demand:} \quad p = -0.05q + 65$$
$$\text{Supply:} \quad p = 0.05q + 10$$

If a $5 tax per item is levied on the supplier and this tax is passed on to the consumer, find the market equilibrium point after the tax.

46. Suppose that a certain product has the following demand and supply functions.

$$\text{Demand:} \quad p = -8q + 2800$$
$$\text{Supply:} \quad p = 3q + 35$$

If a $15 tax per item is levied on the supplier, who passes it on to the consumer as a price increase, find the market equilibrium point after the tax.

OTHER LINEAR MODELS

47. **Insulation R-values** Rock wool is another material used for insulation. Suppose that 4 and 6 inches of rock wool have R-values of R-11 and R-16, respectively. If the relationship between the R-value and the thickness is linear, write an equation relating those for rock wool.

48. **Insulation costs**
    (a) If rock wool costs $3.25 per cubic foot, use the result of problem 47 to find the R-value per dollar for rock wool.
    (b) Use the information in Example 7 for fiberglass and cellulose to decide which of the three types of insulation gives the best R-value per dollar.

49. **Weight-height norms** Suppose that the relationship between recommended weight and height for medium-framed adult men is linear.

Suppose further that a man 6'0" tall should weigh 178 lb, and that a man 5'5" tall should weigh 148 lb. Write the equation that gives the recommended weight y of an adult male with a medium frame in terms of his height in inches x.

50. **Insurance rates** Insurance companies charge a surcharge for women whose weights are 25% or more above the values in Table 1.1. Use the equation developed in Example 8(a) to write the equation for weights that are exactly 25% above the recommended weights.

Federal income tax The federal income tax for certain types of filing status in 1991 is summarized in the following table. For a single return, the table is used by applying the 15% rate for income up to $20,350, then, adding to that amount of tax, 28% of the income over $20,350 up to $49,300, etc. Use the table to solve problems 51 and 52.

Taxable income brackets

Tax rate	Single returns	Joint returns
15%	0–$20,350	0–$34,000
28%	$20,351–$49,300	$34,001–$82,150
31%	> $49,300	> $82,150

51. Develop an equation for the amount of federal income tax that must be paid by someone who files a single return and has a taxable income of x dollars, if
    (a) $x \le \$20,350$ (b) $x > \$49,300$

52. Develop an equation for the amount of federal income tax that must be paid by a couple who file a joint return and have taxable income of x dollars, if
    (a) $x \le \$34,000$ (b) $x > \$82,150$

53. **Depreciation** When property is depreciated over its useful life of n years by the straight-line depreciation method, the same amount is depreciated in each of the n years after the salvage value s is subtracted from the cost.

(a) Use this method to write the formula for the annual depreciation, d.

(b) Write the equation for the total amount D depreciated after t years, if $t \leq n$.

54. **Depreciation** Suppose that a truck costs $30,000, and has a useful life of 5 years and a salvage value of $5000. If the straight-line method is used, how much depreciation will have occurred at the end of 4 years?

55. **Investments** The amount of money that will accrue if P dollars are invested for t years at an annual simple interest rate r is given by

$$A = Prt + P.$$

Suppose that $1000 is invested at 6% simple interest.

(a) Write the equation that gives the dollar amount A as a function of the time t, in years.

(b) What will the value of this investment be in 18 months?

56. **Investments** If an investment of $2500 yields an amount of $3100 in 3 years, what simple interest rate is being paid?

57. **Residential heating costs** Residential customers who heat their homes with natural gas have their monthly bills calculated by the addition of a base service charge of $5.19 per month and an energy charge of 51.91 cents per hundred cubic feet (CCF). Write an equation for the monthly charge, y, in terms of the number of CCF, x, that are used.

58. **Residential electrical costs** An electric utility company determines the monthly bill for a residential customer by adding an energy charge of 7.97 cents per kilowatt hour (kWh) to its base charge of $6.30 per month. Write an equation for the monthly charge y in terms of the number of kWh (x) that are used.

59. **Inflation** A labor contract assumes that the annual inflation rate will average 5% over the next 4 years, and gives raises based on this assumption. If a person is making x dollars when the contract is signed, write an equation

(a) that gives his/her salary one year later.

(b) for his/her salary two years later.

60. **Pollution effects** It has been estimated that a certain stream can support 85,000 fish if it is pollution-free. It has further been estimated that for each ton of pollutants in the stream, 1700 fewer fish can be supported. Write the equation that gives the population of fish p in terms of the tons of pollutants x.

61. **Television purchases** The following data give the number of color television sets (in thousands) sold in 15 different years, along with the corresponding average price per set for the year.

(a) If the price p is written as a linear function of the number of sets sold N, then the "best fit" to these data (see Section 7.5) has slope $m = -0.0104$ and p-intercept 574.96. Write p as a linear function of N.

(b) Check this model for some of the data points. The equation in (a) is the best linear fit to the data; does the model appear to be an extremely good fit or only a fairly good fit? Explain.

N in thousands of sets	p in dollars
9,793	471.56
10,236	487.79
9,107	487.32
7,700	510.78
6,485	504.39
8,411	466.29
10,071	449.81
7,908	509.86
6,349	524.96
4,822	514.10
5,962	515.43
5,981	520.82
5,777	525.01
5,892	462.32
2,646	560.09

Source: U.S. Bureau of the Census, Statistical Abstract of the United States, Washington, D.C.

1.4 | QUADRATIC FUNCTIONS

OBJECTIVES

- To determine if a vertex is a maximum point or a minimum point
- To find the vertex of the graph of a quadratic function
- To find the zeros of a quadratic function
- To graph quadratic functions

A function that models suspension bridges, profit functions in business, and the paths of projectiles is the second-degree polynomial function, or **quadratic function.** The general equation of a quadratic function has the form $y = ax^2 + bx + c$, where a, b, and c are real numbers and $a \neq 0$. The graph of a quadratic function has a distinctive shape, called a **parabola.** (See Figure 1.30.)

FIGURE 1.30

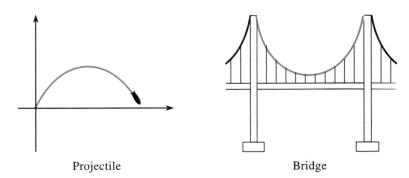

Projectile   Bridge

The basic function $y = x^2$ and a variation of it, $y = -\frac{1}{2}x^2$, are parabolas whose graphs are shown in Figure 1.31.

FIGURE 1.31

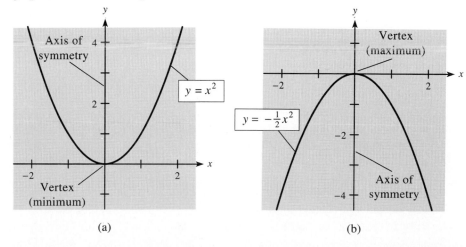

(a)   (b)

As these examples illustrate, the graph of $y = ax^2$ is a parabola that opens upward if $a > 0$ and downward if $a < 0$. The turning point, or **vertex,** is a **minimum point** if $a > 0$ and a **maximum point** if $a < 0$. The vertical line through the vertex of a parabola is called the **axis of symmetry** because one half of the graph is a reflection of the other half through this line.

The graph of $y = (x - 2)^2 - 1$ is the graph of $y = x^2$ shifted to a new location that is 2 units to the right and 1 unit down; its vertex is shifted from $(0, 0)$ to $(2, -1)$ and its axis of symmetry is shifted 2 units to the right. (See Figure 1.32.) The graph of $y - 2 = -\frac{1}{2}(x + 1)^2$ is the graph of $y = -\frac{1}{2}x^2$ shifted 1 unit to the left and 2 units upward, with its vertex at $(-1, 2)$. (See Figure 1.33.)

FIGURE 1.32

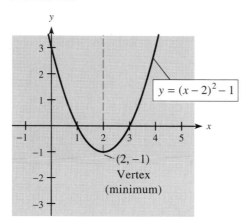

FIGURE 1.33

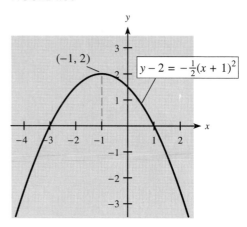

In general, if a quadratic function $y = f(x) = ax^2 + bx + c$ has the form

$$y = a(x - h)^2 + k,$$

then its graph is that of $y = ax^2$, with its vertex shifted to $(h, k) = (h, f(h))$. In addition, $f(x) = ax^2 + bx + c$ can be written in the form

$$f(x) = a\left(x + \frac{b}{2a}\right)^2 + \left(c - \frac{b^2}{4a}\right),$$

so we have the following.

Vertex of a Parabola

The quadratic function $y = f(x) = ax^2 + bx + c$ has its **vertex** at

$$\left(\frac{-b}{2a}, f\left(\frac{-b}{2a}\right)\right).$$

See Figure 1.34.

FIGURE 1.34

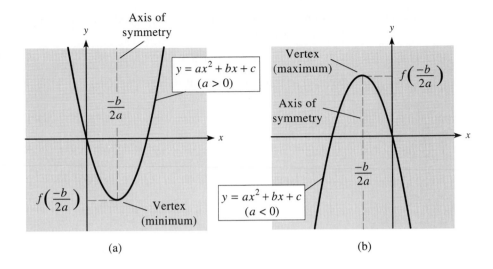

(a)   (b)

Knowing the location of the vertex of a parabola and whether the parabola opens upward or downward, we need very few other points to make a good sketch.

EXAMPLE 1

Find the vertex and sketch the graph of

$$f(x) = 2x^2 - 4x + 4.$$

Solution Since the graph of $f(x)$ opens upward, the vertex is the minimum point. We can calculate its coordinates as follows:

$$x = \frac{-b}{2a} = \frac{-(-4)}{2(2)} = 1$$
$$y = f(1) = 2.$$

Thus the vertex is $(1, 2)$. Using x-values on either side of the vertex to plot additional points allows us to sketch the graph accurately. (See Figure 1.35.)

FIGURE 1.35

x	y
-1	10
0	4
1	2
2	4
3	10

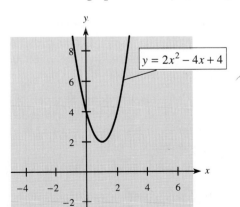

$y = 2x^2 - 4x + 4$

EXAMPLE 2

Suppose that the profit received from the production and sale of x units ($x \geq 0$) of a product is given by

$$P(x) = -0.4x^2 + 40x - 360.$$

(a) Find the maximum profit.

(b) Sketch the graph.

Solution

(a) Since the graph of $P(x)$ is a parabola that opens downward, its vertex is a maximum point. Thus maximum profit can be found by finding the vertex of the parabola.

$$x = \frac{-b}{2a} = \frac{-40}{2(-0.4)} = \frac{-40}{-0.8} = 50$$
$$P(50) = -0.4(50^2) + 40(50) - 360 = 640.$$

Hence, $(50, 640)$ is the maximum point and the maximum profit is $640.

(b) Using x-values around the vertex to plot additional points gives the graph in Figure 1.36.

FIGURE 1.36

x	P
0	-360
30	480
50	640
70	480
100	-360

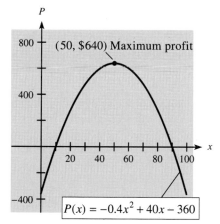

$$P(x) = -0.4x^2 + 40x - 360$$

Notice in Figure 1.36 that the P-intercept is -360, corresponding to a profit of -360 (dollars) or a loss of $360. Notice also that the graph of this parabola has *two* x-intercepts.

The x-intercepts of the graph of a function $y = f(x)$ are the values of x for which $f(x) = 0$, so they are also called the **zeros** of the function. The zeros of the quadratic function $y = f(x) = ax^2 + bx + c$ are the solutions to the quadratic equation

$$ax^2 + bx + c = 0.$$

One method of solving quadratic equations is by factoring. Solution by factoring is based on the following.

Property of Zero For real numbers a and b, $ab = 0$ if and only if $a = 0$ or $b = 0$ or both.

EXAMPLE 3 Find the zeros of the profit function (of Example 2)

$$P(x) = -0.4x^2 + 40x - 360.$$

Solution We find the zeros of the function by solving the following equation.

$$0 = -0.4x^2 + 40x - 360$$
$$0 = 4x^2 - 400x + 3600 \qquad \text{(Multiplying by } -10.\text{)}$$
$$0 = 4(x^2 - 100x + 900)$$
$$0 = 4(x - 90)(x - 10)$$

Thus

$$x - 90 = 0 \quad \text{or} \quad x - 10 = 0$$
$$x = 90 \quad \text{or} \quad x = 10$$

The zeros occur at $x = 10$ and $x = 90$. Note that the profit is zero at these two points of the function; thus break-even occurs at $x = 10$ units and $x = 90$ units. The graph in Figure 1.36 shows that a profit occurs if the number of units produced and sold is between 10 and 90.

Factoring does not lend itself easily to solving quadratic equations such as

$$x^2 - 5 = 0.$$

However, we can solve this equation by writing

$$x^2 = 5$$
$$x = \pm\sqrt{5}$$

In general, we can solve quadratic equations of the form $x^2 = C$ (no x term) by taking the square roots of both sides.

Solution of $x^2 = C$ The solution of $x^2 = C$ is

$$x = \pm\sqrt{C}.$$

By using the fact that for variable x and constant k

$$(x + k)^2 = x^2 + 2kx + k^2,$$

we can solve the general quadratic equation

$$ax^2 + bx + c = 0 \qquad (a \neq 0)$$

by creating the square of a binomial on one side of the equation and then taking the square roots of both sides.* This procedure, which follows, results in a formula for solving any quadratic equation.

COMPLETING THE SQUARE/DERIVATION OF THE QUADRATIC FORMULA

PROCEDURE	EXAMPLE
	Solve $ax^2 + bx + c = 0$.
1. Divide by a: then subtract $\dfrac{c}{a}$ from both sides.	1. $x^2 + \dfrac{bx}{a} = \dfrac{-c}{a}$
2. Set $2kx$ equal to the linear term and solve for k.	2. $2kx = \dfrac{bx}{a} \Rightarrow k = \dfrac{b}{2a}$
3. Add $k^2 = \dfrac{b^2}{4a^2}$ to both sides.	3. $x^2 + \dfrac{bx}{a} + \dfrac{b^2}{4a^2} = \dfrac{-c}{a} + \dfrac{b^2}{4a^2}$
4. Write as a square and simplify.	4. $\left(x + \dfrac{b}{2a}\right)^2 = \dfrac{b^2 - 4ac}{4a^2}$
5. Take the square roots of both sides.	5. $x + \dfrac{b}{2a} = \pm\sqrt{\dfrac{b^2 - 4ac}{4a^2}}$
6. Simplify.	6. $x + \dfrac{b}{2a} = \pm\dfrac{\sqrt{b^2 - 4ac}}{2|a|} = \pm\dfrac{\sqrt{b^2 - 4ac}}{2a}$
7. Solve for x.	7. $x = \dfrac{-b}{2a} \pm \dfrac{\sqrt{b^2 - 4ac}}{2a}$

Quadratic Formula   If $ax^2 + bx + c = 0$, where $a \neq 0$, then
$$x = \frac{-b + \sqrt{b^2 - 4ac}}{2a} \quad \text{or} \quad x = \frac{-b - \sqrt{b^2 - 4ac}}{2a}.$$

We may use the quadratic formula to solve all quadratic equations, but especially those in which factorization is difficult or impossible to see. The proper identification of values for a, b, and c to be substituted into the formula requires that the equation be in general form.

*This technique is called **completing the square** and can be used to solve any quadratic equation.

EXAMPLE 4 | Use the quadratic formula to solve $2x^2 - 3x - 6 = 0$ for x.

Solution The equation is already in general form, with $a = 2$, $b = -3$, and $c = -6$. Hence,

$$x = \frac{-b \pm \sqrt{b^2 - 4ac}}{2a}$$

$$= \frac{-(-3) \pm \sqrt{(-3)^2 - 4(2)(-6)}}{2(2)}$$

$$= \frac{3 \pm \sqrt{9 + 48}}{4}$$

$$= \frac{3 \pm \sqrt{57}}{4}.$$

Thus the solutions are

$$x = \frac{3 + \sqrt{57}}{4} \quad \text{and} \quad x = \frac{3 - \sqrt{57}}{4}.$$

The part of the quadratic formula given by $b^2 - 4ac$ is called the **quadratic discriminant** because it tells us what types of solutions we will obtain.

Quadratic Discriminant

Given $ax^2 + bx + c = 0$ with $a \neq 0$,

if $b^2 - 4ac > 0$, the equation has 2 distinct real solutions.
if $b^2 - 4ac = 0$, the equation has 1 real solution.
if $b^2 - 4ac < 0$, the equation has no real solutions.

CHECKPOINT

1. Name the graph of a quadratic function.

2. (a) What is the x-coordinate of the vertex of $y = ax^2 + bx + c$?

    (b) For $y = 12x - \frac{1}{2}x^2$, what is the x-coordinate of the vertex? What is the y-coordinate of the vertex?

3. (a) How can you tell whether the vertex of $f(x) = ax^2 + bx + c$ is a maximum point or a minimum point?

    (b) In 2(b), is the vertex a maximum point or a minimum point?

4. The zeros of a function correspond to what feature of its graph?

5. (a) What is the quadratic formula?

    (b) In order to use the quadratic formula, what form must the quadratic equation have?

EXAMPLE 5

The height s (in feet) of a projectile fired straight upward at 60 ft/sec from a point 32 feet above the ground is given by

$$s = -16t^2 + 60t + 32 \qquad (t \text{ in seconds}).$$

To the nearest tenth of a second, when does the projectile strike the ground?

Solution Since the projectile strikes the ground when $s = 0$, we must solve the following equation for t.

$$0 = -16t^2 + 60t + 32$$
$$0 = 4t^2 - 15t - 8 \qquad \text{Dividing both sides by } -4.$$

Using the quadratic formula with $a = 4$, $b = -15$, and $c = -8$ gives

$$t = \frac{-(-15) \pm \sqrt{(-15)^2 - 4(4)(-8)}}{2(4)}$$
$$= \frac{15 \pm \sqrt{225 + 128}}{8}$$
$$= \frac{15 \pm \sqrt{353}}{8}.$$

To the nearest tenth this gives $t = 4.2$ sec or $t = -0.5$ sec. Thus the projectile strikes the ground after approximately 4.2 sec (-0.5 is meaningless here). The graph in Figure 1.37 shows the height of the projectile for $0 \le t \le 4.2$.

FIGURE 1.37

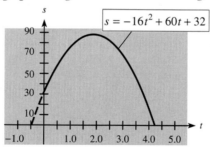

The information that is useful in graphing quadratic functions is summarized below.

Graphs of Quadratic Functions

Form: $y = ax^2 + bx + c$

Graph: parabola (See Figure 1.34 on page 113.)

$a > 0$ parabola opens upward; vertex is a minimum point
$a < 0$ parabola opens downward; vertex is a maximum point

Coordinates of vertex: $x = \dfrac{-b}{2a}$, $\quad y = f\left(\dfrac{-b}{2a}\right)$

Axis of symmetry equation: $x = \dfrac{-b}{2a}$

x-intercepts or zeros (if real*):

$$x = \frac{-b + \sqrt{b^2 - 4ac}}{2a}, \qquad x = \frac{-b - \sqrt{b^2 - 4ac}}{2a}$$

y-intercept: Let $x = 0$; then $y = c$.

*If the zeros are not real, the graph does not cross the x-axis.

TECHNOLOGY CORNER

Many politicians are discussing national health insurance because health care costs are increasing so rapidly.

Health care costs in the United States are given in the table at the right.

Year	Costs (in millions)
1960	27.1
1965	41.6
1970	74.4
1975	132.9
1980	249.1
1985	420.1
1989	539.9

Source: *World Almanac*, 1991.

1. Plot the points from the table. Use x to represent the number of years since 1960 and y to represent costs in millions of dollars.

2. Determine what type of function appears to be the best fit for these points.

3. Graph different quadratic functions of the form $y = ax^2 + c$ until you find a curve that is a reasonable fit for the points.

4. Use your "model" function to predict health care costs in 1990.

5. Actual health care costs for 1990 were $666.2 million. Do health care costs seem to be increasing even faster than your model predicts? Does it appear that some measures are necessary to help slow the growth of health care costs?

CHECKPOINT
SOLUTIONS

1. parabola

2. (a) $x = \dfrac{-b}{2a}$

(b) $x = \dfrac{-12}{2(-1/2)} = \dfrac{-12}{(-1)} = 12$

$y = 12(12) - \dfrac{1}{2}(12)^2 = 144 - 72 = 72$

3. (a) Maximum point if $a < 0$; minimum point if $a > 0$.

(b) $(12, 72)$ is a maximum point because $a = -\dfrac{1}{2}$

4. x-coordinates of the x-intercepts

5. (a) $x = \dfrac{-b \pm \sqrt{b^2 - 4ac}}{2a}$

(b) The general form: $ax^2 + bx + c = 0$.

■

EXERCISE 1.4

In problems 1–4, find the vertex of the graph and determine if it is a maximum point or a minimum point.

1. $y = \frac{1}{2}x^2 + x$ 2. $y = x^2 - 2x$
3. $y = 8 + 2x - x^2$ 4. $y = 6 - 4x - 2x^2$

For each function given in problems 5 and 6, find (a) where the function has its maximum and (b) the maximum value of the function.

5. $f(x) = 6x - x^2$ 6. $f(x) = 4 + 3x - x^2$

For each function given in problems 7 and 8, find (a) where the function has its minimum and (b) the minimum value of the function.

7. $f(x) = x^2 + 2x - 3$ 8. $f(x) = \frac{1}{2}x^2 + 2x$

In problems 9–12, find the zeros of each function and sketch its graph. (See problems 1–4 for information.)

9. $y = \frac{1}{2}x^2 + x$ 10. $y = x^2 - 2x$
11. $y = 8 + 2x - x^2$ 12. $y = 6 - 4x - 2x^2$

In problems 13–22, determine whether each function's vertex is a maximum point or a minimum point and find the coordinates of this point. Find the zeros, if any exist, and sketch the graph of the function.

13. $y = x^2 - 4$ 14. $y = x^2 - 2$
15. $y = x - \frac{1}{4}x^2$ 16. $y = -2x^2 + 18x$
17. $y = x^2 + 4x + 4$ 18. $y = x^2 - 6x + 9$
19. $x^2 + 5x - y + 4 = 0$
20. $y - x^2 - 10x = 16$
21. $\frac{1}{4}x^2 + x - y + 4 = 0$
22. $x^2 + x + y + 2 = 0$

In problems 23–30, sketch the graph of each function.

23. $y = x^2 + 5$ 24. $y = x^2 + 4$
25. $y = -4 + 7x - 4x^2$ 26. $y = \frac{1}{2}x^2 + x - 1$
27. $y = -30 + 4x - 0.1x^2$
28. $y = -9 + x - 0.01x^2$

29. $y = 0.2x^2 + 0.4x + 1.8$
30. $y = 9 - 0.2x - 0.1x^2$
31. Graph
    (a) $y = x^2$ (b) $y = -x^2$
    (c) $y = x^2 - 1$ (d) $y = (x - 1)^2$
32. Graph
    (a) $y = 2x^2$ (b) $y = -2x^2$
    (c) $y = 2x^2 - 2$ (d) $y = 2(x - 2)^2$

APPLICATIONS

33. **Profit** If the daily profit from the sale of a product is given by $P = 16x - 0.1x^2 - 100$,
    (a) what level of production maximizes profit?
    (b) what is the maximum possible profit?

34. **Profit** If the daily profit from the sale of x units of a product is $P = 80x - 0.4x^2 - 200$,
    (a) what level of production maximizes profit?
    (b) what is the maximum possible profit?

35. **Population of organisms** The population size y of a certain organism at time t in hours is given by $y = 5t^2 + 2t$. Graph this function for $0 \le t \le 5$.

36. **Cost** The total cost of producing a product is given by
    $$C = 2000 + 200x + 0.1x^2,$$
    where x is the number of units. Graph this function for $0 \le x \le 5$.

37. **Wind and pollution** The amount of particulate pollution x depends on the wind velocity v, among other things. If the relationship between x and v can be approximated by
    $$x = 20 - 0.01v^2,$$
    sketch the graph relating these quantities with v on the horizontal axis.

38. **Velocity of blood** The velocity v_r of a blood corpuscle in a vessel depends on the distance of the corpuscle from the center of the vessel, r, according to
    $$v_r = v_m\left(1 - \frac{r^2}{R^2}\right),$$

where v_m is the maximum velocity and R is the radius of the vessel.

The blood pressure also affects the velocity of a corpuscle. If we make some simplifications in the formula, namely, let $v_m = 1$ and let $x^2 = r^2/R^2$, then we can observe the following.

Pressure	Equation
$p = 20$ mm	$v(x) = 8(1 - x^2)$
$p = 10$ mm	$v(x) = 3(1 - x^2)$
$p = 5$ mm	$v(x) = 1 - x^2$

Graph each of these equations on the same set of axes.

39. **Flow rates of water** The speed at which water travels in a pipe can be measured by directing the flow through an elbow and measuring the height it spurts out the top. If the elbow height is 10 cm, the equation relating the height h (in centimeters) of the water above the elbow and its velocity v (in centimeters per second) is given by
    $$v^2 = 1960(h + 10).$$
    Solve this equation for h and graph the result, using the velocity as the independent variable.

40. **Stimulus-response** One of the early results in psychology relating the magnitude of a stimulus x to the magnitude of a response y is expressed by the equation
    $$y = kx^2,$$
    where k is an experimental constant. Sketch this graph for $k = 1$, $k = 2$, and $k = 4$.

41. **Drug sensitivity** The sensitivity S to a drug is related to the dosage x by
    $$S = 1000x - x^2.$$
    Determine what dosage gives maximum sensitivity and what the maximum sensitivity is.

42. **Maximizing an enclosed area** If 100 feet of fence is used to fence in a rectangular yard,

then the resulting area is given by

$$A = x(50 - x),$$

where x is the width of the rectangle and $50 - x$ is the length. Determine the length and width that give maximum area.

43. **Photosynthesis** The rate of photosynthesis R for a certain plant depends on the intensity of light x according to

$$R = 270x - 90x^2.$$

Determine the intensity that gives the maximum rate.

44. **Crop yield** The yield from a grove of orange trees is given by $Y = x(800 - x)$, where x is the number of orange trees per acre. How many trees will maximize the yield?

45. **Projectiles** Two projectiles are shot into the air from the same location. The paths of the projectiles are parabolas and are given by
(a) $y = -0.0013x^2 + x + 10$ and
(b) $y = \dfrac{-x^2}{81} + \dfrac{4}{3}x + 10.$
Determine which projectile goes higher by locating the vertex of each parabola.

46. **Projectiles** A projectile shot vertically into the air has its height above ground given by

$$s = 100 + 960t - 16t^2.$$

Find its maximum height.

47. **Revenue** Find the maximum revenue for the revenue function $R(x) = 385x - 0.9x^2$.

48. **Revenue** Find the maximum revenue for the revenue function $R(x) = 1600x - x^2$.

49. **Profit** The profit function for a product is given by

$$P(x) = 90x - 2000 - x^2.$$

Find the break-even points for this product.

50. **Profit** If the profit function for a firm is given by $P(x) = -1100 + 120x - x^2$ and limitations on space require that production is less than 100 units, find the break-even points.

51. **Projectiles** Two projectiles that are shot into the air have their paths given by

$$y = -0.0013x^2 + x + 10 \quad \text{and}$$
$$y = \frac{-x^2}{81} + \frac{4x}{3} + 10.$$

Determine which projectile travels farther by finding the zeros of each function.

52. **Projectiles** The vertical height (in meters) of a projectile is given by $s = -9.8t^2 + 60t$ (t in seconds). At what times is the projectile on the ground (when $s = 0$)?

53. **Maximum revenue and profit** Suppose that a company has fixed costs of \$28,000 and variable costs of $\frac{2}{5}x + 222$ dollars per unit, where x is the total number of units produced. Suppose further that the selling price of its product is $1250 - \frac{3}{5}x$ dollars per unit.
(a) Find the maximum revenue.
(b) Form the profit function from the cost and revenue functions and find maximum profit.
(c) Compare the level of production to maximize profit with the level to maximize revenue. Do they agree?

54. **Maximum revenue and profit** Suppose that a company has fixed costs of \$300 and variable costs of $\frac{3}{4}x + 1460$ dollars per unit, where x is the total number of units produced. Suppose further that the selling price of its product is $1500 - \frac{1}{4}x$ dollars per unit.
(a) Find the maximum revenue.
(b) Form the profit function from the cost and revenue functions and find maximum profit.
(c) Compare the level of production to maximize profit with the level to maximize revenue. Do they agree?

55. **Optimization with fixed budget** A rectangular field along a river is to be fenced, with no fence required along the river. The material for the fence costs \$4 per running foot for the two ends and \$6 per running foot for the side opposite the river, which has length x. Express the area of the field as a function of x if \$1800

worth of fence can be used. What is the maximum area?

56. ***Maximum income*** The Quick Car Rental Company can rent 100 cars per day at a rate of $10 per day. For each $1.00 increase in rate, five fewer cars are rented. If x represents the increase in rate, express the total income in terms of x. What is the maximum income?

Union participation The following table shows the percentages of U.S. workers who belonged to unions for selected years from 1930 to 1989.

Year	Percentage
1930	11.6
1940	26.9
1950	31.5
1960	31.4
1970	27.3
1975	25.5
1980	21.9
1985	18
1989	16.4

Source: *World Almanac*, 1991.

Assume that this data can be modeled with the function

$$u(x) = -39.3 + 2.38x - 0.02x^2,$$

where x is the number of years past 1900. Use this information in problems 57–59.

57. (a) Plot the values from the table.
    (b) Graph the function $u(x)$ on the same set of axes with the data points.

58. (a) For what year does the model $u(x)$ indicate that a maximum percentage of U.S. workers belonged to unions?
    (b) Does your answer in (a) agree with the data in the table?

59. (a) For what years does the model $u(x)$ predict that 0% of U.S. workers will belong to unions?
    (b) When can you guarantee that $u(x)$ can no longer be used to model the percentage of U.S. workers who belong to unions?

1.5 | SPECIAL FUNCTIONS AND THEIR GRAPHS

OBJECTIVES

- To graph and apply basic functions
- To graph and apply polynomial functions
- To graph and apply rational functions
- To graph and apply piecewise defined functions

Linear equations that can be written in the form $y = ax + b$ express y as a function of x, so they are called **linear functions.**

The special function

$$y = f(x) = x$$

is called the **identity function** [Figure 1.38(a)], and a function defined by

$$y = f(x) = C, \qquad C \text{ a constant}$$

is called a **constant function.** Figure 1.38(b) shows the graph of the constant function $y = f(x) = 2$.

Some additional basic functions are $y = 1/x$, $y = x^2$, and $y = x^3$. [See Figure 1.38(c), (d), and (e).]

FIGURE 1.38

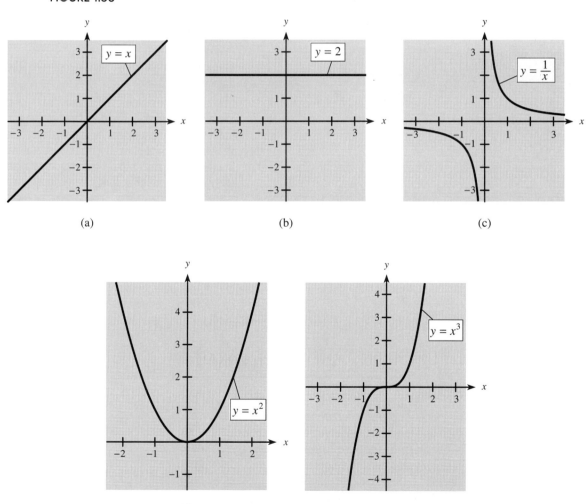

(a)   (b)   (c)

(d)   (e)

These basic functions are the starting points for learning about classes of functions, such as the linear and quadratic functions we have already studied. But linear and quadratic functions and $y = x^3$ are part of a more general class of functions called **polynomial functions,** and $y = 1/x$ belongs to a class called **rational functions.**

POLYNOMIAL AND RATIONAL FUNCTIONS

A **polynomial function of degree n** has the form

$$y = a_n x^n + a_{n-1} x^{n-1} + \cdots + a_1 x + a_0,$$

where $a_n \neq 0$.

A linear function is a polynomial function of degree 1, and a quadratic function is a polynomial function of degree 2.

Accurate graphing of a polynomial function of degree greater than 2 requires the methods of calculus; we will investigate these methods in Chapter 3. For now, we will observe some characteristics of the graphs of polynomial functions of degrees 2, 3, and 4; these are summarized in Table 1.2. Using this information and plotting some points yields the graphs of these functions.

TABLE 1.2   Graphs of some polynomials

	Degree 2	Degree 3	Degree 4
Turning points	1	0 or 2	1 or 3
x-intercepts	0, 1, or 2	1, 2, or 3	0, 1, 2, 3, or 4
Possible shapes			

EXAMPLE 1

Graph $y = x^3 - 16x$ for $-5 \le x \le 5$.

Solution This function is a third-degree polynomial function, so it has one of the four shapes shown in the "Degree 3" column in Table 1.2. By constructing a table for integer values from $x = -5$ to $x = 5$ and plotting the points, we see that the graph appears to turn near $x = -2$ and near $x = 2$ and has a shape like (b) in Table 1.2. [See Figure 1.39(a) on the following page.]

x	y	x	y
-5	-45	1	-15
-4	0	2	-24
-3	21	3	-21
-2	24	4	0
-1	15	5	45
0	0		

Checking points near $x = -2$ and $x = 2$ tells us more about how the graph looks near the turning points.

x	y	x	y
-2.4	24.58	2.1	-24.34
-2.3	24.63	2.2	-24.55
-2.2	24.55	2.3	-24.63
-2.1	24.34	2.4	-24.58

This table indicates that the graph turns at $x = -2.3$ and at $x = 2.3$ (to the nearest tenth). The methods of calculus will make it much easier to find these turning points. The graph is shown in Figure 1.39(b).

FIGURE 1.39

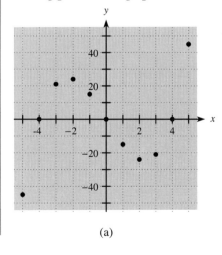

(a)

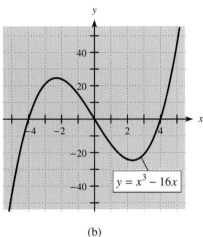

$y = x^3 - 16x$

(b)

EXAMPLE 2

Graph $y = x^4 - 2x^2$ for $-2 \le x \le 2$.

Solution This is a polynomial function of degree 4. Thus it has one, two, or three turning points and has one of the six shapes in the "Degree 4" column of Table 1.2. We begin by constructing a table of values for integer values of x from -2 to 2 and plotting the points [see Figure 1.40(a)].

x	y
−2	8
−1	−1
0	0
1	−1
2	8

The points appear to fit only shape (f) from Table 1.2, with turning points near $x = -1$, $x = 0$, and $x = 1$. Evaluating the function near these x-values and plotting the points gives the graph [shown in Figure 1.40(b)].

x	y
−1.1	−0.96
−0.9	−0.96
−0.1	−0.02
0.1	−0.02
0.9	−0.96
1.1	−0.96

FIGURE 1.40

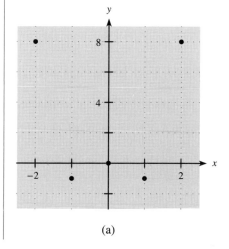

(a)

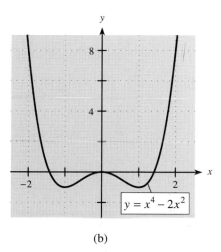

$$y = x^4 - 2x^2$$

(b)

A **rational function** is a function that can be written as the ratio of two polynomials. The graph of the rational function

$$y = \frac{1}{x}$$

is shown in Figure 1.41 on the following page. This graph is constructed by using a table of values for $x = -3$ to $x = 3$. Because division by 0 is not possible, $x = 0$ is not in the domain of the function. To see the shape of the graph near 0, we use additional points near 0.

FIGURE 1.41

x	y	x	y
-3	-0.33	0.02	50
-2	-0.5	0.04	25
-1	-1	0.1	10
-0.1	-10	1	1
-0.04	-25	2	0.5
-0.02	-50	3	0.33

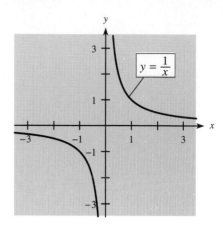

The graph of $y = 1/x$ approaches the y-axis but does not touch it. In this case, we call the y-axis a **vertical asymptote.**

On the graphs of polynomial functions, the turning points are usually the features of greatest interest. However, on the graphs of rational functions, vertical asymptotes frequently are the most interesting features. (Rational functions may or may not have turning points.)

In general, when a rational function has its denominator equal to 0 at a value $x = a$, then we should plot points very close to $x = a$ to see what shape the graph is taking near $x = a$. When $|y|$ becomes large as x gets close to a, we say $x = a$ is a **vertical asymptote.**

Rational functions sometimes have **horizontal asymptotes** as well as vertical asymptotes. Whenever the values of y approach some finite number b as $|x|$ becomes very large, we say that there is a **horizontal asymptote** at $y = b$.

Notice that the graph of $y = 1/x$ appears to get close to the x-axis as $|x|$ becomes large. Testing values of x for which $|x|$ is large, we see that y is close to 0. Thus we say $y = 0$ (or the x-axis) is a **horizontal asymptote** for the graph of $y = 1/x$. The graph in the following example has both a vertical and a horizontal asymptote.

EXAMPLE 3

(a) Use values of x from -5 to 5 to develop a table of function values for the graph of

$$y = \frac{12x + 8}{3x - 9}.$$

(b) Sketch the graph.

Solution

(a) Because $3x - 9 = 0$ when $x = 3$, it follows that $x = 3$ is not in the domain of this function. When we plot points corresponding to integer values of x from

−5 to 5, we also plot additional points near $x = 3$.

x	y	x	y
−5	2.17	2	−10.7
−4	1.90	2.5	−25.33
−3	1.56	2.9	−142.67
−2	1.07	3.1	150.67
−1	0.33	3.5	33.33
0	−0.89	4	18.67
1	−3.33	5	11.33

(b) Figure 1.42(a) shows enough of these points to see that there is a vertical asymptote at $x = 3$.

To see if the function has a horizontal asymptote, we calculate y as $|x|$ becomes larger.

x	$y = f(x)$
−10,000	3.998
−1000	3.98
1000	4.01
10,000	4.001

We can see that the graph is approaching $y = 4$ as $|x|$ increases, so we have a horizontal asymptote at $y = 4$. The graph is shown in Figure 1.42(b).

FIGURE 1.42

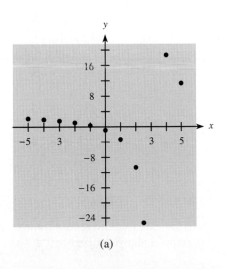

(a)

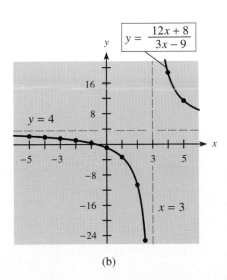

(b)

The graph of the rational function in the following example has a vertical asymptote and a turning point.

EXAMPLE 4 | Consider the following total cost function for x units of a product.

$$C = 900 + 3x + x^2$$

Graph the average cost function for this product.

Solution The average cost per unit is

$$\overline{C} = \frac{C}{x} = \frac{900 + 3x + x^2}{x}$$

or

$$\overline{C} = \frac{900}{x} + 3 + x.$$

Because x represents the number of units produced, $x \geq 0$. Because $x = 0$ cannot be in the domain of the function, we plot points for positive values of x, with some points close to $x = 0$. [See Figure 1.43(a).]

x	$\overline{C}$
0.1	9003.1
1	904
10	103
20	68
30	63
40	65.5
50	71
60	78
70	85.9

Because $\overline{C}$ becomes very large as x approaches 0, we know that $x = 0$, (the y-axis) is a vertical asymptote for the graph. Because the graph appears to have a minimum value near $x = 30$, we can plot additional points near $x = 30$.

x	$\overline{C}$
28	63.14
29	63.03
31	63.03
32	63.13

These points seem to indicate that the minimum average cost is $63 when 30 units are produced. The graph is shown in Figure 1.43(b).

FIGURE 1.43

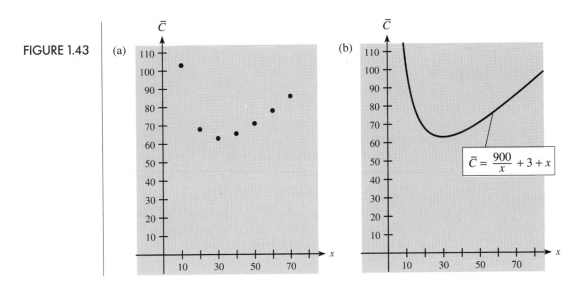

(a)

(b)

$$\bar{C} = \frac{900}{x} + 3 + x$$

PIECEWISE DEFINED FUNCTIONS

Another special function comes from the definition of $|x|$. The **absolute value function** can be written as

$$f(x) = |x| \quad \text{or} \quad f(x) = \begin{cases} x & \text{if } x \geq 0 \\ -x & \text{if } x < 0 \end{cases}$$

Notice that restrictions on the domain of the absolute value function specify different formulas for different parts of the domain. To graph $f(x) = |x|$, we graph the portion of the line $y = x$ for $x \geq 0$ [see Figure 1.44(a)] and the portion of the line $y = -x$ for $x < 0$ [see Figure 1.44(b)]. When we put these pieces on the same graph [Figure 1.44(c)], they give us the graph of $f(x) = |x|$. Since the absolute value function is defined by two equations, we say it is a **piecewise defined function.**

FIGURE 1.44

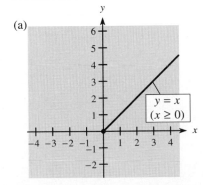

(a)

$y = x$
$(x \geq 0)$

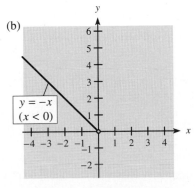

(b)

$y = -x$
$(x < 0)$

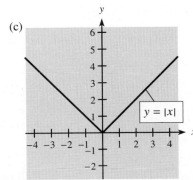

(c)

$y = |x|$

It is possible for the selling price S of a product to be defined as a piecewise function of the cost C of the product. For example, the selling price might be defined by two different equations on two different intervals, as follows:

$$S = f(C) = \begin{cases} 3C & \text{if } 0 \le C \le 20 \\ 1.5C + 30 & \text{if } C > 20 \end{cases}$$

Written in this way, the value of S depends on the value of C, so C is the **independent variable** and S is the **dependent variable.** The set of possible values of C (the domain) is the set of nonnegative real numbers (because cost cannot be negative), and the range is the set of nonnegative real numbers (since all values of C will result in nonnegative values for S).

Note that the selling price of a product that costs \$15 would be $f(15) = 3(15) = 45$ (dollars) and the selling price of a product that costs \$25 would be $f(25) = 1.5(25) + 30 = 67.50$ (dollars).

EXAMPLE 5 | Graph the selling price function

$$S = f(C) = \begin{cases} 3C & \text{if } 0 \le C \le 20 \\ 1.5C + 30 & \text{if } C > 20 \end{cases}$$

Solution Each of the two pieces of the graph of this function is a line and is easily graphed. It remains only to graph each in the proper interval. The graph is shown in Figure 1.45.

FIGURE 1.45

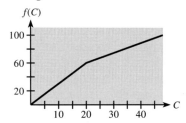

1. All constant functions [such as $f(x) = 8$] have graphs that are _____.

2. Which of the following are polynomial functions, which are rational functions, and which are neither?

(a) $f(x) = x^3 - x + 4$ 　　　　　　(b) $f(x) = \dfrac{x + 1}{4x}$

(c) $f(x) = 1 + \sqrt{x}$ 　　　　　　(d) $g(x) = \dfrac{1 + \sqrt{x}}{1 + x + \sqrt{x}}$

(e) $h(x) = 5$

3. A third-degree polynomial can have at most _____ turning points.

4. Given $f(x) = \dfrac{3x}{x - 4}$, decide whether the following are true or false.

 (a) $f(x)$ has a vertical asymptote at $x = 4$.

 (b) $f(x)$ has a horizontal asymptote at $x = 3$.

5. If $f(x) = \begin{cases} 0 & \text{if } x \le 0 \\ 12x & \text{if } 0 < x < 10, \\ 10x + 20 & \text{if } x \ge 10 \end{cases}$ find the following.

 (a) $f(-5)$ (b) $f(5)$ (c) $f(20)$

TECHNOLOGY CORNER

The table below gives a demand schedule for a product.

Price	Quantity
96	9
80	11
64	14
30	31
16	59
10	95

1. Let x represent quantity and y represent price, and then plot the points.

2. The data from (1) fit a curve of the form

$$y = \frac{a}{x + b},$$

 where a and b are positive constants. Try different values of a and b until you find a curve that fits the points. (You can look at fewer points with a smaller range once you get a "close" approximation.)

3. Check the values from the table in your equation to see if your equation is correct.

4. In (2), as you tried different values of a and b, what did you notice about the resulting graphs? In particular, what happened to the asymptotes and the basic shape of the graph?

1. horizontal lines

2. polynomial functions are (a) and (e); also (e) is a constant function; the only rational function is (b); both (c) and (d) are neither because of $\sqrt{x}$.

3. two

4. (a) True.   (b) False. The horizontal asymptote is $y = 3$.

5. (a) $f(-5) = 0$ In fact, for any negative value of x, $f(x) = 0$.
   (b) $f(5) = 12(5) = 60$
   (c) $f(20) = 10(20) + 20 = 220$

EXERCISE 1.5

In problems 1–20, match each of the given functions with one of the graphs labeled (a)–(t) shown following these functions. Recognizing special features of certain types of functions and plotting points for the functions will be helpful.

1. $y = 4x + 2$

2. $y = 2.5 - 2x$

3. $y = (x - 1)^2$

4. $y = 2x^2$

5. $y = -2(x - 4)^2$

6. $y = -x^2 + 2x + 4$

7. $y = x^3$

8. $y = -x^4$

9. $y = x^3 - x$

10. $y = (x - 3)^2(x + 1)$

11. $y = 16x^2 - x^4$

12. $y = (x + 1)(x - 3)(x - 1)$

13. $y = \dfrac{1}{x - 1}$

14. $y = \dfrac{1 - 2x}{x}$

15. $y = \dfrac{x - 3}{x + 1}$

16. $y = \dfrac{1 - 3x}{2x + 5}$

17. $y = |x + 1|$

18. $y = |x - 2|$

19. $y = \begin{cases} -x & \text{if } x < -1 \\ 1 & \text{if } -1 \le x \le 1 \\ x & \text{if } x > 1 \end{cases}$

20. $y = \begin{cases} x & \text{if } x \le 0 \\ 7x/2 & \text{if } 0 < x < 2 \\ 7 & \text{if } x \ge 2 \end{cases}$

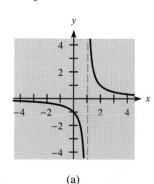

(a)

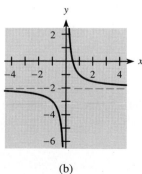

(b)

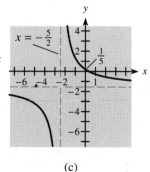

(c)

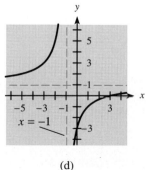

(d)

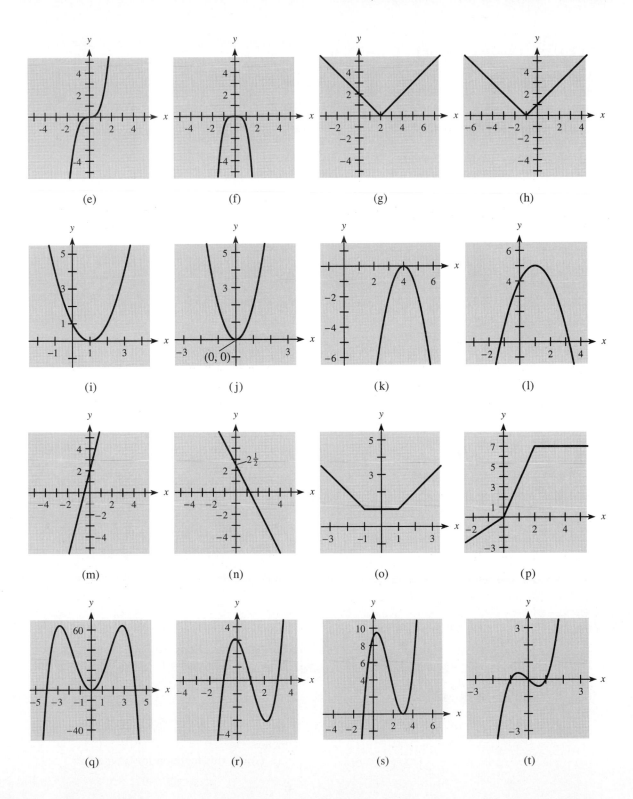

(e)

(f)

(g)

(h)

(i)

(j)

(k)

(l)

(m)

(n)

(o)

(p)

(q)

(r)

(s)

(t)

21. If $F(x) = \dfrac{|x|}{x}$, find the following.
   (a) $F(-\frac{1}{3})$ (b) $F(10)$
   (c) $F(0.001)$ (d) Is $F(0)$ defined?

22. If $H(x) = |x - 1|$, find the following.
   (a) $H(-1)$ (b) $H(1)$
   (c) $H(0)$
   (d) Does $H(-x) = H(x)$?

23. If $f(x) = \begin{cases} |x| + 1 & \text{if } x < 1 \\ 3 - 1/x & \text{if } x > 1 \end{cases}$,

   find the following, if they exist.
   (a) $f(-6)$ (b) $f(1)$
   (c) $f(100)$ (d) $f(0.9)$

24. If $k(x) = \begin{cases} 2 & \text{if } x < 0 \\ x + 4 & \text{if } 0 < x < 1, \\ |1 - x| & \text{if } x \geq 1 \end{cases}$

   find the following, if they exist.
   (a) $k(-0.1)$ (b) $k(0.1)$
   (c) $k(0.9)$ (d) $k(1.1)$

25. If $f(x) = \begin{cases} x^2 + 1 & \text{if } x < 1 \\ 3 - 1/x & \text{if } x > 1 \end{cases}$,

   find the following, if they exist.
   (a) $f(-6)$ (b) $f(1)$
   (c) $f(100)$ (d) $f(0.9)$

26. If $f(x) = \begin{cases} 1 - 4x & \text{if } x < -1 \\ -x^2 & \text{if } x \geq -1 \end{cases}$,

   find the following, if they exist.
   (a) $f(-3)$ (b) $f(-1.1)$
   (c) $f(-1)$ (d) $f(10)$

27. If $k(x) = \begin{cases} 2 & \text{if } x < 0 \\ x + 4 & \text{if } 0 \leq x < 1, \\ 1 - x & \text{if } x \geq 1 \end{cases}$

   find the following, if they exist.
   (a) $k(-5)$ (b) $k(0)$
   (c) $k(1)$ (d) $k(-0.001)$

28. If $g(x) = \begin{cases} 0.5x + 4 & \text{if } x < 0 \\ 4 - x & \text{if } 0 \leq x < 4, \\ 0 & \text{if } x > 4 \end{cases}$

   find the following, if they exist.
   (a) $g(-4)$ (b) $g(1)$
   (c) $g(7)$ (d) $g(3.9)$

Some functions that have special features near $x = 0$ are given in problems 29–38. Graph them.

29. $y = -x^3$ 30. $y = -x^4$

31. $y = -x^4 + 2x^2$ 32. $y = x^4 - 4x^2$

33. $y = \dfrac{1}{x^2}$ 34. $y = -\dfrac{1}{x^2}$

35. $y = \dfrac{1}{1 - x}$ 36. $y = \dfrac{x}{x - 1}$

37. $y = \begin{cases} -x & \text{if } x < 0 \\ 5x & \text{if } x \geq 0 \end{cases}$

38. $y = \begin{cases} 2x - 1 & \text{if } x < 1 \\ -x & \text{if } x \geq 1 \end{cases}$

APPLICATIONS

39. **Fixed costs** Fixed costs FC are business costs that remain constant regardless of the number of units produced. Some items that might contribute to fixed costs are rent and utilities. The equation

   $$FC = 2000$$

   indicates that a business has fixed costs of $2000. Graph $FC = 2000$ by putting x (the number of units produced) on the horizontal axis. (Note that FC does not mean the product of F and C.)

40. **Photosynthesis** The amount of photosynthesis that takes place in a certain plant depends on the intensity of light x according to the equation

   $$f(x) = 145x^2 - 30x^3.$$

   Graph this function for values of x from 0 to 4.

41. **Parcel restrictions** If a box with a square base is to be sent by UPS, the volume of the box is restricted by

   $$V = 108x^2 - 4x^3,$$

   where x is the length of one side of the base in inches.
   (a) Graph this function for $0 \leq x \leq 27$.

(b) Estimate the maximum volume, in cubic inches, that can be sent by UPS.

42. **Container design** A rectangular box with a square base is to be formed from a square piece of cardboard with 12-in. sides. If a square piece with side x is cut from each corner of the cardboard and the sides are folded up to form an open box, the volume of the box is

$$V = (12 - 2x)^2 x.$$

(a) What domain makes sense for this problem?
(b) Sketch the graph of this function for values of x from $x = 0$ to $x = 6$.

43. **Intensity of light** The relationship between the intensity C of light (in candlepower) and the distance x from the source of light (in meters) is given by

$$C = \frac{k}{x^2}.$$

If $k = 5000$, graph this function.

44. **Demand** The demand function for a product is given by

$$p = \frac{200}{2 + 0.1x},$$

where x is the number of units and p is the price. Graph this demand function for $0 \le x \le 250$, with x on the horizontal axis.

45. **Minimum costs** A printer has a contract to run 10,000 posters for a fire company benefit. He can use any number of printing plates from 1 to 10 to run the posters, with the cost of printing given by

$$C(x) = 3x + \frac{48}{x},$$

where x is the number of plates he uses.
(a) Graph this function for $1 \le x \le 10$.
(b) Estimate how many plates would give him the lowest cost (1, 2, 3, 4, 5, etc.).

46. **Production costs** A manufacturer estimates that the cost of a production run for a product is

$$C(x) = 30(x - 1) + \frac{3000}{x + 10}$$

where x is the number of machines used. Graph this total cost function for values of $x \ge 0$.

47. **Mob behavior** In studying lynchings between 1899 and 1946, psychologist Brian Mullin found that the size of a lynch mob relative to the number of victims predicted the level of brutality. He developed a formula for the other-total ratio (y) that predicts the level of self-attentiveness of people in a crowd of size x with 1 victim.

$$y = \frac{1}{x + 1}$$

The lower the value of y, the more likely an individual is to be influenced by "mob psychology." Graph this function; use positive integers as its domain.

48. **Gravitational force** A person weighing 150 pounds on earth has weight given by

$$w = w(d) = \frac{2,400,000,000}{(4000 + d)^2}$$

d miles above the earth's surface.
(a) Find $w(0)$ and interpret this.
(b) How much would this person weigh while flying in an airplane at 29,000 feet?
(c) An astronaut orbits the earth at an average of 80 miles above the surface. If he weighs 150 pounds on earth, how much does he weigh while in orbit?

49. **Water usage costs** The monthly charge for water in a small town is given by

$$f(x) = \begin{cases} 18 & \text{if } 0 \le x \le 20 \\ 18 + 0.1\,(x - 20) & \text{if } x > 20 \end{cases}$$

where x is in hundreds of gallons and $f(x)$ is in dollars. Find the monthly charge for each of the following usages: (a) 30 gallons, (b) 3000 gallons, and (c) 4000 gallons. (d) Graph the function for $0 \leq x \leq 100$.

50. ***Commercial electrical usage*** The monthly charge (in dollars) for x kilowatt hours (kWh) of electricity used by a commercial customer is given by the following function.

$$C(x) = \begin{cases} 7.52 + 0.1079x & \text{if } 0 \leq x \leq 5 \\ 19.22 + 0.1079x & \text{if } 5 < x \leq 750 \\ 20.795 + 0.1058x & \text{if } 750 < x \leq 1500 \\ 131.345 + 0.0321x & \text{if } x > 1500 \end{cases}$$

Find the monthly charges for the following usages.
(a) 5 kWh
(b) 6 kWh
(c) 3000 kWh

51. ***Calories and temperature*** The temperature of 1 g of H_2O as it changes from ice at $-10°C$ to steam at $110°C$ is given by

$$T = f(x) = \begin{cases} x - 10 & \text{if } 0 \leq x < 10 \\ 0 & \text{if } 10 \leq x < 100 \\ x - 100 & \text{if } 100 \leq x < 200 \\ 100 & \text{if } 200 \leq x < 700 \\ x - 600 & \text{if } 700 \leq x \leq 710 \end{cases}$$

where x represents calories of heat. Find the temperature for each of the following values of x.
(a) 5   (b) 50
(c) 150   (d) 500
(e) 705
(f) For $10 < x < 100$, the value of T is 0. Over this interval, what is happening to the 1 g of substance?

1.6 | POINTS OF INTERSECTION AND THEIR APPLICATIONS

OBJECTIVES
- To find break-even points
- To find market equilibrium

BREAK-EVEN POINTS

In Section 1.3, we discussed linear cost and revenue functions. Functions other than linear functions (for example, quadratic functions) may also be used to describe the revenue and cost for a product.

For example, the monthly total cost curve for a commodity may be the parabola with equation $C(x) = 2000 + 10x + x^2$. If the total revenue function is given by the equation $R(x) = 130x$, we can find break-even by finding the quantity x that makes $C(x) = R(x)$. (See Figure 1.46.)

FIGURE 1.46

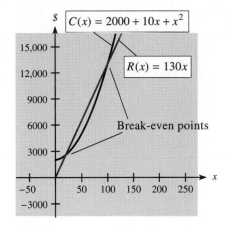

$$C(x) = 2000 + 10x + x^2$$

$$R(x) = 130x$$

Break-even points

Setting $C(x) = R(x)$, we have

$$2000 + 10x + x^2 = 130x$$
$$x^2 - 120x + 2000 = 0$$
$$(x - 20)(x - 100) = 0$$

Thus $C(x) = R(x)$ at $x = 20$ and at $x = 100$. If 20 items are produced and sold, $C(x)$ and $R(x)$ are both $2600; if 100 items are sold, $C(x)$ and $R(x)$ are both $13,000. Thus there are two break-even points.

In a monopoly market, the revenue of a company is restricted by the demand for the product. In this case, the relationship between the price p of the product and the number of units sold x is described by the demand function $p = f(x)$, and the total revenue function for the product is given by

$$R = px = [f(x)]x.$$

If, for example, the demand for a product is given by

$$p = 300 - x,$$

where x is the number of units sold and p is the price, then the revenue function for this product is the quadratic function

$$R = px = (300 - x)x$$

or

$$R = 300x - x^2.$$

EXAMPLE 1

Suppose that in a monopoly market the total cost per week of producing a high-tech product is given by $C = 3600 + 100x + 2x^2$. Suppose further that the weekly demand function for this product is $p = 500 - 2x$. Find the number of units that will give break-even for the product.

Solution The total cost function is $C(x) = 3600 + 100x + 2x^2$, and the total revenue function is $R(x) = (500 - 2x)x = 500x - 2x^2$.

Setting $C(x) = R(x)$ and solving for x gives

$$3600 + 100x + 2x^2 = 500x - 2x^2$$
$$4x^2 - 400x + 3600 = 0$$
$$x^2 - 100x + 900 = 0$$
$$(x - 90)(x - 10) = 0$$
$$x = 90 \quad \text{or} \quad x = 10.$$

Does this mean that the firm will break even at 10 units and at 90 units? Yes. Figure 1.47 shows the graphs of $C(x)$ and $R(x)$. From the graph we can observe that the firm makes a profit after $x = 10$ *until* $x = 90$. At $x = 90$, the profit is 0, and the firm loses money if more than 90 units are produced per week.

FIGURE 1.47

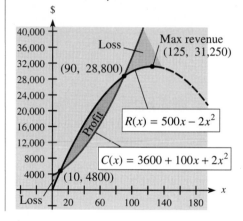

Notice that for Example 1 the revenue function

$$R(x) = (500 - 2x)x = 500x - 2x^2$$

is a parabola that opens downward. Thus the vertex is the point at which revenue is maximum. We can locate this vertex by using the methods discussed in Section 1.4.

$$\text{Vertex:} \quad x = \frac{-b}{2a} = \frac{-500}{2(-2)} = \frac{500}{4} = 125 \text{ (units)}$$

It is interesting to note that when $x = 125$, the firm achieves its maximum revenues of

$$R(125) = 500(125) - 2(125)^2 = 31{,}250 \text{ (dollars)},$$

but the costs when $x = 125$ are

$$C(125) = 3600 + 100(125) + 2(125)^2 = 47{,}350 \text{ (dollars)},$$

which results in a loss. This illustrates that maximizing revenue is not a good goal. We should seek to maximize profit.

EXAMPLE 2

If total costs are given by $C(x) = 3600 + 100x + 2x^2$ and total revenues are given by $R(x) = 500x - 2x^2$, form the profit function and find the maximum profit.

Solution Note that these are the same cost and revenue functions that appear in the previous example.

Profit = revenue − cost,

so we have

$$P(x) = (500x - 2x^2) - (3600 + 100x + 2x^2),$$

or

$$P(x) = -3600 + 400x - 4x^2.$$

This profit function is a parabola that opens downward, so the vertex will be the maximum point.

$$\text{Vertex:} \quad x = \frac{-b}{2a} = \frac{-400}{2(-4)} = \frac{-400}{-8} = 50$$

Furthermore, when $x = 50$, we have

$$P(50) = -3600 + 400(50) - 4(50)^2 = 6400 \text{ (dollars)}.$$

Thus when 50 items are produced and sold, a maximum profit of $6400 results (see Figure 1.48).

FIGURE 1.48

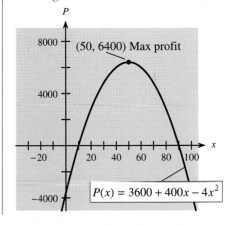

Comparing Figures 1.47 and 1.48, notice first that the maximum profit of $6400 at 50 units in Figure 1.48 corresponds to the vertical distance between revenue and cost at 50 units in Figure 1.47. In addition, the break-even points at $x = 10$ and $x = 90$ in Figure 1.47 correspond to x-intercepts (Profit = 0) in Figure 1.48.

It is important to note that the procedures for finding maximum revenue and profit in these examples depend on the fact that these functions are parabolas. For more general functions, procedures for finding maximum or minimum values are discussed in Chapter 3.

CHECKPOINT

1. The point of intersection of the revenue function and the cost function is called _____.

2. If $C(x) = 120x + 15{,}000$ and $R(x) = 370x - x^2$, finding the break-even points requires solution of what equation?

MARKET EQUILIBRIUM

The first-quadrant parts of parabolas or other quadratic equations are frequently used to represent supply and demand functions. For example, the first-quadrant part of $p - q^2 + q + 2$ (Figure 1.49) may represent a supply curve, while the first-quadrant part of $q^2 + 2q + 6p - 23 = 0$ (Figure 1.50) may represent a demand curve.

FIGURE 1.49

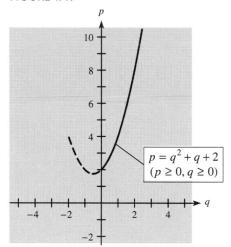

$$p = q^2 + q + 2$$
$$(p \geq 0, q \geq 0)$$

FIGURE 1.50

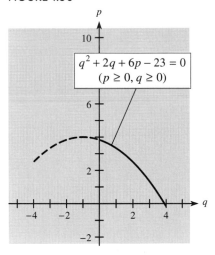

$$q^2 + 2q + 6p - 23 = 0$$
$$(p \geq 0, q \geq 0)$$

Because both supply and demand have the same price p at market equilibrium, we can solve them simultaneously to find the market equilibrium point. If the supply function for a commodity is given by $p = q^2 + 100$ and the demand function is given by $p = -20q + 2500$, we find the point of market equilibrium as follows.

$$q^2 + 100 = -20q + 2500$$
$$q^2 + 20q - 2400 = 0$$
$$(q - 40)(q + 60) = 0$$
$$q = 40 \quad \text{or} \quad q = -60$$

Since a negative quantity has no meaning, the equilibrium point occurs when 40 units are sold, at $(40, 1700)$. The graphs of the functions are shown (in the first quadrant only) in Figure 1.51.

FIGURE 1.51

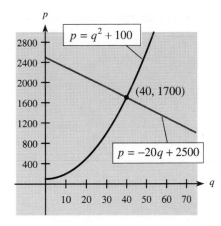

EXAMPLE 3

If the demand function for a commodity is given by $p(q + 4) = 400$ and the supply function is given by $2p - q - 38 = 0$, find the market equilibrium.

Solution Solving $2p - q - 38 = 0$ for p gives $p = \frac{1}{2}q + 19$. Solving $p(q + 4) = 400$ for p gives $p = 400/(q + 4)$. Thus market equilibrium occurs where

$$\frac{1}{2}q + 19 = \frac{400}{q + 4}$$

$$\left(\frac{1}{2}q + 19\right)(q + 4) = 400$$

$$\frac{1}{2}q^2 + 21q - 324 = 0$$

$$q^2 + 42q - 648 = 0$$
$$(q - 12)(q + 54) = 0$$
$$q = 12 \quad \text{or} \quad q = -54.$$

Thus the market equilibrium occurs when 12 items are sold at a price of \$25 each. The graphs of the demand and supply functions are shown in Figure 1.52.

FIGURE 1.52

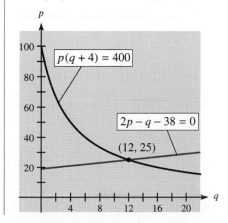

3. The point of intersection of the supply and demand functions is called _____.

4. If the demand and supply functions for a product are

$$p + \frac{1}{10}q^2 = 1000 \quad \text{and} \quad p = \frac{1}{10}q + 10,$$

respectively, finding the market equilibrium point requires solution of what equation?

TECHNOLOGY CORNER

Suppose that a company's total costs (in dollars) are given by

$$C(x) = (x - 10)^3 + 10{,}000 + 100x,$$

where x is the number of hundreds of units. Suppose further that the firm wants to set its price at $49 per unit (that is, at $4900 per hundred units).

1. Form the total revenue function for this company, and graph it and the total cost function.

2. From the graphs in (1), estimate the number of units that need to be produced for the company to break even.

3. From the graphs in (1), estimate the number of units the company should produce to obtain maximum profit. Explain how you reached your conclusion.

4. Form the profit function for this company, and graph it with the total revenue and total cost functions.

5. Check your conclusions in (2) and (3) by using the graph of the profit function. Explain what feature of the graph of the profit function was used in each case.

6. Use trace to determine the maximum profit.

1. the break-even point

2. Solution of $C(x) = R(x)$. That is, solution of $120x + 15{,}000 = 370x - x^2$, or $x^2 - 250x + 15{,}000 = 0$.

3. the market equilibrium point or market equilibrium

4. Demand: $p = -\frac{1}{10}q^2 + 1000$; supply: $p = \frac{1}{10}q + 10$

Solution of $-\frac{1}{10}q^2 + 1000 = \frac{1}{10}q + 10$

$$-q^2 + 10{,}000 = q + 100$$
$$0 = q^2 + q - 9900. \qquad \blacksquare$$

EXERCISE 1.6

BREAK-EVEN POINTS

1. The total costs for a company are given by

$$C(x) = 2000 + 40x + x^2$$

and the total revenues are given by $R(x) = 130x$. Find the break-even points.

2. If a firm has cost function $C(x) = 3600 + 25x + \frac{1}{2}x^2$ and revenue function $R(x) = (175 - \frac{1}{2}x)x$, find the break-even points.

3. If a company has total costs given by $C(x) = 15{,}000 + 35x + 0.1x^2$ and total revenues given by $R(x) = 385x - 0.9x^2$, find the break-even points.

4. If a company's total costs are $C(x) = 1600 + 1500x$ and total revenues are $R(x) = 1600x - x^2$, find the break-even points.

5. Given $C(x) = 150 + x + 0.09x^2$ and $R(x) = 12.5x - 0.01x^2$, and given that production is restricted to fewer than 75 units, find the break-even points.

6. If the profit function for a firm is given by $P(x) = -1100 + 120x - x^2$ and limitations on space require that production be less than 100 units, find the break-even points.

7. Suppose, in a monopoly market, that the demand for a product is $p = 175 - 0.50x$ and the revenue function is $R = px$, where x is the number of units sold. Suppose also that fixed costs are $5000 and the cost per unit is $75. Find the break-even points. Is it possible for this company to make a profit?

8. Suppose, in a monopoly market, that the demand for a product is $p = 1600 - x$ and the revenue function is $R = px$, where x is the number of units sold. Suppose further that fixed costs are $90,000 and the cost per unit is $600. Find the break-even points. Is it possible for this company to make a profit?

9. Suppose that a company in a monopoly market has fixed costs of $28,000 and variable costs of $\frac{2}{5}x + 222$ dollars per unit. Suppose further that the demand function for the product is $p = 1250 - \frac{3}{5}x$. Find the break-even points.

10. In a monopoly market, suppose that a firm has fixed costs of $300 and variable costs of $\frac{3}{4}x + 1460$ dollars per unit for its product. If the demand function for the product is $p = 1500 - \frac{1}{4}x$, find the break-even points.

SUPPLY, DEMAND, AND MARKET EQUILIBRIUM

11. Sketch the first quadrant portions of the following on the same set of axes.
    (a) The supply function whose equation is $p = \frac{1}{4}q^2 + 10$.

(b) The demand function whose equation is $p = 86 - 6q - 3q^2$.

(c) Label the market equilibrium point.

(d) Algebraically determine the equilibrium point for the supply and demand functions.

12. Sketch the first-quadrant portions of the following on the same set of axes.

(a) The supply function whose equation is $p = q^2 + 8q + 16$.

(b) The demand function whose equation is $p = 216 - 2q$.

(c) Label the market equilibrium point.

(d) Algebraically determine the equilibrium point for the supply and demand functions.

13. Sketch the first quadrant portions of the following on the same set of axes.

(a) The supply function whose equation is $p = 0.2q^2 + 0.4q + 1.8$.

(b) The demand function whose equation is $p = 9 - 0.2q - 0.1q^2$.

(c) Label the market equilibrium point.

(d) Algebraically determine the market equilibrium point.

14. Sketch the first-quadrant portions of the following on the same set of axes.

(a) The supply function whose equation is $p = q^2 + 8q + 10$.

(b) The demand function whose equation is $p = 240 - \frac{1}{2}q^2$.

(c) Label the market equilibrium point.

(d) Algebraically determine the market equilibrium point for the supply and demand functions.

15. If the supply function for a commodity is $p = q^2 + 8q + 16$ and the demand function is $p = -3q^2 + 6q + 436$, find the equilibrium quantity and equilibrium price.

16. If the supply function for a commodity is $p = q^2 + 8q + 20$ and the demand function is $p = 100 - 4q - q^2$, find the equilibrium quantity and equilibrium price.

17. If the demand function for a certain commodity is given by $p^2 + 4q = 1600$ and the supply function is given by $300 - p^2 + 2q = 0$, find the equilibrium quantity and equilibrium price.

18. If the supply and demand functions for a commodity are $4p - q = 42$ and $(p + 2)q = 2100$, respectively, find the price that will result in market equilibrium.

19. If the supply and demand functions for a commodity are $q = p - 10$ and $q = 1200/p$, what is the equilibrium price and what is the corresponding number of units supplied and demanded?

20. If the supply and demand functions for a certain product are $2p - q + 6 = 0$ and $(p + q)(q + 10) = 3696$, respectively, find the price and quantity that give market equilibrium.

21. The supply function for a product is $2p - q - 10 = 0$. The demand function for the product is $(p + 10)(q + 30) = 7200$. Find the market equilibrium point.

22. Supply and demand for a product are given by the equations $2p - q = 50$ and $pq = 100 + 20q$, respectively. Find the market equilibrium point.

23. For the product in problem 21, if a $22 tax is placed on production of the good, then the supplier passes on this tax by adding $22 to his selling price. Find the new equilibrium point for this product when the tax is passed on. (The new supply function is given by $p = \frac{1}{2}q + 27$.)

24. For the product in problem 22, if a $12.50 tax is placed on production and passed through by the supplier, find the new equilibrium point.

KEY TERMS
& FORMULAS

SECTION	KEY TERM	FORMULA
1.1	Coordinate system	
	Ordered pair, origin,	
	x-axis, y-axis	
	Relation	
	Function	
	Vertical line test,	
	Domain, range	
	Operations with functions	
	Sum	$(f + g)(x) = f(x) + g(x)$
	Difference	$(f - g)(x) = f(x) - g(x)$
	Product	$(f \cdot g)(x) = f(x) \cdot g(x)$
	Quotient	$\left(\dfrac{f}{g}\right)(x) = \dfrac{f(x)}{g(x)}, \; g(x) \neq 0$
	Composite	$(f \circ g)(x) = f(g(x))$ and $(g \circ f)(x) = g(f(x))$
1.2	Linear functions	$f(x) = ax + b$
	Intercepts	x-intercept: where $y = 0$
		y-intercept: where $x = 0$
	Slope of a line	$m = \dfrac{y_2 - y_1}{x_2 - x_1}$
	Parallel lines	$m_1 = m_2$
	Perpendicular lines	$m_2 = -1/m_1$
	Point-slope form	$y - y_1 = m(x - x_1)$
	Slope-intercept form	$y = mx + b$
	Vertical line	$x = a$
	Horizontal line	$y = b$
1.3, 1.6	Cost and revenue	$C(x)$ and $R(x)$
	Profit	$P(x) = R(x) - C(x)$
	Marginal profit	Slope of linear profit
	Marginal cost	Slope of linear cost
	Marginal revenue	Slope of linear revenue
	Break-even point	$C(x) = R(x)$ or $P(x) = 0$
	Supply and demand	
	Market equilibrium	

SECTION	KEY TERM	FORMULA

1.4

Quadratic function; parabola $\qquad f(x) = ax^2 + bx + c$

Vertex of a parabola $\qquad (-b/2a, f(-b/2a))$

Maximum point if $a < 0$

Minimum point if $a > 0$

Zeros of a function $\qquad f(x) = 0$

Quadratic formula $\qquad x = \dfrac{-b \pm \sqrt{b^2 - 4ac}}{2a}$, if $ax^2 + bx + c = 0$

Quadratic discriminant $\qquad b^2 - 4ac$

1.5

Special functions

$f(x) = C, \quad C = \text{constant}$
$f(x) = x \quad (\text{identity})$
$f(x) = x^2, \quad f(x) = x^3,$
$f(x) = 1/x$

Polynomial function $\qquad f(x) = a_n x^n + a_{n-1} x^{n-1} + \cdots + a_1 x + a_0$

Rational function $\qquad f(x) = p(x)/q(x)$, where $p(x)$ and $q(x)$ are polynomials

Vertical asymptote

Horizontal asymptote

Absolute value function $\qquad f(x) = |x| = \begin{cases} x & \text{if } x \geq 0 \\ -x & \text{if } x < 0 \end{cases}$

Piecewise defined functions

REVIEW
EXERCISES

1.1

1. If $p = 3q^3$, is p a function of q?

2. If $y^2 = 9x$, is y a function of x?

3. If $R = \sqrt[3]{x + 4}$, is R a function of x?

4. What are the domain and range of the function $y = \sqrt{9 - x}$?

5. What is the domain of $y = \dfrac{\sqrt{x + 3}}{x}$?

6. If $f(x) = x^2 + 4x + 5$, find the following.
   (a) $f(-3)$ (b) $f(4)$ (c) $f(\tfrac{1}{2})$

7. If $g(x) = x^2 + 1/x$, find the following.
   (a) $g(-1)$ (b) $g(\tfrac{1}{2})$ (c) $g(0.1)$

8. If $f(x) = \begin{cases} -x^2 & \text{if } x \leq 0 \\ 1/x & \text{if } x > 0 \end{cases}$, find the following.
   (a) $f(0)$ (b) $f(0.0001)$ (c) $f(-5)$ (d) $f(10)$

9. If $f(x) = 9x - x^2$, find the following.
   (a) $f(-4 + 1)$ (b) $f(x + 1)$ (c) $f(x + h)$

10. If $f(x) = 3 - x - 2x^2$, find $\dfrac{f(x + h) - f(x)}{h}$.

11. Does the graph in Figure 1.53 represent y as a function of x?

12. Does the graph in Figure 1.54 represent y as a function of x?

FIGURE 1.53   FIGURE 1.54

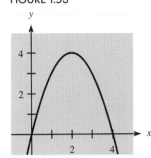   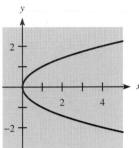

13. For the function f graphed in Figure 1.53 what is $f(2)$?

14. For the function f graphed in Figure 1.53, for what values of x does $f(x) = 0$?

15. For the relation whose graph is in Figure 1.54, when $x = 1$, what values does y assume?

16. If the points $(1, 4)$ and $(-2, 1)$ lie on the graph of $y = f(x)$, what is $f(1)$?

In problems 17 and 18, use $f(x) = 2/x^3$ and $g(x) = 3x^4$ to find the functions indicated.

17. (a) $(f + g)(x)$ (b) $(f - g)(x)$ (c) $(f \cdot g)(x)$ (d) $(f/g)(x)$

18. (a) $(f \circ g)(x)$ (b) $(g \circ f)(x)$ (c) $g(g(x))$ (d) $g^2(x)$

1.2   In problems 19–23, sketch the graph of each equation.

19. $y = 3x$ 20. $y = 5$ 21. $x = -2$

22. $2x - 3y = 6$ 23. $5x + 3y = 6$

In problems 24–26, find the slope of the line passing through each pair of points.

24. $(-1, 2)$ and $(3, -1)$ 25. $(2, -1)$ and $(-1, -4)$

26. $(-3.8, -7.16)$ and $(-3.8, 1.16)$

In problems 27 and 28, find the slope and y-intercept of each line.

27. $2x + 5y = 10$ 28. $x = -\frac{3}{4}y + \frac{3}{2}$

In problems 29–36, write the equation of each line described.

29. slope 4 and y-intercept 2   30. slope $-\frac{1}{2}$ and y-intercept 3

31. passes through $(-2, 1)$ with slope $\frac{2}{5}$ 32. passes through $(6, -11)$ with slope -1
33. passes through $(-2, 7)$ and $(6, -4)$ 34. passes through $(-1, 8)$ and $(-1, -1)$
35. passes through $(1, 6)$ and parallel to $y = 4x - 6$
36. passes through $(-1, 2)$ and perpendicular to $3x + 4y = 12$

1.4   For each function in problems 37–46, find the vertex and determine if it is a maximum or minimum point, find the zeros if they exist, and sketch the graph.

37. $y = \frac{1}{2}x^2 + 2x$ 38. $y = 4 - \frac{1}{4}x^2$ 39. $y = 6 + x - x^2$
40. $y = x^2 - 4x + 5$ 41. $y = x^2 + 6x + 9$ 42. $y = 12x - 9 - 4x^2$
43. $y = x^2 + 2x + 2$ 44. $y = -10 + 7x - x^2$ 45. $y = 20x - 0.1x^2$
46. $y = 50 - 1.5x + 0.01x^2$

1.5   Graph the functions in problems 47–56.

47. $f(x) = x^3$ 48. $f(x) = 4$ 49. $f(x) = |x|$
50. $y = (x - 1)^2$ 51. $y = -x^3 + 16x$ 52. $y = x^3 + 3x^2 - 9x$

53. $y = \dfrac{1}{x - 2}$ 54. $y = \dfrac{x - 1}{x}$ 55. $y = \begin{cases} x & \text{if } x \le 1 \\ 3x - 2 & \text{if } x > 1 \end{cases}$

56. $y = \begin{cases} 1 & \text{if } x < 0 \\ 1 - x & \text{if } x \ge 0 \end{cases}$

APPLICATIONS

1.3   57. **Cost analysis** The owner of a small construction business needs a new truck. He could buy a diesel truck for $18,000 and estimates it would cost him $0.16 per mile to operate. He could buy a gas engine truck for $16,000 and estimates it would cost him $0.21 per mile to operate. Find the number of miles the trucks would have to travel before their costs (purchase price and operating costs) would be equal. If he normally keeps a truck for 5 years and averages 20,000 miles per year, which is the better buy?

58. **Supply and demand** A certain product has supply function given by $p = 4q + 5$ and demand function given by $p = -2q + 81$.
(a) If $p = \$53$, how many units are supplied and how many are demanded?
(b) Does $p = \$53$ give a shortfall or a surplus?
(c) Is p likely to increase from $53 or decrease from it?

59. **Cost** Suppose that a commodity has fixed costs of $500 and variable costs of $2 per unit.
(a) Find the cost function for this commodity.
(b) What is the cost of producing 100 units?

60. **Revenue** Suppose that a commodity sells for $4 per unit.
(a) Find the revenue function for this commodity.
(b) Find the revenue if 100 units are sold.

61. ***Profit*** Suppose that a product has costs given by $C(x) = 2x + 500$ and revenue given by $R(x) = 4x$.
   (a) Form the profit function for this product.
   (b) Find the profit if 100 units are sold.
   (c) Find the number of units that must be sold so that no money is lost.

62. ***Investments*** A retired couple has $150,000 to invest and wants to earn $15,000 per year in interest. The safest investment yields 9.5%, but they could also put some of their money in a somewhat riskier investment earning 11%. How much should they invest at each rate to earn $15,000 per year?

63. ***Supply and demand*** Of the equations $p + 6q = 420$ and $p = 6q + 60$, one is the supply function for a product and one is the demand function for that product.
   (a) Graph these equations on the same set of axes.
   (b) Label the supply function and the demand function.
   (c) Find the market equilibrium point.

64. ***Marginals and break-even*** A certain product has its costs and its revenues given by $C(x) = 38.80x + 4500$ and $R(x) = 61.30x$, respectively. Find the
   (a) marginal cost.
   (b) marginal revenue.
   (c) marginal profit.
   (d) number of units required to break even.

65. ***Profit analysis*** A certain commodity has the following costs for a period.

   Fixed costs: $1500
   Variable costs: $22 per unit

   If the commodity is sold for $52 per unit, what is the
   (a) total cost function?
   (b) total revenue function?
   (c) profit function?
   (d) marginal cost?
   (e) marginal revenue?
   (f) marginal profit?
   (g) break-even point?

66. ***Market equilibrium*** If the supply function for a product is linear and determined by Table 1.3, and the demand function is linear and determined by Table 1.4, find the price that will give market equilibrium.

TABLE 1.3

Price	Quantity
100	200
200	400
300	600

TABLE 1.4

Price	Quantity
200	200
100	400
0	600

1.4, 1.6   67. **Maximum area** A rectangular lot is to be fenced in, then divided down the middle to create two identical fenced lots (see Figure 1.55). If 1200 ft of fence is to be used, the area of each lot is given by

$$A = x\left(\frac{1200 - 3x}{4}\right)$$

FIGURE 1.55

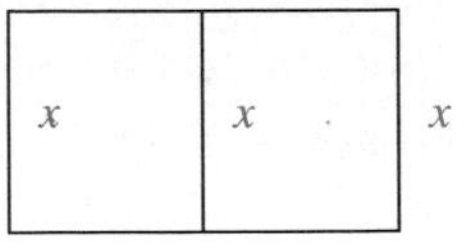

(a) Find the x value that maximizes this area.   (b) Find the maximum area.

68. **Market equilibrium**
   (a) Suppose that the supply function for a product is $p = 0.1q^2 + 1$ and that the demand function is $p = 85 - 0.2q - 0.1q^2$. Sketch the first quadrant portion of the graph of each function. Use the same set of axes for both and label the market equilibrium point.
   (b) Use algebraic methods to find the equilibrium price and quantity.

69. **Market equilibrium** The supply function for a product is given by $p = q^2 + 300$, and the demand function is given by $p + q = 410$. Find the equilibrium quantity and price.

70. **Market equilibrium** If the demand function for a certain commodity is given by $p^2 + 5q = 200$ and the supply function is given by $40 - p^2 + 3q = 0$, find the equilibrium quantity and price.

71. **Break-even** If total costs for a product are given by $C(x) = 1760 + 8x + 0.6x^2$ and total revenues are given by $R(x) = 100x - 0.4x^2$, find the break-even points.

72. **Break-even** If total costs for a commodity are given by $C(x) = 900 + 25x$ and total revenues are given by $R(x) = 100x - x^2$, find the break-even points. .

73. **Maximum revenue and profit** Find the maximum revenue and maximum profit for a product with costs given by $C(x) = 900 + 25x$ and revenues given by $R(x) = 100x - x^2$.

74. **Break-even and profit maximization** Given total profit $P(x) = 1.3x - 0.01x^2 - 30$, find the maximum profit and the break-even points. Sketch the graph.

75. **Maximum profit** Given $C(x) = 360 + 10x + 0.2x^2$ and $R(x) = 50x - 0.2x^2$, find the level of production that gives maximum profit and find the maximum profit.

76. **Break-even and maximum profit** A certain company in a monopoly market has fixed costs of $15,000 for its product and variable costs given by $140 + 0.04x$ dollars per unit, where x is the total number of units. The demand function for the product is given by $p = 300 - 0.06x$.
   (a) Formulate the functions for total cost and total revenue.
   (b) Find the break-even points.
   (c) Find the level of sales that maximizes revenue.
   (d) Form the profit function and find the level of production and sales that maximizes profit.
   (e) Find the profit (or loss) at the production levels found in parts (c) and (d).

HOSPITAL ADMINISTRATION

Southwest Hospital has an operating room used only for eye surgery. The annual cost of rent, heat, and electricity for the operating room and its equipment is $180,000, and the annual salaries of the people who staff this room total $270,000.

Each surgery performed requires the use of $380 worth of medical supplies and drugs. To promote goodwill, every patient receives a bouquet of flowers the day after surgery. In addition, one quarter of the patients require dark glasses, which the hospital provides free of charge. It costs the hospital $15 for each bouquet of flowers and $20 for each pair of glasses.

The hospital receives a payment of $1000 for each eye operation performed.

1. Identify the revenue per case and the annual fixed and variable costs for running the operating room.

2. How many eye operations must the hospital perform each year in order to break even?

3. Southwest Hospital currently averages 70 eye operations per month. One of the nurses has just learned about a machine that would reduce by $50 per patient the amount of medical supplies needed. It can be leased for $50,000 annually. Keeping in mind the financial costs/benefits, advise the hospital on whether or not they should lease this machine.

4. An advertising agency has proposed to the hospital's president that she spend $10,000 per month on television and radio advertising to persuade people that Southwest Hospital is the best place to have any eye surgery performed. The advertising firm estimates that such publicity would increase business by 40 operations per month. If they are correct and if this increase is not big enough to affect fixed costs, what impact would this advertising have on the hospital's profits?

5. In case the advertising agency is being overly optimistic, how many extra operations per month will be needed to cover the cost of the proposed ads?

6. If the ad campaign is approved and subsequently meets its projections, should the hospital review its decision about the machine discussed in (3)?

PREREQUISITE PROBLEM TYPE	REVIEW SECTION/ANSWER
Sections 2.1, 2.8	Section 1.1, Functional notation
If $f(x) = \dfrac{x^2 - x - 6}{x + 2}$, find	
(a) $f(-2.5)$ (b) $f(-2.1)$ (c) $f(-2)$	(a) -5.5 (b) -5.1 (c) undefined
Sections 2.1, 2.7	Section 0.5, Factoring
Factor:	
(a) $x^2 - x - 6$ (b) $x^2 - 4$	(a) $(x + 2)(x - 3)$ (b) $(x - 2)(x + 2)$
(c) $(x^2 + 1)^5(12x + 1) - 12(x^2 + 1)^4(x^3 + x + 1)$	(c) $(x^2 + 1)^4(x^2 - 11)$
Sections 2.4, 2.5, 2.6, 2.7, 2.8	Sections 0.2, 0.3, Exponents and radicals
Write as a power:	
(a) $\sqrt{t}$ (b) $\dfrac{1}{x}$ (c) $\dfrac{1}{\sqrt[3]{x^2 + 1}}$	(a) $t^{1/2}$ (b) x^{-1} (c) $(x^2 + 1)^{-1/3}$
Sections 2.3, 2.5, 2.7, 2.8	Section 0.4, Simplifying algebra expressions
Simplify:	
(a) $\dfrac{4(x + h)^2 - 4x^2}{h}$ (b) $\dfrac{x(3x^2) - x^3(1)}{x^2}$	(a) $8x + 4h$ (b) $2x$
(c) $(2x^3 + 3x + 1)(2x) + (x^2 + 4)(6x^2 + 3)$	(c) $10x^4 + 33x^2 + 2x + 12$
Sections 2.1, 2.7	Section 0.6, Simplifying fractions
Simplify:	
(a) $\dfrac{x^2 - x - 6}{x + 2}$ if $x \neq -2$	(a) $x - 3$
(b) $\dfrac{2(x^2 + 1)^3(x - 1) - 6x(x - 1)^2(x^2 + 1)^2}{(x^2 + 1)^6}$	(b) $\dfrac{2(x - 1)(-2x^2 + 3x + 1)}{(x^2 + 1)^4}$
Section 2.3	Section 1.1, Functional notation
If $f(x) = 3x^2 + 2x$, find $\dfrac{f(x + h) - f(x)}{h}$	$6x + 3h + 2$
Sections 2.3, 2.4, 2.6	Section 1.2, Equations of lines
(a) Find the slope of the line passing through $(1, 2)$ and $(2, 4)$.	(a) 2
(b) Write the equation of the line passing through $(1, 5)$ with slope 8.	(b) $y = 8x - 3$

2 | DERIVATIVES

If a firm receives $30,000 in revenue during a 30-day month, its average revenue per day is $30,000/30 = $1000. This does not necessarily mean that the actual revenue was $1000 on any one day, just that the average is $1000 per day. Similarly, if a person drives a car 50 miles in an hour's time, the car's average velocity is 50 miles per hour, but the driver could have gotten a speeding ticket for traveling 70 miles per hour on this trip. When we say a car is moving at a velocity of 50 miles per hour, we are talking about the velocity of the car at an instant in time (the instantaneous velocity). We can use the average velocity to find the instantaneous velocity, as follows.

If a car travels in a straight line from position y_1 at time x_1 and arrives at position y_2 at time x_2, then it has traveled the distance $y_2 - y_1$ in the elapsed time $x_2 - x_1$. If we represent the distance traveled by Δy and the elapsed time by Δx, the average velocity is given by

$$V_{\text{av}} = \frac{\Delta y}{\Delta x}.$$

The smaller the time interval, the more nearly the average velocity will approximate the instantaneous velocity. For example, knowing that a car traveled 50 miles in an hour does not tell us much about its instantaneous velocity at any time during that hour. But knowing that it traveled 1 mile in 1 minute, or 50 feet in one second, tells us much more about the velocity at a given time. Continuing to decrease the length of the time interval (Δx) will get us closer and closer to the instantaneous velocity.

Some police departments have equipment that measures how fast a car is traveling by measuring how much time elapses while the car travels between two sensors placed 60 inches apart on the road. This is not the instantaneous velocity of the car, but it is an excellent approximation.

We define the **instantaneous velocity** to be the *limit* of $\Delta y / \Delta x$ as Δx approaches 0. We write this as

$$V = \lim_{\Delta x \to 0} \frac{\Delta y}{\Delta x}.$$

Thus we may think of velocity as the instantaneous rate of change of distance with respect to time.

This chapter is concerned with *limits* and *rates of change*. We will see that the *derivative* of a function can be used to determine the rate of change of the dependent variable with respect to the independent variable. In this chapter, the derivative will be used to find the marginal profit, marginal cost, and marginal revenue, given the respective profit, total cost, and total revenue functions, and we will find other rates of change, such as rates of change of populations and velocity. We will also use the derivative to determine the slope of a tangent to a curve at a point on the curve. In Chapter 3, more applications of the derivative will be discussed. For example, we will use differentiation to minimize average cost, maximize total revenue, maximize profit, and find the maximum dosage for certain medications.

2.1 | LIMITS: POLYNOMIAL AND RATIONAL FUNCTIONS

OBJECTIVES

- To use graphs and numerical tables to find limits of functions, when they exist
- To find limits of polynomial functions
- To find limits of rational functions

INTRODUCTION TO LIMITS

We have used the notation $f(c)$ to indicate the value of a function $f(x)$ at $x = c$. If we need to discuss a value that $f(x)$ approaches as x approaches c, we use the idea of a **limit.** For example, if $f(x) = x^2$, then we know [and Figure 2.1(a) shows] that

$f(-2) = 4$. In addition, Figure 2.1(a) shows that as x approaches -2 from either side of -2, the graph approaches the point at $(-2, 4)$ and the values of $f(x)$ approach 4. We write this using the notation $f(x) \to 4$ as $x \to -2$, or

$$\lim_{x \to -2} f(x) = 4.$$

FIGURE 2.1   (a)

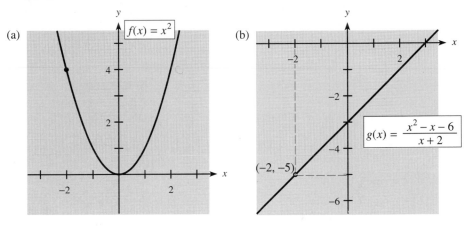

Figure 2.1(b) shows the graph of $g(x) = (x^2 - x - 6)/(x + 2)$. We see from this equation that $g(x)$ is not defined at $x = -2$, and the graph has an open circle at $x = -2$. Even though $g(-2)$ is not defined, Figure 2.1(b) shows that as x approaches -2 from either side of -2, the graph approaches the open circle at $(-2, -5)$ and the values of $g(x)$ approach -5. Thus -5 is the limit of $g(x)$ as x approaches -2, and we write

$$\lim_{x \to -2} g(x) = -5.$$

This limit is fairly obvious from the graph, but not so obvious from the equation for $g(x)$.

From our discussion of the graphs in Figure 2.1, we see that as x approaches -2 from either side of -2, the limit of the function is the value L that the function approaches. This limit L is not necessarily the value of the function at $x = -2$.

The preceding discussion forms a basis for our definition of limit.

Limit   Let $f(x)$ be defined on an open interval containing c, except perhaps at c. The statement

$$\lim_{x \to c} f(x) = L$$

is read "the limit of $f(x)$ as x approaches c equals L" and means that for all x sufficiently close to c, but not equal to c, the value of $f(x)$ can be made as close as desired to the single number L. When the values of $f(x)$ do not approach a single finite value as x approaches c, we say the limit does not exist.

Note that $f(x)$ may or may not be defined at $x = c$, but it must be defined on both sides of c.

Although our definition of limit is informal (because we have not specified what is meant by "sufficiently close" and "as close as desired"), we can interpret it graphically (as we did in Figure 2.1) to mean that as x approaches c, the limit is the y-coordinate of the point or open circle that the graph of the function approaches.

EXAMPLE 1   Figure 2.2 shows three functions for which the limit exists as x approaches 2. Use this figure to find the following:

(a) $\lim\limits_{x \to 2} f(x)$ and $f(2)$ (if it exists)

(b) $\lim\limits_{x \to 2} g(x)$ and $g(2)$ (if it exists)

(c) $\lim\limits_{x \to 2} h(x)$ and $h(2)$ (if it exists)

FIGURE 2.2

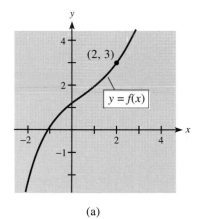

(a)

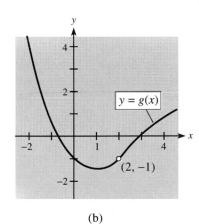

(b)

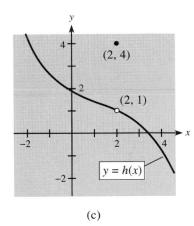

(c)

Solution

(a) From the graph in Figure 2.2(a), we see that as x approaches 2 from both the left and the right, the graph approaches the point $(2, 3)$. Thus $f(x)$ approaches the single value 3. That is,

$$\lim_{x \to 2} f(x) = 3.$$

The value of $f(2)$ is the y-coordinate of the point on the graph at $x = 2$. Thus $f(2) = 3$.

(b) Figure 2.2(b) shows that as x approaches 2 from both the left and the right, the graph approaches the open circle at $(2, -1)$. Thus

$$\lim_{x \to 2} g(x) = -1.$$

The figure also shows that at $x = 2$ there is no point on the graph. Thus $g(2)$ is undefined.

(c) Figure 2.2(c) shows that

$$\lim_{x \to 2} h(x) = 1.$$

The figure also shows that at $x = 2$ there is a point on the graph at $(2, 4)$. Thus $h(2) = 4$, and we see that $\lim_{x \to 2} h(x) \neq h(2)$.

Note that in the preceding example we looked at functions as x approached a particular value from both the left and right sides of that value. Note also that in each case the limit was a single, *finite* value. These will be important considerations in the next example, in which we present cases where limits do not exist.

EXAMPLE 2   Figure 2.3 contains the graphs of three functions for which the limit as x approaches -1 does not exist.

(a) Determine why $\lim_{x \to -1} f(x)$ does not exist.

(b) Determine why $\lim_{x \to -1} h(x)$ does not exist.

(c) Determine why $\lim_{x \to -1} g(x)$ does not exist.

FIGURE 2.3

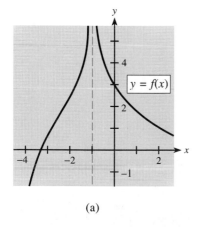

(a)

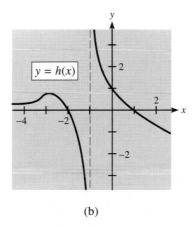

(b)

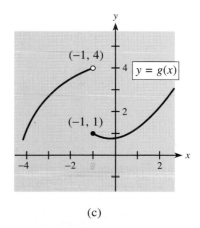

(c)

Solution

(a) Figure 2.3(a) shows that as x approaches -1, the values of $f(x)$ become larger without bound. In this case, the values of $f(x)$ do not approach a finite value, so the limit does not exist.

(b) Figure 2.3(b) shows that as x approaches -1 from the left, the values of $h(x)$ decrease without bound. Also, as x approaches -1 from the right, the values of $h(x)$ increase without bound. Thus, in this case, the values of $h(x)$ do not approach a finite value (real number), so the limit does not exist.

(c) Figure 2.3(c) shows that as x approaches -1 from the left, the graph approaches the open circle at $(-1, 4)$, but as x approaches -1 from the right, the graph approaches the point at $(-1, 1)$. Because $g(x)$ approaches two different numbers as x approaches -1, the limit does not exist.

In the preceding example we could have used the notation $x \to -1^-$ to indicate that x is approaching -1 from the left (that is, while $x < -1$) and the notation $x \to -1^+$ to indicate that x is approaching -1 from the right (that is, while $x > -1$). Thus for part (c) we could have written

$$\lim_{x \to -1^-} g(x) = 4 \quad \text{and} \quad \lim_{x \to -1^+} g(x) = 1.$$

Because these two **one-sided limits** are different, $\lim_{x \to -1} g(x)$ does not exist.

In addition, the fact that the values of a function increase without bound as x approaches c is denoted by

$$\lim_{x \to c} f(x) = +\infty.$$

and the fact that the values of a function decrease without bound as x approaches c is denoted by

$$\lim_{x \to c} f(x) = -\infty.$$

These notations indicate that the limit does not exist; the symbol ∞ (read "infinity") is not a number.

In Figure 2.3(a) we see that

$$\lim_{x \to -1} f(x) = +\infty,$$

and in Figure 2.3(b) we see that

$$\lim_{x \to -1^-} h(x) = -\infty \quad \text{and} \quad \lim_{x \to -1^+} h(x) = +\infty.$$

Examples 1 and 2 illustrate the following two important facts regarding limits.

Facts About Limits

1. The limit of a function as x approaches c is independent of the value of the function at c. When $\lim_{x \to c} f(x)$ exists, the value of the function at c may be (i) the same as the limit, (ii) undefined, or (iii) defined but different from the limit (see Figure 2.2 and Example 1.)

2. The limit is said to exist only if the following conditions are satisfied:
   (a) The limit L is a finite value (real number).
   (b) The limit as x approaches c from the left equals the limit as x

approaches c from the right. That is, we must have

$$\lim_{x \to c^-} f(x) = \lim_{x \to c^+} f(x).$$

Figure 2.3 and Example 2 illustrate cases where $\lim_{x \to c} f(x)$ does not exist.

Figure 2.1(b) on page 157 shows the graph of

$$g(x) = \frac{x^2 - x - 6}{x + 2}.$$

We have already used this graph to conclude that

$$\lim_{x \to -2} g(x) = -5.$$

We can also use a table of values to evaluate $\lim_{x \to -2} g(x)$. In Table 2.1, we calculate

values of $g(x)$ for specific values of x that approach (get closer and closer to) -2 from the left and the right. We use these values of $g(x)$ to predict the limit and again conclude that

$$\lim_{x \to -2} g(x) = -5.$$

TABLE 2.1

Left		Right	
x	y	x	y
-3	-6	-1	-4
-2.5	-5.5	-1.5	-4.5
-2.3	-5.3	-1.7	-4.7
-2.1	-5.1	-1.9	-4.9
-2.01	-5.01	-1.99	-4.99
-2.001	-5.001	-1.999	-4.999

CHECKPOINT

1. Can $\lim_{x \to c} f(x)$ exist if $f(c)$ is undefined?

2. Does $\lim_{x \to c} f(x)$ exist if $f(c) = 1$?

3. Does $f(c) = 4$ if $\lim_{x \to c} f(x) = 4$?

4. If $\lim_{x \to c^-} f(x) = 4$, does $\lim_{x \to c} f(x)$ exist?

LIMITS OF POLYNOMIAL AND RATIONAL FUNCTIONS

Fact 1 regarding limits tells us that the value of the limit of a function as $x \to c$ will not always be the same as the value of the function at $x = c$. However, there are many functions for which the limit and the functional value agree [see Figures 2.1(a) and 2.2(a) on pages 157 and 158], and for these functions we can easily evaluate limits. The following properties of limits allow us to identify certain classes or types of functions for which $\lim_{x \to c} f(x)$ equals $f(c)$.

PROPERTIES OF LIMITS

PROPERTY	EXAMPLE
I. $\lim_{x \to c} k = k$, where k is constant	I. (a) $\lim_{x \to 2} 4 = 4$; (b) $\lim_{x \to -1} 5 = 5$
II. $\lim_{x \to c} x = c$	II. (a) $\lim_{x \to 3} x = 3$; (b) $\lim_{x \to -5} x = -5$
III. If $\lim_{x \to c} f(x) = L$ and $\lim_{x \to c} g(x) = M$, then $\lim_{x \to c} [f(x) \pm g(x)] =$ $\lim_{x \to c} f(x) \pm \lim_{x \to c} g(x) = L \pm M.$	III. (a) $\lim_{x \to 2} (x + 4) = \left(\lim_{x \to 2} x\right) + \left(\lim_{x \to 2} 4\right)$ $= 2 + 4 = 6$ (b) $\lim_{x \to -1} (x - 1) = \left(\lim_{x \to -1} x\right) - \left(\lim_{x \to -1} 1\right)$ $= -1 - 1 = -2$
IV. If $\lim_{x \to c} f(x) = L$ and $\lim_{x \to c} g(x) = M$, then $\lim_{x \to c} [f(x) \cdot g(x)] =$ $\left[\lim_{x \to c} f(x)\right]\left[\lim_{x \to c} g(x)\right] = LM.$ *Note:* $\lim_{x \to c} kf(x) = k \cdot \lim_{x \to c} f(x) = k \cdot L.$	IV. (a) $\lim_{x \to 3} x^2 = \left(\lim_{x \to 3} x\right)\left(\lim_{x \to 3} x\right) = 3 \cdot 3 = 9$ (b) $\lim_{x \to 2} 4x = 4\left(\lim_{x \to 2} x\right) = 4 \cdot 2 = 8$ (c) $\lim_{x \to -1} 2x^2 = 2\left(\lim_{x \to -1} x\right)\left(\lim_{x \to -1} x\right)$ $= 2(-1)(-1) = 2$
V. If $\lim_{x \to c} f(x) = L$ and $\lim_{x \to c} g(x) = M$, with $M \neq 0$, then $\lim_{x \to c} \dfrac{f(x)}{g(x)} = \dfrac{\lim_{x \to c} f(x)}{\lim_{x \to c} g(x)} = \dfrac{L}{M}.$	V. (a) $\lim_{x \to 2} \dfrac{x^2 + 4}{x + 2} = \dfrac{\lim_{x \to 2} (x^2 + 4)}{\lim_{x \to 2} (x + 2)} = \dfrac{8}{4} = 2$ (b) $\lim_{x \to 3} \dfrac{x^2 - 4x}{x - 2} = \dfrac{\lim_{x \to 3} (x^2 - 4x)}{\lim_{x \to 3} (x - 2)}$ $= \dfrac{-3}{1} = -3$

Note that if f is a polynomial function, then Properties I–IV imply that $\lim\limits_{x \to c} f(x)$ can be found by evaluating $f(c)$. Moreover, if h is a rational function whose denominator is not zero at $x = c$, then Property V implies that $\lim\limits_{x \to c} h(x)$ can be found by evaluating $h(c)$. We summarize these facts below.

POLYNOMIAL AND RATIONAL FUNCTIONS

DEFINITION	LIMIT
Polynomial Function $f(x) = a_n x^n + a_{n-1} x^{n-1} + \cdots + a_1 x + a_0,$ where n is a positive integer	$\lim\limits_{x \to c} f(x) = f(c)$ for all values c (by Properties I–IV)
Rational Function $h(x) = \dfrac{f(x)}{g(x)}$ where both $f(x)$ and $g(x)$ are polynomial functions	$\lim\limits_{x \to c} \dfrac{f(x)}{g(x)} = \dfrac{f(c)}{g(c)}$ when $g(c) \neq 0$ (by Property V)

EXAMPLE 3

Find the following limits, if they exist.

(a) $\lim\limits_{x \to -1} (x^3 - 2x)$

(b) $\lim\limits_{x \to 4} \dfrac{x^2 - 4x}{x - 2}$

Solution

(a) Note that $f(x) = x^3 - 2x$ is a polynomial, so

$$\lim_{x \to -1} f(x) = f(-1) = (-1)^3 - 2(-1) = 1.$$

Figure 2.4(a) shows the graph of $f(x) = x^3 - 2x$.

(b) Note that this limit has the form

$$\lim_{x \to c} \frac{f(x)}{g(x)},$$

where $f(x)$ and $g(x)$ are polynomials and $g(c) \neq 0$. Therefore, we have

$$\lim_{x \to 4} \frac{x^2 - 4x}{x - 2} = \frac{4^2 - 4(4)}{4 - 2} = \frac{0}{2} = 0.$$

Figure 2.4(b) shows the graph of $g(x) = \dfrac{x^2 - 4x}{x - 2}$.

FIGURE 2.4

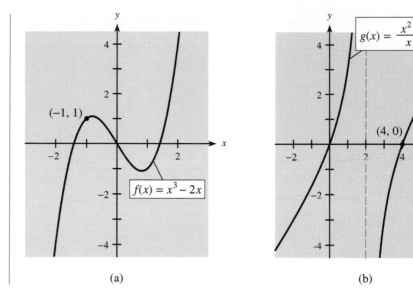

(a)

(b)

We have seen that we can use Property V to find the limit of a rational function $f(x)/g(x)$ as long as the denominator is *not* zero. If the limit of the denominator of $f(x)/g(x)$ *is* zero, then there are two possible cases.

I. Both $\lim\limits_{x \to c} g(x) = 0$ and $\lim\limits_{x \to c} f(x) = 0$, or

II. $\lim\limits_{x \to c} g(x) = 0$ and $\lim\limits_{x \to c} f(x) \neq 0$.

In case I we say that $f(x)/g(x)$ has the form $0/0$ at $x = c$. We call this the **0/0 indeterminate form;** the limit cannot be evaluated until $x - c$ is factored from both $f(x)$ and $g(x)$ and the fraction is reduced. Example 4 illustrates this case.

In case II, the limit has the form $a/0$, where a is a constant, $a \neq 0$. This expression is undefined, and the limit does not exist. Example 5 will illustrate this case.

EXAMPLE 4

Evaluate the following limits, if they exist.

(a) $\lim\limits_{x \to 2} \dfrac{x^2 - 4}{x - 2}$

(b) $\lim\limits_{x \to 1} \dfrac{x^2 - 3x + 2}{x^2 - 1}$

Solution

(a) We cannot find the limit by using Property V because the denominator is zero at $x = 2$. Since the numerator is also zero at $x = 2$, the expression

$$\frac{x^2 - 4}{x - 2}$$

has the 0/0 indeterminate form at $x = 2$. Thus we can factor $x - 2$ from both the numerator and the denominator and reduce the fraction. (We can divide by $x - 2$ because $x - 2 \neq 0$ while $x \rightarrow 2$.)

$$\lim_{x \to 2} \frac{x^2 - 4}{x - 2} = \lim_{x \to 2} \frac{(x - 2)(x + 2)}{x - 2}$$
$$= \lim_{x \to 2} (x + 2)$$
$$= 4$$

Figure 2.5(a) shows the graph of $f(x) = (x^2 - 4)/(x - 2)$. Note the open circle at $(2, 4)$.

(b) By substituting 1 for x in $(x^2 - 3x + 2)/(x^2 - 1)$ we see that the expression has the 0/0 indeterminate form at $x = 1$, so $x - 1$ is a factor of both the numerator and the denominator. (We can then reduce the fraction because $x - 1 \neq 0$ while $x \rightarrow 1$.)

$$\lim_{x \to 1} \frac{x^2 - 3x + 2}{x^2 - 1} = \lim_{x \to 1} \frac{(x - 1)(x - 2)}{(x - 1)(x + 1)}$$
$$= \lim_{x \to 1} \frac{x - 2}{x + 1}$$
$$= \frac{1 - 2}{1 + 1} = \frac{-1}{2} \qquad \text{(by Property V)}$$

Figure 2.5(b) shows the graph of $g(x) = (x^2 - 3x + 2)/(x^2 - 1)$. Note the open circle at $(1, -\frac{1}{2})$.

FIGURE 2.5

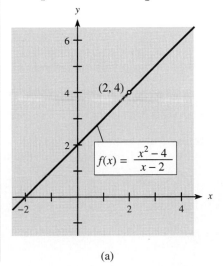

(a)

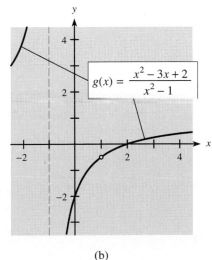

(b)

Notice that although both problems in Example 4 had the 0/0 indeterminate form, they had different answers.

EXAMPLE 5   Find $\lim\limits_{x \to 1} \dfrac{x^2 + 3x + 2}{x - 1}$, if it exists.

Solution   Substituting 1 for x in the function results in 6/0, so this limit has the form $a/0$, with $a \neq 0$, and is like case II discussed previously. Because the numerator is not zero when $x = 1$, we know that $x - 1$ is *not* a factor of the numerator, and we cannot divide numerator and denominator as we did in Example 4. Table 2.2 verifies that this limit does not exist, because the values of the expression are unbounded near $x = 1$.

TABLE 2.2

Left		Right	
x	$\dfrac{x^2 + 3x + 2}{x - 1}$	x	$\dfrac{x^2 + 3x + 2}{x - 1}$
0	-2	2	12
0.5	-7.5	1.5	17.5
0.7	-15.3	1.2	35.2
0.9	-55.1	1.1	65.1
0.99	-595.01	1.01	605.01
0.999	$-5{,}995.001$	1.001	6,005.001
0.9999	$-59{,}999.0001$	1.001	60,005.0001
$\lim\limits_{x \to 1^-} \dfrac{x^2 + 3x + 2}{x - 1} = -\infty$		$\lim\limits_{x \to 1^+} \dfrac{x^2 + 3x + 2}{x - 1} = +\infty$	

Thus $\lim\limits_{x \to 1} \dfrac{x^2 + 3x + 2}{x - 1}$ does not exist.

The results of Examples 4 and 5 can be summarized as follows.

Rational Functions: Evaluating Limits of the Form $\lim\limits_{x \to c} \dfrac{f(x)}{g(x)}$, **where** $\lim\limits_{x \to c} g(x) = 0$

Type I.   If $\lim\limits_{x \to c} f(x) = 0$ and $\lim\limits_{x \to c} g(x) = 0$, then the fractional expression has the **0/0 indeterminate form** at $x = c$. We can factor $x - c$ from $f(x)$ and $g(x)$, reduce the fraction, and then find the limit of the resulting expression, if it exists.

Type II.   If $\lim\limits_{x \to c} f(x) \neq 0$ and $\lim\limits_{x \to c} g(x) = 0$, then $\lim\limits_{x \to c} \dfrac{f(x)}{g(x)}$ does not exist. In this case, the values of $f(x)/g(x)$ are unbounded near $x = c$.

In Example 5, even though the left-hand and right-hand limits do not exist (see Table 2.2), knowledge that the functional values are unbounded (that is, that they become infinite) is helpful in graphing. The graph is shown in Figure 2.6. We see that $x = 1$ is a vertical asymptote.

FIGURE 2.6

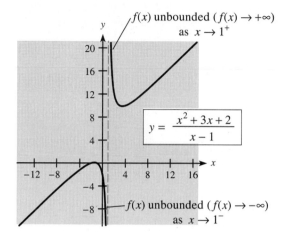

$f(x)$ unbounded ($f(x) \to +\infty$) as $x \to 1^+$

$$y = \frac{x^2 + 3x + 2}{x - 1}$$

$f(x)$ unbounded ($f(x) \to -\infty$) as $x \to 1^-$

CHECKPOINT

Assume that f, g, and h are polynomials.

5. Does $\lim\limits_{x \to c} f(x) = f(c)$?

6. Does $\lim\limits_{x \to c} \dfrac{g(x)}{h(x)} = \dfrac{g(c)}{h(c)}$?

7. If $g(c) = 0$ and $h(c) = 0$, can we be certain that

   (a) $\lim\limits_{x \to c} \dfrac{g(x)}{h(x)} = 0$?

   (b) $\lim\limits_{x \to c} \dfrac{g(x)}{h(x)}$ exists?

8. If $g(c) \neq 0$ and $h(c) = 0$, what can be said about

   $\lim\limits_{x \to c} \dfrac{g(x)}{h(x)}$ and $\lim\limits_{x \to c} \dfrac{h(x)}{g(x)}$?

TECHNOLOGY CORNER

Graph the following functions. With each one, use trace to see what happens
(a) near $x = -1$ and (b) at $x = -1$, and answer the questions below.

A. $f(x) = x^3 + x^2 + 2$

B. $f(x) = \dfrac{x^3 - x}{x + 1}$

C. $f(x) = \dfrac{x + 2}{(x + 1)^2}$

D. $f(x) = \dfrac{2x}{x + 1}$

E. $f(x) = \dfrac{(x + 1)^2}{x + 2}$

F. $f(x) = \dfrac{2\sqrt{(x + 1)^2}}{x + 1}$ (Don't simplify.)

1. For which of these functions is $f(-1)$ defined?

2. For which of these functions does $\lim\limits_{x \to -1} f(x)$ exist?

3. For which of these functions does $\lim\limits_{x \to -1} f(x) = f(-1)$?

4. Which of the functions has a vertical asymptote?
    Is the asymptote at $x = -1$?

**CHECKPOINT
SOLUTIONS**

1. Yes. For example, Figure 2.1(b) on page 157 and Table 2.1 show that this is
    possible for $g(x) = \dfrac{x^2 - x - 6}{x + 2}$. Remember that $\lim\limits_{x \to c} f(x)$ does not depend on $f(c)$.

2. Not necessarily. Figure 2.3(c) on page 159 shows the graph of $y = g(x)$ with
    $g(-1) = 1$, but $\lim\limits_{x \to -1} g(x)$ does not exist.

3. Not necessarily. Figure 2.2(c) on page 158 shows the graph of $y = h(x)$ with
    $h(2) = 4$, but $\lim\limits_{x \to 2} h(x) = 1$.

4. Not necessarily. For example, Figure 2.3(c) on page 159 shows the graph of $y = g(x)$ with $\lim\limits_{x \to -1^-} g(x) = 4$, but with $\lim\limits_{x \to -1^+} g(x) = 1$, so the limit doesn't exist. Recall that if $\lim\limits_{x \to c^-} f(x) = \lim\limits_{x \to c^+} f(x) = L$, then $\lim\limits_{x \to c} f(x) = L$.

5. Yes, Properties I–IV yield this result.

6. Not necessarily. If $h(c) \neq 0$, then this is true. Otherwise it is not true.

7. For both (a) and (b), $g(x)/h(x)$ has the 0/0 indeterminate form at $x = c$. In this case we can make no general conclusion about the limit. It is possible for the limit to exist (and be zero or nonzero) or not to exist. Consider the following 0/0 indeterminate forms.

    (i) $\lim\limits_{x \to 0} \dfrac{x^2}{x} = \lim\limits_{x \to 0} x = 0$

    (ii) $\lim\limits_{x \to 0} \dfrac{x(x + 1)}{x} = \lim\limits_{x \to 0} (x + 1) = 1$

    (iii) $\lim\limits_{x \to 0} \dfrac{x}{x^2} = \lim\limits_{x \to 0} \dfrac{1}{x}$, which does not exist

8. $\lim\limits_{x \to c} \dfrac{g(x)}{h(x)}$ does not exist and $\lim\limits_{x \to c} \dfrac{h(x)}{g(x)} = 0$ ■

EXERCISE 2.1

In problems 1–8, a graph of $y = f(x)$ is shown. For each problem, use the graph to find (a) $\lim\limits_{x \to c} f(x)$ and (b) $f(o)$, whenever they exist.

1.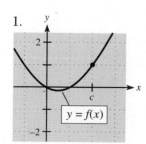

2.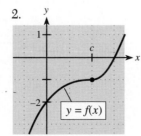

3.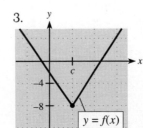

4.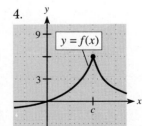

5.

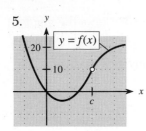

6.

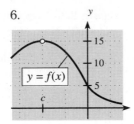

7.

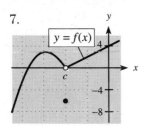

8.

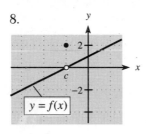

In problems 9–12, use the graph of $y = f(x)$ to find the following, whenever they exist.

(a) $\lim_{x \to c^-} f(x)$ (b) $\lim_{x \to c^+} f(x)$

(c) $\lim_{x \to c} f(x)$ (d) $f(c)$

9.

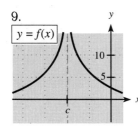

10.

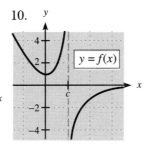

11.

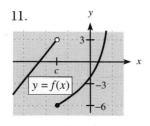

12.

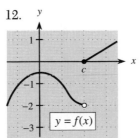

In problems 13–16, complete each table and predict the limit.

13. $f(x) = \dfrac{x^2 - 4x + 4}{x^2 - 2x}$

$\lim_{x \to 2} f(x) = ?$

x	$f(x)$
1.9	
1.99	
1.999	
$\downarrow$	$\downarrow$
2	?
$\uparrow$	$\uparrow$
2.001	
2.01	
2.1	

14. $f(x) = \dfrac{2x - 10}{x^2 - 25}$

$\lim_{x \to 5} f(x) = ?$

x	$f(x)$
4.9	
4.99	
4.999	
$\downarrow$	$\downarrow$
5	?
$\uparrow$	$\uparrow$
5.001	
5.01	
5.1	

15. $f(x) = \dfrac{1 - x^2}{x - 1}$

$\lim\limits_{x \to 1} f(x) = ?$

x	$f(x)$
0.9	
0.99	
0.999	
↓	↓
1	?
↑	↑
1.001	
1.01	
1.1	

16. $f(x) = \dfrac{2x + 1}{\frac{1}{4} - x^2}$

$\lim\limits_{x \to -0.5} f(x) = ?$

x	$f(x)$
−0.51	
−0.501	
−0.5001	
↓	↓
−0.5	?
↑	↑
−0.4999	
−0.499	
−0.49	

In problems 17–44, evaluate the limits, if they exist.

17. $\lim\limits_{x \to -2} 9$

18. $\lim\limits_{x \to 5} \sqrt{3}$

19. $\lim\limits_{x \to 2} (x - 3)$

20. $\lim\limits_{x \to 2} (3x - 4)$

21. $\lim\limits_{x \to -1} (4x^2 + 2)$

22. $\lim\limits_{x \to 3} (2x^3 - 12x^2 + 5x + 3)$

23. $\lim\limits_{x \to 2} \dfrac{x^3 - 4}{x - 3}$

24. $\lim\limits_{x \to -1} \dfrac{x^3 - 3x + 1}{x - 1}$

25. $\lim\limits_{x \to 4} \dfrac{4x^2 - 12x - 16}{x + 4}$

26. $\lim\limits_{x \to 3} \dfrac{x^2 - 9}{x + 2}$

27. $\lim\limits_{x \to -1/2} \dfrac{4x - 2}{4x^2 + 1}$

28. $\lim\limits_{x \to -1/3} \dfrac{1 - 3x}{9x^2 + 1}$

29. $\lim\limits_{x \to 3} \dfrac{x^2 - 9}{x - 3}$

30. $\lim\limits_{x \to -4} \dfrac{x^2 - 16}{x + 4}$

31. $\lim\limits_{x \to -2} \dfrac{x^2 + 4x + 4}{x + 2}$

32. $\lim\limits_{x \to 1} \dfrac{x^2 + x - 2}{x - 1}$

33. $\lim\limits_{x \to 2} \dfrac{x^3 - 4x}{2x^2 - x^3}$

34. $\lim\limits_{x \to 1/2} \dfrac{x^2 - \frac{1}{4}}{2x - 1}$

35. $\lim\limits_{x \to 10} \dfrac{x^2 - 19x + 90}{3x^2 - 30x}$

36. $\lim\limits_{x \to -3} \dfrac{x^4 + 3x^3}{2x^4 - 18x^2}$

37. $\lim\limits_{x \to 2} \dfrac{x^2 + 6x + 9}{x - 2}$

38. $\lim\limits_{x \to 5} \dfrac{x^2 - 6x + 8}{x - 5}$

39. $\lim\limits_{x \to -1} \dfrac{x^2 + 5x + 6}{x + 1}$

40. $\lim\limits_{x \to 3} \dfrac{x^2 + 2x - 3}{x - 3}$

41. $\lim\limits_{x \to -1} \dfrac{x^3 - x}{x^2 + 2x + 1}$

42. $\lim\limits_{x \to 5} \dfrac{x^2 - 7x + 10}{x^2 - 10x + 25}$

43. $\lim\limits_{h \to 0} \dfrac{(x + h)^3 - x^3}{h}$

44. $\lim\limits_{h \to 0} \dfrac{2(x + h)^2 - 2x^2}{h}$

45. Use values 0.1, 0.01, 0.001, 0.0001, and 0.00001 with your calculator to approximate

$$\lim_{a \to 0} (1 + a)^{1/a}$$

to 3 decimal places. This limit equals the special number e that we will discuss in Section 4.1.

46. If $\lim\limits_{x \to 2} [f(x) + g(x)] = 5$ and $\lim\limits_{x \to 2} g(x) = 11$, find

(a) $\lim\limits_{x \to 2} f(x)$.

(b) $\lim\limits_{x \to 2} \{[f(x)]^2 - [g(x)]^2\}$.

(c) $\lim\limits_{x \to 2} \dfrac{3g(x)}{f(x) - g(x)}$.

47. If $\lim\limits_{x \to 3} f(x) = 4$ and $\lim\limits_{x \to 3} g(x) = -2$, find

(a) $\lim\limits_{x \to 3} [f(x) + g(x)]$.

(b) $\lim\limits_{x \to 3} [f(x) - g(x)]$. 6

(c) $\lim\limits_{x \to 3} [f(x) \cdot g(x)]$.   (d) $\lim\limits_{x \to 3} \dfrac{g(x)}{f(x)}$.

48. (a) If $\lim\limits_{x \to 2^+} f(x) = 5$, $\quad \lim\limits_{x \to 2^-} f(x) = 5$, and $f(2) = 0$, find $\lim\limits_{x \to 2} f(x)$, if it exists. Explain your conclusions.

(b) If $\lim\limits_{x \to 0^+} f(x) = 3$, $\quad \lim\limits_{x \to 0^-} f(x) = 0$, and $f(0) = 0$, find $\lim\limits_{x \to 0} f(x)$, if it exists. Explain your conclusions.

APPLICATIONS

49. *Revenue* The total revenue for a product is given by

$$R(x) = 1600x - x^2,$$

where x is the number of units sold. What is $\lim\limits_{x \to 100} R(x)$?

50. *Profit* If the profit function for a product is given by

$$P(x) = 92x - x^2 - 1760,$$

find $\lim\limits_{x \to 40} P(x)$.

51. *Sales and training* The average monthly sales volume (in thousands of dollars) for a firm depends on the number of hours x of training of its sales staff, according to

$$S(x) = \frac{4}{x} + 30 + \frac{x}{4}, \qquad 4 \le x \le 100.$$

(a) Find $\lim\limits_{x \to 4^+} S(x)$.   (b) Find $\lim\limits_{x \to 100^-} S(x)$.

52. *Sales and training* During the first four months of employment, the monthly sales S (in thousands of dollars) for a new salesperson depends on the number of hours x of training, as follows:

$$S = S(x) = \frac{9}{x} + 10 + \frac{x}{4}, \qquad \text{with } x \ge 4.$$

(a) Find $\lim\limits_{x \to 4^+} S(x)$.   (b) Find $\lim\limits_{x \to 10} S(x)$.

53. *Advertising and sales* Suppose that the daily sales S (in dollars) t days after the end of an advertising campaign is

$$S = S(t) = 400 + \frac{2400}{t + 1}.$$

(a) Find $S(0)$.   (b) Find $\lim\limits_{t \to 7} S(t)$.

(c) Find $\lim\limits_{t \to 14} S(t)$.

54. *Advertising and sales* Sales y (in thousands of dollars) are related to advertising expenses x (in thousands of dollars) according to

$$y = y(x) = \frac{200x}{x + 10}, \qquad x \ge 0.$$

(a) Find $\lim\limits_{x \to 10} y(x)$.   (b) Find $\lim\limits_{x \to 0^+} y(x)$.

55. *Productivity* During an 8-hour shift, the rate of change of productivity (in units per hour) of children's phonographs assembled after t hours on the job is

$$r(t) = \frac{128(t^2 + 6t)}{(t^2 + 6t + 18)^2}, \qquad 0 \le t \le 8.$$

(a) Find $\lim\limits_{t \to 4} r(t)$.   (b) Find $\lim\limits_{t \to 8^-} r(t)$.

(c) Is the rate of productivity higher near the lunch break (at $t = 4$) or near quitting time (at $t = 8$)?

56. *Advertising and sales* Suppose that a company's daily sales volume (in thousands of units) that is directly attributable to an advertising campaign is given by

$$\frac{S(t) = 1 + (3t - 9)}{(t + 3)^2},$$

where t is the number of weeks the campaign is run.

(a) Find $\lim\limits_{x \to 3} S(t)$.   (b) Find $\lim\limits_{t \to 15} S(t)$.

57. *Revenue* If the revenue for a product is

$R(x) = 100x - 0.1x^2$, and the average revenue per unit is

$$\overline{R}(x) = \frac{R(x)}{x}, \qquad x > 0,$$

find (a) $\lim\limits_{x \to 100} \dfrac{R(x)}{x}$ and (b) $\lim\limits_{x \to 0^+} \dfrac{R(x)}{x}$.

58. ***Cost-benefit*** Suppose that the cost C of obtaining water that contains p percent impurities is given by

$$C(p) = \frac{120{,}000}{p} - 1200.$$

(a) Find $\lim\limits_{p \to 100^-} C(p)$, if it exists.

(b) Find $\lim\limits_{p \to 0^+} C(p)$, if it exists.

(c) Is complete purity possible?

59. ***Cost-benefit*** Suppose that the cost C of removing p percent of the particulate pollution from the smokestacks of an industrial plant is given by

$$C(p) = \frac{7300p}{100 - p}.$$

(a) Find $\lim\limits_{p \to 80} C(p)$.

(b) Find $\lim\limits_{p \to 100^-} C(p)$, if it exists.

(c) Can 100% of the particulate pollution be removed?

2.2 | CONTINUOUS FUNCTIONS; LIMITS AT INFINITY

OBJECTIVES

- To determine if a function is continuous or discontinuous
- To determine where a function is discontinuous
- To find limits at infinity
- To find limits of piecewise defined functions

We may intuitively think of continuous functions as those functions whose graphs we can draw without lifting the pencil. A formal definition of continuity follows.

Continuity

A function f is said to be **continuous at the point** $x = c$ if the following conditions are satisfied:

1. $f(c)$ exists.

2. $\lim\limits_{x \to c} f(x)$ exists.

3. $\lim\limits_{x \to c} f(x) = f(c)$.

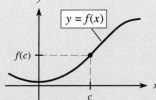

If one or more of these conditions are not satisfied, we say the function is **discontinuous** at $x = c$. (Figure 2.7 shows graphs of some functions that are discontinuous at $x = c$.)

FIGURE 2.7

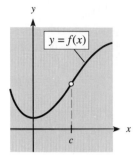

(a) $f(c)$ does not exist

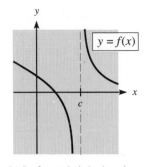

(b) Left- and right-hand limits are infinite. Limit does not exist.

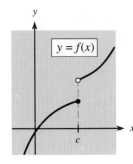

(c) Left- and right-hand limits are *different* finite values. Limit does not exist.

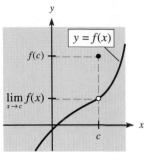

(d) $\lim_{x \to c} f(x) \neq f(c)$

For example, the function $f(x) = 3x + 5$ is continuous at $x = 2$ because

1. $f(2) = 11$,

2. $\lim_{x \to 2} f(x) = 11$, and

3. $\lim_{x \to 2} f(x) = 11 = f(2)$.

Recall that in Section 2.1 we found that we can evaluate $\lim_{x \to c} f(x)$, when $f(x)$ is a polynomial, by evaluating $f(c)$. We can do this because every polynomial is continuous. If a function is not a polynomial, it may have a point where it is not continuous. To determine if a function is continuous, we must investigate the point(s) where it may be discontinuous. As we noted in Section 2.1, a function that can be written as the ratio of two polynomials is called a rational function. A rational function may be discontinuous because any value that makes the denominator 0 will be a point of discontinuity.

EXAMPLE 1   Is the function $f(x) = \dfrac{x^2 - 1}{x + 1}$ continuous at (a) $x = 1$ and (b) $x = -1$?

Solution

(a)   1. $f(1) = 0$ 2. $\lim_{x \to 1} f(x) = 0$ 3. $\lim_{x \to 1} f(x) = 0 = f(1)$

Thus $f(x)$ is continuous at $x = 1$.

(b) $f(-1)$ is undefined. Thus the function is discontinuous at $x = -1$. Note that $\lim_{x \to -1} f(x)$ does exist, since

$$\lim_{x \to -1} \frac{x^2 - 1}{x + 1} = \lim_{x \to -1} \frac{(x - 1)(x + 1)}{x + 1} = \lim_{x \to -1} (x - 1) = -2.$$

We can see from Example 1(b) that there is at least one point where the function $f(x) = (x^2 - 1)/(x + 1)$ is discontinuous. The graph of the function in Example 1 is shown in Figure 2.8.

If there is *no point of discontinuity* for a function we say it is a **continuous function.** The function $y = x^2 - 3x + 1$ is a continuous function because there is no point of discontinuity. However, the function $f(x) = 5/(x - 3)$ has a discontinuity at $x = 3$ because $f(3)$ is undefined.

FIGURE 2.8

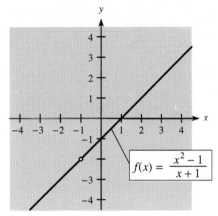

$$f(x) = \frac{x^2 - 1}{x + 1}$$

CHECKPOINT

1. Can we use $f(c)$ to evaluate $\lim_{x \to c} f(x)$ if we know that f is a continuous function?

2. Name one type of function for which $\lim_{x \to c} f(x) = f(c)$ always.

3. For what values of c can we use $f(c)$ to evaluate $\lim_{x \to c} f(x)$ if $f(x) = \dfrac{u(x)}{v(x)}$ is a rational function?

EXAMPLE 2

Is the function $f(x) = \dfrac{1}{x - 1}$ continuous?

Solution The denominator of this function will be 0 if $x = 1$, so the trouble spot is at $x = 1$. We see that

1. the function is undefined at $x = 1$.

2. $\lim_{x \to 1^-} f(x) = -\infty$ and $\lim_{x \to 1^+} f(x) = +\infty$

Thus $f(x) = 1/(x - 1)$ has a discontinuity at $x = 1$. The graph of $f(x) = 1/(x - 1)$ (Figure 2.9) shows that the curve approaches $-\infty$ as x approaches 1 from the left and $+\infty$ as x approaches 1 from the right.

In the graph of $f(x) = 1/(x - 1)$ in the preceding example (and in Figure 2.9), the function approaches the vertical line $x = 1$ but does not touch it. As we saw in Section 1.5, such a line is called a **vertical asymptote** of the graph.

FIGURE 2.9

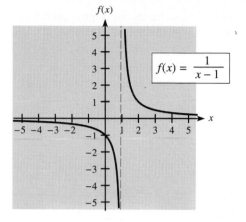

$$f(x) = \frac{1}{x - 1}$$

We also see in Figure 2.9 that the curve approaches $y = 0$ (the x-axis) as x increases without bound.

We can denote this fact with the notation

$$\lim_{x \to +\infty} \frac{1}{x - 1} = 0,$$

and we say that $y = 0$ (the x-axis) is a **horizontal asymptote** for $f(x) = 1/(x - 1)$. In addition, we see that $f(x) = 1/(x - 1)$ approaches 0 as x decreases without bound, and we denote this by

$$\lim_{x \to -\infty} \frac{1}{x - 1} = 0,$$

These limits can also be established with numerical tables.

x	$f(x) = \dfrac{1}{x - 1}$	x	$f(x) = \dfrac{1}{x - 1}$
101	0.01	-99	-0.01
100,001	0.00001	$-99,999$	-0.00001
100,000,001	0.00000001	$-99,999,999$	-0.00000001
$\downarrow$	$\downarrow$	$\downarrow$	$\downarrow$
$+\infty$	0	$-\infty$	0
$\lim\limits_{x \to +\infty} \dfrac{1}{x - 1} = 0$		$\lim\limits_{x \to -\infty} \dfrac{1}{x - 1} = 0$	

By using graphs and tables of values, we can obtain the following results.

Limits at Infinity

If c is any constant, then

1. $\lim\limits_{x \to +\infty} c = c$ and $\lim\limits_{x \to -\infty} c = c$.

2. $\lim\limits_{x \to +\infty} \dfrac{c}{x^p} = 0$, where $p > 0$.

3. $\lim\limits_{x \to -\infty} \dfrac{c}{x^n} = 0$, where $n > 0$ is any integer.

In order to use these properties for finding the limits of rational functions as x approaches $+\infty$ or $-\infty$, we first divide each term of the numerator and denominator by the highest power of x present and then determine the limit of the resulting expression.

EXAMPLE 3

Find each of the following limits, if they exist.

(a) $\lim\limits_{x \to +\infty} \dfrac{2x - 1}{x + 2}$

(b) $\lim\limits_{x \to -\infty} \dfrac{x^2 + 3}{1 - x}$

Solution

(a) The highest power of x present is x^1, so we divide each term in the numerator and denominator by x and then use the properties for limits at infinity.

$$\lim\limits_{x \to +\infty} \frac{2x - 1}{x + 2} = \lim\limits_{x \to +\infty} \frac{\dfrac{2x}{x} - \dfrac{1}{x}}{\dfrac{x}{x} + \dfrac{2}{x}}$$

$$= \lim\limits_{x \to +\infty} \frac{2 - \dfrac{1}{x}}{1 + \dfrac{2}{x}}$$

$$= \frac{2 - 0}{1 + 0} = 2 \qquad \text{(by Properties 1 and 2)}$$

Figure 2.10(a) shows the graph of this function with the y-coordinates of the graph approaching 2 as x approaches $+\infty$ and as x approaches $-\infty$. That is, $y = 2$ is a horizontal asymptote. Note also that there is a discontinuity (vertical asymptote) where $x = -2$.

(b) We divide each term in the numerator and denominator by x^2 and then use the properties.

$$\lim_{x \to -\infty} \frac{x^2 + 3}{1 - x} = \lim_{x \to -\infty} \frac{\dfrac{x^2}{x^2} + \dfrac{3}{x^2}}{\dfrac{1}{x^2} - \dfrac{x}{x^2}}$$

$$= \lim_{x \to -\infty} \frac{1 + \dfrac{3}{x^2}}{\dfrac{1}{x^2} - \dfrac{1}{x}}$$

$$= \frac{1 + 0}{0 - 0} = +\infty$$

This limit is $+\infty$ because the numerator approaches 1 and the denominator approaches 0 through positive values. Thus

$$\lim_{x \to -\infty} \frac{x^2 + 3}{1 - x} \quad \text{does not exist.}$$

The graph of this function, shown in Figure 2.10(b), has y-coordinates that increase without bound as x approaches $-\infty$ and that decrease without bound as x approaches $+\infty$. (There is no horizontal asymptote.) Note also that there is a vertical asymptote at $x = 1$.

FIGURE 2.10

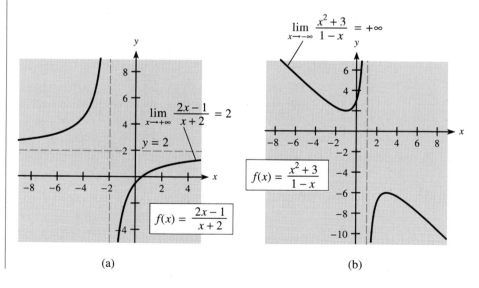

(a) (b)

Whereas the graphs of rational functions will often exhibit discontinuities like those illustrated in Figure 2.7(a) and (b) on page 174, the graphs of piecewise defined functions (defined in Section 1.5) will often have discontinuities like those in Figure 2.7(c) and (d).

Figure 2.11 is the graph of

$$f(x) = \begin{cases} x + 1 & \text{if } x < 0 \\ (x - 1)^2 & \text{if } 0 \le x < 2. \\ 2 - x & \text{if } x \ge 2 \end{cases}$$

The three formulas that define the function result in three separate pieces of the graph. We can see that two of the pieces appear to fit together at $x = 0$, so the function appears to be continuous at $x = 0$. However, at $x = 2$ the graph is broken (the function has a discontinuity). In Example 4, we show how to use the conditions for continuity to justify these conclusions.

FIGURE 2.11

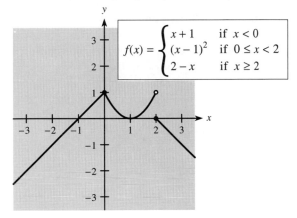

$$f(x) = \begin{cases} x + 1 & \text{if } x < 0 \\ (x - 1)^2 & \text{if } 0 \le x < 2 \\ 2 - x & \text{if } x \ge 2 \end{cases}$$

EXAMPLE 4

Test the function $f(x)$ for continuity if $f(x) = \begin{cases} x + 1 & \text{if } x < 0 \\ (x - 1)^2 & \text{if } 0 \le x < 2. \\ 2 - x & \text{if } x \ge 2 \end{cases}$

Solution This function consists of three polynomial (hence continuous) pieces. Thus if the function has a discontinuity, it will occur at an x-value where there is a formula change, namely at $x = 0$ or $x = 2$. Checking at $x = 0$ first, we see the following.

1. $f(0) = (0 - 1)^2 = 1$

2. Because $f(x)$ has different formulas for $x < 0$ and $x \ge 0$, we must use one-sided limits on the different pieces of $f(x)$ to evaluate $\lim\limits_{x \to 0} f(x)$.

$$\left. \begin{array}{l} \lim\limits_{x \to 0^-} f(x) = \lim\limits_{x \to 0^-} (x + 1) = 1 \\ \lim\limits_{x \to 0^+} f(x) = \lim\limits_{x \to 0^+} (x - 1)^2 = 1 \end{array} \right\} \Rightarrow \lim\limits_{x \to 0} f(x) = 1$$

3. $\lim\limits_{x \to 0} f(x) = f(0) = 1$

So $f(x)$ is continuous at $x = 0$.

Checking at $x = 2$, we have

1. $f(2) = 2 - 2 = 0$

2. Once again, we need one-sided limits to evaluate $\lim\limits_{x \to 2} f(x)$.

$$\left.\begin{array}{l} \lim\limits_{x \to 2^-} f(x) = \lim\limits_{x \to 2^-} (x-1)^2 = 1 \\[2mm] \lim\limits_{x \to 2^+} f(x) = \lim\limits_{x \to 2^+} (2-x) = 0 \end{array}\right\} \Rightarrow \lim\limits_{x \to 2} f(x) \text{ does not exist.}$$

Thus the function has a discontinuity at $x = 2$.

Piecewise defined functions that have discontinuities may seem abstract, but they are very much a part of our everyday life. For example, first-class postage is 29 cents for the first ounce or part of an ounce that a letter weighs and is an additional 23 cents for each additional ounce or part of an ounce above one ounce. Thus we can find the cost of mailing a first-class letter that weighs 5 ounces or less by using Table 2.3 or Figure 2.12. From the figure it is obvious why the post-office function is called a **step function.**

TABLE 2.3

Weight x	Postage $f(x)$
$0 < x \le 1$	\$0.29
$1 < x \le 2$	0.52
$2 < x \le 3$	0.75
$3 < x \le 4$	0.98
$4 < x \le 5$	1.21

FIGURE 2.12

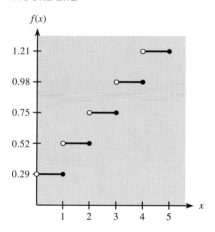

From Figure 2.12 we see that the post-office function is discontinuous at each whole ounce (that is, at $x = 1, 2, 3,$ and 4) because the left- and right-hand limits differ. In fact, any step function that has a "step" at $x = a$ is discontinuous at $x = a$ because the limit as x approaches a does not exist.

SUMMARY

The following information is useful in discussing continuity of functions.

A. A polynomial function is continuous everywhere.

B. A rational function is a function of the form $\dfrac{f(x)}{g(x)}$, where $f(x)$ and $g(x)$ are polynomials.

1. If $g(x) \neq 0$ at any value of x, the function is continuous everywhere.
2. If $g(c) = 0$, the function is discontinuous at $x = c$.
   (a) If $g(c) = 0$ and $f(c) \neq 0$, then there is a vertical asymptote at $x = c$.
   (b) If $g(c) = 0$ and $\lim\limits_{x \to c} \dfrac{f(x)}{g(x)} = L$, then the graph has an open circle at $x = c$.

C. A piecewise defined function *may* have a discontinuity at any x-value where the function changes its formula. One-sided limits must be used to see if the limit exists.

The following steps are useful when evaluating limits at infinity for a rational function $f(x) = p(x)/q(x)$.

1. Divide both $p(x)$ and $q(x)$ by the highest power of x found in either polynomial.
2. Use the properties of limits at infinity to complete the evaluation.

TECHNOLOGY CORNER

Graph the following functions. With each one, use trace to see what happens (a) near $x = -1$ and (b) at $x = -1$, and answer the questions below.

A. $f(x) = \dfrac{x^2 + 1}{x + 1}$

B. $f(x) = \dfrac{x^2 + 2x + 1}{x^2 - 1}$

C. $f(x) = \dfrac{|x + 1|}{x + 1}$

D. $f(x) = \begin{cases} -\dfrac{1}{2}x^2 - 2x & \text{if } x \leq -1 \\ \dfrac{1}{2}x + 2 & \text{if } x > -1 \end{cases}$

1. For each function, evaluate $f(-1)$, if it exists.
2. For each function, evaluate $\lim\limits_{x \to -1} f(x)$, if it exists.
3. Which of these functions is continuous at $x = -1$?
4. What happens at $x = -1$ for the discontinuous functions*?
5. Which of these functions is discontinuous at an x-value other than $x = -1$?

*On some graphics calculators or computers, changing the mode from connected to dot may make it easier to locate jumps or holes in a graph.

1. Yes, because if f is a continuous function, then $\lim_{x \to c} f(x) = f(c)$.

2. polynomial functions

3. Those values for which $v(c) \neq 0$.

EXERCISE 2.2

Problems 1 and 2 refer to the figure below. For each given x-value, use the figure to determine whether the function is continuous or discontinuous at that x-value. If the function is discontinuous, state which of the three conditions that define continuity are not satisfied.

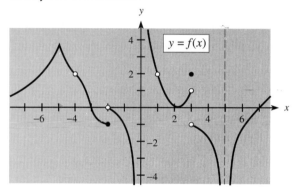

1. (a) $x = -5$ (b) $x = 1$
   (c) $x = 3$ (d) $x = 0$
2. (a) $x = 2$ (b) $x = -4$
   (c) $x = -2$ (d) $x = 5$

In problems 3–14, determine whether each function is continuous or discontinuous at the given x-value. Examine the three conditions in the definition of continuity.

3. $f(x) = x^2 - 5x$, $x = 0$

4. $f(x) = 3x - 5x^3$, $x = 2$

5. $f(x) = \dfrac{x^2 - 4}{x - 2}$, $x = -2$

6. $y = \dfrac{x^2 - 9}{x + 3}$, $x = 3$

7. $y = \dfrac{x^2 - 9}{x + 3}$, $x = -3$

8. $f(x) = \dfrac{x^2 - 4}{x - 2}$, $x = 2$

9. $y = \dfrac{x^2 + 5x - 6}{x + 1}$, $x = -1$

10. $y = \dfrac{x^2 - 2x - 3}{x - 1}$, $x = 1$

11. $f(x) = \begin{cases} 2 & \text{if } x \le 0 \\ x + 2 & \text{if } x > 0 \end{cases}$, $x = 0$

12. $f(x) = \begin{cases} x - 3 & \text{if } x \le 2 \\ 4x - 7 & \text{if } x > 2 \end{cases}$, $x = 2$

13. $f(x) = \begin{cases} x^2 + 1 & \text{if } x \le 1 \\ 2x^2 - 1 & \text{if } x > 1 \end{cases}$, $x = 1$

14. $f(x) = \begin{cases} x^2 - x & \text{if } x \le 2 \\ 8 - 3x & \text{if } x > 2 \end{cases}$, $x = 2$

In problems 15–26, determine whether or not the given function is continuous. If it is not, identify where it is discontinuous and which condition fails to hold.

15. $f(x) = 4x^2 - 1$

16. $y = 5x^2 - 2x$

17. $g(x) = \dfrac{x^2 + 4x + 4}{x + 2}$

18. $y = \dfrac{x^2 - 5x + 4}{x + 4}$

19. $g(x) = \dfrac{4x^2 + 3x + 2}{x + 2}$

20. $y = \dfrac{4x^2 + 4x + 1}{x + 1/2}$

21. $y = \dfrac{x}{x^2 + 1}$

22. $y = \dfrac{2x - 1}{x^2 + 2x + 3}$

23. $f(x) = \begin{cases} 3 & \text{if } x \le 1 \\ x^2 + 2 & \text{if } x > 1 \end{cases}$

24. $f(x) = \begin{cases} x^3 + 1 & \text{if } x \le 1 \\ 2 & \text{if } x > 1 \end{cases}$

25. $f(x) = \begin{cases} x - 4 & \text{if } x \le 3 \\ x^2 - 8 & \text{if } x > 3 \end{cases}$

26. $f(x) = \begin{cases} x^2 + 4 & \text{if } x \ne 1 \\ 5 & \text{if } x = 1 \end{cases}$

In problems 27–30, use the graphs to find each of the following, if they exist:
(a) vertical asymptotes
(b) $\lim\limits_{x \to \infty} f(x)$
(c) $\lim\limits_{x \to -\infty} f(x)$
(d) horizontal asymptotes

27.
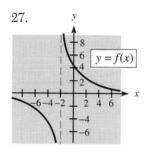

28.
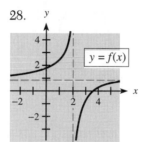

29.
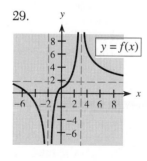

30.
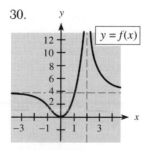

Evaluate the limits in problems 31–40.

31. $\lim\limits_{x \to +\infty} \dfrac{3}{x + 1}$

32. $\lim\limits_{x \to -\infty} \dfrac{4}{x^2 - 2x}$

33. $\lim\limits_{x \to +\infty} \dfrac{x^3 - 1}{x^3 + 4}$

34. $\lim\limits_{x \to 0\infty} \dfrac{3x^2 + 2}{x^2 - 4}$

35. $\lim\limits_{x \to -\infty} \dfrac{5x^3 - 4x}{3x^3 - 2}$

36. $\lim\limits_{x \to +\infty} \dfrac{4x^2 + 5x}{x^2 - 4x}$

37. $\lim\limits_{x \to -\infty} \dfrac{4x + 3}{x^2 - 1}$

38. $\lim\limits_{x \to -\infty} \dfrac{5x^2 + 4x}{2x^3 - 1}$

39. $\lim\limits_{x \to +\infty} \dfrac{3x^2 + 5x}{6x + 1}$

40. $\lim\limits_{x \to -\infty} \dfrac{5x^3 - 8}{4x^2 + 5x}$

APPLICATIONS

41. **Sales volume** Suppose that the weekly sales volume (in thousands of units) for a product is given by

$$y = \dfrac{32}{(p + 8)^{2/3}}, \quad p \ge 0,$$

where p is the price in dollars per unit. Is this function continuous
(a) at $p = 24$?
(b) for all $p \ge 0$?

42. **Worker productivity** Suppose that the average number of minutes M that it takes a new employee to assemble one unit of a product is given by

$$M = \dfrac{40 + 30t}{2t + 1}, \quad t \ge 0,$$

where t is the number of days on the job. Is this function continuous
(a) at $t = 14$?
(b) for all $t \ge 0$?

43. **Demand** Suppose that the demand for a product is defined by the equation

$$p = \dfrac{200{,}000}{(q + 1)^2},$$

where p is the price and q is the quantity demanded.
(a) Is this function discontinuous at any value of q? What value?
(b) Because q represents quantity, we know that $q \ge 0$. Is this function continuous for $q \ge 0$?

44. **Advertising and sales** The sales volume y (in thousands of dollars) is related to advertis-

ing expenditures x (in thousands of dollars) according to

$$y = \frac{200x}{x + 10}.$$

(a) Does this function have any points of discontinuity?

(b) Since advertising expenditures x must be nonnegative, is this function continuous for these values of x?

45. **Calories and temperature** Suppose that the number of calories of heat required to raise 1 gram of water (or ice) from $-40°C$ to $x°C$ is given by

$$f(x) = \begin{cases} \frac{1}{2}x + 20, & \text{if } -40 \le x < 0. \\ x + 100, & \text{if } 0 \le x. \end{cases}$$

(a) What can be said about the continuity of the function?

(b) What accounts for the behavior of the function at $0°C$?

46. **Response to adrenalin** Experimental evidence suggests that the response y of the body to the concentration x of injected adrenalin is given by

$$y = \frac{x}{a + bx}$$

where a and b are experimental constants.

(a) Is this function continuous for all x?

(b) Based on your conclusion in (a) and the fact that in reality $x \ge 0$ and $y \ge 0$, must a and b be both positive, be both negative, or have opposite signs?

47. **Cost-benefit** Suppose that the cost C of removing p percent of the impurities from the waste water in a manufacturing process is given by

$$C(p) = \frac{9800p}{101 - p}.$$

Is this function continuous for all those p-values for which the problem makes sense?

48. **Cost-benefit** Suppose that the cost C of removing p percent of the particulate pollution from the exhaust gases at an industrial site is given by

$$C(p) = \frac{8100p}{100 - p}.$$

Describe any discontinuities for $C(p)$.

49. **Cost-benefit** The percentage p of particulate pollution that can be removed from the smokestacks of an industrial plant by spending C dollars is given by

$$p = \frac{100C}{7300 + C}.$$

Find the percentage of the pollution that could be removed if spending C was allowed to increase without bound. Can 100% of the pollution be removed?

50. **Cost-benefit** The percentage p of impurities that can be removed from the waste water of a manufacturing process at a cost of C dollars is given by

$$p = \frac{100C}{8100 + C}.$$

Find the percentage of the impurities that could be removed if cost were no object (that is, if cost were allowed to increase without bound). Can 100% of the impurities be removed?

51. **Annuities** If an annuity makes an infinite series of equal payments at the end of the interest periods, it is called a **perpetuity.** If a lump-sum investment of A_n is needed to result in n periodic payments of R when the interest rate per period is i, then

$$A_n = R \frac{1 - (1 + i)^{-n}}{i}.$$

Evaluate $\lim_{n \to \infty} A_n$ to find a formula for the lump-sum payment for a perpetuity.

52. ***Annuities*** Find the lump-sum investment needed to make payments of $100 per month in perpetuity if interest is 12%, compounded monthly. Use the formula developed in problem 51.

53. ***Federal income tax*** The U.S. federal income tax schedule for single taxpayers in 1991 is given below.

Tax rate	Taxable income (in dollars)
15%	0–20,350
28%	20,351–49,300
31%	> 49,300

This means that the tax T is a function of income x as follows:

$$T(x) - \begin{cases} 0.15x & \text{if } 0 \le x \le 20{,}350 \\ 3052.50 + 0.28(x - 20{,}350) \\ \quad \text{if } 20{,}350 < x < 49{,}300 \\ 11{,}158.50 + 0.31(x - 49{,}300) \\ \quad \text{if } x > 49{,}300 \end{cases}$$

Is $T(x)$ continuous?

54. ***Parking costs*** The Ace Parking Garage charges $2.00 for parking for 2 hours or less, and 50 cents for each extra hour or part of an hour after the 2-hour minimum. The parking charges for the first 5 hours could be written as a function of the time as follows.

$$f(t) = \begin{cases} \$2.00 & \text{if } 0 < t \le 2 \\ \$2.50 & \text{if } 2 < t \le 3 \\ \$3.00 & \text{if } 3 < t \le 4 \\ \$3.50 & \text{if } 4 < t \le 5 \end{cases}$$

(a) Find $\lim_{t \to 1} f(t)$, if it exists.
(b) Find $\lim_{t \to 2} f(t)$, if it exists.
(c) Is $f(t)$ continuous at $t = 2$?

55. ***Water usage costs*** The monthly charge for water in a small town is given by

$$f(x) = \begin{cases} 18 & \text{if } 0 \le x \le 20 \\ 0.1x + 16 & \text{if } x > 20 \end{cases}$$

(a) Find $\lim_{x \to 20} f(x)$, if it exists.
(b) Is $f(x)$ continuous?

56. ***Electrical usage costs*** The monthly charge in dollars for x kilowatt hours (kWh) of electricity used by a commercial customer is given by the following function.

$$C(x) = \begin{cases} 7.52 + 0.1079x & \text{if } 0 \le x \le 5 \\ 19.22 + 0.1079x & \text{if } 5 < x \le 750 \\ 20.795 + 0.1058x & \text{if } 750 < x \le 1500 \\ 131.345 + 0.0321x & \text{if } x > 1500 \end{cases}$$

(a) Find $\lim_{x \to 1500} C(x)$, if it exists.
(b) Find $\lim_{x \to 5} C(x)$, if it exists.
(c) Is $C(x)$ continuous at $x = 5$?

57. ***Postage costs*** For the post-office function discussed in this section (see Table 2.3 and Figure 2.12 on page 180), find the following.
(a) $\lim_{x \to 2.5} f(x)$ (b) $f(2.5)$
(c) $\lim_{x \to 4^-} f(x)$ (d) $\lim_{x \to 4} f(x)$ (e) $f(4)$

2.3 | THE DERIVATIVE: RATES OF CHANGE; TANGENT TO A CURVE

OBJECTIVES

- To define the derivatives as a rate of change
- To use the definition of derivative to find derivatives of functions
- To use derivatives to find slopes of tangents to curves

Suppose that a ball is thrown straight upward at 64 feet per second from a spot 96 feet above ground level. The equation that describes the height y of the ball after x seconds is

$$y = f(x) = 96 + 64x - 16x^2.$$

Figure 2.13 shows the graph of this function for $0 \le x \le 5$.

FIGURE 2.13

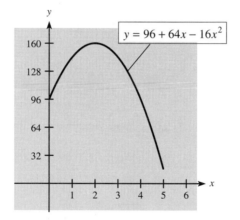

$$y = 96 + 64x - 16x^2$$

The average velocity of the ball over a given time interval is the change in the height divided by the length of time that has passed. Table 2.4 shows some average velocities over time intervals beginning at $x = 1$.

TABLE 2.4 Average velocities

TIME			HEIGHT			
Beginning	*Ending*	*Change*	*Beginning*	*Ending*	*Change*	*AVERAGE VELOCITY*
1	2	1	144	160	16	16/1 = 16
1	1.5	0.5	144	156	12	12/0.5 = 24
1	1.1	0.1	144	147.04	3.04	3.04/0.1 = 30.4
1	1.01	0.01	144	144.3184	0.3184	0.3184/0.01 = 31.84

In Table 2.4, the smaller the time interval, the more closely the average velocity approximates the instantaneous velocity at $x = 1$. Thus the instantaneous velocity at $x = 1$ is closer to 31.84 ft/s than to 30.4 ft/s.

If we represent the change in time by h, then the average velocity from $x = 1$ to $x = 1 + h$ approaches the instantaneous velocity at $x = 1$ as h approaches 0. This is illustrated in the following example.

EXAMPLE 1

Suppose that a ball is thrown straight upward so that its height $f(x)$ (in feet) is given by the equation

$$f(x) = 96 + 64x - 16x^2,$$

where x is time (in seconds).
(a) Find the average velocity from $x = 1$ to $x = 1 + h$.
(b) Find the instantaneous velocity at $x = 1$.

Solution
(a) Let h represent the change in x (time) from 1 to $1 + h$. Then the corresponding change in $f(x)$ (height) is

$$\begin{aligned}
f(1 + h) - f(1) &= [96 + 64(1 + h) - 16(1 + h)^2] - [96 + 64 - 16] \\
&= 96 + 64 + 64h - 16(1 + 2h + h^2) - 144 \\
&= 16 + 64h - 16 - 32h - 16h^2 \\
&= 32h - 16h^2.
\end{aligned}$$

The average velocity V_{av} is then the change in height divided by the change in time.

$$\begin{aligned}
V_{av} &= \frac{f(1 + h) - f(1)}{h} \\
&= \frac{32h - 16h^2}{h} \\
&= 32 - 16h
\end{aligned}$$

(b) The instantaneous velocity V is the limit of the average velocity as h approaches 0.

$$\begin{aligned}
V &= \lim_{h \to 0} V_{av} = \lim_{h \to 0} (32 - 16h) \\
&= 32 \text{ ft/s}
\end{aligned}$$

Instantaneous velocity is usually called **velocity,** and it can be found at any time x as follows.

Velocity　Suppose that an object moving in a straight line has its position y at time x given by $y = f(x)$. Then the **velocity** of the object at time x is

$$V = \lim_{h \to 0} \frac{f(x + h) - f(x)}{h},$$

provided this limit exists.

The instantaneous rate of change of any function can be found in the same way we find velocity. The function that gives this instantaneous rate of change of a function f is called the **derivative** of f.

Derivative　If f is a function defined by $y = f(x)$, then the **derivative** of $f(x)$ at any value x, denoted $f'(x)$, is

$$f'(x) = \lim_{h \to 0} \frac{f(x + h) - f(x)}{h},$$

if this limit exists. If $f'(x_0)$ exists, we say f is **differentiable** at x_0.

The following procedure illustrates how to find the derivative of a function $y = f(x)$ at any value x.

DERIVATIVE USING THE DEFINITION

PROCEDURE	EXAMPLE
To find the derivative of $y = f(x)$ at any value x:	Find the derivative of $f(x) = 4x^2$.
1. Let h represent the change in x from x to $x + h$.	1. The change in x from x to $x + h$ is h.
2. The corresponding change in $y = f(x)$ is $f(x + h) - f(x)$.	2. The change in $f(x)$ is $$\begin{aligned} f(x + h) - f(x) &= 4(x + h)^2 - 4x^2 \\ &= 4(x^2 + 2xh + h^2) - 4x^2 \\ &= 4x^2 + 8xh + 4h^2 - 4x^2 \\ &= 8xh + 4h^2. \end{aligned}$$
3. Form the difference quotient $$\frac{f(x + h) - f(x)}{h}$$ and simplify.	3. $$\begin{aligned} \frac{f(x + h) - f(x)}{h} &= \frac{8xh + 4h^2}{h} \\ &= 8x + 4h \end{aligned}$$

4. Find

$$\lim_{h \to 0} \frac{f(x + h) - f(x)}{h}$$

to determine $f'(x)$, the derivative of $f(x)$.

4. $f'(x) = \lim_{h \to 0} \frac{f(x + h) - f(x)}{h}$

$f'(x) = \lim_{h \to 0} (8x + 4h) = 8x$

Note that in the previous example, we could have found the derivative of the function $f(x) = 4x^2$ at a particular value of x, say $x = 3$, by evaluating the derivative formula at that value:

$$f'(x) = 8x \quad \text{so} \quad f'(3) = 8(3) = 24.$$

In addition to $f'(x)$, the derivative at any point x may be denoted by

$$\frac{dy}{dx}, \quad y', \quad \frac{d}{dx} f(x), \quad D_x y, \quad \text{or} \quad D_x f(x).$$

We can, of course, use variables other than x and y to represent functions and their derivatives. For example, we can represent the derivative of the function defined by $p = 2q^2 - 1$ by dp/dq.

CHECKPOINT

1. For the function

$$y = f(x) = x^2 - x + 1,$$

find

(a) $f(x + h) - f(x)$

(b) $\dfrac{f(x + h) - f(x)}{h}$

(c) $f'(x) = \lim_{h \to 0} \dfrac{f(x + h) - f(x)}{h}$

(d) $f'(2)$

In Section 1.3 we defined the **marginal revenue** for a product as the rate of change of the total revenue function for the product and noted that the slope of a linear total revenue function gave the marginal revenue. If the total revenue function for a product is not linear, we define the marginal revenue for the product as the instantaneous rate of change, or the derivative, of the revenue function.

Marginal Revenue

Suppose that the total revenue function for a product is given by $R = R(x)$, where x is the number of units sold. Then the **marginal revenue** at x units is

$$\overline{MR} = R'(x) = \lim_{h \to 0} \frac{R(x + h) - R(x)}{h},$$

provided the limit exists.

EXAMPLE 2

Suppose that an oil company's revenue (in thousands of dollars) is given by the equation

$$R = R(x) = 100x - x^2, \quad x \geq 0,$$

where x is the number of units of oil sold each day.

(a) Find the function that gives the marginal revenue at any value of x.

(b) Find the marginal revenue at $x = 20$.

Solution

(a) The marginal revenue function is found by evaluating

$$
\begin{aligned}
R'(x) &= \lim_{h \to 0} \frac{R(x + h) - R(x)}{h} \\
&= \lim_{h \to 0} \frac{[100(x + h) - (x + h)^2] - (100x - x^2)}{h} \\
&= \lim_{h \to 0} \frac{100x + 100h - (x^2 + 2xh + h^2) - 100x + x^2}{h} \\
&= \lim_{h \to 0} \frac{100h - 2xh - h^2}{h} \\
&= \lim_{h \to 0} (100 - 2x - h) \\
&= 100 - 2x.
\end{aligned}
$$

(b) The marginal revenue function found in part (a) gives the marginal revenue at *any* value of x. To find the marginal revenue when 20 units are sold, we evaluate $R'(20)$.

$$R'(20) = 100 - 2(20) = 60$$

The marginal revenue at $x = 20$ is 60 thousand dollars.

As mentioned earlier, the rate of change of revenue (the marginal revenue) for a linear revenue function is given by the slope of the line. In fact, the slope of the revenue curve gives us the marginal revenue even if the revenue function is not linear. We will show that the slope of the graph of a function at any point is the same as the derivative at that point. In order to show this, we must define the slope of a curve at a point on the curve. We will define the slope of a curve at a point as the slope of the line tangent to the curve at the point.

In geometry, a **tangent** to a circle is defined as a line that has one point in common with the circle. [See Figure 2.14(a).] This definition does not apply to all curves, as Figure 2.14(b) shows. Many lines can be drawn through the point A that touch the curve only at A. One of the lines, line l, looks like it is tangent to the curve.

FIGURE 2.14

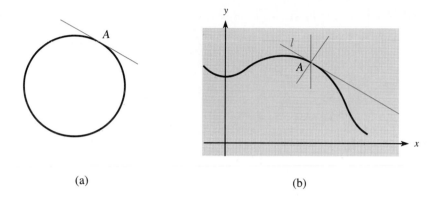

(a)   (b)

We can use **secant lines** (lines intersecting the curve at two points) to determine the tangent to a curve at a point. In Figure 2.15, we have a set of secant lines s_1, s_2, s_3, and s_4 that pass through a point A on the curve and points Q_1, Q_2, Q_3, and Q_4 on the curve near A. The line l represents the tangent line to the curve at point A. We can get a secant line as close as we wish to the tangent line l by choosing a "second point" Q sufficiently close to point A.

FIGURE 2.15

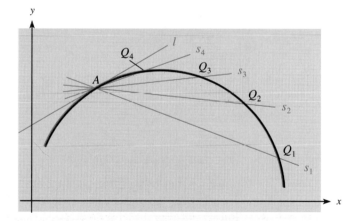

As we choose points on the curve closer and closer to A, the limiting position of the secant lines that pass through A is the **tangent line** to the curve at point A, and the slopes of those secant lines approach the slope of the tangent line at A. Thus we can find the slope of the tangent line by finding the slope of a secant line and taking the limit of this slope as the "second point" Q approaches A. To find the slope of the tangent to the graph of $y = f(x)$ at A $(x_1, f(x_1))$, we first draw a secant line from point A to a second point Q $(x_1 + h, f(x_1 + h))$ on the curve (see Figure 2.16).

FIGURE 2.16

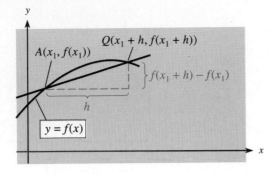

The slope of this secant line is

$$m_{AQ} = \frac{f(x_1 + h) - f(x_1)}{h}.$$

As Q approaches A, we see that the difference between the x-coordinates of these two points decreases, so h approaches 0. Thus the slope of the tangent is given by the following.

Slope of the Tangent

The **slope of the tangent** to the graph of $y = f(x)$ at point $A(x_1, f(x_1))$ is

$$m = \lim_{h \to 0} \frac{f(x_1 + h) - f(x_1)}{h}$$

if this limit exists. That is, $m = f'(x_1)$.

EXAMPLE 3

Find the slope of $y = f(x) = x^2$ at the point A (2, 4).

Solution The formula for the slope of the tangent to $y = f(x)$ at (2, 4) is

$$m = f'(2) = \lim_{h \to 0} \frac{f(2 + h) - f(2)}{h}.$$

So for $f(x) = x^2$, we have

$$m = f'(2) = \lim_{h \to 0} \frac{(2 + h)^2 - 2^2}{h}.$$

Taking the limit immediately would result in both the numerator and the denominator approaching 0. To avoid this, we simplify the fraction before taking the limit.

$$m = \lim_{h \to 0} \frac{4 + 4h + h^2 - 4}{h} = \lim_{h \to 0} \frac{4h + h^2}{h} = \lim_{h \to 0} (4 + h) = 4$$

Thus the slope of the tangent to $y = x^2$ at (2, 4) is 4 (see Figure 2.17).

FIGURE 2.17

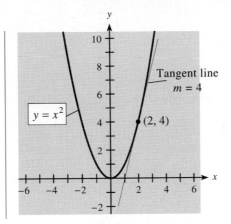

The statement "the slope of the tangent to the curve at (2, 4) is 4" is frequently simplified to the statement "the slope of the curve at (2, 4) is 4." Knowledge that the slope is a positive number on an interval tells us that the function is increasing on that interval, which means that a point moving along the graph of the function rises as it moves to the right on that interval. If the derivative (and thus the slope) is negative on an interval, the curve is decreasing on the interval; that is, a point moving along the graph falls as it moves to the right on that interval.

EXAMPLE 4

Given $y = f(x) = 3x^2 + 2x$, find

(a) the derivative of $f(x)$ at any point $(x, f(x))$.

(b) the slope of the curve at $(1, 5)$.

(c) the equation of the line tangent to $y = 3x^2 + 2x$ at $(1, 5)$.

Solution

(a) The derivative of $f(x)$ at any value x is denoted by $f'(x)$, and is

$$y' = f'(x) = \lim_{h \to 0} \frac{f(x + h) - f(x)}{h}$$
$$= \lim_{h \to 0} \frac{[3(x + h)^2 + 2(x + h)] - (3x^2 + 2x)}{h}$$
$$= \lim_{h \to 0} \frac{3(x^2 + 2xh + h^2) + 2x + 2h - 3x^2 - 2x}{h}$$
$$= \lim_{h \to 0} \frac{6xh + 3h^2 + 2h}{h}$$
$$= \lim_{h \to 0} (6x + 3h + 2)$$
$$= 6x + 2.$$

(b) The derivative is $f'(x) = 6x + 2$, so the slope of the tangent to the curve at $(1, 5)$ is $f'(1) = 6(1) + 2 = 8$.

(c) The equation of the tangent line uses the given point $(1, 5)$ and the slope $m = 8$. It is $y - 5 = 8(x - 1)$, or $y = 8x - 3$.

The discussion in this section indicates that the derivative of a function can be used to accomplish the following.

1. Find the velocity of an object moving in a straight line.

2. Find the instantaneous rate of change of a function.

3. Find the marginal revenue function for a given revenue function.

4. Find the slope of the tangent to the graph of a function.

So far we have talked about how the derivative is defined, what it represents, and how to find it. However, there are functions for which derivatives do not exist at every value of x. Figure 2.18 shows some common cases where $f'(c)$ does not exist but where $f'(x)$ exists for all other values of x.

FIGURE 2.18

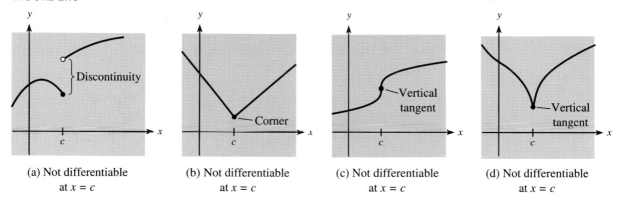

(a) Not differentiable at $x = c$

(b) Not differentiable at $x = c$

(c) Not differentiable at $x = c$

(d) Not differentiable at $x = c$

From Figure 2.18 we see that a function may be continuous at $x = c$ even though $f'(c)$ does not exist. Thus continuity does not imply differentiability at a point. However, differentiability does imply continuity.

Differentiability Implies Continuity

If a function f is differentiable at $x = c$, then f is continuous at $x = c$.

EXAMPLE 5

The monthly charge for water in a small town is given by

$$y = f(x) = \begin{cases} 18 & \text{if } 0 \le x \le 20. \\ 0.1x + 16 & \text{if } x > 20 \end{cases}$$

(a) Is this function continuous at $x = 20$?

(b) Is this function differentiable at $x = 20$?

Solution

(a) We must check the three properties for continuity.

(1) $f(x) = 18$ for $x \leq 20$, so $f(20) = 18$.

(2) $\left.\begin{array}{l} \lim\limits_{x \to 20^-} f(x) = \lim\limits_{x \to 20^-} 18 = 18 \\[2mm] \lim\limits_{x \to 20^+} f(x) = \lim\limits_{x \to 20^+} (0.1x + 16) = 18 \end{array}\right\} \Rightarrow \lim\limits_{x \to 20} f(x) = 18.$

(3) $\lim\limits_{x \to 20} f(x) = f(20)$.

Thus $f(x)$ is continuous at $x = 20$.

(b) Because the function is defined differently on either side of $x = 20$, we must evaluate both

(i) $\lim\limits_{h \to 0^-} \dfrac{f(20 + h) - f(20)}{h}$ and (ii) $\lim\limits_{h \to 0^+} \dfrac{f(20 + h) - f(20)}{h}$

to see if $f'(20)$ exists.

(i) $\lim\limits_{h \to 0^-} \dfrac{f(20 + h) - f(20)}{h} = \lim\limits_{h \to 0^-} \dfrac{18 - 18}{h}$

$= \lim\limits_{h \to 0^-} 0 = 0.$

(ii) $\lim\limits_{h \to 0^+} \dfrac{f(20 + h) - f(20)}{h} = \lim\limits_{h \to 0^+} \dfrac{[0.1(20 + h) + 16] - 18}{h}$

$= \lim\limits_{h \to 0^+} \dfrac{0.1h}{h}$

$= \lim\limits_{h \to 0^+} 0.1 = 0.1.$

Because these limits are not equal, the derivative does not exist.

CHECKPOINT 2. Which of the following are given by $f'(c)$?
   (a) The slope of the tangent when $x = c$.
   (b) The y-coordinate of the point where $x = c$.
   (c) The instantaneous rate of change of $f(x)$ at $x = c$.
   (d) The marginal revenue at $x = c$, if $f(x)$ is the revenue function.

3. Must a graph that has no discontinuity, corner, or cusp at $x = c$ be differentiable at $x = c$?

TECHNOLOGY CORNER

If the point (a, b) lies on the graph of $y = x^2$, then the equation of the secant line to $y = x^2$ from $(1, 1)$ to (a, b) has the equation

$$y = \frac{b - 1}{a - 1}(x - 1) + 1.$$

1. Graph $y = x^2$ in a range near $(1, 1)$ and graph the secant line for each of the following values for a and b.

   (a) $a = 5, b = 25$

   (b) $a = 3, b = 9$

   (c) $a = 1.01, b = 1.0201$

2. Which secant line graphed in (1) appears as if it might be closest to the tangent line at $(1, 1)$?

3. (a) What is the slope of each secant line you graphed?

   (b) Do your graphs illustrate that, as (a, b) approaches $(1, 1)$, the slopes of the secant lines approach the slope of the tangent line?

   (c) What would you guess to be the slope of the tangent line?

4. (a) Express the slope of the secant line to (a, b) in terms of a. That is, express $(b - 1)/(a - 1)$ in terms of a.

   (b) Graph the function of a found in part (a) and evaluate the slope of the tangent line at $(1, 1)$ by using trace to find $\displaystyle\lim_{a \to 1} \frac{b - 1}{a - 1}$.

CHECKPOINT

SOLUTIONS

1. (a) $f(x + h) - f(x) = [(x + h)^2 - (x + h) + 1] - (x^2 - x + 1)$
   $$= x^2 + 2xh + h^2 - x - h + 1 - x^2 + x - 1$$
   $$= 2xh + h^2 - h$$

   (b) $\dfrac{f(x + h) - f(x)}{h} = \dfrac{2xh + h^2 - h}{h}$
   $$= 2x + h - 1$$

   (c) $f'(x) = \displaystyle\lim_{h \to 0} \frac{f(x + h) - f(x)}{h}$
   $$= \lim_{h \to 0} (2x + h - 1)$$
   $$= 2x - 1$$

   (d) $f'(x) = 2x - 1$, so $f'(2) = 3$.

2. Parts (a), (c), and (d) are given by $f'(c)$. The y-coordinate where $x = c$ is given by $f(c)$.

3. No. Figure 2.18(c) shows such an example.

EXERCISE 2.3

1. In the Procedure/Example table in this section we were given $f(x) = 4x^2$ and found $f'(x) = 8x$. Find the
   (a) instantaneous rate of change of $f(x)$ at $x = 4$.
   (b) slope of the tangent to the graph of $f(x)$ at $x = 4$.
   (c) point on the graph of $f(x)$ at $x = 4$.

2. In Example 4 of this section we were given $f(x) = 3x^2 + 2x$ and found $f'(x) = 6x + 2$. Find the
   (a) instantaneous rate of change of $f(x)$ at $x = 6$.
   (b) slope of the tangent to the graph of $f(x)$ at $x = 6$.
   (c) point on the graph of $f(x)$ at $x = 6$.

In problems 3–6, find the derivative of each function.

3. $f(x) = 1 - 6x$
4. $f(x) = 4 - 5x$
5. $f(x) = 4x^2 - 2x + 1$
6. $f(x) = 16x^2 - 4x + 2$

In problems 7–10, (a) find the instantaneous rate of change of the function at any point and (b) find the instantaneous rate of change at the given value.

7. (a) $p(q) = q^2 + 4q + 1$
   (b) $q = 5$
8. (a) $p(q) = 2q^2 - 4q + 5$
   (b) $q = 2$
9. (a) $C(x) = 14x^3 + 5x + 60$
   (b) $x = 4$
10. (a) $C(x) = 500 + 40x + 0.5x^2$
    (b) $x = 5$

In problems 11–14, (a) find the slope of the tangent to the graph of $f(x)$ at any point, (b) find the slope of the tangent at the given x-value, and (c) write the equation of the line tangent to the graph of $f(x)$ at the given point.

11. (a) $f(x) = x^2 + x$
    (b) $x = 2$
    (c) $(2, 6)$
12. (a) $f(x) = x^2 + 3x$
    (b) $x = -1$
    (c) $(-1, -2)$
13. (a) $f(x) = x^3 + 3$
    (b) $x = 1$
    (c) $(1, 4)$
14. (a) $f(x) = 5x^3 + 2$
    (b) $x = -1$
    (c) $(-1, -3)$

In problems 15–18, the tangent line to the graph of $f(x)$ at $x = 1$ is shown. On the tangent line, P is the point of tangency and A is another point on the line.
(a) Find the coordinates of the points P and A.
(b) Use the coordinates of P and A to find the slope of the tangent line.
(c) Find $f'(1)$.
(d) Find the instantaneous rate of change of $f(x)$ at

15.

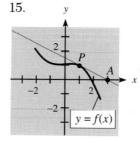

16.

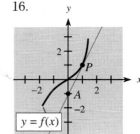

17.

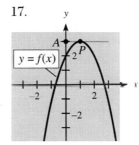

18.

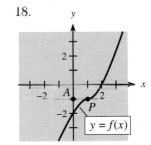

In problems 19 and 20, a point (a, b) on the graph of $y = f(x)$ is given and the equation of the line tangent to the graph of $f(x)$ at (a, b) is given. In each case, find $f'(a)$ and $f(a)$.

19. $(-3, -9);$ $5x - 2y = 3$

20. $(-1, 6);$ $x + 10y = 59$

21. If the instantaneous rate of change of $f(x)$ at $(1, -1)$ is 3, write the equation of the line tangent to the graph of $f(x)$ at $x = 1$.

22. If the instantaneous rate of change of $g(x)$ at $(-1, -2)$ is $1/2$, write the equation of the line tangent to the graph of $g(x)$ at $x = -1$.

Since the derivative of a function represents both the slope of the tangent to the curve and the instantaneous rate of change of the function, it is possible to use information about one to gain information about the other. In problems 23 and 24, use the graph of the function $y = f(x)$ given by Figure 2.19.

FIGURE 2.19

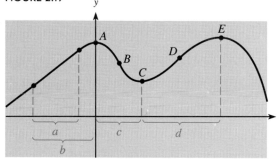

23. (a) Over what interval(s) (a) through (d) is the rate of change of $f(x)$ positive?
    (b) Over what interval(s) (a) through (d) is the rate of change of $f(x)$ negative?
    (c) At what point(s) A through E is the rate of change of $f(x)$ equal to zero?

24. (a) At what point(s) A through E does the rate of change of $f(x)$ change from positive to negative?
    (b) At what point(s) A through E does the rate of change of $f(x)$ change from negative to positive?

25. Given the graph of $y = f(x)$ in Figure 2.20, determine for which x-values A, B, C, D, or E the function is
    (a) continuous.   (b) differentiable.

26. Given the graph of $y = f(x)$ in Figure 2.20 below, determine for which x-values F, G, H, I, or J the function is
    (a) continuous.   (b) differentiable.

Applications

27. **Average velocity** When a ball is dropped from a height of 256 feet, its position (height above the ground) after x seconds is given by

    $$S(x) = 256 - 16x^2.$$

    (a) What is the average velocity in the first 2 seconds of the fall?
    (b) What does the negative average velocity in part (a) mean?

28. **Average velocity** If an object is thrown upward at 64 ft/s from a height of 20 feet, its height S after x seconds is given by

    $$S(x) = 20 + 64x - 16x^2.$$

    What is the average velocity in the
    (a) first 2 seconds after it is thrown?
    (b) next 2 seconds?

FIGURE 2.20

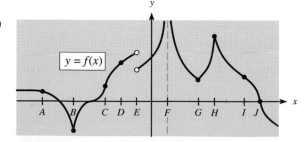

29. **Demand** If the demand for a product is given by

$$D(p) = \frac{1000}{\sqrt{p}} - 1,$$

what is the average rate of change of demand if p increases from
(a) 1 to 25?
(b) 25 to 100?

30. **Revenue** If the total revenue function for a blender is

$$R(x) = 36x - 0.01x^2,$$

where x is the number of units sold, what is the average rate of change in revenue $R(x)$ as x increases from 10 to 20 units?

31. **Speed limit enforcement** If 0.05 second elapses while a car on a road travels over two sensors that are 5 feet apart, what is the average velocity (in miles per hour) of the car as it travels between the sensors (88 feet per second is equivalent to 60 miles per hour)?

32. **Speed limit enforcement** One speed-check system used by local police measures the elapsed time between two marks 0.1 mile apart. If 5.85 seconds elapse while a car on the highway travels between the two marks, find the average velocity of the car (in miles per hour) as it travels between the two marks.

33. **Marginal revenue** If the revenue function for a stereo system is

$$R(x) = 300x - x^2,$$

where x denotes the number of units sold, what is
(a) the marginal revenue if 50 units are sold?
(b) the marginal revenue if 100 units are sold?
(c) the marginal revenue if 150 units are sold?
(d) happening to revenue when 150 units are sold?

34. **Marginal revenue** If the total revenue function for a blender is

$$R(x) = 36x - 0.01x^2,$$

where x is the number of units sold, what

(a) function gives the marginal revenue?
(b) is the marginal revenue when 600 units are sold?
(c) is the marginal revenue when 2000 units are sold?
(d) is the marginal revenue when 1800 units are sold?

35. **Labor force and output** The monthly output at the Olek Carpet Mill is

$$Q(x) = 15{,}000 + 2x^2 \text{ units}, \quad (40 \le x \le 60),$$

where x is the number of workers employed at the mill. If there are currently 50 workers, find the instantaneous rate of change of monthly output with respect to the number of workers. [That is, find $Q'(50)$.]

36. **Consumer expenditure** Suppose that the demand x for a product is

$$x = 10{,}000 - 100p,$$

where p dollars is the price per unit. Then the consumer expenditure for the product is

$$E(p) = px = p(10{,}000 - 100p)$$
$$= 10{,}000p - 100p^2.$$

What is the instantaneous rate of change of consumer expenditure with respect to price at
(a) any price p?
(b) $p = 5$?
(c) $p = 20$?

37. **Profit** Suppose that the profit function for the monthly sales of a car by a dealership is

$$P(x) = 500x - x^2 - 100,$$

where x is the number of cars sold. What is the instantaneous rate of change of profit when
(a) 200 cars are sold?
(b) 300 cars are sold?

38. **Profit** If the total revenue function for a toy is

$$R(x) = 2x,$$

and the total cost function is

$$C(x) = 100 + 0.2x^2 + x,$$

what is the instantaneous rate of change of profit if 10 units are produced and sold?

39. ***Bacterial weight*** The weight of a culture of bacteria is given by the following chart.

Time (h)	Weight (g)
0	5
1	10
2	20
3	40
4	80

Find the average rate of change of the weight in the

(a) first hour. (b) first 2 hours.
(c) first 4 hours.
(d) period from 2 to 4 hours.

40. ***Velocity*** When a ball is dropped from a height of 256 feet, the distance it travels in t seconds is given by $s = 16t^2$.

(a) Find the average rate of change of the distance (average velocity) in the first 2 seconds of the fall.
(b) Find the average rate in the next 2 seconds.
(c) Find the instantaneous rate at $t = 2$ seconds.

41. ***Average speed*** On an 80-mile trip, a driver averages 40 mph for the first 40 miles and 60 mph for the last 40 miles. What is the average speed for the trip? Careful!

2.4 | DERIVATIVE FORMULAS

OBJECTIVES

- To find derivatives of powers of x
- To find derivatives of constant functions
- To find derivatives of functions involving constant coefficients
- To find derivatives of sums and differences of functions

We can use the definition of derivative to show the following:

If $f(x) = x^2$, then $f'(x) = 2x$.
If $f(x) = x^3$, then $f'(x) = 3x^2$.
If $f(x) = x^4$, then $f'(x) = 4x^3$.
If $f(x) = x^5$, then $f'(x) = 5x^4$.

Do you recognize a pattern that could be used to find the derivative of $f(x) = x^6$? What is the derivative of $f(x) = x^n$? If you said that the derivative of $f(x) = x^6$ is $f'(x) = 6x^5$ and the derivative of $f(x) = x^n$ is $f'(x) = nx^{n-1}$, you're right. We can use the definition of derivative to show this. If n is a positive integer, then

$$f'(x) = \lim_{h \to 0} \frac{f(x+h) - f(x)}{h}$$
$$= \lim_{h \to 0} \frac{(x+h)^n - x^n}{h}.$$

Since we are assuming that n is a positive integer, we can use the binomial formula to expand $(x + h)^n$. You may recall from an algebra course that this formula is stated as follows:

$$(a + b)^n = a^n + na^{n-1}b + \frac{n(n-1)}{1 \cdot 2}a^{n-2}b^2 + \cdots + b^n.$$

Thus replacing a with x and b with h gives the following.

$$f'(x) = \lim_{h \to 0} \frac{\left[x^n + nx^{n-1}h + \dfrac{n(n-1)}{1 \cdot 2}x^{n-2}h^2 + \cdots + h^n\right] - x^n}{h}$$

$$= \lim_{h \to 0} \left[nx^{n-1} + \frac{n(n-1)}{1 \cdot 2}x^{n-2}h + \cdots + h^{n-1}\right]$$

Now, each term after nx^{n-1} contains h as a factor, so all terms except nx^{n-1} will approach 0 as $h \to 0$. Thus

$$f'(x) = nx^{n-1}.$$

Even though we proved this derivative rule only for the case when n is a positive integer, the rule applies for any real number n.

Powers of x Rule	If $f(x) = x^n$, where n is a real number, then $f'(x) = nx^{n-1}$.

EXAMPLE 1

Find the derivatives of the following functions.

(a) $g(x) = x^6$ (b) $f(x) = x^{-2}$

(c) $y = x^4$ (d) $y = x^{1/3}$

Solution

(a) If $g(x) = x^6$, then $g'(x) = 6x^{6-1} = 6x^5$.

(b) The Powers of x Rule applies for all real values. Thus for $f(x) = x^{-2}$, we have

$$f'(x) = -2x^{-2-1} = -2x^{-3} = \frac{-2}{x^3}.$$

(c) If $y = x^4$, then $dy/dx = 4x^{4-1} = 4x^3$.

(d) The Powers of x Rule applies to $y = x^{1/3}$.

$$\frac{dy}{dx} = \frac{1}{3}x^{1/3-1} = \frac{1}{3}x^{-2/3} = \frac{1}{3x^{2/3}}.$$

In Example 1 we took the derivative with respect to x of *both sides* of each equation. We denote the operation "take the derivative with respect to x" by $\dfrac{d}{dx}$.

Thus for $y = x^4$ [in part (c)],

$$\frac{d}{dx}(y) = \frac{d}{dx}(x^4) \quad \text{gives} \quad \frac{dy}{dx} = 4x^3.$$

Similarly, for $f(x) = x^{-2}$ [in part (b)],

$$\frac{d}{dx}[f(x)] = \frac{d}{dx}(x^{-2}) \quad \text{gives} \quad f'(x) = -2x^{-3}.$$

The differentiation rules are stated and proved for the independent variable x, but they also apply to other independent variables. The following examples illustrate differentiation with variables other than x.

EXAMPLE 2

Find the derivatives of the following functions.

(a) $u(s) = s^8$ (b) $p = q^{2/3}$ (c) $C(t) = \sqrt{t}$ (d) $s = \dfrac{1}{\sqrt{t}}$

Solution

(a) If $u(s) = s^8$, then $u'(s) = 8s^{8-1} = 8s^7$.

(b) If $p = q^{2/3}$, then

$$\frac{dp}{dq} = \frac{2}{3}q^{2/3-1} = \frac{2}{3}q^{-1/3} = \frac{2}{3q^{1/3}}.$$

(c) Writing $\sqrt{t}$ in its equivalent form, $t^{1/2}$, permits us to use the derivative formula.

$$C'(t) = \frac{1}{2}t^{1/2-1} = \frac{1}{2}t^{-1/2}$$

Writing the derivative in radical form gives

$$C'(t) = \frac{1}{2} \cdot \frac{1}{t^{1/2}} = \frac{1}{2\sqrt{t}}.$$

(d) Writing $1/\sqrt{t}$ as a power of t gives

$$s = \frac{1}{t^{1/2}} = t^{-1/2}, \quad \text{so} \quad \frac{ds}{dt} = -\frac{1}{2}t^{-1/2-1} = -\frac{1}{2}t^{-3/2}.$$

Writing the derivative in a form similar to that of the original function gives

$$\frac{ds}{dt} = -\frac{1}{2} \cdot \frac{1}{t^{3/2}} = -\frac{1}{2\sqrt{t^3}}.$$

EXAMPLE 3

Find the slope of the tangent to the curve $y = x^3$ at $x = 1$.

Solution   The derivative of $y = x^3$ is $y' = 3x^2$. The slope of the tangent to $y = x^3$ at $x = 1$ is $y'|_{x=1} = 3(1)^2 = 3$. The graph and the tangent line are shown in Figure 2.21.

FIGURE 2.21

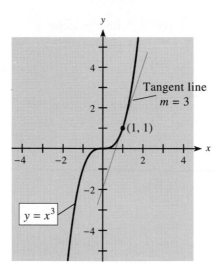

A function of the form $y = f(x) = c$, where c is a constant, is called a **constant function.** We can show that the derivative of a constant function is 0, as follows.

$$f'(x) = \lim_{h \to 0} \frac{f(x + h) - f(x)}{h} = \lim_{h \to 0} \frac{c - c}{h} = \lim_{h \to 0} 0 = 0$$

We can state this rule formally.

Constant Function Rule   If $f(x) = c$, where c is a constant, then $f'(x) = 0$.

EXAMPLE 4   Find the derivative of the function defined by $y = 4$.

Solution   Because 4 is a constant, $\dfrac{dy}{dx} = 0$.

Recall that the function defined by $y = 4$ has a horizontal line as its graph. Thus the slope of the line (and the derivative of the function) is 0.

We now can take derivatives of constant functions and powers of x. But we do not yet have a rule for taking derivatives of functions of the form $f(x) = 4x^5$ or $g(t) = \frac{1}{2}t^2$. The following rule provides a method for handling functions of this type.

Coefficient Rule   If $f(x) = c \cdot u(x)$, where c is a constant and $u(x)$ is a differentiable function of x, then $f'(x) = c \cdot u'(x)$.

The above formula says that the derivative of a constant times a function is the constant times the derivative of the function.

We can use the fact that

$$\lim_{h \to 0} c \cdot g(h) = c \cdot \lim_{h \to 0} g(h),$$

which was discussed in Section 2.1, to verify the coefficient rule. If $f(x) = c \cdot u(x)$, then

$$f'(x) = \lim_{h \to 0} \frac{f(x + h) - f(x)}{h}$$

$$= \lim_{h \to 0} \frac{c \cdot u(x + h) - c \cdot u(x)}{h}$$

$$= \lim_{h \to 0} c \cdot \left[\frac{u(x + h) - u(x)}{h} \right]$$

$$= c \cdot \lim_{h \to 0} \frac{u(x + h) - u(x)}{h}, \text{ so}$$

$$f'(x) = c \cdot u'(x).$$

EXAMPLE 5

Find the derivatives of the following functions.

(a) $f(x) = 4x^5$

(b) $g(t) = \frac{1}{2}t^2$

(c) $p = \dfrac{5}{\sqrt{q}}$

Solution

(a) $f'(x) = 4(5x^4) = 20x^4$

(b) $g'(t) = \frac{1}{2}(2t) = t$

(c) $p = \dfrac{5}{\sqrt{q}} = 5q^{-1/2}$, so

$$\frac{dp}{dq} = 5\left(-\frac{1}{2}q^{-3/2} \right) = -\frac{5}{2\sqrt{q^3}}.$$

In Example 4 of Section 2.3 we found the derivative of $f(x) = 3x^2 + 2x$ to be $f'(x) = 6x + 2$. This result, along with the results of several of the derivatives calculated in Exercise 2.3, suggest that we can find the derivative of a function by finding the derivatives of its terms and combining them. The following rules state this formally.

Sum Rule   If $f(x) = u(x) + v(x)$, where u and v are differentiable functions of x, then

$f'(x) = u'(x) + v'(x)$.

We can prove this rule as follows. If $f(x) = u(x) + v(x)$, then

$$f'(x) = \lim_{h \to 0} \frac{f(x + h) - f(x)}{h} = \lim_{h \to 0} \frac{[u(x + h) + v(x + h)] - [u(x) + v(x)]}{h}$$

$$= \lim_{h \to 0} \left[\frac{u(x + h) - u(x)}{h} + \frac{v(x + h) - v(x)}{h} \right]$$

$$= \lim_{h \to 0} \frac{u(x + h) - u(x)}{h} + \lim_{h \to 0} \frac{v(x + h) - v(x)}{h}$$

$$= u'(x) + v'(x).$$

In a similar fashion, we can prove that the derivative of the difference of two functions is the difference of their derivatives. (This proof is left to the student in problem 44 of Exercise 2.4.)

Difference Rule   If $f(x) = u(x) - v(x)$, where u and v are differentiable functions of x, then

$f'(x) = u'(x) - v'(x)$.

EXAMPLE 6   Find the derivatives of the following functions.

(a) $y = x^2 + 3$ (b) $p = q^2 - 4q$ (c) $y = 3x + 5$

Solution

(a) $y' = 2 \cdot x + 0 = 2x$

(b) $dp/dq = 2 \cdot q - 4 \cdot 1 = 2q - 4$

(c) $y' = 3 \cdot 1 + 0 = 3$

In Example 6(c) we saw that the derivative of $y = 3x + 5$ is 3. Because the slope of a line is the same at all points on the line, it is reasonable that the derivative of a linear equation is a constant. In particular, the slope of the graph of the equation $y = mx + b$ is m at all points on its graph because the derivative of $y = mx + b$ is $y' = f'(x) = m$.

The rules regarding the derivatives of sums and differences of two functions also apply if more than two functions are involved. For example, the derivative of $f(x) = 4x^3 - 2x^2 + 5x - 3$ is $f'(x) = 12x^2 - 4x + 5$. We may think of the functions that are added and subtracted as terms of the function f. Then it would be correct to say that we may take the derivative of a function term by term.

EXAMPLE 7 | Find the derivatives of the following functions.

(a) $y = 3x^3 - 4x^2$ (b) $p = \frac{1}{3}q^3 + 2q^2 - 3$ (c) $u(x) = 5x^4 + x^{1/3}$

Solution

(a) $y' = 3(3x^2) - 4(2x) = 9x^2 - 8x$

(b) $\dfrac{dp}{dq} = \frac{1}{3}(3q^2) + 2(2q) - 0 = q^2 + 4q$

(c) $u'(x) = 5(4x^3) + \frac{1}{3}x^{-2/3} = 20x^3 + \dfrac{1}{3x^{2/3}}$

EXAMPLE 8 | Find the derivatives of the following functions.

(a) $y = 4x^3 + \sqrt{x}$ (b) $s = 5t^6 - \dfrac{1}{t^2}$

Solution

(a) We may write the equation as

$$y = 4x^3 + x^{1/2},$$

so

$$y' = 4(3x^2) + \frac{1}{2}x^{-1/2}$$

$$= 12x^2 + \frac{1}{2x^{1/2}},$$

$$= 12x^2 + \frac{1}{2\sqrt{x}}.$$

(b) We may write $s = 5t^6 - 1/t^2$ as

$$s = 5t^6 - t^{-2},$$

so

$$\frac{ds}{dt} = 5(6t^5) - (-2t^{-3})$$

$$= 30t^5 + 2t^{-3}$$

$$= 30t^5 + \frac{2}{t^3}.$$

EXAMPLE 9 | Find the slope of the tangent to $f(x) = \frac{1}{2}x^2 + 5x$ at each of the following.

(a) $x = 2$ (b) $x = -5$

Solution The derivative of $f(x) = \frac{1}{2}x^2 + 5x$ is $f'(x) = x + 5$.

(a) At $x = 2$, the slope is $f'(2) = 2 + 5 = 7$.

(b) At $x = -5$, the slope is $f'(-5) = -5 + 5 = 0$. Thus when $x = -5$, the tangent to the curve is a horizontal line.

CHECKPOINT

1. True or false: The derivative of a constant times a function is equal to the constant times the derivative of the function.

2. True or false: The derivative of the sum of two functions is equal to the sum of the derivatives of the two functions.

3. True or false: The derivative of the difference of two functions is equal to the difference of the derivatives of the two functions.

4. Does the Coefficient Rule apply to $f(x) = x^n/c$, where c is a constant? Explain.

The marginal revenue $R'(x)$ is used to estimate the change in revenue caused by the sale of one additional unit.

EXAMPLE 10

Suppose that a manufacturer of a product knows that because of the demand for this product, his revenue is given by

$$R(x) = 1500x - 0.02x^2, \qquad 0 \le x \le 1000,$$

where x is the number of units sold and $R(x)$ is in dollars.

(a) Find the marginal revenue at $x = 500$.

(b) Find the change in revenue caused by the increase in sales from 500 to 501 units.

(c) Find the difference between the marginal revenue found in part (a) and the change in revenue found in part (b).

Solution

(a) The marginal revenue for any value of x is

$$R'(x) = 1500 - 0.04x.$$

The marginal revenue at $x = 500$ is

$$R'(500) = 1500 - 20 = 1480 \text{ (dollars)}.$$

(b) The revenue at $x = 500$ is $R(500) = 745{,}000$, and the revenue at $x = 501$ is $R(501) = 746{,}479.98$, so the change in revenue is

$$R(501) - R(500) = 746{,}479.98 - 745{,}000 = 1479.98 \text{ (dollars)}.$$

(c) The difference is $1480 - 1479.98 = 0.02$. Thus we see that the marginal revenue at $x = 500$ is a good estimate of the revenue from the 501st unit.

TECHNOLOGY CORNER

1. Graph $y = x^3 - 3x + 3$ and its derivative on the same set of axes.

2. Are the points where $y' = 0$ the x-intercepts of the graph of y'? Use trace to see where $y' = 0$.

3. Trace the graph of y near the x-values found in 2(a). Does the graph of y appear to turn at the points corresponding to these x-values?

4. Determine intervals where $y' > 0$ and where $y' < 0$.

5. As you trace the graph of y from left to right, determine intervals where the graph is rising and intervals where the graph is falling.

6. Use your answers to (4) and (5) to write a statement that explains how $y' > 0$ or $y' < 0$ gives us information about whether the graph of y is rising or falling.

7. Graph the following functions and their derivatives to see if your conclusions from (6) still hold.

   (a) $y = x^{2/3}$ (b) $y = x^4 - 8x^2 + 2$

CHECKPOINT
SOLUTIONS

1. True, by the Coefficient Rule.

2. True, by the Sum Rule.

3. True, by the Difference Rule.

4. Yes, $f(x) = x^n/c = (1/c)x^n$, so the coefficient is $(1/c)$.

EXERCISE 2.4

Find the derivatives of the following functions.

1. $y = 4$

2. $f(s) = 6$

3. $y = x$

4. $s = t^2$

5. $c(x) = x^3$

6. $u(x) = x^5$

7. $y = 3x^5$

8. $y = 10x^{12}$

9. $p = 5q^8$

10. $f(q) = 8q^3$

11. $f(x) = 3x + 8$

12. $y = 5x^3 - 3x^2$

13. $y = 3x^6 - 12x^2$

14. $f(s) = s^2 + 4s + 1$

15. $p = 5q^3 + 4q^2 + 2$

16. $c(x) = x^3 - 5x^2 + 4x$

17. $y = x^{-3}$

18. $y = x^{-1}$

19. $y = \dfrac{1}{x^2}$

20. $y = \dfrac{1}{x^5}$

21. $y = x^{2/3}$

22. $f(q) = q^{11/5}$

23. $f(x) = x^{-4/5}$

24. $y = x^{-7/4}$

25. $p = \sqrt[4]{q^3}$

26. $f(q) = \sqrt[5]{q^3}$

27. $y = 5x^{-4/5} + 2x^{1/5}$

28. $y = 6x^{-8/3} - x^{-2/3}$

29. $y = 3x^3 - \dfrac{2}{x^5}$

30. $y = 4x^2 - \dfrac{2}{x^2}$

31. $y = \dfrac{3}{x^3} - \dfrac{1}{x^{1/3}} - 5\sqrt{x}$

32. $y = \dfrac{3}{x^4} - \dfrac{2}{3x} + 5$

33. $y = 2\sqrt{x} + 4\sqrt{x^3} - 3$

34. $y = \sqrt[3]{x} + 6\sqrt[3]{x^4} - 5$

In problems 35–38, find the slopes of the tangents to the following curves at the indicated points.

35. $y = 4x^2 + 3x, \quad x = 2$

36. $C(x) = 3x^2 - 5, \quad (3, 22)$

37. $P(x) = x^2 - 4x. \quad (2, -4)$

38. $R(x) = 16x + x^2, \quad x = 1$

In problems 39–42, write the equations of the tangent lines to the curves at the indicated points.

39. $y = 3x^2 + 2x, \quad (1, 5)$

40. $y = 4x - x^2, \quad (5, -5)$

41. $f(x) = 4x^2 - \dfrac{1}{x} \quad$ at $x = -\dfrac{1}{2}$

42. $f(x) = \dfrac{x^3}{3} - \dfrac{3}{x^3} \quad$ at $x = -1$

43. (a) Find the derivatives of $y = x^3$, $u(x) = x$, and $v(x) = x^2$.

(b) Does $\dfrac{d}{dx}[x \cdot x^2] = \dfrac{d}{dx}[x] \cdot \dfrac{d}{dx}[x^2]$?

(c) We know that
$$\dfrac{d}{dx}[u(x) + v(x)] = \dfrac{d}{dx}[u(x)] + \dfrac{d}{dx}[v(x)].$$
Does $\dfrac{d}{dx}[u(x) \cdot v(x)] = \dfrac{d}{dx}[u(x)] \cdot \dfrac{d}{dx}[v(x)]$

for all differentiable functions $u(x)$ and $v(x)$?

44. If $u(x)$ and $v(x)$ are differentiable functions of x, prove the Difference Rule:
If $f(x) = u(x) - v(x)$, then $f'(x) = u'(x) - v'(x)$.

APPLICATIONS

45. **Revenue** Suppose that a wholesaler expects that his monthly revenue for small television sets will be
$$R(x) = 100x - 0.1x^2, \quad 0 \le x \le 800,$$
where x is the number of units sold. Find his marginal revenue and interpret it when the quantity sold is
(a) $x = 300$. (b) $x = 600$.

46. **Demand** The demand q for a product depends on the price p (in dollars) according to
$$q = \dfrac{1000}{\sqrt{p}} - 1, \quad \text{for } p > 0.$$
Find the instantaneous rate of change of demand with respect to price when price is
(a) \$25. (b) \$100.

47. **Workers and output** The weekly output of a certain product is
$$Q(x) = 200x + 6x^2,$$
where x is the number of workers on the assembly line. If there are presently 60 workers on the line,
(a) find $Q'(x)$ and estimate the change in the weekly output caused by the addition of one worker.
(b) calculate $Q(61) - Q(60)$ to see the actual change in the weekly output.

48. **Capital investment and output** The monthly output of a certain product is
$$Q(x) = 800x^{5/2},$$
where x is the capital investment in millions of dollars. Find dQ/dx, which can be used to estimate the effect on the output if an additional capital investment of \$1 million is made.

49. **Pollution** The tons of pollutants dumped into a stream by a factory is given by

$$p = \frac{t^{7/4}}{1050},$$

where t is the number of weeks after manufacturing of a new product begins. Find the rate of change in the number of tons of pollutants with respect to the number of weeks at
(a) $t = 4$. (b) $t = 36$.

50. **Demand** Suppose that the demand for a product depends on the price p according to

$$D(p) = \frac{50,000}{p^2} - \frac{1}{2}, \qquad p > 0,$$

where p is in dollars. Find the instantaneous rate of change of demand with respect to price when
(a) $p = 50$. (b) $p = 100$.

51. **Population** Suppose that the population of a city is predicted by

$$P(t) = 500t^{3/2}, \qquad t \geq 0,$$

where t is the number of years from 1992 and $P(t)$ is in thousands. What is the instantaneous rate of change of population when
(a) $t = 4$? (b) $t = 16$?

52. **Advertising and sales** Suppose that sales decrease after the end of an advertising campaign according to

$$S(x) = 1200 - 0.1x - 0.01x^2, \qquad 0 \leq x \leq 100,$$

where $S(x)$ is the sales in dollars and x is the number of days since the end of the campaign. Find the instantaneous rate of change at $x = 10$.

53. **Cost and average cost** Suppose that the total cost function for the production of x units of a product is given by

$$C(x) = 4000 + 55x + 0.1x^2.$$

Then the average cost of producing x items is

$$\overline{C(x)} = \frac{\text{total cost}}{x} = \frac{4000}{x} + 55 + 0.1x.$$

(a) Find the instantaneous rate of change of average cost with respect to the number of units produced, at any level of production.
(b) Find the level of production at which this rate of change equals zero.

54. **Cost and average cost** Suppose that the total cost function for a certain commodity is given by

$$C(x) = 40,500 + 190x - 0.2x^2,$$

where x is the number of units produced.
(a) Find the instantaneous rate of change of the average cost

$$\overline{C} = \frac{40,500}{x} + 190 + 0.2x$$

for any level of production.
(b) Find the level of production where this rate of change equals zero.

55. **Cost-benefit** Suppose that for a certain city the cost C of obtaining drinking water that contains p percent impurities (by volume) is given by

$$C = \frac{120,000}{p} - 1200.$$

Find the rate of change of cost with respect to p when impurities account for 1% (by volume).

56. **Revenue** The total revenue for a commodity is described by the function

$$R = 300x - 0.02x^2.$$

(a) What is the marginal revenue when 40 units are sold?
(b) Interpret your answer to part (a).

57. **Population of organisms** The population size y of a certain organism at time t is given by

$$y = 4t^2 + 2t.$$

Find the rate of change of population.

58. **Bacterial populations** The number of organisms of a certain bacteria at time t can be modeled according to the equation

$$N(t) = 2500(1 + 2t^2).$$

Find the rate of change of the number.

59. **Rate of flow** A swimming pool is filled by an inlet pipe. The number of gallons N in the pool at time t is

$$N = 2t^2 + 30t,$$

where t is in minutes. At what rate is the pool filling when t is 10?

60. **Boyle's law** Pressure P of a gas is related to volume V according to Boyle's law, and this relationship is expressed by the equation

$$P = \frac{C}{V},$$

where C is a constant. Find the rate of change of pressure with respect to volume.

61. **Union participation** The following table shows the percentage of U.S. workers who belonged to unions for selected years from 1930 to 1989. Assume that these data can be modeled with the function

$$u(x) = -39.3 + 2.38x - 0.02x^2,$$

where x is the number of years past 1900. This function and the data points are graphed in the figure below.

(a) For the period from 1980 to 1985, use the data points to find the average rate of change of the percentage of U.S. workers who belonged to unions.

(b) Find the instantaneous rate of change of the modeling function $u(x)$ for the year 1980.

Year	Percentage
1930	11.6
1940	26.9
1950	31.5
1960	31.4
1970	27.3
1975	25.5
1980	21.9
1985	18
1989	16.4

Source: *World Almanac*, 1991.

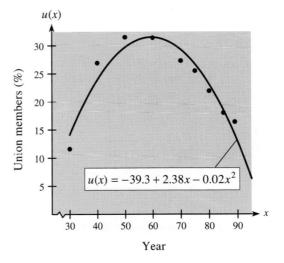

2.5 | PRODUCT AND QUOTIENT RULES

OBJECTIVES

- To use the Product Rule to find the derivative of certain functions
- To use the Quotient Rule to find the derivative of certain functions

We have simple formulas for finding the derivatives of the sums and differences of functions. But we are not so lucky with products. The derivative of a product is *not* the product of the derivatives. To see this, we consider the function $f(x) = x \cdot x$. Since this function is $f(x) = x^2$, its derivative is $f'(x) = 2x$. But the product of the derivatives of x and x would give $1 \cdot 1 = 1 \neq 2x$. Thus we need a different formula to find the derivative of a product. This formula is given by the **Product Rule.**

Product Rule   If $f(x) = u(x) \cdot v(x)$, where u and v are differentiable functions of x, then

$$f'(x) = u(x) \cdot v'(x) + v(x) \cdot u'(x).$$

Thus the derivative of a product of two functions is the first function times the derivative of the second plus the second function times the derivative of the first.

We can prove the Product Rule as follows. If $f(x) = u(x) \cdot v(x)$, then

$$\lim_{h \to 0} \frac{f(x + h) - f(x)}{h} = \lim_{h \to 0} \frac{u(x + h) \cdot v(x + h) - u(x) \cdot v(x)}{h}.$$

Subtracting and adding $u(x + h) \cdot v(x)$ in the numerator gives

$$f'(x) = \lim_{h \to 0} \frac{u(x + h) \cdot v(x + h) - u(x + h) \cdot v(x) + u(x + h) \cdot v(x) - u(x) \cdot v(x)}{h}$$

$$= \lim_{h \to 0} \left(u(x + h) \left[\frac{v(x + h) - v(x)}{h} \right] + v(x) \left[\frac{u(x + h) - u(x)}{h} \right] \right).$$

Properties III and IV of limits give

$$f'(x) = \lim_{h \to 0} u(x + h) \cdot \lim_{h \to 0} \frac{v(x + h) - v(x)}{h} + \lim_{h \to 0} v(x) \cdot \lim_{h \to 0} \frac{u(x + h) - u(x)}{h}$$

Now, because u is differentiable and hence continuous, it follows that $\lim_{h \to 0} u(x + h) = u(x)$. So we have $f'(x) = u(x) \cdot v'(x) + v(x) \cdot u'(x)$.

EXAMPLE 1

Use the Product Rule to find the derivative of $f(x) = x^2 \cdot x$.

Solution Using the formula with $u(x) = x^2$, $v(x) = x$, we have

$$
\begin{aligned}
f'(x) &= u(x) \cdot v'(x) + v(x) \cdot u'(x) \\
&= x^2 \cdot 1 + x(2x) \\
&= x^2 + 2x^2 \\
&= 3x^2.
\end{aligned}
$$

Note that we could have found the same result by multiplying the factors and finding the derivative of $f(x) = x^3$. But we will soon see how valuable the Product Rule is.

EXAMPLE 2

Find dy/dx if $y = (2x^3 + 3x + 1)(x^2 + 4)$.

Solution Using the Product Rule with $u(x) = 2x^3 + 3x + 1$ and $v(x) = x^2 + 4$, we have

$$
\begin{aligned}
\frac{dy}{dx} &= (2x^3 + 3x + 1)(2x) + (x^2 + 4)(6x^2 + 3) \\
&= 4x^4 + 6x^2 + 2x + 6x^4 + 3x^2 + 24x^2 + 12 \\
&= 10x^4 + 33x^2 + 2x + 12.
\end{aligned}
$$

We could, of course, avoid using the Product Rule by multiplying the two factors before taking the derivative. But multiplying the factors first may involve more work than using the Product Rule.

EXAMPLE 3

Given $f(x) = (4x^3 + 5x^2 - 6x + 5)(x^3 - 4x^2 + 1)$, find the slope of the tangent to the graph of $y = f(x)$ at $x = 1$.

Solution
$f'(x) = (4x^3 + 5x^2 - 6x + 5)(3x^2 - 8x) + (x^3 - 4x^2 + 1)(12x^2 + 10x - 6)$. If we substitute $x = 1$ into $f'(x)$, we find that the slope of the curve at $x = 1$ is $f'(1) = 8(-5) + (-2)(16) = -72$.

The rule for finding the derivative of a function that is the quotient of two functions requires a new formula.

Quotient Rule

If $f(x) = u(x)/v(x)$, where u and v are differentiable functions of x, with $v(x) \neq 0$, then

$$
f'(x) = \frac{v(x) \cdot u'(x) - u(x) \cdot v'(x)}{[v(x)]^2}.
$$

The preceding formula says that the derivative of a quotient is the denominator times the derivative of the numerator minus the numerator times the derivative of the denominator, all divided by the square of the denominator.

To see that this rule is reasonable, consider the function $f(x) = x^3/x$, $x \neq 0$. Using the Quotient Rule, with $u(x) = x^3$ and $v(x) = x$, we get

$$f'(x) = \frac{x(3x^2) - x^3(1)}{x^2} = \frac{3x^3 - x^3}{x^2} = \frac{2x^3}{x^2} = 2x.$$

Since $f(x) = x^3/x = x^2$ if $x \neq 0$, we see that $f'(x) = 2x$ is the correct derivative. The proof of the Quotient Rule is left for the student in problem 33 of Exercise 2.5.

EXAMPLE 4 | If $f(x) = \dfrac{x^2 - 4x}{x + 5}$, find $f'(x)$.

Solution Using the Quotient Rule with $u(x) = x^2 - 4x$ and $v(x) = x + 5$, we get

$$f'(x) = \frac{(x + 5)(2x - 4) - (x^2 - 4x)(1)}{(x + 5)^2}$$

$$= \frac{2x^2 + 6x - 20 - x^2 + 4x}{(x + 5)^2}$$

$$= \frac{x^2 + 10x - 20}{(x + 5)^2}.$$

EXAMPLE 5 | If $f(x) = \dfrac{x^3 - 3x^2 + 2}{x^2 - 4}$, find $f'(x)$.

Solution Using the Quotient Rule, with $u(x) = x^3 - 3x^2 + 2$ and $v(x) = x^2 - 4$, we get

$$f'(x) = \frac{(x^2 - 4)(3x^2 - 6x) - (x^3 - 3x^2 + 2)(2x)}{(x^2 - 4)^2}$$

$$= \frac{(3x^4 - 6x^3 - 12x^2 + 24x) - (2x^4 - 6x^3 + 4x)}{(x^2 - 4)^2}$$

$$= \frac{x^4 - 12x^2 + 20x}{(x^2 - 4)^2}.$$

EXAMPLE 6 | Use the Quotient Rule to find the derivative of $y = 1/x^3$.

Solution Letting $u(x) = 1$ and $v(x) = x^3$, we get

$$y' = \frac{x^3(0) - 1(3x^2)}{(x^3)^2}$$

$$= -\frac{3x^2}{x^6}$$

$$= -\frac{3}{x^4}.$$

Note that we could have found the derivative more easily by writing

$$y = 1/x^3 = x^{-3},$$

so

$$y' = -3x^{-4} = -\frac{3}{x^4}.$$

Recall that we proved the Powers of x Rule for positive integer powers and assumed that it was true for all real number powers. In problem 34 of Exercise 2.5, you will be asked to use the Quotient Rule to show that the Powers of x Rule applies to negative integers.

It is not necessary to use the Quotient Rule when the denominator of the function in question contains only a constant. For example, the function $y = (x^3 - 3x)/3$ can be written $y = \frac{1}{3}(x^3 - 3x)$, so the derivative is $y' = \frac{1}{3}(3x^2 - 3) = x^2 - 1$.

CHECKPOINT

1. True or false: The derivative of the product of two functions is equal to the product of the derivatives of the two functions.

2. True or false: The derivative of the quotient of two functions is equal to the quotient of the derivatives of the two functions.

3. If $y = \frac{4}{3}(x^2 + 3x - 4)$, does finding y' require the Product Rule? Explain.

4. If $y = f(x)/c$, where c is a constant, does finding y' require the Quotient Rule? Explain.

EXAMPLE 7

Suppose that the revenue function for a product is given by

$$R(x) = 10x + \frac{100x}{3x + 5},$$

where x is the number of units sold and R is in dollars.

(a) Find the marginal revenue function.

(b) Find the marginal revenue when $x = 15$.

Solution

(a) We must use the Quotient Rule to find the marginal revenue (the derivative).

$$\overline{MR} = R'(x) = 10 + \frac{(3x + 5)(100) - 100x(3)}{(3x + 5)^2}$$

$$= 10 + \frac{300x + 500 - 300x}{(3x + 5)^2}$$

$$= 10 + \frac{500}{(3x + 5)^2}$$

(b) The marginal revenue when $x = 15$ is $R'(15)$.

$$R'(15) = 10 + \frac{500}{[(3)(15) + 5]^2}$$

$$= 10 + \frac{500}{(50)^2}$$

$$= 10 + \frac{500}{2500} = 10.20$$

Recall that $R'(15)$ estimates the revenue from the sale of the 16th item.

TECHNOLOGY CORNER

1. Graph $f(x) = \dfrac{8x}{x^2 + 4}$ and its derivative on the same set of axes.

2. Determine x-values where the graph of $f'(x) = 0$, where $f'(x) > 0$, and where $f'(x) < 0$.

3. Determine x-values where the graph of $f(x)$ has high points and low points, where it is rising (from left to right), and where it is falling.

4. What do you notice about your answers to (2) and (3)? Explain.

**CHECKPOINT
SOLUTIONS**

1. False. The derivative of a product is equal to the first function times the derivative of the second plus the second function times the derivative of the first. That is,

$$\frac{d}{dx}(fg) = f \cdot \frac{dg}{dx} + g \cdot \frac{df}{dx}.$$

2. False. The derivative of a quotient is equal to the denominator times the derivative of the numerator minus the numerator times the derivative of the denominator, all divided by the square of the denominator. That is,

$$\frac{d}{dx}\left(\frac{f}{g}\right) = \frac{g \cdot f' - f \cdot g'}{g^2}.$$

3. No, y' can be found with the Coefficient Rule:

$$y' = \frac{4}{3}(2x + 3).$$

4. No, y' can be found with the Coefficient Rule:

$$y' = \left(\frac{1}{c}\right)f'(x).$$

EXERCISE 2.5

1. Find y' if $y = (x + 3)(x^2 - 2x)$.
2. Find $f'(x)$ if $f(x) = (3x - 1)(x^3 + 1)$.
3. Find $\dfrac{dp}{dq}$ if $p = (3q - 1)(q^2 + 2)$.
4. Find $\dfrac{ds}{dt}$ if $s = (t^4 + 1)(t^3 - 1)$.
5. If $f(x) = (x^{12} + 3x^4 + 4)(4x^3 - 1)$, find $f'(x)$.
6. If $y = (3x^7 + 4)(8x^6 - 6x^4 - 9)$, find $\dfrac{dy}{dx}$.
7. If $R(x) = (3x - 1)(100 + 2x^2)$, find $R'(x)$.
8. If $C(x) = (34x + 300)(25 + x^2)$, find $C'(x)$.
9. If $y = (x + 1)\sqrt{x}$, find y'.
10. If $y = \sqrt[3]{x}(x^2 + 1)$, find $\dfrac{dy}{dx}$.
11. If $y = \left(4\sqrt{x} + \dfrac{3}{x}\right)\left(3\sqrt[3]{x} - \dfrac{5}{x^2} - 5^2\right)$, find $\dfrac{dy}{dx}$.
12. If $y = \left(3\sqrt[4]{x^5} - \sqrt[5]{x^4} - 1\right)\left(\dfrac{2}{x^3} - \dfrac{1}{\sqrt{x}}\right)$, find y'.
13. What is the slope of the tangent to $y = (x^2 + 1)(x^3 - 4x)$ at $(1, -6)$?
14. What is the slope of the tangent to $y = (x^3 - 3)(x^2 - 4x + 1)$ at $(2, -15)$?
15. Find y' if $y = \dfrac{x}{x^2 - 1}$.
16. Find $f'(x)$ if $f(x) = \dfrac{x^2}{x - 3}$.

17. Find $\dfrac{dp}{dq}$ if $p = \dfrac{q^2 + 1}{q - 2}$.
18. Find $C'(x)$ if $C(x) = \dfrac{x^2 + 1}{x^2 - 1}$.
19. Find $\dfrac{dy}{dx}$ if $y = \dfrac{1 - x^4}{x^3 + 1}$.
20. Find $\dfrac{dz}{dt}$ if $z = \dfrac{t^3 - 4t}{16 - t^4}$.
21. Find $\dfrac{dp}{dq}$ if $p = \dfrac{3\sqrt{q}}{1 - q}$.
22. Find $\dfrac{dy}{dx}$ if $y = \dfrac{2\sqrt{x} - 1}{1 - 4\sqrt{x^3}}$.
23. Find y' if $y = \dfrac{x(x^2 + 4)}{x - 2}$.
24. Find $f'(x)$ if $f(x) = \dfrac{(x + 1)(x - 2)}{x^2 + 1}$.
25. Find the derivative of $y = \dfrac{x - 2}{x + 1}$ at $\left(1, -\dfrac{1}{2}\right)$.
26. Find the derivative of $y = \dfrac{x^2 + 1}{x - 2}$ at $(1, -2)$.
27. Find the slope of the tangent to $y = \dfrac{x^2 + 1}{x + 3}$ at $(2, 1)$.
28. Find the slope of the tangent to $y = \dfrac{x^2 - 4x}{x^2 + 2x}$ at $\left(2, -\dfrac{1}{2}\right)$.
29. Write the equation of the tangent line to
$$y = \dfrac{3x^4 - 2x - 1}{4 - x^2} \text{ at } x = 1.$$

30. Write the equation of the tangent line to

    $$y = \frac{x^2 - 4x}{2x - x^3} \text{ at } x = 2.$$

31. At what point(s) will the slope of the tangent to $y = (x^2 + 1)(x - 2)$ be 0?

32. At what point(s) will the slope of the tangent to

    $$y = \frac{x^2}{x - 2} \text{ be } 0?$$

33. Prove the Quotient Rule for differentiation. *Hint:* Add $[-u(x) \cdot v(x) + u(x) \cdot v(x)]$ to the expanded numerator and use steps similar to those used to prove the Product Rule.

34. Use the Quotient Rule to show that the Powers of x Rule applies to negative integer powers. That is, show that $(d/dx)x^n = nx^{n-1}$ when $n = -k$, $k > 0$, by finding the derivative of $f(x) = 1/(x^k)$.

APPLICATIONS

35. **Cost-benefit** If the cost C of removing p percent of the particulate pollution from the exhaust gases at an industrial site is given by

    $$C(p) = \frac{8100p}{100 - p},$$

    find the rate of change of C with respect to p.

36. **Cost-benefit** If the cost C of removing p percent of the impurities from the waste water in a manufacturing process is given by

    $$C(p) = \frac{9800p}{101 - p},$$

    find the rate of change of C with respect to p.

37. **Revenue** Suppose that the revenue function for a product is given by

    $$R(x) = \frac{6x^2 - 27x}{2x + 1}.$$

    Find the marginal revenue function.

38. **Nerve response** The number of action potentials produced by a nerve, t seconds after a stimulus, is given by

    $$N(t) = 25t + \frac{4}{t^2 + 2} - 2.$$

    Find the rate at which the action potentials are produced.

39. **Response to a drug** The reaction R to an injection of a drug is related to the dosage x according to

    $$R(x) = x^2\left(500 - \frac{x}{3}\right),$$

    where 1000 mg is the maximum dosage. If the rate of reaction with respect to the dosage defines the sensitivity to the drug, find the sensitivity.

40. **Response to injected adrenalin** Experimental evidence has shown that the concentration of injected adrenaline x is related to the response y of a muscle according to the equation

    $$y = \frac{x}{a + bx},$$

    where a and b are constants. Find the rate of change of response with respect to the concentration.

41. **Advertising and sales** The sales of a product s (in thousands of dollars) are related to advertising expenses (in thousands of dollars) by

    $$s = \frac{200x}{x + 10}.$$

    Find the rate of change of sales with respect to advertising expenses when
    (a) $x = 10$. \qquad (b) $x = 20$.

42. **Productivity** The average number of children's toys assembled by a worker in t hours of an 8-hour shift is given by

    $$N(t) = \frac{64 - 128(t + 3)}{t^2 + 6t + 18}, \qquad 0 \le t \le 8.$$

Find the rate of change in the number of toys assembled when $t = 4$.

43. **Sales and training** The average monthly sales volume (in thousands of dollars) for a firm depends on the number of hours of training x of its sales staff, according to

$$s = \frac{100 + 250x + x^2}{25x}, \quad x > 0.$$

(a) Find the rate of change of sales volume with respect to training hours at $x = 12$.
(b) What does this rate of change mean?

44. **Candidate recognition** Suppose that the proportion P of voters who recognize a candidate's name t months after the start of the campaign is given by

$$P(t) = \frac{13t}{t^2 + 100} + 0.18.$$

(a) Find the rate of change of P when $t = 6$.
(b) Find the rate of change of P when $t = 12$.
(c) One month prior to the election, is it better for $P'(t)$ to be positive or negative?

45. **Bacterial population** Suppose that

$$P = \frac{1000t}{t + 10}$$

represents the size of a population of bacteria, where t represents time. What is the rate of growth of the population?

46. **Endangered species population** It is determined that a wildlife refuge can support a group of up to 120 of a certain endangered species. If 75 are introduced onto the refuge and their population after t years is given by

$$p(t) = 75\left(1 + \frac{4t}{t^2 + 16}\right),$$

find the rate of population growth after t years. Find the rate after each of the first seven years.

47. **Test reliability** If a test having reliability r is lengthened by a factor n, the reliability of the new test is given by

$$R = \frac{nr}{1 + (n - 1)r}, \quad 0 < r \le 1.$$

Find the rate at which R changes with respect to n.

2.6 THE CHAIN RULE AND POWER RULE

OBJECTIVES

• To use the Chain Rule to differentiate functions
• To use the Power Rule to differentiate functions

Up to this point, we have found derivatives of sums of functions, differences of functions, products of functions, and quotients of functions. We will now consider how to find the derivative of a function that is the composite of two functions. Recall that if f and g are functions, then the composite functions g of f (denoted $g \circ f$) and f of g (denoted $f \circ g$) are defined as follows:

$$(g \circ f)(x) = g(f(x)) \quad \text{and} \quad (f \circ g)(x) = f(g(x)).$$

EXAMPLE 1 | If $f(x) = 3x^2$ and $g(x) = 2x - 1$, find $F(x) = f(g(x))$.

Solution Substituting $g(x) = 2x - 1$ for x in $f(x)$ gives

$$f(g(x)) = f(2x - 1) = 3(2x - 1)^2.$$

Thus $F(x) = 3(2x - 1)^2$.

We could find the derivative of the function $F(x) = 3(2x - 1)^2$ by multiplying out the expression $3(2x - 1)^2$. Then

$$F(x) = 3(4x^2 - 4x + 1) = 12x^2 - 12x + 3,$$

so $F'(x) = 24x - 12$. But we can also use a very powerful rule, called the **Chain Rule,** to find derivatives of functions of this type. If we write the composite function $y = f(g(x))$ in the form $y = f(u)$, where $u = g(x)$, we state the Chain Rule as follows.

Chain Rule

If f and g are differentiable functions with $y = f(u)$ and $u = g(x)$, then y is a differentiable function of x, and

$$\frac{dy}{dx} = \frac{d}{du}f(u) \cdot \frac{d}{dx}g(x)$$

or, written another way,

$$\frac{dy}{dx} = \frac{dy}{du} \cdot \frac{du}{dx}.$$

Note that dy/du represents the derivative of $y = f(u)$ *with respect to u* and du/dx represents the derivative of $u = g(x)$ *with respect to x*. For example, if $y = 3(2x - 1)^2$, we may write $y = f(u) = 3u^2$, where $u = 2x - 1$. Then the derivative is

$$\frac{dy}{dx} = \frac{dy}{du} \cdot \frac{du}{dx} = 6u \cdot 2 = 12u.$$

To write this derivative in terms of x, we substitute $2x - 1$ for u. Thus

$$\frac{dy}{dx} = 12(2x - 1) = 24x - 12.$$

Note that we get the same result by using the Chain Rule as we did by multiplying out $F(x) = 3(2x - 1)^2$. The Chain Rule is important because it is not always possible to rewrite the function as a polynomial. Consider the following example.

EXAMPLE 2 | If $y = \sqrt{x^2 - 1}$, find $\dfrac{dy}{dx}$.

Solution If we write this function as $y = f(u) = \sqrt{u}$, where $u = x^2 - 1$, we can find the derivative.

$$\frac{dy}{dx} = \frac{dy}{du} \cdot \frac{du}{dx} = \frac{1}{2} \cdot u^{-1/2} \cdot 2x$$

$$= u^{-1/2} \cdot x = \frac{1}{\sqrt{u}} \cdot x = \frac{x}{\sqrt{u}}$$

To write this derivative in terms of x alone, we substitute $x^2 - 1$ for u. Then

$$\frac{dy}{dx} = \frac{x}{\sqrt{x^2 - 1}}.$$

Note that we could not find the derivative of a function like that of Example 2 by the methods learned previously.

EXAMPLE 3 | If $y = \dfrac{1}{(x^2 + 3x + 1)^2}$, find $\dfrac{dy}{dx}$.

Solution If we let $u = x^2 + 3x + 1$, we can write $y = f(u) = \dfrac{1}{u^2}$, or $y = u^{-2}$. Then

$$\frac{dy}{dx} = \frac{dy}{du} \cdot \frac{du}{dx} = -2u^{-3}(2x + 3) = \frac{-4x - 6}{u^3}.$$

Substituting for u gives

$$\frac{dy}{dx} = \frac{-4x - 6}{(x^2 + 3x + 1)^3}.$$

The Chain Rule is very useful and will be extremely important with functions that we will study later, but a special case of the Chain Rule, called the **Power Rule,** is useful for the algebraic functions we have studied so far.

Power Rule   If $y = u^n$, where u is a differentiable function of x, then

$$\frac{dy}{dx} = nu^{n-1} \cdot \frac{du}{dx}.$$

EXAMPLE 4

If $y = (x^2 - 4x)^6$, find $\dfrac{dy}{dx}$.

Solution The right side of the equation is in the form u^n, with $u = x^2 - 4x$. Thus by the Power Rule

$$\frac{dy}{dx} = nu^{n-1} \cdot \frac{du}{dx} = 6u^5(2x - 4).$$

Substituting for u gives

$$\frac{dy}{dx} = 6(x^2 - 4x)^5(2x - 4)$$
$$= (12x - 24)(x^2 - 4x)^5.$$

EXAMPLE 5

If $y = 3\sqrt[3]{x^2 - 3x + 1}$, find y'.

Solution Since $y = 3(x^2 - 3x + 1)^{1/3}$, we can use the Power Rule with $u = x^2 - 3x + 1$.

$$y' = 3\left(nu^{n-1}\frac{du}{dx}\right)$$
$$= 3\left[\frac{1}{3}u^{-2/3}(2x - 3)\right]$$
$$= (x^2 - 3x + 1)^{-2/3}(2x - 3)$$
$$= \frac{2x - 3}{(x^2 - 3x + 1)^{2/3}}$$

EXAMPLE 6

If $p = \dfrac{4}{3q^2 + 1}$, find $\dfrac{dp}{dq}$.

Solution We can use the Power Rule to find dp/dq if we write the equation in the form

$$p = 4(3q^2 + 1)^{-1}.$$

Then

$$\frac{dp}{dq} = 4[-1(3q^2 + 1)^{-2}(6q)]$$
$$= \frac{-24q}{(3q^2 + 1)^2}.$$

The derivative of the function in Example 6 can also be found by using the Quotient Rule, but the Power Rule provides a more efficient method.

EXAMPLE 7

Find the derivative of $g(x) = \dfrac{1}{\sqrt{(x^2 + 1)^3}}$.

Solution Writing $g(x)$ as a power gives

$$g(x) = (x^2 + 1)^{-3/2}.$$

Then

$$g'(x) = -\frac{3}{2}(x^2 + 1)^{-5/2}(2x)$$

$$= -3x \cdot \frac{1}{(x^2 + 1)^{5/2}}$$

$$= \frac{-3x}{\sqrt{(x^2 + 1)^5}}.$$

CHECKPOINT

1. (a) If $f(x) = (3x^4 + 1)^{10}$, does $f'(x) = 10(3x^4 + 1)^9$?

   (b) If $f(x) = (2x + 1)^5$, does $f'(x) = 10(2x + 1)^4$?

   (c) If $f(x) = \dfrac{[u(x)]^n}{c}$, where c is a constant, does $f'(x) = \dfrac{n[u(x)]^{n-1} \cdot u'(x)}{c}$?

2. (a) If $f(x) = \dfrac{12}{2x^2 - 1}$, find $f'(x)$ by using the Power Rule (not the Quotient Rule).

   (b) If $f(x) = \dfrac{\sqrt{x^3 - 1}}{3}$, find $f'(x)$ by using the Power Rule (not the Quotient Rule). ■

EXAMPLE 8

The demand x for a product is given by

$$x = 98(2p + 1)^{-1/2} - 1,$$

where p is the price per unit. Find the rate of change of the demand with respect to price when $p = 24$.

Solution The rate of change of demand with respect to price is

$$\frac{dx}{dp} = 98\left[-\frac{1}{2}(2p + 1)^{-3/2}(2) \right]$$

$$= -98(2p + 1)^{-3/2}.$$

When $p = 24$, the rate of change is

$$\frac{dx}{dp}\bigg|_{p=24} = -98(48 + 1)^{-3/2}$$

$$= -98 \cdot \frac{1}{49^{3/2}}$$

$$= -98 \cdot \frac{1}{343}$$

$$= -\frac{2}{7}.$$

TECHNOLOGY CORNER

Graph $f(x) = 3(x^2 - 4)^{2/3}$ and its derivative.

1. Use trace to locate x-values where $f'(x)$ is 0 and where it is undefined.

2. (a) What happens to $f(x)$ as x approaches the value where $f'(x) = 0$?
   (b) What happens to $f(x)$ as x approaches the values where $f'(x)$ is undefined?

3. Where is $f'(x) > 0$ and where is $f'(x) < 0$?

4. As you move from left to right on the graph of $f(x)$,
   (a) for what values of x is the graph falling [$f(x)$ decreasing]?
   (b) for what values of x is the graph rising [$f(x)$ increasing]?

5. What do you notice about your answers to (3) and (4)? Form a generalization.

CHECKPOINT
SOLUTIONS

1. (a) No, $f'(x) = 10(3x^4 + 1)^9(12x^3)$.   (b) Yes.   (c) Yes.

2. (a) $f(x) = 12(2x^2 - 1)^{-1}$

$$f'(x) = -12(2x^2 - 1)^{-2}(4x) = \frac{-48x}{(2x^2 - 1)^2}$$

(b) $f(x) = \frac{1}{3}(x^3 - 1)^{1/2}$

$$f'(x) = \frac{1}{6}(x^3 - 1)^{-1/2}(3x^2) = \frac{x^2}{2\sqrt{x^3 - 1}}$$

EXERCISE 2.6

Differentiate the functions in problems 1–20.

1. $y = (x^2 + 1)^3$

2. $p = (q^2 + 4q)^4$

3. $y = (4x^2 - 4x + 1)^4$

4. $r = (s^2 + 5s)^{10}$

5. $f(x) = \dfrac{1}{(x^2 + 2)^3}$

6. $g(x) = \dfrac{1}{4x^3 + 1}$

7. $g(x) = (x^2 + 4x)^{-2}$

8. $p = (q^3 + 1)^{-5}$

9. $c(x) = (x^2 + 3x + 4)^{-3}$

10. $y = (x^2 - 8x)^{2/3}$

11. $g(x) = \dfrac{1}{(2x^3 + 3x + 5)^{3/4}}$

12. $y = \dfrac{1}{(3x^3 + 4x + 1)^{3/2}}$

13. $y = \sqrt{x^2 + 4x + 5}$

14. $y = \sqrt{x^2 + 3x}$

15. $s = 4\sqrt{3x - x^2}$

16. $y = 3\sqrt[3]{(x - 1)^2}$

17. $y = \dfrac{8(x^2 - 3)^5}{5}$

18. $y = \dfrac{5\sqrt{1 - x^3}}{6}$

19. $y = \dfrac{(3x + 1)^5 - 3x}{7}$

20. $y = \dfrac{\sqrt{2x - 1} - \sqrt{x}}{2}$

21. Find the slope of the tangent to $y = (x^3 + 2x)^4$ at $x = 2$.

22. Find the slope of the tangent to $y = \sqrt{5x^2 + 2x}$ at $x = 1$.

23. Find the slope of the tangent to $y = \sqrt{x^3 + 1}$ at $(2, 3)$.

24. Find the slope of the tangent to $y = (4x^3 - 5x + 1)^3$ at $(1, 0)$.

25. Write the equation of the tangent to $y = (x^2 - 3x + 3)^3$ at $(1, 1)$.

26. Write the equation of the tangent to $y = (x^2 + 1)^3$ at $(2, 125)$.

27. Write the equation of the tangent to $y = \sqrt{3x^2 - 2}$ at $x = 3$.

28. Write the equation of the tangent to

$$y = \left(\dfrac{1}{x^3 - x}\right)^3 \text{ at } x = 2.$$

29. At what values of x will the slope of the tangent to $y = (x^2 - 4)^3$ be 0?

30. At what value(s) of x will the slope of the tangent to $y = \sqrt{4 - x^2}$ be 0?

In problems 31 and 32, find the derivative of each function.

31. (a) $y = \dfrac{2x^3}{3}$

 (b) $y = \dfrac{2}{3x^3}$

 (c) $y = \dfrac{(2x)^3}{3}$

 (d) $y = \dfrac{2}{(3x)^3}$

32. (a) $y = \dfrac{3}{(5x)^5}$

 (b) $y = \dfrac{3x^5}{5}$

 (c) $y = \dfrac{3}{5x^5}$

 (d) $y = \dfrac{(3x)^5}{5}$

APPLICATIONS

33. **Productivity** The productivity of a research team on a project is

$$P(t) = 0.01(t + 40)^2 - 0.0001t^3 - 16,$$

where t is the number of hours since the project began. If the marginal productivity is $P'(t)$, what is the marginal productivity after 10 hours?

34. **Typing speed** The typing speed (in words per minute) of a secretarial student is

$$S = 10\sqrt{0.8x + 4}, \qquad 0 \le x \le 100,$$

where x is the number of hours of training he has had. What is the rate at which his speed is changing when he has had
 (a) 15 hours of training?
 (b) 40 hours of training?

35. **Bacterial growth** Suppose that the number of grams of bacteria in a population is given by $y = (t^2 + 1)^2$, where t is the number of hours of growth. Find the rate of growth of the bacteria at
 (a) time t.
 (b) $t = 10$.

36. **Body-heat loss** The description of body-heat loss due to convection involves a coefficient of convection, K_c, which depends on wind velocity according to the equation

$$K_c = 4\sqrt{4v + 1}.$$

Find the rate of change of the coefficient with respect to the wind velocity.

37. **Ballistics** Ballistics experts are able to identify the weapon that fired a certain bullet by studying the markings on the bullet. Tests are conducted by firing into a bale of paper. If the distance s, in inches, that the bullet travels into the paper is given by

$$s = 27 - (3 - 10t)^3$$

for $0 \le t \le 0.3$ seconds, find the velocity of the bullet one-tenth of a second after it hits the paper.

38. **Population of microorganisms** Suppose that the population of a certain microorganism at time t (in minutes) is given by

$$P = 1000 - 1000(t + 10)^{-1}.$$

Find the rate of change of population.

39. **Pricing and sales** Suppose that the weekly sales volume y (in thousands of units sold) depends on the price per unit of the product according to

$$y = 32(3p + 1)^{-2/5}, \qquad p > 0,$$

where p is in dollars. What is the rate of change in sales volume when the price is $21?

40. **Pricing and sales** A chain of auto service stations has found that their monthly sales volume y (in thousands of dollars) is related to the price p (in dollars) of an oil change according to

$$y = \frac{90}{\sqrt{p + 5}}, \qquad p > 10.$$

What is the rate of change of sales volume when the price is $20?

41. **Demand** Suppose that the demand for a product is described by

$$p = \frac{200{,}000}{(q + 1)^2}.$$

What is the rate of change of price with respect to the quantity demanded when $q = 49$?

Stimulus-response The relation between the magnitude of a sensation y and the magnitude of the stimulus x is given by

$$y = k(x - x_0)^n,$$

where k is a constant, x_0 is the threshold of effective stimulus, and n depends on the type of stimulus. Find the rate of change of sensation with respect to the amount of stimulus for each of problems 42–44.

42. For the stimulus of visual brightness $y = k(x - x_0)^{1/3}$.

43. For the stimulus of warmth $y = k(x - x_0)^{8/5}$.

44. For the stimulus of electrical stimulation $y = k(x - x_0)^{7/2}$.

45. **Revenue** The revenue from the sale of x units of a product is

$$R = 1500x + 3000(2x + 3)^{-1} - 1000,$$

where x is the number of units sold. Find the marginal revenue when 100 units are sold.

46. **Revenue** The revenue from the sale of x units of a product is

$$R = 15(3x + 1)^{-1} + 50x - 15.$$

Find the marginal revenue when 40 units are sold.

47. **Demand** If the demand for a product is described by the equation

$$p = \frac{100}{\sqrt{2q + 1}},$$

find the rate of change of p with respect to q.

48. ***Advertising and sales*** The daily sales S (in thousands of dollars) attributed to an advertising campaign are given by

$$S = 1 + \frac{3}{t + 3} - \frac{18}{(t + 3)^2},$$

where t is the number of weeks the campaign runs. What is the rate of change of sales at
(a) $t = 8$?   (b) $t = 10$?
(c) Should the campaign be continued after the 10th week?

49. ***Investments*** If an IRA is a variable-rate investment for 20 years at rate r percent per year, compounded monthly, then the compound amount A that accumulates from an initial investment of $1000 is

$$A = 1000\left(1 + \frac{0.01r}{12}\right)^{240}.$$

What is the rate of change of A with respect to

r if the interest rate is
(a) 6%?   (b) 12%?

50. ***Concentrations of body substances*** The concentration C of a substance in the body depends on the quantity of the substance Q and the volume V through which it is distributed. For a static substance, this relation is given by

$$C = \frac{Q}{V}.$$

For a situation like that in the kidneys, where the fluids are moving, the concentration is the ratio of the rate of change of quantity with respect to time and the rate of change of volume with respect to time.
(a) Formulate the equation for concentration of a moving substance.
(b) Show that this is equal to the rate of change of quantity with respect to volume.

2.7 | USING DERIVATIVE FORMULAS

OBJECTIVE

• To use derivative formulas separately and in combination with each other

We have used the Power Rule to find the derivative of functions like

$$y = (x^3 - 3x^2 + x + 1)^5,$$

but we have not found the derivative of functions like

$$y = [(x^2 + 1)(x^3 + x + 1)]^5.$$

This function is different because the function u (which is raised to the fifth power) is the product of two functions $(x^2 + 1)$ and $(x^3 + x + 1)$. The equation is of the form $y = u^5$, where $u = (x^2 + 1)(x^3 + x + 1)$. This means that the Product

Rule should be used to find du/dx. Then

$$\frac{dy}{dx} = 5u^4 \cdot \frac{du}{dx}$$
$$= 5[(x^2 + 1)(x^3 + x + 1)]^4[(x^2 + 1)(3x^2 + 1) + (x^3 + x + 1)(2x)]$$
$$= 5[(x^2 + 1)(x^3 + x + 1)]^4(5x^4 + 6x^2 + 2x + 1)$$
$$= (25x^4 + 30x^2 + 10x + 5)[(x^2 + 1)(x^3 + x + 1)]^4.$$

A different type of problem involving the Power Rule and the Product Rule is finding the derivative of $y = (x^2 + 1)^5(x^3 + x + 1)$. We may think of y as the *product* of two functions, one of which is a power. Thus the fundamental formula we should use is the Product Rule. The two functions are $u(x) = (x^2 + 1)^5$ and $v(x) = x^3 + x + 1$. The Product Rule gives

$$\frac{dy}{dx} = u(x) \cdot v'(x) + v(x) \cdot u'(x)$$
$$= (x^2 + 1)^5(3x^2 + 1) + (x^3 + x + 1)[5(x^2 + 1)^4 2x].$$

Note that the Power Rule was used to find $u'(x)$, since $u(x) = (x^2 + 1)^5$.

We can simplify dy/dx by factoring $(x^2 + 1)^4$ from both terms:

$$\frac{dy}{dx} = (x^2 + 1)^4[(x^2 + 1)(3x^2 + 1) + (x^3 + x + 1) \cdot 5 \cdot 2x]$$
$$= (x^2 + 1)^4(13x^4 + 14x^2 + 10x + 1).$$

EXAMPLE 1 | If $y = \left(\dfrac{x^2}{x - 1}\right)^2$, find y'.

Solution We again have an equation of the form $y = u^n$, but this time u is a quotient. Thus we will need the Quotient Rule to find du/dx.

$$y' = nu^{n-1} \cdot \frac{du}{dx}$$
$$= 2u \frac{(x - 1) \cdot 2x - x^2 \cdot 1}{(x - 1)^2}$$

Substituting for u and simplifying gives

$$y' = 2 \cdot \frac{x^2}{x - 1} \cdot \frac{2x^2 - 2x - x^2}{(x - 1)^2}$$
$$= \frac{2x^2(x^2 - 2x)}{(x - 1)^3}$$
$$= \frac{2x^4 - 4x^3}{(x - 1)^3}.$$

EXAMPLE 2

Find $f'(x)$ if $f(x) = \dfrac{(x-1)^2}{(x^2+1)^3}$.

Solution This function is the quotient of two functions, $(x-1)^2$ and $(x^2+1)^3$, so we must use the Quotient Rule to find the derivative of $f(x)$, but taking the derivatives of $(x-1)^2$ and $(x^2+1)^3$ will require the Power Rule.

$$f'(x) = \frac{[v(x) \cdot u'(x) - u(x) \cdot v'(x)]}{[v(x)]^2}$$

$$= \frac{(x^2+1)^3[2(x-1)(1)] - (x-1)^2[3(x^2+1)^2 2x]}{[(x^2+1)^3]^2}$$

$$= \frac{2(x^2+1)^3(x-1) - 6x(x-1)^2(x^2+1)^2}{(x^2+1)^6}$$

We see that 2, $(x^2+1)^2$, and $(x-1)$ are all factors in both terms of the numerator, so we can factor them from both terms and reduce the fraction.

$$f'(x) = \frac{2(x^2+1)^2(x-1)[(x^2+1) - 3x(x-1)]}{(x^2+1)^6}$$

$$= \frac{2(x-1)(-2x^2+3x+1)}{(x^2+1)^4}$$

EXAMPLE 3

Find $f'(x)$ if $f(x) = (x^2-1)\sqrt{3-x^2}$.

Solution The function is the product of two functions, x^2-1 and $\sqrt{3-x^2}$. Therefore we will use the Product Rule to find the derivative of $f(x)$, but the derivative of $\sqrt{3-x^2} = (3-x^2)^{1/2}$ will require the Power Rule.

$$f'(x) = u(x) \cdot v'(x) + v(x) \cdot u'(x)$$

$$= (x^2-1)\left[\frac{1}{2}(3-x^2)^{-1/2}(-2x)\right] + (3-x^2)^{1/2}(2x)$$

$$= (x^2-1)[-x(3-x^2)^{-1/2}] + (3-x^2)^{1/2}(2x)$$

$$= \frac{-x^3+x}{(3-x^2)^{1/2}} + 2x(3-x^2)^{1/2}$$

We can combine these terms over the common denominator $(3-x^2)^{1/2}$ as follows.

$$f'(x) = \frac{-x^3+x}{(3-x^2)^{1/2}} + \frac{2x(3-x^2)^1}{(3-x^2)^{1/2}}$$

$$= \frac{-x^3+x+6x-2x^3}{(3-x^2)^{1/2}}$$

$$= \frac{-3x^3+7x}{(3-x^2)^{1/2}}$$

We should note that in Example 3 we could have written $f'(x)$ in the form

$$f'(x) = (-x^3 + x)(3 - x^2)^{-1/2} + 2x(3 - x^2)^{1/2}.$$

Now, the factor $(3 - x^2)$, to different powers, is contained in both terms of the expression. Thus we can factor $(3 - x^2)^{-1/2}$ from both terms. (We choose the $-1/2$ power because it is the smaller of the two powers.) Dividing $(3 - x^2)^{-1/2}$ into the first term gives $(-x^3 + x)$, and dividing it into the second term gives $2x(3 - x^2)^1$. Why? Thus we have

$$f'(x) = (3 - x^2)^{-1/2}[(-x^3 + x) + 2x(3 - x^2)]$$
$$= \frac{-3x^2 + 7x}{(3 - x^2)^{1/2}},$$

which agrees with our previous answer.

CHECKPOINT

1. If a function has the form $y = [u(x)]^n \cdot v(x)$, where n is a constant, we begin to find the derivative by using the _____ Rule and then use the _____ Rule to find the derivative of $[u(x)]^n$.

2. If a function has the form $y = [u(x)/v(x)]^n$, where n is a constant, we begin to find the derivative by using the _____ Rule and then use the _____ Rule.

EXAMPLE 4

Suppose that the weekly revenue function for a product is given by

$$R(x) = \frac{36,000,000x}{(2x + 500)^2},$$

where x is the number of units sold.

(a) Find the marginal revenue function.

(b) Find the marginal revenue when 50 units are sold.

Solution

(a) $\overline{MR} = R'(x) = \dfrac{(2x + 500)^2(36,000,000) - 36,000,000x[2(2x + 500)^1(2)]}{(2x + 500)^4}$

$= \dfrac{36,000,000(2x + 500)(2x + 500 - 4x)}{(2x + 500)^4}$

$= \dfrac{36,000,000(500 - 2x)}{(2x + 500)^3}$

(b) $\overline{MR}(50) = R'(50) = \dfrac{36,000,000(500 - 100)}{(100 + 500)^3}$

$= \dfrac{36,000,000(400)}{(600)^3}$

$= \dfrac{200}{3} = 66.67$

The marginal revenue is $66.67 when 50 units are sold. That is, the predicted revenue from the sale of the 51st unit is approximately $66.67.

It may be helpful to review the formulas needed to find the derivatives of various types of functions. Table 2.5 presents examples of different types of functions and the formulas needed to find their derivatives.

TABLE 2.5   Derivative formulas summary

Example	Formula
$f(x) = 14$	If $f(x) = c$, then $f'(x) = 0$.
$y = x^4$	If $f(x) = x^n$, then $f'(x) = nx^{n-1}$.
$g(x) = 5x^3$	If $g(x) = cf(x)$, then $g'(x) = cf'(x)$.
$y = 3x^2 + 4x$	If $f(x) = u(x) + v(x)$, then $f'(x) = u'(x) + v'(x)$.
$y = (x^2 - 2)(x + 4)$	If $f(x) = u(x) \cdot v(x)$, then $f'(x) = u(x) \cdot v'(x) + v(x) \cdot u'(x)$.
$f(x) = \dfrac{x^3}{x^2 + 1}$	If $f(x) = \dfrac{u(x)}{v(x)}$, then $f'(x) = \dfrac{v(x) \cdot u'(x) - u(x) \cdot v'(x)}{[v(x)]^2}$.
$y = (x^3 - 4x)^{10}$	If $y = u^n$ and $u = g(x)$, then $\dfrac{dy}{dx} = nu^{n-1} \cdot \dfrac{du}{dx}$.
$y = \left(\dfrac{x-1}{x^2+3}\right)^3$	Power Rule, then Quotient Rule to find $\dfrac{du}{dx}$, where $u = \dfrac{x-1}{x^2+3}$
$y = (x + 1)\sqrt{x^3 + 1}$	Product Rule, then Power Rule to find $v'(x)$, where $v(x) = \sqrt{x^3 + 1}$
$y = \dfrac{(x^2 - 3)^4}{x + 1}$	Quotient Rule, then Power Rule to find the derivative of the numerator

CHECKPOINT
SOLUTIONS

1. Product, Power

2. Power, Quotient

EXERCISE 2.7

Find the derivatives of the following functions. Simplify and express the answer using positive exponents only.

1. $f(x) = \pi^4$

2. $f(x) = \dfrac{1}{4}$

3. $g(x) = \dfrac{4}{x^4}$

4. $y = \dfrac{x^4}{4}$

5. $g(x) = 5x^3 + \dfrac{4}{x}$

6. $y = 3x^2 + 4\sqrt{x}$

7. $y = (x^2 - 2)(x + 4)$

8. $y = (x^3 - 5x^2 + 1)(x^3 - 3)$

9. $f(x) = \dfrac{x^3 + 1}{x^2}$

10. $y = \dfrac{1 + x^2 - x^4}{1 + x^4}$

11. $y = \dfrac{(x^3 - 4x)^{10}}{10}$

12. $y = \dfrac{5}{2}(3x^4 - 6x^2 + 2)^5$

13. $y = \dfrac{5}{3}x^3(4x^5 - 5)^3$

14. $y = 3(x^2 + 4x)(x^5 + 1)^3$

15. $y = (x - 1)^2(x^2 + 1)$

16. $f(x) = (5x^3 + 1)(x^4 + 5x)^2$

17. $y = \dfrac{(x^2 - 4)^3}{x^2 + 1}$

18. $y = \dfrac{(x^2 - 3)^4}{x}$

19. $p = [(q + 1)(q^3 - 3)]^3$

20. $y - [(1 - x^2)(x^2 + 5x)]^4$

21. $R(x) = [x^2(x^2 + 3x)]^4$

22. $c(x) = [x^3(x^2 + 1)]^{-3}$

23. $y = \left(\dfrac{2x - 1}{x^2 + x}\right)^4$

24. $y = \left(\dfrac{5 - x^2}{x^4}\right)^3$

25. $g(x) = (8x^4 + 3)^2(x^3 - 4x)^3$

26. $y = (3x^3 - 4x)^3(4x^2 - 8)^2$

27. $f(x) = \dfrac{\sqrt[3]{x^2 + 5}}{4 - x^2}$

28. $g(x) = \dfrac{\sqrt[3]{2x - 1}}{2x + 1}$

29. $y = x^2\sqrt[4]{4x - 3}$

30. $y = 3x^3\sqrt{x^4 + 3}$

31. $c(x) = 2x\sqrt{x^3 + 1}$

32. $R(x) = x\sqrt[3]{3x^3 + 2}$

In problems 33 and 34, find the derivative of each function.

33. (a) $F_1(x) = \dfrac{3(x^4 + 1)^5}{5}$

   (b) $F_2(x) = \dfrac{3}{5(x^4 + 1)^5}$

   (c) $F_3(x) = \dfrac{(3x^4 + 1)^5}{5}$

   (d) $F_4(x) = \dfrac{3}{(5x^4 + 1)^5}$

34. (a) $G_1(x) = \dfrac{2(x^3 - 5)^3}{3}$

   (b) $G_2(x) = \dfrac{(2x^3 - 5)^3}{3}$

   (c) $G_3(x) = \dfrac{2}{3(x^3 - 5)^3}$

   (d) $G_4(x) = \dfrac{2}{(3x^3 - 5)^3}$

APPLICATIONS

35. **Physical output** The total physical output P of workers is a function of the number of workers, x. The function $P = f(x)$ is called the physical productivity function. Suppose that the physical productivity of x construction workers is given by

$$P = 10(3x + 1)^3 - 10.$$

Find the marginal physical productivity, dP/dx.

36. **Revenue** Suppose that the revenue function for a certain product is given by

$$R(x) = 15(2x + 1)^{-1} + 30x - 15,$$

where x is in thousands of units and R is in thousands of dollars.
   (a) Find the marginal revenue when 2000 units are sold.
   (b) How is revenue changing when 2000 units are sold?

37. **Revenue** Suppose that the revenue function for a computer is given by

$$R(x) = 60{,}000x + 40{,}000(10 + x)^{-1} - 4000.$$

   (a) Find the marginal revenue when 10 units are sold.
   (b) How is revenue changing when 10 units are sold?

38. **Production** Suppose that the production of x items of a new line of products is given by

$$x = 200[(t + 10) - 400(t + 40)^{-1}],$$

where t is the number of weeks the line has been in production. Find the rate of production.

39. **National consumption** If the national consumption function is given by

$$C(y) = 2(y + 1)^{1/2} + 0.4y + 4,$$

find the marginal propensity to consume, dC/dy.

40. **Demand** Suppose that the demand function for an appliance is given by

$$p = \frac{400(q + 1)}{(q + 2)^2}.$$

Find the rate of change of price with respect to the number of appliances.

41. **Volume** When squares of side x are cut from the corners of a 12-inch-square piece of cardboard, an open top box can be formed by folding up the sides. The volume of this box is given by

$$V = x(12 - 2x)^2.$$

Find the rate of change of volume with respect to the size of the squares.

42. **Advertising and sales** Suppose that sales (in thousands of dollars) are directly related to an advertising campaign according to

$$S = 1 + \frac{3t - 9}{(t + 3)^2},$$

where t is the number of weeks of the cam-

paign. Find the rate of change of sales after 3 weeks.

43. **Advertising and sales** An inferior product with an extensive advertising campaign does well when it is released, but sales decline as people discontinue use of the product. If the sales S after t weeks are given by

$$S(t) = \frac{200t}{(t + 1)^2}, \qquad t \geq 0,$$

what is the rate of change of sales when $t = 9$?

44. **Advertising and sales** An excellent film with a very small advertising budget must depend largely on word-of-mouth advertising. If attendance at the film after t weeks is given by

$$A = \frac{100t}{(t + 10)^2},$$

what is the rate of change in attendance when
(a) $t = 10$?   (b) $t = 20$?

2.8 | HIGHER-ORDER DERIVATIVES

OBJECTIVE

- To find second derivatives and higher derivatives of certain functions

Earlier in this chapter we introduced the first derivative of a function. Because the derivative of a function is itself a function, we can take a derivative of the derivative. The derivative of a first derivative is called a **second derivative.** We can find the second derivative of a function f by differentiating it twice. If f' represents the first derivative of a function, then f'' represents the second derivative of that function.

EXAMPLE 1 | If $f(x) = 3x^3 - 4x^2 + 5$, find $f''(x)$.

Solution The first derivative is $f'(x) = 9x^2 - 8x$.
The second derivative is $f''(x) = 18x - 8$.

EXAMPLE 2

Find the second derivative of $y = x^4 - 3x^2 + x^{-2}$.

Solution The first derivative is $y' = 4x^3 - 6x - 2x^{-3}$.
The second derivative, which we may denote by y'', is

$$y'' = 12x^2 - 6 + 6x^{-4}.$$

It is also common to use $\dfrac{d^2y}{dx^2}$ and $\dfrac{d^2}{dx^2}f(x)$ to denote the second derivative of a function.

EXAMPLE 3

If $y = \sqrt{2x - 1}$, find d^2y/dx^2.

Solution The first derivative is

$$\frac{dy}{dx} = \frac{1}{2}(2x - 1)^{-1/2}(2) = (2x - 1)^{-1/2}.$$

The second derivative is

$$\frac{d^2y}{dx^2} = -\frac{1}{2}(2x - 1)^{-3/2}(2)$$
$$= -(2x - 1)^{-3/2}$$
$$= \frac{-1}{(2x - 1)^{3/2}} = \frac{-1}{\sqrt{(2x - 1)^3}}.$$

We can also find third, fourth, fifth, and higher derivatives, continuing indefinitely. The third, fourth, and fifth derivatives of a function f are denoted by f''', $f^{(4)}$, and $f^{(5)}$, respectively. Other notations for the third and fourth derivatives include:

$$y''' \qquad y^{(4)}$$
$$\frac{d^3y}{dx^3} \qquad \frac{d^4y}{dx^4}$$
$$\frac{d^3f(x)}{dx^3} \qquad \frac{d^4f(x)}{dx^4}$$

EXAMPLE 4

Find the first four derivatives of $f(x) = 4x^3 + 5x^2 + 3$.

Solution $f'(x) = 12x^2 + 10x$
$f''(x) = 24x + 10$
$f'''(x) = 24$
$f^{(4)}(x) = 0$

Just as the first derivative, $f'(x)$, can be used to determine the rate of change of a function $f(x)$, the second derivative, $f''(x)$, can be used to determine the rate of change of $f'(x)$.

EXAMPLE 5

If $f(x) = 3x^4 + 6x^3 - 3x^2 + 4$,

(a) how fast is $f(x)$ changing at $(1, 10)$?

(b) how fast is $f'(x)$ changing at $(1, 10)$?

(c) is $f'(x)$ increasing or decreasing at $(1, 10)$?

Solution

(a) Since $f'(x) = 12x^3 + 18x^2 - 6x$, we have

$$f'(1) = 12 + 18 - 6 = 24.$$

Thus the rate of change of $f(x)$ at $(1, 10)$ is 24.

(b) Since $f''(x) = 36x^2 + 36x - 6$, we have

$$f''(1) = 66.$$

Thus the rate of change of $f'(x)$ at $(1, 10)$ is 66.

(c) Since $f''(1) = 66 > 0$, $f'(x)$ is increasing at $(1, 10)$.

EXAMPLE 6

Suppose that a particle travels according to the equation

$$s = 100t - 16t^2 + 200,$$

where s is the distance and t is the time. Then ds/dt is the velocity, and $d^2s/dt^2 = dv/dt$ is the acceleration of the particle. Find the acceleration.

Solution The velocity is $v = ds/dt = 100 - 32t$, and the acceleration is

$$\frac{dv}{dt} = \frac{d^2s}{dt^2} = -32.$$

CHECKPOINT

Suppose that the vertical distance a particle travels is given by

$$s = 4x^3 - 12x^2 + 6,$$

where s is in feet and x is in seconds.

1. Find the function that describes the velocity of this particle.

2. Find the function that describes the acceleration of this particle.

3. Is the acceleration always positive?

4. When does the *velocity* of this particle increase?

TECHNOLOGY CORNER

1. Given $f(x) = x^4 - 8x^2 + 2$, graph $f(x), f'(x)$, and $f''(x)$ on the same set of axes.

2. (a) When the graph of $f(x)$ is near or at a "high point," is $f''(x) > 0, f''(x) < 0$, or $f''(x) = 0$?

   (b) Repeat (a) when the graph of $f(x)$ is near or at a "low point."

3. (a) When $f''(x) = 0$, what happens to the graph of $f'(x)$?

   (b) At the points where $f''(x) = 0$, does there appear to be a transition in the way the graph of $f(x)$ "opens?"

   (c) When $f''(x) > 0$, does the graph of $f(x)$ seem to open upward or downward?

   (d) Repeat part (c) when $f''(x) < 0$.

4. Form a generalization about the sign of $f''(x)$ and the manner in which $f(x)$ opens. Test your generalization to see if it holds by graphing the following functions with their second derivatives.

   (a) $f(x) = x^3 - 3x^2$ (b) $f(x) = \frac{1}{4}x^4 - \frac{4}{3}x^3$

CHECKPOINT
SOLUTIONS

1. The velocity is described by $s'(x) = 12x^2 - 24x$.

2. The acceleration is described by $s''(x) = 24x - 24$.

3. No, the acceleration is positive when $s''(x) > 0$, that is, when $24x - 24 > 0$. It is zero when $24x - 24 = 0$ and negative when $24x - 24 < 0$. Thus acceleration is negative when $x < 1$ second, zero when $x = 1$ second, and positive when $x > 1$ second.

4. The velocity increases when the acceleration is positive. Thus the velocity is increasing after 1 second. ■

EXERCISE 2.8

In problems 1–8, find the second derivative.

1. $f(x) = 4x^3 - 15x^2 + 3x + 2$

2. $f(x) = 2x^{10} - 18x^5 - 12x^3 + 4$

3. $y = 10x^3 - x^2 + 14x + 3$

4. $y = 6x^5 - 3x^4 + 12x^2$

5. $g(x) = x^3 - \dfrac{1}{x}$

6. $h(x) = x^2 - \dfrac{1}{x^2}$

7. $y = x^3 - \sqrt{x}$

8. $y = 3x^2 - \sqrt[3]{x^2}$

9. If $y = x^5 - x^{1/2}$, find $\dfrac{d^2y}{dx^2}$.

10. If $y = x^4 + x^{1/3}$, find $\dfrac{d^2y}{dx^2}$.

11. If $f(x) = \sqrt{x - 1}$, find $\dfrac{d^2}{dx^2} f(x)$.

12. If $f(x) = \sqrt[3]{x + 2}$, find $\dfrac{d^2}{dx^2} f(x)$.

13. If $y = \sqrt{x^2 + 4}$, find y''.

14. If $f(x) = \sqrt{4x^2 - 2}$, find $f''(x)$.

15. If $y = x(x + 1)^{-1}$, find y''.

16. If $y = \dfrac{2x}{x^2 + 1}$, find y''.

In problems 17–28, find the third derivative.

17. $y = x^5 - 16x^3 + 12$

18. $y = 6x^3 - 12x^2 + 6x$

19. $f(x) = 2x^9 - 6x^6$ 20. $f(x) = 3x^5 - x^6$

21. $y = 1/x$ 22. $y = 1/x^2$

23. $y = \sqrt{x}$ 24. $y = \sqrt[3]{x}$

25. $f(x) = \sqrt{x + 1}$ 26. $f(x) = \sqrt{x - 5}$

27. $y = \sqrt{x^2 + 4}$ (see problem 13)

28. $y = x(x + 1)^{-1}$ (see problem 15)

29. Find $\dfrac{d^4y}{dx^4}$ if $y = 4x^3 - 16x$.

30. Find $y^{(4)}$ if $y = x^6 - 15x^3$.

31. Find $f^{(4)}(x)$ if $f(x) = \sqrt{x}$.

32. Find $f^{(4)}(x)$ if $f(x) = 1/x$.

33. If $f(x) = 16x^2 - x^3$, what is the rate of change of $f'(x)$ at $(1, 15)$?

34. If $y = 36x^2 - 6x^3 + x$, what is the rate of change of y' at $(1, 31)$?

APPLICATIONS

35. **Acceleration** If a particle travels as a function of time according to the formula

$$s = 100t + 10t^2 + 0.01t^3,$$

find the acceleration of the particle when $t = 2$.

36. **Acceleration** If the formula describing the distance an object travels as a function of time is

$$s = 100 + 160t - 16t^2,$$

what is the acceleration of the object when $t = 4$?

37. **Revenue** If the revenue from sales of a product can be described by

$$R(x) = 100x - 0.01x^2,$$

find the instantaneous rate of change of the marginal revenue.

38. **Revenue** Suppose that the revenue from the sale of a product is given by

$$R = 70x + 0.5x^2 - 0.001x^3,$$

where x is the number of units sold. How fast is the marginal revenue $\overline{MR}$ changing when $x = 100$?

39. **Photosynthesis** The amount of photosynthesis that takes place in a certain plant depends on the intensity of light x according to the equation

$$f(x) = 145x^2 - 30x^3.$$

(a) Find the rate of change of photosynthesis with respect to the intensity.

(b) What is the rate of change when $x = 1$? when $x = 3$?

(c) How fast is the rate found in (a) changing when $x = 1$? when $x = 3$?

40. **Reaction to a drug** The reaction R to an injection of a drug is related to the dosage x

according to

$$R(x) = x^2 \left(500 - \frac{x}{3} \right).$$

(a) If the sensitivity is defined as dR/dx, what is the sensitivity when $x = 350$? when $x = 700$?

(b) What is the rate of change of sensitivity when $x = 350$? when $x = 700$?

41. **Revenue** The revenue (in thousands of dollars) from the sale of x units of a product is

$$R = 15x + 30(4x + 1)^{-1} - 30,$$

where x is the number of units sold. At what rate is the marginal revenue $\overline{MR}$ changing when the number of units being sold is 25?

42. **Advertising and sales** The sales of a product S (in thousands of dollars) are given by

$$S = \frac{600x}{x + 40},$$

where x is the advertising expenditure (in thousands of dollars).

(a) Find the rate of change of sales with respect to advertising expenditure.

(b) Use the second derivative to find how this rate is changing at $x = 20$.

43. **Advertising and sales** The daily sales S (in thousands of dollars) that are attributed to an advertising campaign are given by

$$S = 1 + \frac{3}{t + 3} - \frac{18}{(t + 3)^2},$$

where t is the number of weeks the campaign runs.

(a) Find the rate of change of sales at any time t.

(b) Use the second derivative to find how this rate is changing at $t = 15$.

44. **Advertising and sales** A product with a large advertising budget has its sales S (in millions of dollars) given by

$$S = \frac{500}{t + 2} - \frac{1000}{(t + 2)^2},$$

where t is the number of months the product has been on the market.

(a) Find the rate of change of sales at any time t.

(b) What is the rate of change of sales at $t = 2$?

(c) Use the second derivative to find how this rate is changing at $t = 2$.

2.9 | APPLICATIONS OF DERIVATIVES IN BUSINESS AND ECONOMICS

OBJECTIVES

- To find the marginal cost and marginal revenue at different levels of production
- To find the marginal profit function, given information about cost and revenue

In Chapter 1, we defined marginal cost as the rate of change of the total cost function. For a linear total cost function, the marginal cost was defined as the slope of the function's graph. For any total cost function defined by an equation, we can find the instantaneous rate of change of cost (the marginal cost) at any level of production by finding the derivative of the function.

Marginal Cost	If $C = C(x)$ is a total cost function for a commodity, then its derivative, $\overline{MC} = C'(x)$, is the **marginal cost function.**

The linear cost function with equation

$$C(x) = 300 + 6x \quad \text{(in dollars)}$$

has marginal cost $6 because its slope is 6. Taking the derivative of $C(x)$ gives

$$\overline{MC} = C'(x) = 6,$$

which verifies that the marginal cost is $6 at all levels of production.

The cost function

$$C(x) = 1000 + 6x + x^2$$

has derivative

$$C'(x) = 6 + 2x.$$

Thus the *marginal cost* at $x = 10$ (when 10 units are produced) is

$$C'(10) = 6 + 2(10) = 26,$$

and the marginal cost at 40 units is

$$C'(40) = 6 + 2(40) = 86.$$

Note that when a cost function is linear, the marginal cost gives the amount by which cost would change if production were increased by one unit. When a cost function is *not* linear [as with $C(x) = 1000 + 6x + x^2$], the marginal cost is used to estimate the amount by which cost would change if production were increased by one unit. Thus at 10 units, the marginal cost is $26, so costs would increase by approximately $26 if one more unit were produced. [Note that $C(11) - C(10) = $27 gives the actual increase in costs.] Also, at 40 units, the marginal cost is $86, so costs would increase by approximately $86 if one more unit were produced.

As noted previously, when the derivative of a function is positive (and thus the slope of the tangent to the curve is positive), the function is increasing, and the value of the derivative gives us a measure of how fast it is increasing. As we saw, the marginal cost for

$$C(x) = 1000 + 6x + x^2$$

is 86 at $x = 40$ and 26 at $x = 10$. This tells us that the cost is increasing faster at $x = 40$ than it is at $x = 10$.

Since producing more units can never reduce the total cost of production, the following properties are valid:

1. The total cost can never be negative. If there are fixed costs, the cost of producing 0 units is positive; otherwise, the cost of producing 0 units is 0.

2. The total cost function is always increasing; the more units produced, the higher the total cost. Thus the marginal cost is always positive.

3. There may be limitations on the units produced, by factors such as plant space.

The graphs of many marginal cost functions tend to be U-shaped; they eventually will rise, even though there may be an initial interval where they decrease.

EXAMPLE 1 | If the total cost function for a commodity is $C(x) = x^3 - 9x^2 + 33x + 30$, find the marginal cost.

Solution The marginal cost is $\overline{MC} = C'(x) = 3x^2 - 18x + 33$.

The graph of the total cost function is shown in Figure 2.22(a), and the graph of the marginal cost function is shown in Figure 2.22(b).

FIGURE 2.22

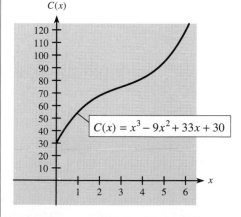

(a) Total cost function

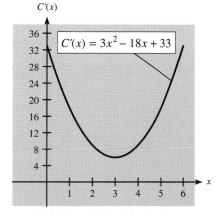

(b) Marginal cost function

As we have seen in Section 2.3, the instantaneous rate of change (the derivative) of the revenue function is the marginal revenue.

Marginal Revenue	If $R = R(x)$ is the total revenue function for a commodity, then the **marginal revenue function** is $\overline{MR} = R'(x)$.

If the demand function for a product in a monopoly market is $p = f(x)$, then the total revenue from the sale of x units is

$$R(x) = px = f(x) \cdot x.$$

EXAMPLE 2 If the demand for a product in a monopoly market is given by

$$p = 16 - 0.02x,$$

where x is the number of units and p is the price per unit, (a) find the total revenue function, and (b) find the marginal revenue for this product at $x = 40$.

Solution

(a) The total revenue function is

$$\begin{aligned}
R(x) = px &= (16 - 0.02x)x \\
&= 16x - 0.02x^2.
\end{aligned}$$

(b) The marginal revenue function is

$$\overline{MR} = R'(x) = 16 - 0.04x.$$

At $x = 40$, $R'(40) = 16 - 1.6 = 14.40$. Thus the 41st item sold will increase the total revenue by approximately $14.40.

The marginal revenue is an approximation of the revenue gained from the sale of one additional unit. We have used marginal revenue in Example 2 to find that the revenue from the sale of the 41st item will be approximately $14.40. The actual increase in revenue from the sale of the 41st item is

$$R(41) - R(40) = 622.38 - 608 = \$14.38.$$

EXAMPLE 3 Use the graphs in Figure 2.23 to determine the x-value where the revenue function has its maximum. What is happening to the marginal revenue at and near this x-value?

Solution Figure 2.23(a) shows that the total revenue function has a maximum value at $x = 400$. After that, the total revenue function decreases. This means that the total revenue will be reduced each time a unit is sold if more than 400 are produced and sold. The graph of the marginal revenue function shows that the marginal revenue is positive to the left of 400. This indicates that the rate at which the total revenue is changing is positive until 400 units are sold; thus the total revenue is increasing. Then, at 400 units, the rate of change is 0. After 400 units are sold, the marginal revenue is negative, which indicates that the total revenue is now decreasing. It is clear from looking at either graph that 400 units should be produced and sold to maximize the total revenue function $R(x)$. That is, the *total revenue* function has its maximum at $x = 400$.

FIGURE 2.23

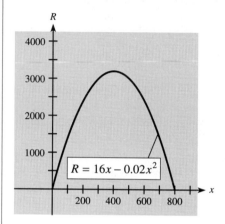

(a) Total revenue function (b) Marginal revenue function

The total cost function for the commodity in Example 1 is $C(x) = x^3 - 9x^2 + 33x + 30$, and the marginal cost is $C'(x) = 3x^2 - 18x + 33$.

1. What is the marginal cost if $x = 10$ units are produced?

2. Use marginal cost to estimate the cost of producing the 11th unit.

3. Calculate $C(11) - C(10)$ to find the actual cost of producing the 11th unit.

4. True or false: For products having linear cost functions, the actual cost of producing the $(x + 1)$st unit is equal to the marginal cost at x.

As with marginal cost and marginal revenue, the derivative of a profit function for a commodity gives us the marginal profit function for the commodity.

Marginal Profit   If $P = P(x)$ is the profit function for a commodity, then the **marginal profit function** is $\overline{MP} = P'(x)$.

EXAMPLE 4   If the total profit, in thousands of dollars, for a product is given by $P(x) = 20\sqrt{x+1} - 2x$, what is the marginal profit at a production level of 15 units?

Solution The marginal profit function is

$$\overline{MP} = P'(x) = 20 \cdot \frac{1}{2}(x+1)^{-1/2} - 2 = \frac{10}{\sqrt{x+1}} - 2.$$

If 15 units are produced, the marginal profit is

$$P'(15) = \frac{10}{\sqrt{15+1}} - 2 = \frac{1}{2}.$$

This means that the profit from the sale of the 16th unit is approximately $\frac{1}{2}$(thousand dollars), or $500.

In a **competitive market,** each firm is so small that its actions in the market cannot affect the price of the product. The price of the product is determined in the market by the intersection of the market demand curve (from all consumers) and the market supply curve (from all firms that supply this product). The firm can sell as little or as much as it desires at the given market price, which it cannot change.

Therefore, a firm in a competitive market has a total revenue function given by $R(x) = px$, where p is the market equilibrium price for the product and x is the quantity sold.

EXAMPLE 5   A firm in a competitive market must sell its product for $200 per unit. The cost per unit (per month) is $80 + x$, where x represents the number of units sold per month. Find the marginal profit.

Solution If the cost per unit is $80 + x$, then the total cost of x units is given by $C(x) = (80 + x)x = 80x + x^2$. The revenue per unit is $200, so the total revenue is given by $R(x) = 200x$. Thus the profit function is

$$P(x) = R(x) - C(x) = 200x - (80x + x^2) \quad \text{or} \quad P(x) = 120x - x^2.$$

The marginal profit is $P'(x) = 120 - 2x$.

The marginal profit in Example 5 is not always positive, so producing and selling a certain number of items will maximize profit. Note that the marginal profit will be negative (that is, profit will decrease) if more than 60 items per month are produced. We will discuss methods of maximizing total revenue and profit, and for minimizing average cost, in Chapter 3.

CHECKPOINT If the total profit function for a product is $P(x) = 20\sqrt{x + 1} - 2x$, then the marginal profit is

$$P'(x) = \frac{10}{\sqrt{x + 1}} - 2 \quad \text{and} \quad P''(x) = \frac{-5}{\sqrt{(x + 1)^3}}.$$

5. Is $P''(x) < 0$ for all values of $x \geq 0$?

6. Is the marginal profit decreasing for all $x \geq 0$?

TECHNOLOGY CORNER

In Example 4, the marginal profit is given by

$$P'(x) = \frac{10}{\sqrt{x + 1}} - 2.$$

1. Use a graphics calculator or computer to graph this marginal profit function and determine where $P'(x) = 0$.

2. Using a different range for y, graph the profit function $P(x) = 20\sqrt{x + 1} - 2x$. Where does the profit function reach its maximum value?

3. What is the slope of the tangent to this graph at $x = 24$?

CHECKPOINT
SOLUTIONS

1. $C'(10) = 153$

2. Since $C'(10) = 153$, it will cost approximately \$153 to produce the 11th unit.

3. $C(11) - C(10) = 635 - 460 = 175$

4. True.

5. Yes.

6. Yes, because $P''(x) < 0$ for $x \geq 0$.

MARGINAL COST, REVENUE, AND PROFIT

Find the marginal cost functions related to the cost functions in problems 1–8.

1. $C(x) = 40 + 8x$
2. $C(x) = 200 + 16x$
3. $C(x) = 500 + 13x + x^2$
4. $C(x) = 300 + 10x + \frac{1}{100}x^2$
5. $C = x^3 - 6x^2 + 24x + 10$
6. $C = x^3 - 12x^2 + 63x + 15$
7. $C = 400 + 27x + x^3$
8. $C(x) = 50 + 48x + x^3$

9. Suppose that the cost function for a commodity is

$$C(x) - 40 + x^2.$$

   (a) Find the marginal cost at $x = 5$ and tell what this predicts about the cost of producing one additional unit.
   (b) Calculate $C(6) - C(5)$ to find the actual cost of producing one additional unit.

10. Suppose that the cost function for a commodity is

$$C(x) = 300 + 6x + \tfrac{1}{20}x^2.$$

   (a) Find the marginal cost at $x = 8$ and tell what this predicts about the cost of producing one additional unit.
   (b) Calculate $C(9) - C(8)$ to find the actual cost of producing one additional unit.

11. If the cost function for a commodity is

$$C(x) = x^3 - 4x^2 + 30x + 20,$$

   find the marginal cost at $x = 4$ and tell what this predicts about the cost of producing one additional unit.

12. If the cost function for a commodity is

$$C(x) = \tfrac{1}{90}x^3 + 4x^2 + 4x + 10,$$

   find the marginal cost at $x = 3$ and tell what this predicts about the cost of producing one additional unit.

13. If the cost function for a commodity is

$$C(x) = 300 + 4x + x^2,$$

   graph the marginal cost function.

14. If the cost function for a commodity is

$$C(x) = x^3 - 12x^2 + 63x + 15,$$

   graph the marginal cost function.

15. (a) If the total revenue function for a product is $R(x) = 4x$, what is the marginal revenue function?
   (b) What does this marginal revenue function tell us?

16. If the total revenue function for a product is $R(x) = 32x$, what is the marginal revenue for the product?

17. Suppose that the total revenue function for a commodity is $R = 36x - 0.01x^2$.
   (a) Find $R(100)$ and tell what it represents.
   (b) Find the marginal revenue function.
   (c) Find the marginal revenue at $x = 100$, and tell what it predicts about the sale of the next unit.
   (d) Find $R(101) - R(100)$ and explain what it represents.

18. Suppose that the total revenue function for a commodity is $R(x) = 25x - 0.05x^2$.
   (a) Find $R(50)$ and tell what it represents.
   (b) Find the marginal revenue function.
   (c) Find the marginal revenue at $x = 50$, and tell what it predicts about the sale of the next unit.
   (d) Find $R(51) - R(50)$ and explain what it represents.

19. (a) Graph the marginal revenue function from problem 17.

(b) At what value of x will total revenue be maximized?

(c) What is the maximum revenue?

20. (a) Graph the marginal revenue function from problem 18.

    (b) Sale of how many units will maximize total revenue?

    (c) What is the maximum revenue?

21. If the total profit function is $P(x) = 5x - 25$, find the marginal profit.

22. If the total profit function is $P(x) = 16x - 32$, find the marginal profit.

23. Suppose that the total revenue function for a product is $R(x) = 32x$ and that the total cost function is $C(x) = 200 + 2x + x^2$.

    (a) Find the profit from the production and sale of 20 units.

    (b) Find the marginal profit function.

    (c) Find $\overline{MP}$ at $x = 20$ and explain what it predicts.

    (d) Find $P(21) - P(20)$ and explain what it represents.

24. Suppose that the total revenue function is given by

    $$R(x) = 46x$$

    and that the total cost function is given by

    $$C(x) = 100 + 30x + \tfrac{1}{10}x^2.$$

    (a) Find $P(100)$.

    (b) Find the marginal profit function.

    (c) Find $\overline{MP}$ at $x = 100$ and explain what it predicts.

    (d) Find $P(101) - P(100)$ and explain what it represents.

25. (a) Graph the marginal profit function for the profit function $P(x) = 30x - x^2 - 200$.

(b) What level of production and sales will give a 0 marginal profit?

(c) At what level of production and sales will profit be at a maximum?

(d) What is the maximum profit?

26. (a) Graph the marginal profit function for the profit function $P(x) = 16x - 0.1x^2 - 100$.

    (b) What level of production and sales will give a 0 marginal profit?

    (c) At what level of production and sales will profit be at a maximum?

    (d) What is the maximum profit?

27. The price of a product in a competitive market is $300. If the cost per unit of producing the product is $160 + x$, where x is the number of units produced per month, how many units should the firm produce and sell to maximize its profit?

28. The cost per unit of producing a product is $60 + 2x$, where x represents the number of units produced per week. If the equilibrium price determined by a competitive market is $220, how many units should the firm produce and sell each week to maximize its profit?

29. If the daily cost per unit of producing a product by the Ace Company is $10 + 2x$, and if the price on the competitive market is $50, what is the maximum daily profit the Ace Company can expect on this product?

30. The Mary Ellen Candy Company produces chocolate Easter bunnies at a cost per unit of $0.10 + 0.01x$, where x is the number produced. If the price on the competitive market for a bunny this size is $2.50, how many should the company produce to maximize its profit?

KEY TERMS
& FORMULAS

SECTION	KEY TERM	FORMULA
2.1	Limit	
	0/0 Indeterminate form	
2.2	Continuous function	
	Vertical asymptote	
	Horizontal asymptote	
	Limit at infinity	
2.3	Average velocity	
	Velocity	
	Instantaneous rate of change	
	Derivative	$f'(x) = \lim\limits_{h \to 0} \dfrac{f(x + h) - f(x)}{h}$
	Marginal revenue	$\overline{MR} = R'(x)$
	Tangent line	
	Secant line	
	Slope of a curve	
	Differentiation	
2.4	Powers of x Rule	$\dfrac{d(x^n)}{dx} = nx^{n-1}$
	Constant Function Rule	$\dfrac{d(c)}{dx} = 0$ for constant c
	Coefficient Rule	$\dfrac{d}{dx}[c \cdot f(x)] = c \cdot f'(x)$
	Sum Rule	$\dfrac{d}{dx}[u + v] = \dfrac{du}{dx} + \dfrac{dv}{dx}$
	Difference Rule	$\dfrac{d}{dx}[u - v] = \dfrac{du}{dx} - \dfrac{dv}{dx}$
2.5	Product Rule	$\dfrac{d}{dx}[uv] = uv' + vu'$
	Quotient Rule	$\dfrac{d}{dx}\left(\dfrac{u}{v}\right) = \dfrac{vu' - uv'}{v^2}$
2.6	Chain Rule	$\dfrac{dy}{dx} = \dfrac{dy}{du} \cdot \dfrac{du}{dx}$

Section	Key Term	Formula
	Power Rule	$\dfrac{d}{dx}(u^n) = nu^{n-1}\dfrac{du}{dx}$
2.8	Second derivative	
2.9	Marginal cost function	$\overline{MC} = C'(x)$
	Marginal revenue function	$\overline{MR} = R'(x)$
	Marginal profit function	$\overline{MP} = P'(x)$

REVIEW
EXERCISES

2.1   In problems 1–6, use the graph of $y = f(x)$ in Figure 2.24 to find the functional values and limits, if they exist.

FIGURE 2.24

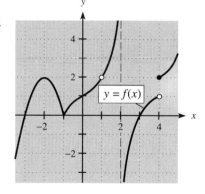

1. (a) $f(-2)$ (b) $\displaystyle\lim_{x \to -2} f(x)$ 2. (a) $f(-1)$ (b) $\displaystyle\lim_{x \to -1} f(x)$

3. (a) $f(4)$ (b) $\displaystyle\lim_{x \to 4^-} f(x)$ 4. (a) $\displaystyle\lim_{x \to 4^+} f(x)$ (b) $\displaystyle\lim_{x \to 4} f(x)$

5. (a) $f(1)$ (b) $\displaystyle\lim_{x \to 1} f(x)$ 6. (a) $f(2)$ (b) $\displaystyle\lim_{x \to 2} f(x)$

In problems 7–18, find each limit, if it exists.

7. $\displaystyle\lim_{x \to 4} (3x^2 + x + 3)$ 8. $\displaystyle\lim_{x \to 4} \frac{x^2 - 16}{x + 4}$ 9. $\displaystyle\lim_{x \to -1} \frac{x^2 - 1}{x + 1}$

10. $\displaystyle\lim_{x \to 3} \frac{x^2 - 9}{x - 3}$ 11. $\displaystyle\lim_{x \to 2} \frac{4x^3 - 8x^2}{4x^3 - 16x}$ 12. $\displaystyle\lim_{x \to -\frac{1}{2}} \frac{x^2 - \frac{1}{4}}{6x^2 + x - 1}$

13. $\lim\limits_{x \to 3} \dfrac{x^2 - 16}{x - 3}$

14. $\lim\limits_{x \to -3} \dfrac{x^2 - 9}{x - 3}$

15. $\lim\limits_{x \to 1} \dfrac{x^2 - 9}{x - 3}$

16. $\lim\limits_{x \to 2} \dfrac{x^2 - 8}{x - 2}$

17. $\lim\limits_{h \to 0} \dfrac{3(x + h)^2 - 3x^2}{h}$

18. $\lim\limits_{h \to 0} \dfrac{[(x + h) - 2(x + h)^2] - [x - 2x^2]}{h}$

2.2

Use the graph of $y = f(x)$ in Figure 2.24 to answer the questions in problems 19 and 20.

19. Is $f(x)$ continuous at
    (a) $x = -1$?   (b) $x = 1$?

20. Is $f(x)$ continuous at
    (a) $x = -2$?   (b) $x = 2$?

In problems 21–26, suppose that

$$f(x) = \begin{cases} x^2 + 1 & \text{if } x \le 0 \\ x & \text{if } 0 < x < 1. \\ 2x^2 - 1 & \text{if } x \ge 1 \end{cases}$$

21. What is $\lim\limits_{x \to -1} f(x)$?

22. What is $\lim\limits_{x \to 0} f(x)$, if it exists?

23. What is $\lim\limits_{x \to 1} f(x)$, if it exists?

24. Is $f(x)$ continuous at $x = 0$?

25. Is $f(x)$ continuous at $x = 1$?

26. Is $f(x)$ continuous at $x = -1$?

Which of the functions in problems 27–30 are continuous?

27. $y = \dfrac{x^2 + 25}{x - 5}$

28. $y = \dfrac{x^2 - 3x + 2}{x - 2}$

29. $f(x) = \begin{cases} x + 2 & \text{if } x \le 2 \\ 5x - 6 & \text{if } x > 2 \end{cases}$

30. $y = \begin{cases} x^4 - 3 & \text{if } x \le 1 \\ 2x - 3 & \text{if } x > 1 \end{cases}$

In problems 31 and 32, use the graphs to find (a) the points of discontinuity, (b) $\lim\limits_{x \to +\infty} f(x)$, and (c) $\lim\limits_{x \to -\infty} f(x)$.

31.

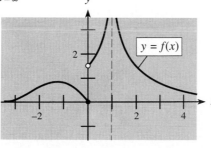

32.

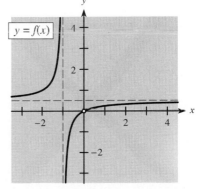

In problems 33 and 34, evaluate the limits, if they exist.

33. $\lim\limits_{x \to -\infty} \dfrac{2x^2}{1 - x^2}$

34. $\lim\limits_{x \to +\infty} \dfrac{3x^{2/3}}{x + 1}$

2.3

In problems 35 and 36, decide whether the statements are true or false.

35. $\lim\limits_{h \to 0} \dfrac{f(x + h) - f(x)}{h}$ gives the formula for the slope of the tangent and the instantaneous rate of change of $f(x)$ at any value of x.

36. $\lim\limits_{h \to 0} \dfrac{f(c + h) - f(c)}{h}$ gives the equation of the tangent line to $f(x)$ at $x = c$.

37. Use the definition of *derivative* to find $f'(x)$ for $f(x) = 3x^2 + 2x - 1$.

38. Use the definition of *derivative* to find $f'(x)$ if $f(x) = x - x^2$.

Use the graph of $y = f(x)$ in Figure 2.24 on page 248 to answer the questions in problems 39 and 40.

39. Is $f(x)$ differentiable at
    (a) $x = -1$?   (b) $x = 1$?

40. Is $f(x)$ differentiable at
    (a) $x = -2$?   (b) $x = 2$?

2.4

41. If $c = 4x^5 - 6x^3$, find c'.

42. If $f(x) = 4x^2 - 1$, find $f'(x)$.

43. If $p = 3q + \sqrt{7}$, find dp/dq.

44. If $y = \sqrt{x}$, find y'.

45. If $f(z) = \sqrt[3]{z^4}$, find $f'(z)$.

46. If $v(x) = 4/\sqrt[3]{x}$, find $v'(x)$.

47. If $y = \dfrac{1}{x} - \dfrac{1}{\sqrt{x}}$, find y'.

48. If $f(x) = \dfrac{3}{2x^2} - \sqrt[3]{x} + 4^5$, find $f'(x)$.

49. Write the equation of the line tangent to the graph of $y = 3x^5 - 6$ at $x = 1$.

50. Write the equation of the line tangent to the curve $y = 3x^3 - 2x$ at the point $(2, 20)$.

In problems 51 and 52, find all x-values where the slope of the tangent equals zero.

51. $f(x) = x^3 - 3x^2 + 1$

52. $f(x) = x^6 - 6x^4 + 8$

2.5

53. If $g(x) = (3x - 1)(x^2 - 4x)$, find $g'(x)$.

54. Find y' if $y = (x^2 + 1)(3x^3 + 1)$.

55. If $p = \dfrac{2q - 1}{q^2}$, find $\dfrac{dp}{dq}$.

56. Find $\dfrac{ds}{dt}$ if $s = \dfrac{\sqrt{t}}{(3t + 1)}$.

57. Find $\dfrac{dy}{dx}$ for $y = \sqrt{x}(3x + 2)$.

58. Find $\dfrac{dC}{dx}$ for $C = \dfrac{5x^4 - 2x^2 + 1}{x^3 + 1}$.

2.6

59. If $y = (x^3 - 4x^2)^3$, find y'.

60. If $y = (5x^6 + 6x^4 + 5)^6$, find y'.

61. If $y = (x^3 - 4x^2)^3$, find $\dfrac{dy}{dx}$.

62. Find $g'(x)$ if $g(x) = \dfrac{1}{\sqrt{x^3 - 4x}}$.

2.7

63. Find $f'(x)$ if $f(x) = x^2(2x^4 + 5)^8$.

64. Find S' if $S = \dfrac{(3x + 1)^2}{x^2 - 4}$.

65. Find $\dfrac{dy}{dx}$ if $y = [(3x + 1)(2x^3 - 1)]^{12}$.

66. Find y' if $y = \left(\dfrac{x + 1}{1 - x^2}\right)^3$.

67. Find y' if $y = x\sqrt{x^2 - 4}$.

68. Find $\dfrac{dy}{dx}$ if $y = \dfrac{x}{\sqrt[3]{3x - 1}}$.

2.8

In problems 69 and 70, find the second derivatives.

69. $y = \sqrt{x} - x^2$

70. $y = x^4 - \dfrac{1}{x}$

In problems 71 and 72, find the fifth derivatives.

71. $y = (2x + 1)^4$

72. $y = \dfrac{(1 - x)^6}{24}$

73. If $\dfrac{dy}{dx} = \sqrt{x^2 - 4}$, find $\dfrac{d^3y}{dx^3}$.

74. If $\dfrac{d^2y}{dx^2} = \dfrac{x}{x^2 + 1}$, find $\dfrac{d^4y}{dx^4}$.

APPLICATIONS

2.4

75. **Demand** Suppose that the demand x for a product is given by $x = (100/p) - 1$, where p is the price per unit of the product. Find the rate of change of demand with respect to the price if the price is
(a) \$10.   (b) \$20.

2.6

76. **Demand** The demand q for a product at price p is given by

$$q = 10{,}000 - 50\sqrt{0.02p^2 + 500}.$$

Find the rate of change of demand with respect to price.

77. **Supply** The number of units x of a product that is supplied at price p is given by

$$x = \sqrt{p - 1}, \qquad p \geq 1.$$

If the price p is \$10, what is the rate of change of the supply with respect to the price?

2.9

78. **Cost** If the cost function for a good is $C(x) = 3x^2 + 6x + 600$, what is the
(a) marginal cost function?
(b) marginal cost if 30 units are produced?

79. **Cost** If the total cost function for a commodity is $C(x) = 400 + 5x + x^3$, what is the marginal cost when 4 units are produced?

80. **Revenue** If the total revenue function for a commodity is $R = 40x - 0.02x^2$, with x representing the number of units,
    (a) find the marginal revenue function.
    (b) at what level of production will marginal revenue be 0?

81. **Profit** If the total revenue function is given by $R(x) = 60x$ and the total cost function is given by $C = 200 + 10x + 0.1x^2$, what is the marginal profit at $x = 10$?

82. **Revenue** If the total revenue function for a commodity is given by $R = 80x - 0.04x^2$,
    (a) find the marginal revenue function.
    (b) what is the marginal revenue at $x = 100$?

83. **Revenue** If the revenue function for a product is

$$R(x) = \frac{60x^2}{2x + 1},$$

find the marginal revenue.

84. **Profit** A firm has monthly costs given by

$$C = 45{,}000 + 100x + x^3,$$

where x is the number of units produced per month. The firm can sell its product in a competitive market for \$4600 per unit. Find the marginal profit.

85. **Profit** A small business has weekly costs of

$$C = 100 + 30x + \frac{x^2}{10},$$

where x is the number of units produced each week. The competitive market price for this business' product is \$46 per unit. Find the marginal profit.

Marginal Return to Sales

A tire manufacturer studying the effectiveness of television advertising and other promotions on sales of its GRIPPER-brand tires attempted to fit data it had gathered to the equation

$$S = a_0 + a_1x + a_2x^2 + b_1y,$$

where S is sales in millions of dollars, x is millions of dollars spent on television advertising, y is millions of dollars spent on other promotions, and a_0, a_1, a_2, and b_1 are constants. The data, gathered in two different regions of the country where expenditures for other promotions were kept constant (at B_1 and B_2), resulted in the following quadratic equations relating TV advertising and sales.

Region 1: $S_1 = 30 + 20x - 0.4x^2 + B_1$

Region 2: $S_2 = 20 + 36x - 0.6x^2 + B_2$

The company wants to know how to make the best use of its advertising dollars in the regions, and whether the current allocation could be improved. Advise management about current advertising effectiveness, allocation of additional expenditures, and reallocation of current advertising expenditures by answering the following questions.

1. In the analysis of sales and advertising, **marginal return to sales** is usually used, and it is given by dS_1/dx for Region 1 and dS_2/dx for Region 2.

    (a) Find $\dfrac{dS_1}{dx}$ and $\dfrac{dS_2}{dx}$.

    (b) If \$10 million is being spent on TV advertising in each region, what is the marginal return to sales in each region?

2. Which region would benefit more from each additional dollar of advertising expenditure, if \$10 million is currently being spent in each region?

3. If any additional money is made available for advertising, in which region should it be spent?

4. How could money already being spent be reallocated to produce more sales?

PREREQUISITE PROBLEM TYPE	REVIEW SECTION/ANSWER
Sections 3.1–3.5 Factor: (a) $x^3 - x^2 - 6x$ (b) $8000 - 80x - 3x^2$	Section 0.5, Factoring (a) $x(x - 3)(x + 2)$ (b) $(40 - x)(200 + 3x)$

Sections 3.1–3.3
 	
 (a) For what values of x is
    $\frac{1}{3}(x^2 - 1)^{-2/3}(2x)$ undefined?
 (b) If $f(x) = \frac{1}{3}x^3 - x^2 - 3x + 2$ and
    $f'(x) = x^2 - 2x - 3$, find
    (i) $f(-1)$.   (ii) $f'(-2)$.
	Section 1.1, Functions
	
	 (a) $x = -1, x = 1$
	
	 (b) (i) $\frac{11}{3}$ (ii) 5

Sections 3.1, 3.7 (a) Vertical lines have _____ slopes. (b) Horizontal lines have _____ slopes. (c) Write the equation of the line passing through $(-2, -2)$ with slope 5.	Section 1.2, Equations of lines (a) Undefined (b) 0 (c) $y = 5x + 8$
Sections 3.1, 3.2, 3.3, 3.4, 3.5, 3.7, 3.8 Solve: (a) $0 = 12x^3 - 12x^2$ (b) $0 = 3x^2 - 3$	Section 1.4, Quadratic equations (a) $x = 1, x = 0$ (b) $x = -1, x = 1$
Section 3.3 Does $\displaystyle\lim_{x \to -2} \frac{2x - 4}{3x + 6}$ exist?	Section 2.1, Limits No; unbounded
Sections 3.1– 3.8 Find the derivatives: (a) $\frac{df}{dx}$ if $f = x + 2\left(\frac{80,000}{x}\right)$ (b) $p'(t)$ if $p(t) = 1 + \frac{4t}{t^2 + 16}$ (c) $f''(x)$ if $f(x) = x^3 - 4x^2 + 3$	Sections 2.3, 2.4, 2.5, 2.6, 2.8, Derivatives (a) $\frac{df}{dx} = 1 - \frac{160,000}{x^2}$ (b) $p'(t) = \frac{64 - 4t^2}{(t^2 + 16)^2}$ (c) $f''(x) = 6x - 8$

WARM UP

3 | APPLICATIONS OF DERIVATIVES

In Chapter 2 we learned that the derivative could be used to determine rates of change, including velocity, marginal cost, marginal revenue, marginal profit, and rates of growth. We also used the derivative to determine the slope of the tangent to a curve at a given point.

In this chapter we will consider methods of determining when functions are maximized and minimized. We will see that the derivative can be used to determine the "turning points" of the graph of a function, so we can determine when a curve reaches its highest (or lowest) point. Knowledge of where a function attains its relative maxima and relative minima will be very helpful in sketching its graph.

While relative maxima and relative minima are important features of the graph of a function, the absolute maximum and absolute minimum are necessary elements in the solution of many applied problems. For example, we will use them in determining the levels of production that will maximize profit functions and revenue functions and in minimizing average cost functions.

The second derivative can be used to determine where the graph of an equation will be concave up, where it will be concave down, and where it will change from concave up to concave down, or vice versa. (Points where this occurs are called **points of inflection.**) The second-derivative test uses concavity to determine where the graph of an equation has a relative maximum or minimum.

We will carefully define horizontal and vertical asymptotes and sketch graphs of functions by using horizontal and vertical asymptotes, along with other important features of graphs.

The differential is introduced and used to approximate changes in a function for a given change in x. We will also develop methods for finding derivatives of one variable with respect to another variable even though the relationship between them may not be functional. This method is called **implicit differentiation** and will be used in elasticity of demand applications. Finally, we will use implicit differentiation with respect to time to solve problems involving the rates of change of two or more variables. These problems are called related rate problems.

3.1 | RELATIVE MAXIMA AND MINIMA; CURVE SKETCHING

OBJECTIVES

- To find relative maxima and minima and horizontal points of inflection of functions
- To sketch graphs of functions by using information about maxima, minima, and horizontal points of inflection

Except for very simple graphs (straight lines and parabolas, for example), plotting points may not give a very accurate graph of a function. In addition to intercepts and asymptotes, we can use the first derivative as an aid in graphing. The first derivative identifies the "turning points" of a curve, which will help determine the general shape of the curve.

In Figure 3.1 we see that the graph of $y = \frac{1}{3}x^3 - x^2 - 3x + 2$ has two "turning points," at $(-1, \frac{11}{3})$ and $(3, -7)$. The curve has a relative maximum at $(-1, \frac{11}{3})$ because this point is higher than any other point "near" it on the curve; the curve has a relative minimum at $(3, -7)$ because this point is lower than any other point "near" it on the curve. A formal definition follows.

| **Relative Maxima and Minima** | A function f has a **relative maximum** at $x = x_1$ if there is an interval around x_1 on which $f(x_1) \geq f(x)$ for all x in the interval. A function f has a **relative minimum** at $x = x_2$ if there is an interval around x_2 on which $f(x_2) \leq f(x)$ for all x in the interval. |

FIGURE 3.1

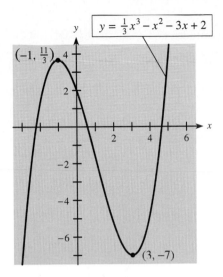

In order to determine whether a turning point of a function is a maximum point or a minimum point, it is frequently helpful to know what the graph of the function does in intervals on either side of the turning point. We say a function is **increasing** on an interval if the functional values increase as the x-values increase (that is, if the graph rises as we move from left to right on the interval). Similarly, a function is **decreasing** on an interval if the functional values decrease as the x-values increase (that is, if the graph falls as we move from left to right on the interval).

We have seen that if the slope of a line is positive, then the linear function is increasing and its graph is rising. Similarly, if $f(x)$ is differentiable over an interval and if each tangent line to the curve over that interval has positive slope, then the curve is rising over the interval and the function is increasing. Because the derivative of the function gives the slope of the tangent to the curve, we see that if $f'(x) > 0$ on an interval, then $f(x)$ is increasing on that interval. A similar conclusion can be reached when the derivative is negative on the interval.

| **Increasing and Decreasing Functions** | If f is a function that is differentiable on an interval (a, b), then

 if $f'(x) > 0$ for all x in (a, b), f is increasing on (a, b).
 if $f'(x) < 0$ for all x in (a, b), f is decreasing on (a, b). |

The derivative $f'(x)$ can change signs only at values of x where $f'(x) = 0$ or $f'(x)$ is undefined. We call these values of x **critical values.** The point corresponding to a critical value for x is a **critical point.*** Because a curve changes from increasing to decreasing at a relative maximum (see Figure 3.1), we have the following fact.

---

*There may be some critical values where $f'(x)$ and $f(x)$ are undefined. Critical points do not occur at these values, but studying the derivative on either side of such values may be of interest.

| **Relative Maximum** | If f has a relative maximum at $x = x_0$, then $f'(x_0) = 0$ or $f'(x_0)$ is undefined. |

From Figure 3.2, we see that this function has two relative maxima, one at $x = x_1$ and the second at $x = x_3$. At $x = x_1$ the derivative is 0, and at $x = x_3$ the derivative does not exist. In Figure 3.2, we also see that a relative minimum occurs at $x = x_2$ and $f'(x_2) = 0$.

FIGURE 3.2

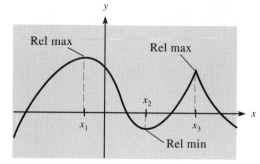

As Figure 3.2 shows, the function changes from decreasing to increasing at a relative minimum. Thus we have the following fact.

| **Relative Minimum** | If f has a relative minimum at $x = x_0$, then $f'(x_0) = 0$ or $f'(x_0)$ is undefined. |

Thus we can find relative maxima and minima for a curve by finding values of x for which the function has critical points. The behavior of the derivative to the left and right of (and near) these points will tell us if they are relative maxima or relative minima, or neither one.

Because the critical values are the only values where the graph can have turning points, the derivative cannot change sign anywhere except at a critical value. Thus in an interval between two critical values, the sign of the derivative at any value in the interval will be the sign of the derivative at all values in the interval.

Using the critical values of $f(x)$ and the sign of $f'(x)$ between those critical values, we can create a **sign diagram for $f'(x)$.** The sign diagram for the graph in Figure 3.2 is shown in Figure 3.3.

FIGURE 3.3

Direction of graph of $f(x)$:

Signs and values of $f'(x)$: $\quad + + + 0 - - - 0 + + + * - - -$

x-axis with critical values:

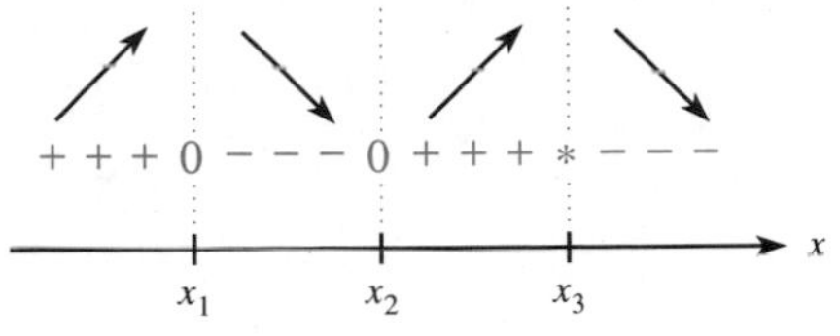

$\qquad\qquad\qquad\qquad\qquad\qquad x_1 \qquad x_2 \qquad x_3 \qquad\qquad x$

* means $f'(x_3)$ is undefined.

Suppose that the point (x_1, y_1) is a critical point. If $f'(x)$ is positive to the left of, and near, this critical point, and if $f'(x)$ is negative to the right of, and near, this critical point, then the curve is increasing to the left of the point and decreasing to the right. This means that a relative maximum occurs at the point. If we draw tangent lines to the curve on the left and right of this critical point, they would fit on the curve in one of the two ways shown in Figure 3.4.

FIGURE 3.4

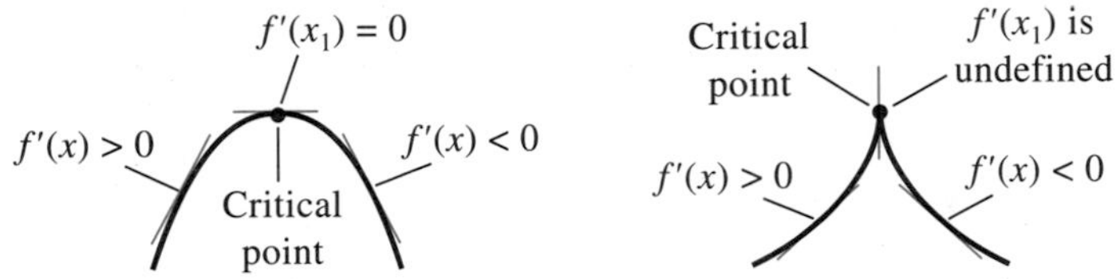

$f'(x_1) = 0$

$f'(x) > 0 \qquad\qquad f'(x) < 0$

Critical point

Relative maximum

(a)

Critical point

$f'(x_1)$ is undefined

$f'(x) > 0 \qquad\qquad f'(x) < 0$

Relative maximum

(b)

Similarly, suppose that the point (x_2, y_2) is a critical point, $f'(x)$ is negative to the left of and near (x_2, y_2), and $f'(x)$ is positive to the right of and near this critical point. Then the curve is decreasing to the left of the point and increasing to the right, and a relative minimum occurs at the point. If we draw tangent lines to the curve to the left of and to the right of this critical point, they would fit on the curve in one of the two ways shown in Figure 3.5.

FIGURE 3.5

Critical point

$f'(x) < 0 \qquad\qquad f'(x) > 0$

$f'(x_2) = 0$

Relative minimum

(a)

$f'(x) < 0 \qquad f'(x) > 0$

Critical point

$f'(x_2)$ is undefined

Relative minimum

(b)

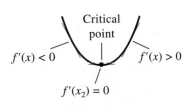

EXAMPLE 1 | Show that the graph of $f(x) = 3x^2 - 2x^3$ has a relative maximum at $x = 1$.

Solution We need to show that:

$f'(1) = 0$ or $f'(1)$ is undefined,

$f'(x) > 0$ to the left of and near $x = 1$, and

$f'(x) < 0$ to the right of and near $x = 1$.

Because $f'(x) = 6x - 6x^2 = 6x(x - 1)$ is 0 only at $x = 0$ and at $x = 1$, we can test (evaluate) the derivative at any value in the interval $(0, 1)$ to see what the curve is doing to the left of $x = 1$, and we can test the derivative at any value to the right of $x = 1$ to see what the curve is doing for $x > 1$.

$$f'\left(\frac{1}{2}\right) = 3 - \frac{3}{2} = \frac{3}{2} > 0 \Rightarrow \text{increasing to left of } x = 1$$

$$f'(1) = 0 \Rightarrow \text{horizontal tangent at } x = 1$$

$$f'\left(\frac{3}{2}\right) = 9 - \frac{27}{2} = -\frac{9}{2} < 0 \Rightarrow \text{decreasing to right of } x = 1$$

A partial sign diagram for $f'(x)$ is

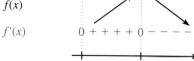

The sign diagram shows that the graph of the function has a relative maximum at $x = 1$.

The preceding discussion suggests the following procedure for finding relative maxima and minima of a function.

First-Derivative Test

Procedure	Example
To find relative maxima and minima of a function:	Find the relative maxima and minima of $f(x) = \frac{1}{3}x^3 - x^2 - 3x + 2$.
1. Find the first derivative of the function.	1. $f'(x) = x^2 - 2x - 3$
2. Set the derivative equal to 0, and solve for values of x that satisfy $f'(x) = 0$. These are called **critical values.** Values that make $f'(x)$ undefined are also critical values.	2. $0 = x^2 - 2x - 3 = (x + 1)(x - 3)$ has solutions $x = -1$, $x = 3$. No values of x make $x^2 - 2x - 3$ undefined. Critical values are -1 and 3.

3. Substitute the critical values into the *original function* to find the **critical points.**

4. Evaluate $f'(x)$ at some value of x to the left and right of each critical point:
   (a) If $f'(x) > 0$ to the left and $f'(x) < 0$ to the right of the critical value, the critical point is a relative maximum point.
   (b) If $f'(x) < 0$ to the left and $f'(x) > 0$ to the right of the critical value, the critical point is a relative minimum point.

5. Develop a sign diagram and use the information and selected points to sketch the graph.

3. $f(-1) = \frac{11}{3}$
   $f(3) = -7$
   The critical points are $(-1, \frac{11}{3})$ and $(3, -7)$.

4. $f'(-2) = 5 > 0$ and
   $f'(0) = -3 < 0$
   Thus $(-1, 11/3)$ is a relative maximum point.
   $f'(2) = -3 < 0$ and
   $f'(4) = 5 > 0$
   Thus $(3, -7)$ is a relative minimum point.

5. The sign diagram for $f'(x)$ is

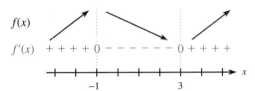

The information from this sign diagram is shown in Figure 3.6(a). Plotting additional points gives the graph of the function, which is shown in Figure 3.6(b).

FIGURE 3.6

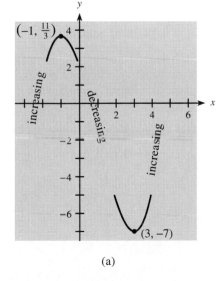

(a)

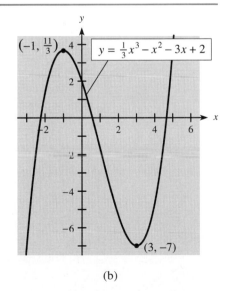

(b)

Note that if the critical point $(c, f(c))$ is a relative maximum point, then we say that the relative maximum *occurs at* $x = c$ and that $f(c)$ is the *relative maximum*. If the point $(b, f(b))$ is a relative minimum point, we say that the relative minimum *occurs at* $x = b$ and that $f(b)$ *is the relative minimum.*

Because the critical values are the only x-values where the graph can have turning points, we can test to the left and right of each critical value by testing to the left of the smallest critical value, then testing a value *between* each critical value, and then testing to the right of the largest critical value. The following example illustrates this procedure.

EXAMPLE 2

Find the relative maxima and minima of $f(x) = \frac{1}{4}x^4 - \frac{1}{3}x^3 - 3x^2 + 8$, and sketch its graph.

Solution

1. $f'(x) = x^3 - x^2 - 6x$

2. Setting $f'(x) = 0$ gives $0 = x^3 - x^2 - 6x$

   Solving for x gives
   $0 = x(x - 3)(x + 2)$

$x = 0$	$x - 3 = 0$	$x + 2 = 0$
	$x = 3$	$x = -2$

   Thus the critical values are $x = 0$, $x = 3$, and $x = -2$.

3. Substituting the critical values into the original function gives the critical points:

   $f(-2) = \frac{8}{3}$,   so $(-2, \frac{8}{3})$ is a critical point.
   $f(0) = 8$,   so $(0, 8)$ is a critical point.
   $f(3) = -\frac{31}{4}$,   so $(3, -\frac{31}{4})$ is a critical point.

4. Testing $f'(x)$ to the left of the smallest critical value, then between the critical values, then to the right of the largest critical value gives

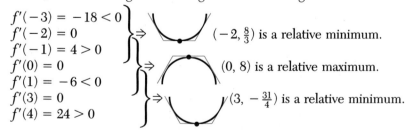

   $f'(-3) = -18 < 0$
   $f'(-2) = 0$
   $f'(-1) = 4 > 0$ $\Rightarrow$ $(-2, \frac{8}{3})$ is a relative minimum.
   $f'(0) = 0$ $\Rightarrow$ $(0, 8)$ is a relative maximum.
   $f'(1) = -6 < 0$
   $f'(3) = 0$ $\Rightarrow$ $(3, -\frac{31}{4})$ is a relative minimum.
   $f'(4) = 24 > 0$

5. The sign diagram for $f'(x)$ is

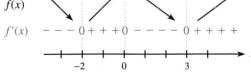

Figure 3.7(a) shows the graph of the function near the critical points, and Figure 3.7(b) shows the graph of the function.

FIGURE 3.7

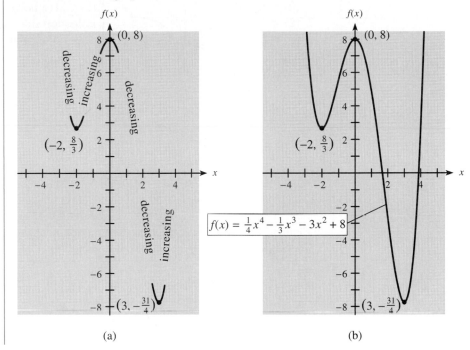

$f(x)$

$f(x)$

(a)

(b)

Note that we substitute the critical values into the *original function $f(x)$* to find the y-values of the critical points, but we test for relative maxima and minima by substituting values near the critical values into the *derivative of the function, $f'(x)$*.

Only four values were needed to test three critical points in Example 2. This method will work *only if* the critical values are tested in order from smallest to largest.

If the first derivative of f is 0 at x_0 but does not change from positive to negative or negative to positive as x passes through x_0, then the critical point at x_0 is neither a relative maximum nor a relative minimum. We say that f has a **horizontal point of inflection** at x_0.

EXAMPLE 3

Find the relative maxima, relative minima, and horizontal points of inflection of $h(x) = \frac{1}{4}x^4 - \frac{2}{3}x^3 - 2x^2 + 8x + 4$, and sketch its graph.

Solution

1. $h'(x) = x^3 - 2x^2 - 4x + 8$

2. $0 = x^3 - 2x^2 - 4x + 8$ or $0 = x^2(x - 2) - 4(x - 2)$. Therefore, we have $0 = (x - 2)(x^2 - 4)$. Thus $x = -2$ and $x = 2$ are solutions.

3. The critical points are $(-2, -\frac{32}{3})$ and $(2, \frac{32}{3})$.

4. $h'(-3) = -25 < 0$
   $h'(-2) = 0$
   $h'(0) = 8 > 0$
   $h'(2) = 0$
   $h'(3) = 5 > 0$

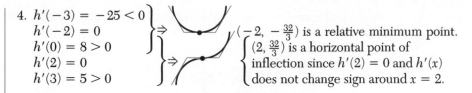

$\left. \right\} \Rightarrow$

$(-2, -\frac{32}{3})$ is a relative minimum point.
$(2, \frac{32}{3})$ is a horizontal point of inflection since $h'(2) = 0$ and $h'(x)$ does not change sign around $x = 2$.

5. The sign diagram for $h'(x)$ is

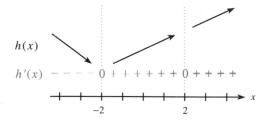

Figure 3.8(a) shows the graph of the function near the critical points, and Figure 3.8(b) shows the graph of the function.

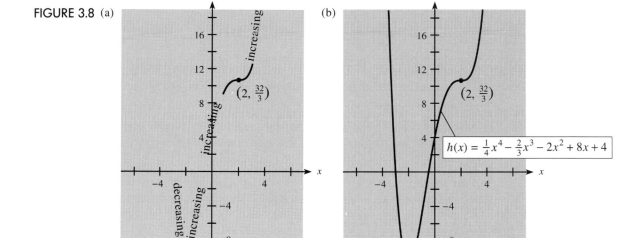

FIGURE 3.8 (a)

(b)

$h(x) = \frac{1}{4}x^4 - \frac{2}{3}x^3 - 2x^2 + 8x + 4$

EXAMPLE 4   Find the relative maxima and minima (if any) of the graph of $y = (x + 2)^{2/3}$.

Solution

1. $y' = f'(x) = \frac{2}{3}(x + 2)^{-1/3} = \dfrac{2}{3\sqrt[3]{x + 2}}$

2. $0 = \dfrac{2}{3\sqrt[3]{x + 2}}$ has no solutions; $f'(x)$ is undefined at $x = -2$.

3. $f(-2) = 0$, so the critical point is $(-2, 0)$.

4. $\left.\begin{array}{l} f'(-3) = -\frac{2}{3} < 0 \\ f'(-2) \text{ undefined} \\ f'(-1) = \frac{2}{3} > 0 \end{array}\right\} \Rightarrow$ a relative minimum occurs at $(-2, 0)$.

5. The sign diagram for $f'(x)$ is

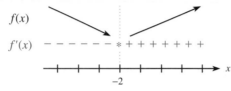

$f(x)$

$f'(x)$ $- - - - - - * + + + + + + + +$

$\qquad\qquad\qquad\quad -2$

* means $f'(-2)$ is undefined.

Figure 3.9(a) shows the graph of the function near the critical point, and Figure 3.9(b) shows the graph.

FIGURE 3.9

(a)
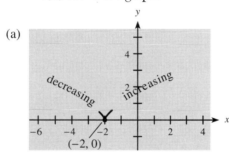

(b)
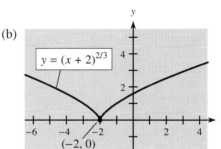

$y = (x + 2)^{2/3}$

CHECKPOINT

1. The x-values of critical points are found where $f'(x)$ is _____ or _____.

2. Decide whether the following are true or false.

   (a) If $f'(1) = 7$, then $f(x)$ is increasing at $x = 1$.

   (b) If $f'(-2) = 0$, then a relative maximum or a relative minimum occurs at $x = -2$.

   (c) If $f'(-3) = 0$ and $f'(x)$ changes from positive on the left to negative on the right of $x = -3$, then a relative minimum occurs at $x = -3$.

3. If $f(x) = 7 + 3x - x^3$, then $f'(x) = 3 - 3x^2$. Use these to decide whether the following are true or false.

   (a) The only critical value is $x = 1$.

   (b) The critical points are $(1, 0)$ and $(-1, 0)$.

4. If $f'(x)$ has the following partial sign diagram, make a "stick-figure" sketch of $f(x)$ and label where any maxima and minima occur. Assume that $f(x)$ is defined for all real numbers.

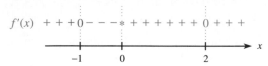

$f'(x)$ $+ + + 0 - - - * + + + + + + 0 + + +$

-1 0 2 x

* means $f'(0)$ is undefined.

EXAMPLE 5 | The weekly sales S of a product during an advertising campaign are given by

$$S = \frac{100t}{t^2 + 100}, \qquad 0 \le t \le 20,$$

where t is the number of weeks since the beginning of the campaign and S is in thousands of dollars.

(a) Over what interval are sales increasing? decreasing?

(b) What is the maximum weekly sales?

(c) Sketch the graph for $0 \le t \le 20$.

Solution

(a) To find where S is increasing, we first find $S'(t)$.

$$S'(t) = \frac{(t^2 + 100)100 - (100t)2t}{(t^2 + 100)^2}$$

$$= \frac{10{,}000 - 100t^2}{(t^2 + 100)^2}$$

We see that $S'(t) = 0$ when $10{,}000 - 100t^2 = 0$, or

$$100(100 - t^2) = 0$$
$$(10 + t)(10 - t) = 0$$
$$t = -10 \text{ or } t = 10$$

Because $S'(t)$ is never undefined ($t^2 + 100 \neq 0$ for any real t) and because $0 \le t \le 20$, our only critical value is $t = 10$. Testing $S'(t)$ to the left and right of $t = 10$ gives

left of $t = 10$: $S'(9) = \dfrac{10{,}000 - 8100}{(81 + 100)^2} > 0$,

so S is increasing on the interval $[0, 10)$, and

right of $t = 10$: $S'(11) = \dfrac{10{,}000 - 12{,}100}{(121 + 100)^2} < 0$,

so S is decreasing on the interval $(10, 20]$.

(b) Because S is increasing to the left of $t = 10$ and S is decreasing to the right of

$t = 10$, the maximum value of S occurs at $t = 10$ and is

$$S = S(10) = \frac{100(10)}{10^2 + 100} = \frac{1000}{200} = 5 \text{ (thousand dollars)}.$$

(c) The sign graph for S' on $[0, 20]$ is

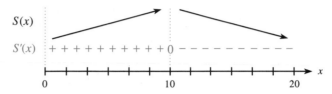

Plotting some additional points gives the graph, as shown in Figure 3.10.

FIGURE 3.10

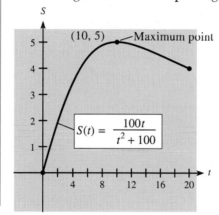

TECHNOLOGY CORNER

Given $f'(x) = 12x^2 - 4x^3$:

1. Graph $f'(x)$.

2. From the graph of $f'(x)$, determine the critical values for $f(x)$.

3. From the graph of $f'(x)$, determine where $f(x)$ would be increasing and where it would be decreasing.

4. From the graph of $f'(x)$, determine the x-values where $f(x)$ would have any relative maxima, relative minima, and any horizontal points of inflection.

5. Sketch a graph that could be the graph of $f(x)$. Make your graph pass through $(0, 0)$.

6. The function graphed in (5) should be $f(x) = 4x^3 - x^4$. Graph this function and check your sketch in (5).

1. $f'(x) = 0$ or $f'(x)$ is undefined.

2. (a) True, $f(x)$ is increasing when $f'(x) > 0$.

    (b) False. There may be a horizontal point of inflection at $x = -2$ (see Figure 3.8 on page 264).

    (c) False. A relative maximum occurs at $x = -3$.

3. (a) False. Critical values are solutions to $3 - 3x^2 = 0$ or $x = 1$ and $x = -1$.

    (b) False, y-coordinates of critical points come from $f(x) = 7 + 3x - x^3$. Thus critical points are $(1, 9)$ and $(-1, 5)$.

4. Shape of $f(x)$

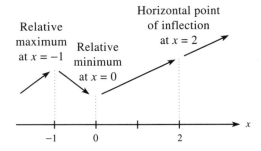

EXERCISE 3.1

For each function in problems 1–8,
(a) find dy/dx.
(b) find the critical values.
(c) find the critical points.
(d) classify the critical points as relative maxima, relative minima, or horizontal points of inflection.

1. $y = \frac{1}{2}x^2 - x$
2. $y = x^2 + 4x$
3. $y = x^3 - 3x$
4. $y = x - \frac{1}{3}x^3$
5. $y = x^3 + 3x^2 + 3x$
6. $y = x^3 - 6x^2 + 12x$
7. $y = x^{2/3}$
8. $y = -(x - 3)^{2/3}$

For each function in problems 9–12,
(a) find dy/dx.
(b) find the critical values.
(c) find the critical points.

(d) classify the critical points as relative maxima, relative minima, or horizontal points of inflection.
(e) sketch the graph.

9. $y = \frac{x^3}{3} + \frac{x^2}{2} - 2x + 1$

10. $y = \frac{x^4}{4} - \frac{x^3}{3}$

11. $y = x^3 - 3x^2$

12. $y = x^4 - 2x^2$

In problems 13–20, both a function and its derivative are given. Use these to find critical values, relative maxima, relative minima, and horizontal points of inflection; sketch the graph of each function.

13. $y = (x^2 - 2x)^2$

    $\dfrac{dy}{dx} = 4x(x - 1)(x - 2)$

14. $y = x(x - 1)^2$

$\dfrac{dy}{dx} = (x - 1)(3x - 1)$

15. $f(x) = x(x - 2)^3$

$f'(x) = 2(2x - 1)(x - 2)^2$

16. $f(x) = (x^2 - 4)^2$

$f'(x) = 4x(x + 2)(x - 2)$

17. $y = \dfrac{x^3(x - 5)^2}{27}$

$\dfrac{dy}{dx} = \dfrac{5x^2(x - 3)(x - 5)}{27}$

18. $y = \dfrac{x^2(x - 5)^3}{27}$

$\dfrac{dy}{dx} = \dfrac{5x(x - 2)(x - 5)^2}{27}$

19. $f(x) = x^{2/3}(x - 5)$

$f'(x) = \dfrac{5(x - 2)}{3x^{1/3}}$

20. $f(x) = x - 3x^{2/3}$

$f'(x) = \dfrac{x^{1/3} - 2}{x^{1/3}}$

For each function in problems 21–30, find the relative maxima, relative minima, and horizontal points of inflection, and sketch the graphs.

21. $y = \frac{1}{3}x^3 - x^2 + x + 1$

22. $y = \frac{1}{4}x^4 - \frac{2}{3}x^3 + \frac{1}{2}x^2 - 2$

23. $y = x^4 - 4x^3$

24. $y = x^3(x - 1)$

25. $p = q^3 - 3q^2 + 4$

26. $p = \frac{1}{3}q^3 - 2q^2 - 12q$

27. $p = q^3 + q^2 - 8q + 3$

28. $C(x) = x^3 - \frac{3}{2}x^2 - 6x + 4$

29. $y = 3x^5 - 5x^3 + 1$

30. $y = \frac{1}{2}x^6 - 3x^4 + 7$

APPLICATIONS

31. **Advertising and sales** Suppose that the daily sales (in dollars) t days after the end of an advertising campaign are given by

$$S = 1000 + \dfrac{400}{t + 1}, \quad t \geq 0.$$

Does S increase for all $t \geq 0$, decrease for all

$t \geq 0$, or change direction at some point in time?

32. **Pricing and sales** Suppose that a chain of auto service stations, Quick-Oil, Inc., has found that their monthly sales volume y (in thousands of dollars) is related to the price p (in dollars) of an oil change by

$$y = \dfrac{90}{\sqrt{p + 5}}, \quad p > 10.$$

Is y increasing or decreasing for all values of $p > 10$?

33. **Productivity** A time study showed that, on average, the productivity of a worker after t hours on the job can be modeled by

$$P(t) = 27t + 6t^2 - t^3, \quad 0 \leq t \leq 8,$$

where P is the number of units produced per hour.
(a) Find the critical values for this function.
(b) Which critical value makes sense in this model?
(c) For what values of t is P increasing?
(d) Graph the function for $0 \leq t \leq 8$.

34. **Production** Analysis of daily output of a factory shows that, on average, the number of units per hour y produced after t hours of production is

$$y = 70t + \frac{1}{2}t^2 - t^3, \quad 0 \leq t \leq 8.$$

(a) Find the critical values for this function.
(b) Which critical values make sense in this problem?
(c) For what values of t, for $0 \leq t \leq 8$, is y increasing?
(d) Graph this function.

35. **Revenue** A recently released film has its weekly revenue given by

$$R(t) = \dfrac{50t}{t^2 + 36}, \quad t \geq 0,$$

where R is in millions of dollars and t is in weeks.
(a) Find the critical values.

(b) For how many weeks will weekly revenue increase?

36. **Production costs** Suppose that the total cost of producing a shipment of a certain product is

$$C = 5000x + \frac{125,000}{x}, \qquad x > 0,$$

where x is the number of machines used in production.
(a) Find the critical values for this function.
(b) Over what interval does the total cost decrease?
(c) Over what interval does the total cost increase?

37. **Earnings** Suppose that the rate of change $f'(x)$ of the average annual earnings of new car salespersons is shown in Figure 3.11.
(a) If a, b, and c represent certain years, what is happening to $f(x)$, the average annual earnings of the salespersons, at a, b, and c?

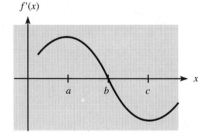

FIGURE 3.11

(b) Over what interval (involving a, b, or c) is there an increase in $f(x)$, the average annual earnings of the salespersons?

38. **Medication** Suppose that the concentration C of a medication in the bloodstream t hours after an injection is given by

$$C(t) = \frac{0.2t}{t^2 + 1}.$$

(a) Find the number of hours before C attains its maximum.
(b) Find the maximum concentration. Do not graph.

39. **Candidate recognition** Suppose that the proportion P of voters who recognize a candidate's name t months after the start of the campaign is given by

$$P(t) = \frac{13t}{t^2 + 100} + 0.18.$$

(a) How many months after the start of the campaign is recognition at its maximum?
(b) To have greatest recognition on November 1, when should a campaign be launched?

40. **Medication** The number of milligrams x of a medication in the bloodstream t hours after taking a dosage can be modeled by

$$x(t) = \frac{2000t}{t^2 + 16}.$$

(a) For what t-values is x increasing?
(b) Find the t-value at which x is maximum.
(c) Find the maximum value for x. Do not graph.

41. **Poverty in the United States** The following table shows the number of people in the United States who lived below the poverty level for selected years between 1960 and 1988. Assume that these data can be modeled with the function $p(x) = 1184.01 - 43.163x + 0.5296x^2 - 0.00214x^3$, where x is the number of years past 1900.

Year	Number of people below the poverty level (in millions)
1960	39.9
1965	33.2
1970	25.4
1973	24.5
1975	25.9
1980	29.3
1986	32.4
1987	32.5
1988	31.7

Source: *World Almanac*, 1991.

(a) For which year does the model $p(x)$ indicate that a minimum number of people lived below the poverty level?
(b) Does your answer to (a) agree with the data in the table?

3.2 | CONCAVITY; POINTS OF INFLECTION

OBJECTIVES

- To find points of inflection of graphs of functions
- To use the second-derivative test to graph functions

Suppose that in 1993 a retailer wishes to sell his store, and uses the graph in Figure 3.12 to show how profits have increased since he opened the store and the potential for profit in the future. Can we conclude that profits will continue to grow, or should we be concerned about future earnings?

FIGURE 3.12

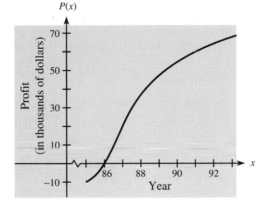

Notice that although profits are still increasing in 1992, they are increasing more slowly than in previous years. Indeed, they appear to have been growing at a decreasing rate since about 1987. We say that this profit curve is **concave down** over the interval from 1987 to 1992. Based on Figure 3.12, it would be unwise to expect a large increase in profit after 1992.

Just as we used the first derivative to determine if a curve was increasing or decreasing on a given interval, we can use the second derivative to determine if the curve is concave up or concave down on an interval.

A curve is said to be **concave up** on an interval $[a, b]$ if at each point on the interval the curve is above its tangent at the point [Figure 3.13(a)]. If the curve is below all its tangents on a given interval, it is **concave down** on the interval [Figure 3.13(b)].

Looking at Figure 3.13(a), we see that the *slopes* of the tangent lines increase over the interval where the graph is concave up. Because $f'(x)$ gives the slopes of those tangents, it follows that $f'(x)$ is increasing over the interval where $f(x)$ is concave up. However, if we know that $f'(x)$ is increasing, then its derivative, $f''(x)$, must be positive. That is, the second derivative is positive if the curve is concave up. Conversely, it can be shown that the graph of a function is concave up if the second derivative is positive.

FIGURE 3.13

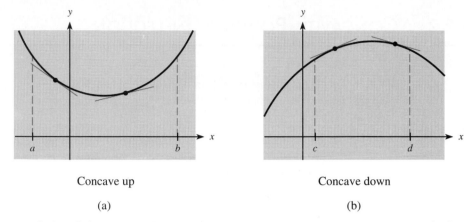

Concave up

(a)

Concave down

(b)

Similarly, if the second derivative of a function is negative over an interval, the slopes of the tangents to the graph decrease over that interval. This happens when the tangent lines are above the graph, as in Figure 3.13(b), so the graph must be concave down on this interval.

Thus we see that the second derivative can be used to determine the concavity of a curve.

Concave Up and Concave Down

Assume that the first and second derivatives of function f exist.
If $f''(x) > 0$ on an interval I, the graph of f is **concave up** on the interval.
If $f''(x) < 0$ on an interval I, then the graph of f is **concave down** on I.

EXAMPLE 1

Is the graph of $f(x) = x^3 - 4x^2 + 3$ concave up or down at
(a) $(1, 0)$? (b) $(2, -5)$?

Solution
(a) We must find $f''(x)$ before we can answer this question.

$$f'(x) = 3x^2 - 8x$$
$$f''(x) = 6x - 8$$

Then $f''(1) = 6(1) - 8 = -2$, so the graph is concave down at $(1, 0)$.

(b) Since $f''(2) = 6(2) - 8 = 4$, the graph is concave up at $(2, -5)$. The graph of $f(x) = x^3 - 4x^2 + 3$ is shown in Figure 3.14.

Looking at the graph of $y = x^3 - 4x^2 + 3$ (Figure 3.14), we see that the curve is concave down on the left and concave up on the right. Thus it has changed from concave down to concave up at some point. But at what point? According to the discussion earlier, it is the point where the second derivative changes from negative to positive. This point is called a **point of inflection.**

FIGURE 3.14

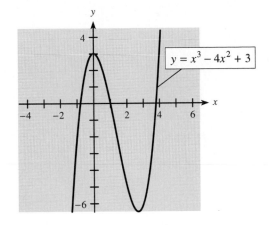

$$y = x^3 - 4x^2 + 3$$

Point of Inflection	A point (x_0, y_0) on the graph of a function f is called a **point of inflection** if the curve is concave up on one side of the point and concave down on the other side. The second derivative at this point, $f''(x_0)$, will be 0 or undefined.

In general, we can find points of inflection as follows.

FINDING POINTS OF INFLECTION

PROCEDURE	EXAMPLE
To find the point(s) of inflection of a curve:	Find the points of inflection of the graph of $y = \dfrac{x^4}{2} - x^3 + 5$.
1. Find the second derivative of the function.	1. $y' = f'(x) = 2x^3 - 3x^2$ $y'' = f''(x) = 6x^2 - 6x$
2. Set the second derivative equal to 0, and solve for x. Potential points of inflection occur at these values of x or at values of x where $f(x)$ is defined and $f''(x)$ is undefined.	2. $0 = 6x^2 - 6x = 6x(x - 1)$ has solutions $x = 0, x = 1$. $f''(x)$ is defined everywhere.
3. Find the potential points of inflection.	3. $(0, 5)$ and $(1, \frac{9}{2})$ are potential points of inflection.
4. If the second derivative has opposite signs on the two sides of one of these values of x, a point of inflection occurs.	4. $\left.\begin{array}{l} f''(-1) = 12 > 0 \\ f''(0) = 0 \\ f''(\frac{1}{2}) = -\frac{3}{2} < 0 \\ f''(0) = 0 \\ f''(2) = 12 > 0 \end{array}\right\}$ $\begin{array}{l}(0, 5) \text{ is a point of} \\ \Rightarrow \text{ inflection} \\ \\ \Rightarrow (1, \frac{9}{2}) \text{ is a point of} \\ \text{inflection}\end{array}$ See the graph in Figure 3.15.

FIGURE 3.15

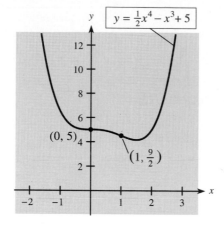

The graph of $y = \frac{1}{2}x^4 - x^3 + 5$ is shown in Figure 3.15. Note the points of inflection at $(0, 5)$ and $(1, \frac{9}{2})$. The point of inflection at $(0, 5)$ is a horizontal point of inflection because $f'(x)$ is also 0 at $x = 0$. A sign diagram for the second derivative of this function is shown below. The changes in the sign of $f''(x)$ correspond to changes in concavity and occur at points of inflection.

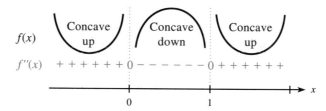

EXAMPLE 2

Suppose that a real estate developer wishes to remove pollution from a small lake so he can sell lakefront homes on a "crystal clear" lake. The graph in Figure 3.16 shows the relation between dollars spent on cleaning the lake and the purity of the water. The point of inflection on the graph is called the **point of diminishing returns** on his investment because it is where the *rate* of return on his investment changes from increasing to decreasing. Show that the rate of change in the purity of the lake, $f'(x)$, is maximized at this point, $x = c$. [Assume that $f(c)$, $f'(c)$, and $f''(c)$ are defined.]

FIGURE 3.16

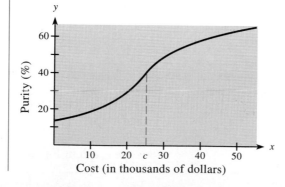

Solution Because $x = c$ is a point of inflection for $f(x)$, we know that the concavity must change at $x = c$. From the figure we see the following.

$x < c$: $f(x)$ is concave up, so $f''(x) > 0$;
$\qquad\quad f''(x) > 0$ means that $f'(x)$ is increasing.

$x > c$: $f(x)$ is concave down, so $f''(x) < 0$;
$\qquad\quad f''(x) < 0$ means that $f'(x)$ is decreasing.

Thus $f'(x)$ has $f'(c)$ as its relative maximum.

EXAMPLE 3

Suppose that the daily sales (in thousands of dollars) of a product is given by

$$S = \frac{(-x^3 + 9x^2 + 6)}{6}$$

where x is thousands of dollars spent on advertising. Find the point of diminishing returns for money spent on advertising.

Solution We seek the point where the graph of this function changes from concave up to concave down, if such a point exists.

$$\frac{dS}{dx} = S'(x) = \frac{1}{6}(-3x^2 + 18x)$$

$$S''(x) = \frac{1}{6}(-6x + 18) = -x + 3$$

$$S''(x) = 0 \quad \text{when} \quad 0 = -x + 3 \quad \text{or} \quad x = 3.$$

Thus $x = 3$ is a possible point of inflection. We test $S''(x)$ to the left and right of $x = 3$.

$S''(2) = 1 > 0 \Rightarrow$ concave up to the left of $x = 3$.
$S''(4) = -1 < 0 \Rightarrow$ concave down to the right of $x = 3$.

Thus the point of diminishing returns occurs when $x = 3$ (thousand dollars) and $S = 10$ (thousand dollars). See Figure 3.17.

FIGURE 3.17

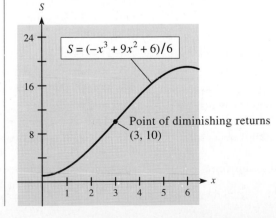

$S = (-x^3 + 9x^2 + 6)/6$

Point of diminishing returns
(3, 10)

We can use information about points of inflection and concavity to help sketch graphs. For example, if we know that the curve is concave up at a critical point where $f'(x) = 0$, then the point must be a relative minimum because the tangent to the curve is horizontal at the critical point, and only a point at the bottom of a "concave up" curve could have a horizontal tangent [see Figure 3.18(a)].

On the other hand, if the curve is concave down at a critical point where $f'(x) = 0$, then the point is a relative maximum [see Figure 3.18(b)].

Thus we can use the **second-derivative test** to determine if a critical point where $f'(x) = 0$ is a relative maximum or minimum.

FIGURE 3.18   (a) 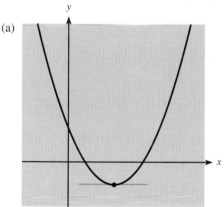   (b)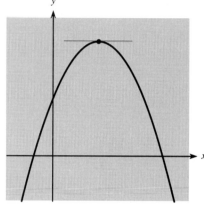

SECOND-DERIVATIVE TEST

PROCEDURE	EXAMPLE
To find relative maxima and minima of a function:	Find the relative maxima and minima of $y = f(x) = \frac{1}{3}x^3 - x^2 - 3x + 2$.
1. Find the critical values of the function.	1. $f'(x) = x^2 - 2x - 3$ $0 = (x - 3)(x + 1)$ has solutions $x = -1$ and $x = 3$. No values of x make $x^2 - 2x - 3$ undefined.
2. Substitute the critical values into $f(x)$ to find the critical points.	2. $f(-1) = \frac{11}{3}$ $f(3) = -7$ The critical points are $(-1, \frac{11}{3})$ and $(3, -7)$.
3. Evaluate $f''(x)$ at each critical value for which $f'(x) = 0$. (a) If $f''(x_0) < 0$, a relative maximum occurs at x_0. (b) If $f''(x_0) > 0$, a relative minimum occurs at x_0.	3. $f''(x) = 2x - 2$ $f''(-1) = 2(-1) - 2 = -4 < 0$, so $(-1, \frac{11}{3})$ is a relative maximum point. $f''(3) = 2(3) - 2 = 4 > 0$, so $(3, -7)$ is a relative minimum point. (The graph is shown in Figure 3.19.)

(c) If $f''(x_0) = 0$, or if $f''(x_0)$ is undefined, the second-derivative test fails; use the first-derivative test.

FIGURE 3.19

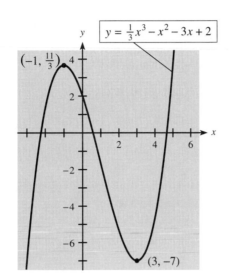

$$y = \tfrac{1}{3}x^3 - x^2 - 3x + 2$$

CHECKPOINT

1. If $f''(x) > 0$, then $f(x)$ is concave _____.

2. Where do possible points of inflection occur?

3. On the graph below, locate any points of inflection (approximately) and label where the curve satisfies $f''(x) > 0$ and $f''(x) < 0$.

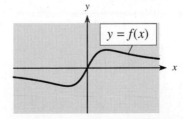

$y = f(x)$

4. Determine whether the following are true or false.

   (a) Let $f(x) = x^4$. Then $f''(x) = 12x^2$ and $f''(0) = 0$. Hence, $f(x)$ has a point of inflection at $x = 0$.

   (b) Let $f(x) = x^5$. Then $f''(x) = 20x^3$ and $f''(0) = 0$. Hence, $f(x)$ has a point of inflection at $x = 0$.

EXAMPLE 4

Find the relative maxima and minima and points of inflection of $y = 3x^4 - 4x^3$.

Solution

$$y' = f'(x) = 12x^3 - 12x^2$$

Solving $0 = 12x^3 - 12x^2 = 12x^2(x - 1)$ gives $x = 1$ and $x = 0$. Thus the critical points are $(1, -1)$ and $(0, 0)$.

$$y'' = f''(x) = 36x^2 - 24x$$
$$f''(1) = 12 > 0 \Rightarrow (1, -1) \text{ is a relative minimum point.}$$
$$f''(0) = 0 \Rightarrow \text{the second-derivative test fails.}$$

Since the second-derivative test fails, we must use the first-derivative test at the critical point $(0, 0)$.

$$\left.\begin{array}{l} f'(-1) = -24 < 0 \\ f'(\frac{1}{2}) = -\frac{3}{2} < 0 \end{array}\right\} \Rightarrow (0, 0) \text{ is a horizontal point of inflection.}$$

We look for points of inflection by setting $f''(x) = 0$ and solving for x. We find that $0 = 36x^2 - 24x$ has solutions $x = 0$ and $x = \frac{2}{3}$.

$$\left.\begin{array}{l} f''(-1) = 60 > 0 \\ f''(\frac{1}{2}) = -3 < 0 \end{array}\right\} \Rightarrow (0, 0) \text{ is a point of inflection.}$$

Thus we see again that $(0, 0)$ is a horizontal point of inflection. This is a special point, where the curve changes concavity *and* has a horizontal tangent (see Figure 3.20). Testing for concavity on either side of $x = \frac{2}{3}$ gives

$$\left.\begin{array}{l} f''(\frac{1}{2}) = -3 < 0 \\ f''(1) = 12 > 0 \end{array}\right\} \Rightarrow (\frac{2}{3}, -\frac{16}{27}) \text{ is a point of inflection.}$$

FIGURE 3.20

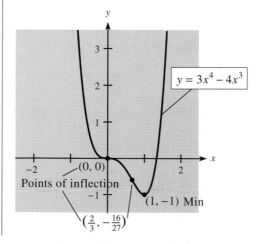

TECHNOLOGY CORNER

1. Suppose that $f(x) = \frac{1}{6}(2x^3 - 3x^2 - 12x + 12)$.

   (a) Graph $f(x)$.

   (b) From the graph of $f(x)$, identify points where $f''(x) = 0$ and where $f''(x)$ is undefined.

   (c) From the graph of $f(x)$, observe intervals where $f''(x) > 0$ and where $f''(x) < 0$.

   (d) Check your observations in parts (b) and (c) by calculating $f''(x)$ and graphing it.

2. Use the graph of the third degree function $y = f(x)$ below to complete the following.

   (a) Estimate where $f'(x) = 0$, where $f'(x) < 0$, and where $f'(x) > 0$.

   (b) Sketch a possible graph of $y = f'(x)$.

   (c) Estimate where $f''(x) = 0$, where $f''(x) < 0$, and where $f''(x) > 0$.

   (d) Sketch a possible graph of $y = f''(x)$.

   (e) Use addition, subtraction, multiplication, or division of all or some of the functions

   $$y_1 = \frac{1}{2}x^2, \quad y_2 = \frac{1}{3}x^3, \quad y_3 = x + 1, \quad y_4 = -x^2 + 3$$

   to create a function f whose graph is shown. Graph the function you created to verify that you have the proper function.

   (f) Use the function you created in (e) to find $f'(x)$ and $f''(x)$. Graph these functions and compare their graphs with the graphs you drew in (b) and (d).

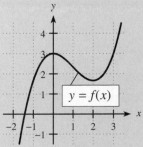
$y = f(x)$

CHECKPOINT
SOLUTIONS

1. up

2. Possible points of inflection occur where $f''(x) = 0$ or $f''(x)$ is undefined.

3.

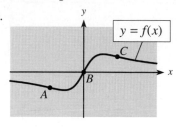

Points of inflection at A, B, and C
$f''(x) < 0$ to the left of A and between B and C
$f''(x) > 0$ between A and B and to the right of C

4. (a) False, $f''(x) = 12x^2$ does not change sign from $x < 0$ to $x > 0$.

 (b) True, $f''(x) = 20x^3$ satisfies $f''(x) < 0$ for $x < 0$ and $f''(x) > 0$ for $x > 0$.

EXERCISE 3.2

Find the points of inflection of the graphs of the following functions, if they exist.

1. $y = x^3 - 3x^2$
2. $y = x^3 + 6x$
3. $y = 2x^3 + 4x$
4. $y = 4x^3 - 3x^2$
5. $y = x^2 - 4x + 3$
6. $y = 4x^2 + 5x + 6$
7. $f(x) = x^3 - 6x^2 + 5x + 6$
8. $f(x) = 2x^3 - 4x^2 + 5x - 2$
9. $y = \frac{1}{4}x^4 + \frac{1}{2}x^3 - 3x^2 + 3$
10. $f(x) = \dfrac{x^4}{4} + 2x^3 - 48x^2 + 8x + 4$
11. $p = q^3 - 9q^2$
12. $p = 2q^4 - 6q^2 + 4$
13. $y = x^{1/3}$
14. $y = x^{2/3}$
15. $y = x^{4/3} - 4x^{1/3}$
16. $y = x^{7/3} - 7x^{4/3}$
17. $y = \dfrac{4x}{x^2 + 1}$
18. $y = \dfrac{8x}{x^2 + 4}$

In problems 19–24, a function and its first and second derivatives are given. Use these to find critical values, relative maxima, relative minima, and points of inflection; sketch the graph of each function.

19. $p = 3q^4 - 4q^3 + 1$
$$\frac{dp}{dq} = 12q^2(q - 1)$$
$$\frac{d^2p}{dq^2} = 12q(3q - 2)$$

20. $f(w) = 4w^3 - 6w^2 - 24w$
$f'(w) = 12(w - 2)(w + 1)$
$f''(w) = 12(2w - 1)$

21. $f(x) = 3x^5 - 20x^3$
$f'(x) = 15x^2(x - 2)(x + 2)$
$f''(x) = 60x(x^2 - 2)$

22. $f(x) = x^5 - 5x^4$
$f'(x) = 5x^3(x - 4)$
$f''(x) = 20x^2(x - 3)$

23. $y = x^{1/3}(x - 4)$
$$y' = \frac{4(x - 1)}{3x^{2/3}}$$
$$y'' = \frac{4(x + 2)}{9x^{5/3}}$$

24. $y = x^{4/3}(x - 7)$
$$y' = \frac{7x^{1/3}(x - 4)}{3}$$
$$y'' = \frac{28(x - 1)}{9x^{2/3}}$$

Find the relative maxima, relative minima, and points of inflection, and sketch the graph of the following functions.

25. $y = x^2 - 4x + 2$
26. $y = x^3 - x^2$

27. $y = x^3 - 3x^2 + 6$

28. $y = x^4 - 8x^3 + 16x^2$

29. $y = x^4 - 16x^2$

30. $y = x^3 + 1$

31. $y = x^4 - 4$

32. $y = \frac{1}{3}x^3 - 2x^2 + 3x + 2$

APPLICATIONS

33. **Productivity—diminishing returns** Figure 3.21 is a typical graph of worker productivity as a function of time on the job.
    (a) If P represents the productivity and t represents the time, write a symbol that represents the rate of change of productivity with respect to time.
    (b) Which of A, B, or C is the critical point for the rate of change found in part (a)? This point actually corresponds to the point at which the rate of production is maximized, or the point for maximum worker efficiency. In economics, this is called the point of diminishing returns.
    (c) Which of A, B, or C corresponds to the maximum production?

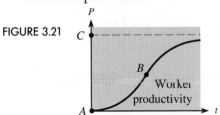

FIGURE 3.21

34. **Population growth** Figure 3.22 shows the growth of a population as a function of time.
    (a) If P represents the population and t represents the time, write a symbol that represents the rate of change (growth rate) of the population with respect to time.
    (b) Which of A, B, or C corresponds to the point at which the growth *rate* attains its maximum?

    (c) Which of A, B, or C corresponds to the maximum population?

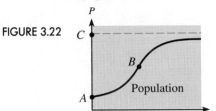

FIGURE 3.22

35. **Advertising and sales** Figure 3.23 shows the daily sales volume S as a function of time t since an ad campaign began.
    (a) Which of A, B, or C is the point of inflection for the graph in Figure 3.23?
    (b) On which side of C is $d^2S/dt^2 > 0$?
    (c) Does the *rate of change* of sales volume attain its minimum at C?

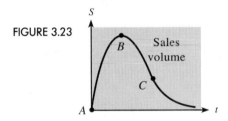

FIGURE 3.23

36. **Oxygen purity** Figure 3.24 shows the oxygen level P (for purity) in a lake t months after an oil spill.
    (a) Which of A, B, or C is the point of inflection for the graph in Figure 3.24?
    (b) On which side of C is $d^2P/dt^2 < 0$?
    (c) Does the *rate of change* of purity attain its maximum at C?

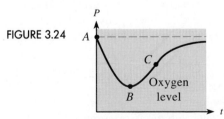

FIGURE 3.24

37. **Production** Suppose that the total number of units produced by a worker in t hours of an

8-hour shift can be modeled by the **production function** $P(t)$:

$$P(t) = 27t + 12t^2 - t^3.$$

Find the number of hours before
(a) production is maximized.
(b) the rate of production is maximized. That is, find the point of diminishing returns.

38. ***Poiseuille's law—velocity of blood*** According to Poiseuille's law, the speed S of blood through an artery of radius r at a distance x from the artery wall is given by

$$S = k[r^2 - (r - x)^2],$$

where k is a constant. Find the distance x that maximizes the speed.

39. ***Spread of disease*** Suppose that the rate of change R of the number of people affected by a flu virus in a community of 10,000 is given by

$$R = kN(10,000 - N),$$

where N is the number affected and k is a constant. Find the number N at which the rate of spread (that is, R) is maximized.

40. ***Oxygen purity—diminishing returns*** Suppose that the oxygen level P (for purity) in a body of water t months after an oil spill is given by

$$P(t) = 500\left[1 - \frac{4}{t + 4} + \frac{16}{(t + 4)^2}\right].$$

How long before the
(a) oxygen level reaches its minimum?
(b) rate of change of P is maximized? That is, find the point of diminishing returns.

41. ***Advertising and sales—diminishing returns*** Suppose that a company's daily sales volume attributed to an advertising campaign is given by

$$S(t) = \frac{3}{t + 3} - \frac{18}{(t + 3)^2} + 1.$$

How long before
(a) sales volume is maximized?
(b) the rate of change of sales volume is minimized? That is, find the point of diminishing returns.

42. ***Poverty in the United States*** The following figure shows the number of people in the United States who lived below the poverty level for selected years between 1960 and 1988. The figure also contains the graph of the function used to model these data:

$$p(x) = 1184.01 - 43.136x + 0.5296x^2 - 0.00214x^3,$$

where x is the number of years past 1900.

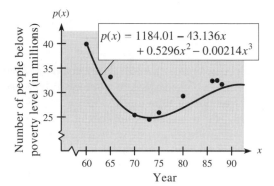

Year	Number of people below the poverty level (in millions)
1960	39.9
1965	33.2
1970	25.4
1973	24.5
1975	25.9
1980	29.3
1986	32.4
1987	32.5
1988	31.7

Source: *World Almanac*, 1991.

The data points show a downturn in the number of people below the poverty line in the late 1980s, but the model does not reflect this. During which year does the model begin to be concave downward, indicating that it may also have a downturn in the future?

3.3 | ASYMPTOTES; MORE CURVE SKETCHING

OBJECTIVES

- To locate horizontal asymptotes
- To locate vertical asymptotes
- To sketch graphs of functions that have vertical and/or horizontal asymptotes

The procedures for using the first-derivative test and the second-derivative test are given in the previous sections, but none of the graphs discussed in those sections contain vertical asymptotes or horizontal asymptotes. In this section, we consider how to use information about asymptotes along with the first and second derivatives and present a unified approach to curve sketching.

ASYMPTOTES

In Section 1.5, we first discussed asymptotes and saw that they are important features of the graphs that have them. Then, in our discussion of limits, we discovered the relationship between certain limits and asymptotes. Limits are used to precisely define and locate asymptotes.

Because a horizontal asymptote tells us the behavior of the functional values (y-coordinates) when x increases or decreases without bound, we use limits at infinity to determine the existence of horizontal asymptotes.

Horizontal Asymptote

The graph of a rational function $y = f(x)$ will have a horizontal asymptote at $y = b$, for a constant b, if

$$\lim_{x \to +\infty} f(x) = b \quad \text{or} \quad \lim_{x \to -\infty} f(x) = b.$$

Otherwise, the graph has no horizontal asymptote.

Note that, for a rational function f, $\lim_{x \to +\infty} f(x) = b$, if and only if $\lim_{x \to -\infty} f(x) = b$; so we only need to find one of these limits to locate a horizontal asymptote.

Just as with horizontal asymptotes, the formal definition of vertical asymptotes uses limits.

Vertical Asymptote

The line $x = x_0$ is a **vertical asymptote** of the graph of $y = f(x)$ if the values of $f(x)$ approach $+\infty$ or $-\infty$ as x approaches x_0 (from the left or the right).

From our work with limits, recall that a vertical asymptote will occur on the graph of a function at an x-value where the function has its denominator (but not its numerator) equal to zero. These observations allow us to determine where vertical asymptotes occur.

Vertical Asymptote of a Rational Function

The graph of the rational function

$$h(x) = \frac{f(x)}{g(x)}$$

has a vertical asymptote at $x = c$ if $g(c) = 0$ and $f(c) \neq 0$.

EXAMPLE 1

Find any vertical and horizontal asymptotes for

(a) $f(x) = \dfrac{2x - 1}{x + 2}$ (b) $f(x) = \dfrac{x^2 + 3}{1 - x}$.

Solution

(a) The denominator of this function is 0 at $x = -2$, and because this value does not make the numerator 0, there is a vertical asymptote at $x = -2$.

Because the function is rational, we can find horizontal asymptotes by evaluating

$$\lim_{x \to +\infty} \frac{2x - 1}{x + 2} \quad \text{or} \quad \lim_{x \to -\infty} \frac{2x - 1}{x + 2}.$$

We will evaluate both.

$$\lim_{x \to +\infty} \frac{2x - 1}{x + 2} = \lim_{x \to +\infty} \frac{2 - 1/x}{1 + 2/x} = \frac{2 - 0}{1 + 0} = 2$$

$$\lim_{x \to -\infty} \frac{2x - 1}{x + 2} = \lim_{x \to -\infty} \frac{2 - 1/x}{1 + 2/x} = \frac{2 - 0}{1 + 0} = 2$$

Thus there is a horizontal asymptote at $y = 2$. The graph is shown in Figure 3.25(a).

(b) The denominator of this function is 0 at $x = 1$, and because this value does not make the numerator 0, there is a vertical asymptote at $x = 1$.

To find horizontal asymptotes, we evaluate the following.

$$\lim_{x \to +\infty} \frac{x^2 + 3}{1 - x} = \lim_{x \to +\infty} \frac{1 + 3/x^2}{1/x^2 - 1/x} = \frac{1 + 0}{0 - 0} = -\infty.$$

This limit is $-\infty$ because the numerator approaches 1 and the denominator approaches 0 through negative values. Thus

$$\lim_{x \to +\infty} \frac{x^2 + 3}{1 - x} \quad \text{does not exist}$$

and the graph has no horizontal asymptotes. Note also that

$$\lim_{x \to -\infty} \frac{x^2 + 3}{1 - x} \quad \text{does not exist.}$$

The graph is shown in Figure 3.25(b).

FIGURE 3.25

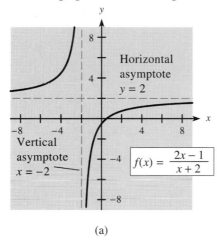

Horizontal asymptote
$y = 2$

Vertical asymptote
$x = -2$

$f(x) = \dfrac{2x - 1}{x + 2}$

(a)

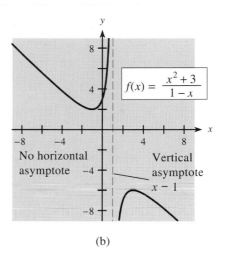

$f(x) = \dfrac{x^2 + 3}{1 - x}$

No horizontal asymptote

Vertical asymptote
$x - 1$

(b)

MORE CURVE SKETCHING

We now extend our first- and second-derivative techniques of curve sketching to include functions that have asymptotes.

In general, the following steps are helpful when we sketch the graph of a function.

1. Determine the domain of the function. The domain may be restricted by the nature of the problem or by the equation.

2. Look for vertical asymptotes, especially if the function is a rational function.

3. Look for horizontal asymptotes, especially if the function is a rational function.

4. Find the relative maxima and minima by using the first-derivative test or the second-derivative test.

5. Use the second derivative to find the points of inflection if this derivative is easily found.

6. Use other information (intercepts, for example) and plot additional points to complete the sketch of the graph.

EXAMPLE 2

Sketch the graph of $y = f(x) = \dfrac{2x - 1}{x - 1}$.

Solution

1. The domain is the set of all real numbers except $x = 1$.

2. The denominator of $f(x)$ is 0 at $x = 1$, and the numerator is not 0 at $x = 1$, so a vertical asymptote occurs at $x = 1$.

3. Because $\displaystyle\lim_{x \to +\infty} \frac{2x - 1}{x - 1} = \lim_{x \to +\infty} \frac{2 - 1/x}{1 - 1/x} = 2$, $y = 2$ is a horizontal asymptote for the graph.

4. To find the critical values, we first find $f'(x)$.

$$f'(x) = \frac{(x - 1)2 - (2x - 1)1}{(x - 1)^2} = \frac{-1}{(x - 1)^2}$$

The only critical value is $x = 1$, where the vertical asymptote occurs, so the graph has no maxima or minima. Note that $f'(x) < 0$ for all $x \neq 1$, so $f(x)$ is decreasing for all values of x for which $f'(x)$ and $f(x)$ exist. [See the sign diagram for $f'(x)$.]

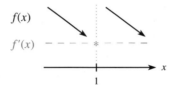

$* x = 1$ is a vertical asymptote.

5. $f'(x) = -(x - 1)^{-2}$,

so $f''(x) = 2(x - 1)^{-3}$ or $f''(x) = \dfrac{2}{(x - 1)^3}$.

Because no value of x gives $f''(x) = 0$ and $f(x)$ is undefined where $f''(x)$ is undefined, there can be no points of inflection. The graph is concave down to the left of $x = -1$ and concave up to the right of $x = -1$. [See the sign diagram for $f''(x)$.]

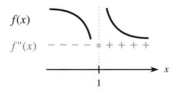

$* x = 1$ is a vertical asymptote.

6. Plotting additional points [including $(0, 1)$] gives the graph in Figure 3.26.

FIGURE 3.26

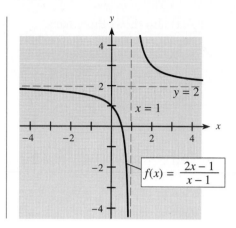

$$f(x) = \frac{2x-1}{x-1}$$

EXAMPLE 3

Sketch the graph of $y = f(x) = \dfrac{4x}{x^2+4}$.

Solution

1. The domain of this function contains all real numbers.

2. Because the domain contains all real numbers, there is no vertical asymptote.

3. $\displaystyle\lim_{x\to+\infty}\frac{4x}{x^2+4} = \lim_{x\to+\infty}\frac{4/x}{1+4/x^2} = \frac{0}{1+0} = 0$, thus $y = 0$,
   the x-axis, is a horizontal asymptote.

4. $f'(x) = \dfrac{(x^2+4)(4) - 4x(2x)}{(x^2+4)^2} = \dfrac{-4x^2+16}{(x^2+4)^2}$

   $f'(x) = 0$ when $-4x^2 + 16 = 0$ (that is, at $x = -2$ or $x = 2$) and $f'(x)$ is never undefined. Thus the only critical values are $x = -2$ and $x = 2$.

   $$f''(x) = \frac{(x^2+4)^2(-8x) - (-4x^2+16)[2(x^2+4)(2x)]}{(x^2+4)^4}$$

   $$= \frac{(x^2+4)(4x)[-2(x^2+4) - (-4x^2+16)]}{(x^2+4)^4}$$

   $$= \frac{4x(2x^2-24)}{(x^2+4)^3}$$

   $$= \frac{8x(x^2-12)}{(x^2+4)^3}$$

   Using the second derivative test gives

   $$f''(-2) = \frac{1}{4} > 0 \Rightarrow \text{relative minimum at } (-2, f(-2)) = (-2, -1)$$

   $$f''(2) = -\frac{1}{4} < 0 \Rightarrow \text{relative maximum at } (2, f(2)) = (2, 1)$$

The sign diagram for $f'(x)$ also shows these facts.

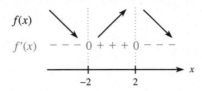

5. $f''(x) = 0$ where $8x(x^2 - 12) = 0$, at $x = 0$, $x = -2\sqrt{3}$, and $x = 2\sqrt{3}$. Checking $f''(x)$ on either side of these values shows that $(0, 0)$, $(-2\sqrt{3}, -\sqrt{3}/2)$, and $(2\sqrt{3}, \sqrt{3}/2)$ are points of inflection [see the sign diagram for $f''(x)$].

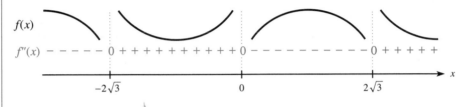

6. Using the information above, with intercept $(0, 0)$ and the fact that the graph is symmetric about the origin, we can sketch the graph, which is shown in Figure 3.27.

FIGURE 3.27

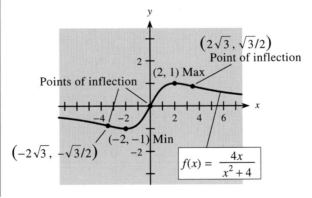

CHECKPOINT

1. Let $f(x) = \dfrac{2x + 10}{x - 1}$ and decide whether the following are true or false.

   (a) $f(x)$ has a vertical asymptote at $x = 1$.

   (b) $f(x)$ has $y = 2$ as its horizontal asymptote.

2. Let $f(x) = \dfrac{x^3 - 16}{x} + 1$; then $f'(x) = \dfrac{2x^3 + 16}{x^2}$ and $f''(x) = \dfrac{2x^3 - 32}{x^3}$.

   Use these to determine whether the following are true or false.

(a) There are no asymptotes.

(b) $f'(x) = 0$ when $x = -2$

(c) A partial sign diagram for $f'(x)$ is

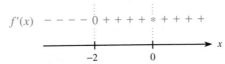

$f'(x) \quad - - - - 0 + + + + * + + + +$

$-2 \qquad 0$

* means $f'(0)$ is undefined.

(d) There is a relative minimum at $x = -2$.

(e) A partial sign diagram for $f''(x)$ is

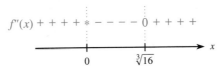

$f''(x) + + + + * - - - - 0 + + + +$

$0 \qquad \sqrt[3]{16}$

* means $f''(0)$ is undefined.

(f) There are points of inflection at $x = 0$ and $x = \sqrt[3]{16}$.

EXAMPLE 4

Graph the function

$$y = f(x) = \frac{x^2 + 3}{1 + x}.$$

Solution

1. The domain is the set of all real numbers except $x = -1$.

2. The denominator is 0 at $x = -1$, and the numerator is not 0 at $x = -1$, so a vertical asymptote occurs at $x = 1$.

3. Because $\lim\limits_{x \to +\infty} \dfrac{x^2 + 3}{1 + x} = \lim\limits_{x \to +\infty} \dfrac{1 + 3/x^2}{1/x^2 + 1/x} = +\infty$, there is no horizontal asymptote.

4. To find the critical values, we first find $f'(x)$.

$$f'(x) = \frac{(1 + x)2x - (x^2 + 3)(1)}{(1 + x)^2} = \frac{x^2 + 2x - 3}{(1 + x)^2}$$

The derivative is undefined at $x = -1$, where the vertical asymptote occurs, and $f'(x) = 0$ when $0 = (x + 3)(x - 1)$ or when $x = -3$ or $x = 1$.

The second derivative is

$$f''(x) = \frac{(1 + x)^2(2x + 2) - (x^2 + 2x - 3)2(1 + x)}{(1 + x)^4}$$

$$= \frac{(1 + x)[2x^2 + 4x + 2 - (2x^2 + 4x - 6)]}{(1 + x)^4}$$

$$= \frac{8}{(1 + x)^3}$$

$$f''(-3) = \frac{8}{-8} < 0 \Rightarrow \text{relative maximum at } (-3, -6)$$

$$f''(1) = \frac{8}{8} > 0 \Rightarrow \text{relative minimum at } (1, 2)$$

The sign diagram for $f'(x)$ also shows these.

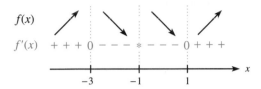

* $x = -1$ is a vertical asymptote.

5. The graph does change concavity at $x = -1$, but there is no point of inflection because $x = -1$ is the vertical asymptote.

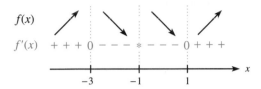

* $x = -1$ is a vertical asymptote.

6. The graph is concave down on the interval $(-\infty, -1)$ and concave up on $(-1, +\infty)$ [see the sign diagram]. The sign diagram for f' shows the behavior of the graph near the vertical asymptote $x = -1$. The graph of the function is shown in Figure 3.28.

FIGURE 3.28

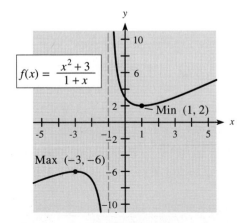

$$f(x) = \frac{x^2 + 3}{1 + x}$$

Min $(1, 2)$

Max $(-3, -6)$

EXAMPLE 5 | Sketch the graph of the function $f(x) = \dfrac{x^2}{(x+1)^2}$.

Solution

1. The domain is the set of all real numbers except $x = -1$.

2. Because $x = -1$ makes the denominator 0 and does not make the numerator 0, there is a vertical asymptote at $x = -1$.

3. Because
$$\lim_{x \to +\infty} \frac{x^2}{(x+1)^2} = \lim_{x \to +\infty} \frac{x^2}{x^2 + 2x + 1}$$
$$= \lim_{x \to +\infty} \frac{1}{1 + \dfrac{2}{x} + \dfrac{1}{x^2}}$$
$$= \frac{1}{1 + 0 + 0} = 1,$$

there is a horizontal asymptote at $y = 1$.

4. To find any maxima and minima, we first find $f'(x)$.

$$f'(x) = \frac{(x+1)^2(2x) - x^2[2(x+1)]}{(x+1)^4}$$
$$= \frac{2x(x+1)[(x+1) - x]}{(x+1)^4}$$
$$= \frac{2x}{(x+1)^3}$$

Thus $f'(x) = 0$ when $x = 0$ (and $y = 0$), and $f'(x)$ is undefined at $x = -1$ (where the vertical asymptote occurs). Testing $f'(x)$ on either side of $x = 0$ and $x = -1$ gives the following sign diagram. The sign diagram for f' shows that the critical point $(0, 0)$ is a relative minimum and shows how the graph approaches the vertical asymptote at $x = -1$.

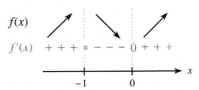

* $x = -1$ is a vertical asymptote.

5. The second derivative is

$$f''(x) = \frac{(x+1)^3(2) - 2x[3(x+1)^2]}{(x+1)^6}$$

Factoring $(x+1)^2$ from the numerator and simplifying gives

$$f''(x) = \frac{2 - 4x}{(x+1)^4}.$$

We can see that $f''(0) = 2 > 0$, so the second derivative test also shows that $(0, 0)$ is a relative minimum. We see that $f''(x) = 0$ when $x = \frac{1}{2}$. Checking $f''(x)$ between $x = -1$ (where it is undefined) and $x = \frac{1}{2}$ shows the graph is concave up on this interval. Also, note that $f''(x) < 0$ for $x > \frac{1}{2}$, so the point $(\frac{1}{2}, \frac{1}{9})$ is a point of inflection. Also see the sign diagram for $f''(x)$.

$f(x)$

$f''(x)$ $+ + + * + + + 0 - - -$

-1 $\frac{1}{2}$ x

* $x = -1$ is a vertical asymptote.

6. To see how the graph approaches the horizontal asymptote, we check $f(x)$ for large values of $|x|$.

$$f(-100) = \frac{(-100)^2}{(-99)^2} = \frac{10{,}000}{9{,}801} > 1, \qquad f(100) = \frac{100^2}{101^2} = \frac{10{,}000}{10{,}201} < 1$$

Thus the graph has the characteristics shown in Figure 3.29(a). The graph is shown in Figure 3.29(b).

FIGURE 3.29

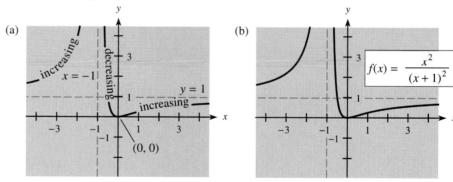

(a)

(b)

$$f(x) = \frac{x^2}{(x+1)^2}$$

When we wish to learn about a function $f(x)$ or sketch its graph, it is important to understand what information we obtain from $f(x)$, from $f'(x)$, and from $f''(x)$. The following summary may be helpful.

Summary

Source	Information provided
$f(x)$	y-coordinates; horizontal asymptotes; vertical asymptotes; domain restrictions
$f'(x)$	Increasing [$f'(x) > 0$]; decreasing [$f'(x) < 0$]; critical points [$f'(x) = 0$ or $f'(x)$ undefined]; sign diagram tests for maxima and minima
$f''(x)$	Concave up [$f''(x) > 0$]; concave down [$f''(x) < 0$]; possible points of inflection [$f''(x) = 0$ or $f''(x)$ undefined]; sign-diagram tests for points of inflection; second-derivative test for maxima and minima

TECHNOLOGY CORNER

1. (a) Graph $f(x) = \dfrac{71x^2}{28(3 - 2x^2)}$.

   (b) From the graph of $f(x)$, estimate $\lim\limits_{x \to \infty} f(x)$.

   (c) From the graph, estimate the x-values where any vertical asymptotes occur.

   (d) Can your work in (b) and (c) be done more accurately from the graph or by applying the techniques of this chapter?

2. Use the graph of $y = f(x)$ shown below to complete the following.

   (a) Determine where $f'(x) = 0$ and where $f'(x)$ is undefined.

   (b) Determine intervals where $f'(x) > 0$ and where $f'(x) < 0$.

   (c) Use the results from (a) and (b) to graph $f'(x)$.

   (d) Of the functions

   $$y_1 = \frac{(x - 2)(x - 3)}{x + 1}, \quad y_2 = \frac{x^2 - 5x + 6}{x - 1}, \quad \text{and} \quad y_3 = \frac{6 - 5x - x^2}{x - 1},$$

   one is the function $f(x)$ whose graph is shown. Choose the correct equation and explain why you chose it. Graph this equation to verify that your choice is correct.

   (e) For the function found in (d), find $f'(x)$ and graph it. Compare the graph to the one you sketched in (c).

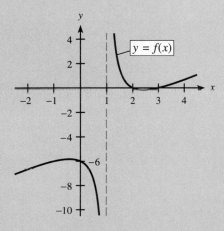

1. (a) True, $x = 1$ makes the denominator of $f(x)$ equal to zero, but not the numerator.

   (b) True, $\lim\limits_{x \to \infty} \dfrac{2x + 10}{x - 1} = 2$ and $\lim\limits_{x \to -\infty} \dfrac{2x + 10}{x - 1} = 2$.

2. (a) False. There are no horizontal asymptotes, but $x = 0$ is a vertical asymptote.

   (b) True

   (c) True

   (d) True. The relative minimum point is $(-2, f(-2)) = (-2, 13)$.

   (e) True

   (f) False. There is a point of inflection only at $(\sqrt[3]{16}, 1)$. At $x = 0$ the vertical asymptote occurs, so there is no point on the graph, and hence no point of inflection. ∎

EXERCISE 3.3

In problems 1–4, use the graphs to find each of the following, if they exist:

(a) vertical asymptotes   (b) $\lim\limits_{x \to \infty} f(x)$

(c) horizontal asymptotes   (d) $\lim\limits_{x \to -\infty} f(x)$

1.

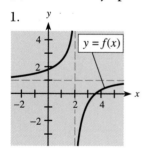

2.

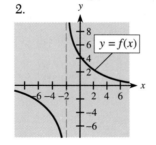

3.

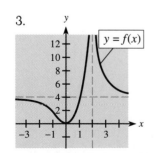

4.

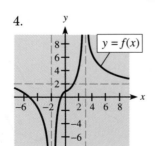

In problems 5–12, find any horizontal and vertical asymptotes for each function.

5. $y = \dfrac{2x}{x - 3}$

6. $y = \dfrac{3x - 1}{x + 5}$

7. $y = \dfrac{x + 1}{x^2 - 4}$

8. $y = \dfrac{4x}{9 - x^2}$

9. $y = \dfrac{3x^2 - 6}{2x - 5}$

10. $y = \dfrac{4x^2 - 1}{4x + 9}$

11. $f(x) = \dfrac{x - 1}{x^2 + 4x + 5}$

12. $f(x) = \dfrac{4x}{x^2 + 2x + 5}$

In problems 13–18, a function and its first and second derivatives are given. Use these to find any horizontal and vertical asymptotes, critical points, relative maxima, relative minima, and points of inflection; then sketch the graph of each function.

13. $y = \dfrac{x}{(x - 1)^2}$

$y' = -\dfrac{x + 1}{(x - 1)^3}$

$y'' = \dfrac{2x + 4}{(x - 1)^4}$

14. $y = \dfrac{(x - 1)^2}{x^2}$

$y' = \dfrac{2(x - 1)}{x^3}$

$y'' = \dfrac{6 - 4x}{x^4}$

15. $y = x + \dfrac{3}{\sqrt[3]{x - 3}}$

$y' = \dfrac{(x - 3)^{2/3} - 1}{(x - 3)^{2/3}}$

$y'' = \dfrac{2}{3(x - 3)^{5/3}}$

16. $y = 3\sqrt[3]{x} + \dfrac{1}{x}$

$y' = \dfrac{x^{4/3} - 1}{x^2}$

$y'' = \dfrac{6 - 2x^{4/3}}{3x^3}$

17. $f(x) = \dfrac{3x^{2/3}}{x + 1}$

$f'(x) = \dfrac{2 - x}{x^{1/3}(x + 1)^2}$

$f''(x) = \dfrac{2(2x^2 - 8x - 1)}{3x^{4/3}(x + 1)^3}$

18. $f(x) = \dfrac{9(x - 2)^{2/3}}{x^2}$

$f'(x) = \dfrac{12(3 - x)}{x^3(x - 2)^{1/3}}$

$f''(x) = \dfrac{4(7x^2 - 42x + 54)}{x^4(x - 2)^{4/3}}$

For each function in problems 19–28, find any horizontal and vertical asymptotes, and use information from the derivative to sketch the graph.

19. $y = 1/x^2$

20. $y = 4/(x - 4)^2$

21. $y = 1/(x - 1)^3$

22. $y = 1/x^3$

23. $y = \dfrac{x^2 + 4}{x}$

24. $y = \dfrac{x^2 + 4}{x^2}$

25. $y = \dfrac{27x^2}{(x + 1)^3}$

26. $y = \left(\dfrac{x}{x - 2}\right)^2$

27. $f(x) = \dfrac{16x}{x^2 + 1}$

28. $f(x) = \dfrac{4x^2}{x^4 + 1}$

APPLICATIONS

29. **Cost-benefit** The percentage p of particulate pollution that can be removed from the smokestacks of an industrial plant by spending C dollars is given by

$$p = \dfrac{100C}{7300 + C}.$$

(a) Find any C-values where the rate of change of p with respect to C does not exist. Make sure that these make sense in the problem.
(b) Find C-values for which p is increasing.
(c) If there is a horizontal asymptote, find it.
(d) Can 100% of the pollution be removed?

30. **Cost-benefit** The percentage p of impurities that can be removed from the waste water of a manufacturing process at a cost of C dollars is given by

$$p = \dfrac{100C}{8100 + C}.$$

(a) Find any C-values where the rate of change of p with respect to C does not exist. Make sure that these make sense in the problem.
(b) Find C-values for which p is increasing.
(c) Find any horizontal asymptotes.
(d) Can 100% of the pollution be removed?

31. **Revenue** A recently released film has its weekly revenue given by

$$R(t) = \dfrac{50t}{t^2 + 36}, \qquad t \ge 0,$$

where $R(t)$ is in millions of dollars and t is in weeks.
(a) Graph $R(t)$.
(b) When will revenue be maximized?
(c) Suppose that if revenue decreases for 4 consecutive weeks, the film will be removed from theaters and will be released as a video 12 weeks later. When will the video come out?

32. **Production costs** Suppose that the total cost of producing a shipment of a certain product is

$$C = 5000x + \dfrac{125,000}{x}, \qquad x > 0,$$

where x is the number of machines used in production.
(a) Graph this total cost function.
(b) Using how many machines will minimize the total cost?

33. ***Profit*** An entrepreneur starts new companies and sells them when their growth is maximized. Suppose that the annual profit for a new company is given by

$$P(x) = 22 - \frac{1}{2}x - \frac{18}{x+1},$$

where P is in thousands of dollars and x is the number of years after the company is formed. If she wants to sell the company before profits begin to decline, after how many years should she sell it?

34. ***Sales volume*** Figure 3.30 shows a typical curve that gives the volume of sales S as a function of time t since an ad campaign.
    (a) What is the horizontal asymptote?
    (b) What is $\lim_{t \to \infty} S(t)$?
    (c) What is the horizontal asymptote for $S'(t)$?
    (d) What is $\lim_{t \to \infty} S'(t)$?

FIGURE 3.30

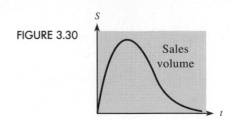

35. ***Productivity*** Figure 3.31 is a typical graph of worker productivity per hour P as a function of time t on the job.
    (a) What is the horizontal asymptote?
    (b) What is $\lim_{t \to \infty} P(t)$?
    (c) What is the horizontal asymptote for $P'(t)$?
    (d) What is $\lim_{t \to \infty} P'(t)$?

FIGURE 3.31

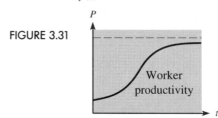

3.4 | OPTIMIZATION IN BUSINESS AND ECONOMICS

OBJECTIVES

- To find absolute maxima and minima
- To maximize revenue, given the total revenue function
- To minimize the average cost, given the total cost function
- To find the maximum profit from total cost and total revenue functions, or from a profit function
- To find the tax per unit, under pure competition, that maximizes tax revenue

Thus far, when we have discussed finding maxima and minima of functions, we have focused on the general case of **relative** extrema. However, in most applications, we are really interested in what we call **absolute extrema.** As the name implies, absolute extrema are the functional values that are the largest or smallest values over the entire domain of the function (or over the interval of interest).

Most companies are interested in obtaining the greatest possible profit (as opposed to making a profit that is relatively large). Similarly, a manufacturer of a certain product is concerned about producing this product for the lowest possible average cost.

In this section we will discuss how to find the absolute extrema of a function and then use these techniques to solve applications involving revenue, cost, and profit.

Let us begin by considering the graph of $y = (x - 1)^2$, shown in Figure 3.32(a). This graph has a relative minimum at $(1, 0)$.

Notice in Figure 3.32(a) that the relative minimum is the lowest point on the graph. In this case, we call the point an **absolute minimum** for the function. Similarly, when there is a point that is the highest point on the graph over the domain of the function, we call the point an **absolute maximum** for the function.

In Figure 3.32(a), we see that there is no relative maximum. However, if the domain of the function is restricted to the interval $\left[\frac{1}{2}, 2\right]$, then we get the graph shown in Figure 3.32(b). In this case, there is an absolute maximum at point $(2, 1)$, and the absolute minimum is still at $(1, 0)$.

If the domain of $y = (x - 1)^2$ is restricted to the interval $[2, 3]$, the resulting graph is shown in Figure 3.32(c). In this case, the absolute minimum occurs at point $(2, 1)$, and its absolute maximum occurs at $(3, 4)$.

FIGURE 3.32

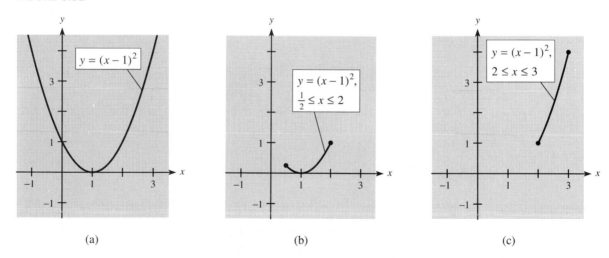

(a)   (b)   (c)

As the preceding discussion indicates, if the domain of a function is limited, an absolute maximum or minimum may occur at the endpoints of the domain. In testing functions with limited domains for absolute maxima and minima, we must compare the endpoints of the domain with the relative maxima and minima found by taking derivatives. In applications to management, life, and social sciences, a limited domain occurs very often, since many quantities are required to be positive, or at least nonnegative.

MAXIMIZING REVENUE

Since the marginal revenue is the first derivative of the total revenue, it should be obvious that the total revenue function will have a critical point at the point where the marginal revenue equals 0. With the total revenue function $R(x) = 16x - 0.02x^2$, the point where $R'(x) = 0$ is clearly a maximum since $R(x)$ is a parabola that opens downward. But the revenue function may not always be a parabola and the critical point may not always be a maximum, so it is wise to verify that the maximum value occurs at the critical point.

EXAMPLE 1

If total revenue for a firm is given by

$$R(x) = 8000x - 40x^2 - x^3,$$

where x is the number of units sold, find the number of units that must be sold to maximize revenue. Find the maximum revenue.

Solution $R'(x) = 8000 - 80x - 3x^2$, so we must solve $8000 - 80x - 3x^2 = 0$ for x.

$$(40 - x)(200 + 3x) = 0$$
$$40 - x = 0 \qquad 200 + 3x = 0,$$

so

$$x = 40 \quad \text{or} \quad x = -\frac{200}{3}.$$

Now, we reject the negative value for x, but we must verify that $x = 40$ will yield maximum revenue.

$$\left.\begin{array}{l} R'(0) = 8000 > 0 \\ R'(100) = 8000 - 8000 - 30{,}000 < 0 \end{array}\right\} \Rightarrow \text{relative maximum}$$

This test shows that a relative maximum occurs at $x = 40$, giving revenue $R(40) = \$192{,}000$. Because $R(x) < 0$ for all $x > 40$, the revenue function is decreasing to the right of $x = 40$. The revenue at $x = 0$ is $R(0) = 0$, so $R = \$192{,}000$ at $x = 40$ is the (absolute) maximum revenue.

EXAMPLE 2

A travel agency will plan group tours for groups of 25 or larger. If the group contains exactly 25 people, the cost is \$300 per person. However, each person's cost is reduced by \$10 for each additional person above the 25. What size group will produce the largest revenue for the agency?

Solution The total revenue is

$$R = (\text{number of people})(\text{cost per person}).$$

If 25 people go, the total revenue will be

$$R = 25 \cdot \$300 = \$7500.$$

But if x additional people go, the number of people will be $25 + x$, and the cost per person will be $(300 - 10x)$ dollars. Then the total revenue will be a function of x,

$$R = R(x) = (25 + x)(300 - 10x),$$

or

$$R(x) = 7500 + 50x - 10x^2.$$

This function will have its maximum where $\overline{MR} = R'(x) = 0$; $R'(x) = 50 - 20x$, and the solution to $0 = 50 - 20x$ is $x = 2.5$. Thus adding 2.5 people to the group should maximize the total revenue. But we cannot add half a person. So we will test the total revenue function for 27 people and 28 people. This will determine the most profitable number because $R(x)$ is concave downward for all x.

For $x = 2$ (giving 27 people) we get $R(2) = 7500 + 50(2) - 10(2)^2 = 7560$. For $x = 3$ (giving 28 people) we get $R(3) = 7500 + 50(3) - 10(3)^2 = 7560$. Note that both 27 and 28 people give the same total revenue and that this revenue is greater than the revenue for 25 people. Thus the revenue is maximized at either 27 or 28 people in the group.

MINIMIZING AVERAGE COST

Since the total cost function is always increasing, we cannot find the number of units that will make the total cost a minimum (except for producing 0 units, which is an absolute minimum). However, we usually can find the number of units that will make the average cost per unit a minimum.

Average Cost   If the total cost is represented by $C = C(x)$, then the **average cost per unit** is

$$\overline{C} = \frac{C(x)}{x}.$$

For example, if $C = 3x^2 + 4x + 2$ is the total cost function for a commodity, the **average cost function** is

$$\overline{C} = \frac{3x^2 + 4x + 2}{x} = 3x + 4 + \frac{2}{x}.$$

Note that the average cost per unit is undefined if no units are produced.

We can use the first-derivative test to find the minimum of the average cost function, as the following example shows.

EXAMPLE 3

If the total cost function for a commodity is given by $C = \frac{1}{4}x^2 + 4x + 100$, where x represents the number of units produced, producing how many units will result in a minimum *average cost* per unit? Find the minimum average cost.

Solution The average cost function is given by

$$\overline{C} = \frac{\frac{1}{4}x^2 + 4x + 100}{x} = \frac{1}{4}x + 4 + \frac{100}{x}.$$

Then

$$\overline{C}' = \overline{C}'(x) = \frac{1}{4} - \frac{100}{x^2}.$$

Setting $\overline{C}' = 0$ gives

$$0 = \frac{1}{4} - \frac{100}{x^2},$$
$$0 = x^2 - 400, \quad \text{or} \quad x = \pm 20.$$

Since the quantity produced must be positive, 20 units should minimize the average cost per unit. We show it is an absolute minimum by using the second derivative.

$$\overline{C}''(x) = \frac{200}{x^3} \quad \text{so} \quad \overline{C}''(x) > 0 \text{ when } x > 0.$$

Thus the minimum average cost per unit occurs if 20 units are produced. The graph of the average cost per unit is shown in Figure 3.33. The minimum average cost per unit is $\overline{C}(20) = \$14$.

FIGURE 3.33

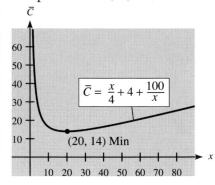

$$\overline{C} = \frac{x}{4} + 4 + \frac{100}{x}$$

(20, 14) Min

MAXIMIZING PROFIT

In Chapter 2, we defined the marginal profit function as the derivative of the profit function. That is,

$$\overline{MP} = P'(x).$$

In this chapter we have seen how to use the derivative to find maxima and minima for various functions. Now we can apply those same techniques, in the context of marginal profit, in order to maximize profit functions.

If there is a physical limitation on the number of units that can be produced in a given period of time, then the endpoints of the interval caused by these limitations should also be checked.

EXAMPLE 4

Suppose that the production capacity for a certain commodity cannot exceed 30. If the total profit function for this commodity is

$$P(x) = 4x^3 - 210x^2 + 3600x - 200,$$

where x is the number of units sold, find the number of items that will maximize profit.

Solution The restrictions on capacity mean that $P(x)$ is restricted by $0 \leq x \leq 30$. The marginal profit function is

$$P'(x) = 12x^2 - 420x + 3600.$$

Setting $P'(x)$ equal to 0, we get

$$0 = 12(x - 15)(x - 20),$$

so $P'(x) = 0$ at $x = 15$ *and* $x = 20$. Testing to the right and left of these values (as in the first-derivative test) we get

$$\left.\begin{array}{l} P'(0) = 3600 > 0 \\ P'(18) = -72 < 0 \\ P'(25) = 600 > 0 \end{array}\right\} \begin{array}{l} \Rightarrow \text{relative maximum at } x = 15. \\ \Rightarrow \text{relative minimum at } x = 20. \end{array}$$

Thus the total profit function has a *relative* maximum at $(15, 20{,}050)$, but we must check the endpoints (0 and 30) before deciding if it is the absolute maximum.

$$P(0) = -200 \quad \text{and} \quad P(30) = \$26{,}800$$

Thus the absolute maximum profit is $\$26{,}800$, and it occurs at the endpoint, $x = 30$. Figure 3.34 shows the graph of the profit function.

FIGURE 3.34

x	P
0	-200
10	18,800
15	20,050
20	19,800
25	21,050
30	26,800

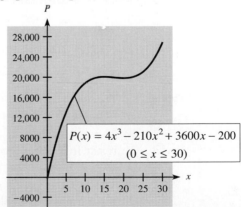

We have seen that a seller who has a monopoly can control the price by regulating the supply of the product. Since the seller controls the supply, he or she can force the price higher by limiting supply.

If the demand function for the product is $p = f(x)$, the total revenue for the sale of x units is $R(x) = px = f(x) \cdot x$. Note that the price p is fixed by the market in a competitive market, but varies with output for the monopolist.

If $\overline{C} = \overline{C}(x)$ represents the average cost per unit sold, then the total cost for the x units sold is $C = \overline{C} \cdot x = \overline{C}x$. Since we have both total cost and total revenue as a function of the quantity, x, we can maximize the profit function, $P(x) = px - \overline{C}x$, where p represents the demand function $p = f(x)$ and $\overline{C}$ represents the average cost function $\overline{C} = \overline{C}(x)$.

EXAMPLE 5

The daily demand function for a product is

$$p = 168 - 0.2x.$$

If a monopolist finds that the average cost is

$$\overline{C} = 120 + x,$$

(a) how many units must be sold to maximize profit?
(b) what is the selling price at this "optimal" level of production?
(c) what is the maximum possible profit?

Solution

(a) The total revenue function for the product is

$$R(x) = px = (168 - 0.2x)x = 168x - 0.2x^2,$$

and the total cost function is

$$C(x) = \overline{C} \cdot x = (120 + x)x = 120x + x^2.$$

Thus the profit function is

$$P(x) = R(x) - C(x) = 168x - 0.2x^2 - (120x + x^2),$$

or

$$P(x) = 48x - 1.2x^2.$$

Then, $P'(x) = 48 - 2.4x$, so $P'(x) = 0$ when $x = 20$.

We see that $P''(20) = -2.4$, so by the second-derivative test, $P(x)$ has a maximum at $x = 20$. That is, selling 20 units will maximize profit.

(b) The selling price is determined by $p = 168 - 0.2x$, so the price that will result from supplying 20 units per day is $p = 168 - 0.2(20) = 164$. That is, the "optimal" selling price is $164 per unit.

(c) The profit at $x = 20$ is $P(20) = 48(20) - 1.2(20)^2 = 960 - 480 = 480$. Thus the maximum possible profit is $480 per day.

In a *competitive market*, each firm is so small that its actions in the market cannot affect the price of the product. The price of the product is determined in the market by the intersection of the market demand curve (from all consumers) and market supply curve (from all firms that supply this product). The firm can sell as little or as much as it desires at the given market price, which it cannot change.

Therefore, a firm in a competitive market has a total revenue function given by $R(x) = px$, where p is the market equilibrium price for the product and x is the quantity sold.

EXAMPLE 6

A firm in a competitive market must sell its product for $200 per unit. The average cost per unit (per month) is $\overline{C} = 80 + x$, where x represents the number of units sold per month. How many units should be sold to maximize profit?

Solution If the average cost per unit is $\overline{C} = 80 + x$, then the total cost of x units is given by $C(x) = (80 + x)x = 80x + x^2$. The revenue per unit is $200, so the total revenue is given by $R(x) = 200x$. Thus the profit function is

$$P(x) = R(x) - C(x) = 200x - (80x + x^2), \quad \text{or} \quad P(x) = 120x - x^2.$$

Then $P'(x) = 120 - 2x$. Setting $P'(x) = 0$ and solving for x gives $x = 60$. Since $P''(60) = -2$, the profit is maximized when the firm sells 60 units per month.

TAXATION IN A COMPETITIVE MARKET

Many taxes imposed by governments are "hidden." That is, the tax is levied on goods produced, and the producers must pay the tax. Of course, the tax becomes a cost to the producers, and they pass the tax on to the consumer in the form of higher prices for goods. But it isn't quite that simple, as the following discussion shows.

Suppose that the government imposes a tax of t dollars on each unit produced and sold by producers. If we are in pure competition in which the consumers' demand depends only on price, the *demand function* will not change. The tax will change the supply function, of course, because at each level of output q, the firm will want to charge a price higher by the amount of the tax. This will shift the entire supply curve upward by the amount of the tax t, and market equilibrium will occur at a point where quantity demanded is lower.

The graphs of the market demand function, the original market supply function, and the market supply function after taxes are shown in Figure 3.35 on the following page. Since the tax added to each item is a constant, the supply function is parallel to the original supply function and t units above it.

Note in this case that after the taxes are imposed, *no* items are supplied at the price that was the equilibrium price before taxation. After the taxes are imposed, the consumers will simply have to pay more for the product. Since taxation does not change the demand curve, the quantity purchased at market equilibrium will

FIGURE 3.35

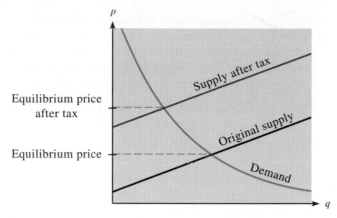

be less than it was before taxation. Thus governments planning taxes should rec-ognize that they will not collect taxes on the original equilibrium quantity. They will collect on the *new* equilibrium quantity, a quantity reduced by their taxation. Thus a large tax on each item may reduce the quantity demanded at the new mar-ket equilibrium so much that very little revenue would result from the tax.

If the tax revenue is represented by $T = tq$, where t is the tax per unit and q is the equilibrium quantity of the supply and demand functions after taxation, we can use the following procedure for maximizing the total tax revenue.

MAXIMIZING TAX REVENUE

PROCEDURE	EXAMPLE
To find the tax per item (under pure competition) that will maximize total tax revenue:	If the demand and supply functions are given by $p = 600 - q$ and $p = 200 + \frac{1}{3}q$, respectively, find the tax rate t that will maximize the total tax revenue T.
1. Write the supply function after taxation.	1. $p = 200 + \frac{1}{3}q + t$
2. Set the demand and (new) supply functions equal, and solve for t.	2. $600 - q = 200 + \frac{1}{3}q + t$ $400 - \frac{4}{3}q = t$
3. Form the total tax revenue function, $T = tq$, and take its derivative with respect to q.	3. $T = tq = 400q - \frac{4}{3}q^2$ $T'(q) = \dfrac{dT}{dq} = 400 - \dfrac{8}{3}q$
4. Set $T' = 0$, solve for q. This is the q that should maximize T. Use the second-derivative test to verify it.	4. $0 = 400 - \frac{8}{3}q$ $q = 150$ $T''(q) = -\frac{8}{3}$. Thus T is maximized at $q = 150$.
5. Substitute the value of q into the equation for t (in step 2). This is the value of t that will maximize T.	5. $t = 400 - \frac{4}{3}(150) = 200$ A tax of \$200 per item will maximize the total tax revenue. The total tax revenue for the period would be \$200 · (150) = \$30,000.

Note that in the example just given, if a tax of $300 were imposed, the total tax revenue the government would receive would be

($300)(75) = $22,500.

This means that consumers would spend $100 more for each item, suppliers would sell 75 fewer items, and the government would lose $7500 in tax revenue. Thus everyone would suffer if the tax rate were raised above $200.

CHECKPOINT

1. True or false: If $R(x)$ is the revenue function, we find all possible points where $R(x)$ could be maximized by solving $\overline{MR} = 0$ for x.

2. If $C(x) = \dfrac{x^2}{20} + 10x + 2500$, form $\overline{C}(x)$, the average cost function.

3. (a) If $p = 5000 - x$ gives the demand function in a monopoly market, find $R(x)$, if it is possible with this information.

   (b) If $p = 5000 - x$ gives the demand function in a competitive market, find $R(x)$, if it is possible with this information.

4. For problems involving taxation in a competitive market, if supply is $p = f(q)$ and demand is $p = g(q)$, is the tax t added to $f(q)$ or to $g(q)$? ■

TECHNOLOGY CORNER

A profit function formed from total cost and total revenue will normally be concave down, and, in this case, a critical point is a maximum point. Given

$$R(x) = 3000 - \frac{3000}{x + 1} \quad \text{and} \quad C(x) = 500 + 12x + x^2,$$

complete the following.

1. Find $\overline{MR}$ and $\overline{MC}$, then graph them and find the x-value of their point of intersection.

2. Form $P(x)$, graph it, and find the x-value where maximum profit occurs.

3. (a) What do you notice about your answers to (1) and (2)?

   (b) Would you conclude that profit can be maximized when $\overline{MR} = \overline{MC}$ for these functions? Justify this by finding where the maximum value of $P(x) = R(x) - C(x)$ occurs.

1. False, $\overline{MR} = R'(x)$, but there may also be critical points where $R'(x)$ is undefined or at endpoints of a restricted domain for $R(x)$.

2. $\overline{C}(x) = \dfrac{C(x)}{x} = \dfrac{x^2/20 + 10x + 2500}{x} = \dfrac{x}{20} + 10 + \dfrac{2500}{x}$

3. (a) $R(x) = p \cdot x = (5000 - x)x = 5000x - x^2$

   (b) In a competitive market, $R(x) = p \cdot x$, where p is the constant equilibrium price. Thus we need to know the supply function and find the equilibrium price before we can form $R(x)$.

4. Tax t is added to supply; $p = f(q) + t$.

EXERCISE 3.4

MAXIMIZING REVENUE

1. If the total revenue function for a radio is $R = 36x - 0.01x^2$, sale of how many units will maximize the total revenue? Find the maximum revenue.

2. If the total revenue function for a blender is $R(x) = 25x - 0.05x^2$, sale of how many units will provide the maximum total revenue? Find the maximum revenue.

3. If the total revenue function for a computer is $R(x) = 2000x - 20x^2 - x^3$, find the level of sales that maximizes revenue and find the maximum revenue.

4. A firm has total revenues given by

$$R(x) = 2800x - 8x^2 - x^3$$

for a product. Find the maximum revenue from sales of that product.

5. An agency charges $10 per person for a trip to a concert if 30 people travel in a group. But for each person above the 30, the charge will be reduced by $.20. How many people will maximize the total revenue for the agency?

6. A company handles an apartment building with 50 units. Experience has shown that if the rent for each of the units is $360 per month, all the units will be filled, but one unit will become vacant for each $10 increase in the monthly rate. What rent should be charged to maximize the total revenue from the building?

7. A cable TV company has 1000 customers paying $20 each month. If each $1 reduction in price attracts 100 new customers, find the price that yields maximum revenue. Find the maximum revenue.

8. A company has determined that its monthly sales revenue S is related to the number of dollars x spent on advertising, with

$$S = 5000 + 8000x - 0.2x^2.$$

Spending how much money on advertising will maximize their revenue? Find the maximum sales revenue.

9. The function $\overline{R}(x) = R(x)/x$ defines the average revenue for selling x units. For

$$R(x) = 2000x + 20x^2 - x^3,$$

   (a) find the maximum average revenue.
   (b) show that $\overline{R}(x)$ attains its maximum at the x-value where $\overline{R}(x) = \overline{MR}$.

10. For the revenue function given by

$$R(x) = 2800x + 8x^2 - x^3,$$

(a) find the maximum average revenue.

(b) show that $\overline{R}(x)$ attains its maximum at the x-value where $\overline{R}(x) = \overline{MR}$.

MINIMIZING AVERAGE COST

11. If the total cost function for a lamp is $C(x) = 25 + 13x + x^2$, producing how many units will result in a minimum average cost per unit? Find the minimum average cost.

12. If the total cost function for a product is $C(x) = 300 + 10x + 0.03x^2$, producing how many units will result in a minimum average cost per unit? Find the minimum average cost.

13. If the total cost function for a product is $C(x) = 100 + x^2$, producing how many units will result in a minimum average cost per unit? Find the minimum average cost.

14. If the total cost function for a product is $C(x) = 250 + 6x + 0.1x^2$, producing how many units will minimize the average cost? Find the minimum average cost.

15. If the total cost function for a product is $C(x) = (x + 4)^3$, where x represents the number of hundreds of units produced, producing how many units will minimize average cost? Find the minimum average cost.

16. If the total cost function for a product is $C(x) = (x + 5)^3$, where x represents the number of hundreds of units produced, producing how many units will minimize average cost? Find the minimum average cost.

17. For the cost function $C(x) = 25 + 13x + x^2$, show that average costs are minimized at the x-value where

$$\overline{C}(x) = \overline{MC}.$$

18. For the cost function $C(x) = 300 + 10x + 0.03x^2$, show that average costs are minimized at the x-value where

$$\overline{C}(x) = \overline{MC}.$$

MAXIMIZING PROFIT

19. If the profit function for a product is $P(x) = 5600x + 85x^2 - x^3 - 200{,}000$, selling how many items will produce a maximum profit? Find the maximum profit.

20. If the profit function for a commodity is $P = 6400x - 18x^2 - \frac{1}{3}x^3 - 40{,}000$, selling how many units will result in a maximum profit? Find the maximum profit.

21. A manufacturer estimates that x units of its product can be produced at a total cost of $C(x) = 45{,}000 + 100x + x^3$. If the manufacturer's total revenue from the sale of x units is $R(x) = 4600x$, determine the level of production x that will maximize the profit. Find the maximum profit.

22. A product can be produced at a total cost $C(x) = 800 + 100x^2 + x^3$, where x is the number produced. If the total revenue is given by $R(x) = 60{,}000x - 50x^2$, determine the level of production that will maximize the profit. Find the maximum profit.

23. A firm can produce only 1000 units per month. The monthly total cost is given by $C(x) = 300 + 200x$, where x is the number produced. If the total revenue is given by $R(x) = 250x - \frac{1}{100}x^2$, how many items should they produce for maximum profit? Find the maximum profit.

24. A firm can produce 100 units per week. If its total cost function is $C = 500 + 1500x$ and its total revenue function is $R = 1600x - x^2$, how many units should it produce to maximize its profit? Find the maximum profit.

25. A firm has monthly average costs given by

$$\overline{C} = \frac{45{,}000}{x} + 100 + x^2,$$

where x is the number of units produced per month. The firm can sell its product in a competitive market for \$4600 per unit. Find the number of units that gives maximum profit, and find the maximum profit.

26. A small business has weekly average costs of

$$\overline{C} = \frac{100}{x} + 30 + \frac{x}{10},$$

where x is the number of units produced each week. The competitive market price for this business' product is $46 per unit. Find the level of production that yields maximum profit, and find the maximum profit.

27. The weekly demand function for a product sold by only one firm is $p = 600 - \frac{1}{2}x$, and the average cost of production and sale is $\overline{C} = 300 + 2x$.
    (a) Find the quantity that will maximize profit.
    (b) Find the selling price at this optimal level of production.
    (c) What is the maximum profit?

28. The monthly demand function for a product sold by a monopoly is $p = 8000 - x$, and its average cost is $\overline{C} = 4000 + 5x$. Determine
    (a) the quantity that will maximize profit.
    (b) the selling price at the optimal quantity.
    (c) the maximum profit.

29. If the monthly demand function for a product sold by a monopoly is $p = 1960 - \frac{1}{3}x^2$, and the average cost is $\overline{C} = 1000 + 2x + x^2$, find
    (a) the quantity that will give maximum profit.
    (b) the maximum profit.

30. The monthly demand function for a product sold by a monopoly is $p = 5900 - \frac{1}{2}x^2$, and its average cost is $\overline{C} = 3020 + 2x$. Will the maximum profit result in a profit or loss?

31. An industry having a monopoly on a product has its average weekly costs given by

$$\overline{C} = \frac{10,000}{x} + 60 - 0.03x + 0.00001x^2.$$

The weekly demand for the product is given by $p = 120 - 0.015x$. Find the price the industry should set and the number of units it should produce to obtain maximum profit. Find the maximum profit.

32. A large corporation having monopolistic control in the marketplace has its average daily costs given by

$$\overline{C} = \frac{800}{x} + 100x + x^2.$$

The daily demand for its product is given by $p = 60,000 - 50x$. Find the quantity that gives maximum profit, and find the maximum profit. What selling price should the corporation set for its product?

33. A company handles an apartment building with 50 units. Experience has shown that if the rent of each of the units is $360 per month, all of the units will be filled, but one unit will become vacant for each $10 increase in this monthly rate. If the monthly cost of maintaining the apartment building is $6 per rented unit, what rent should be charged per month to maximize the profit?

34. A travel agency will plan a group tour for groups of size 25 or larger. If the group contains exactly 25 people, the cost is $500 per person. However, each person's cost is reduced by $10 for each additional person above the 25. If the travel agency incurs a cost of $125 per person for the tour, what size group will give the agency the maximum profit?

TAXATION IN A COMPETITIVE MARKET

35. If the weekly demand function is $p = 30 - q$ and the supply function before taxation is $p = 6 + 2q$, what tax per item will maximize the total tax revenue?

36. If the demand function for a fixed period of time is $p = 38 - 2q$ and the supply function before taxation is $p = 8 + 3q$, what tax per item will maximize the total tax revenue?

37. If the demand and supply functions for a product are $p = 800 - 2q$ and $p =$

$100 + 0.5q$, respectively, find the tax per unit t that will maximize the tax revenue T.

38. If the demand and supply functions for a product are $p = 2100 - 3q$ and $p = 300 + 1.5q$, respectively, find the tax per unit t that will maximize the tax revenue T.

39. If the weekly demand function is $p = 200 - 2q^2$ and the supply function before taxation is $p = 20 + 3q$, what tax per item will maximize the total tax revenue?

40. If the monthly demand function is $p = 7230 - 5q^2$ and the supply function before taxation is $p = 30 + 30q^2$, what tax per item will maximize the total tax revenue?

41. Suppose that the weekly demand for a product is given by $p + 2q = 840$ and that the weekly supply before taxation is given by

$$p = 0.02q^2 + 0.55q + 7.4.$$

Find the tax per item that produces maximum tax revenue. Find the tax revenue.

42. If the daily demand for a product is given by $p + q = 1000$, and the daily supply before taxation is given by $p = q^2/30 + 2.5q + 920$, find the tax per item that maximizes tax revenue. Find the tax revenue.

43. If the demand and supply functions for a product are $p = 2100 - 10q - 0.5q^2$ and $p = 300 + 5q + 0.5q^2$, respectively, find the tax per unit t that will maximize the tax revenue T.

44. If the demand and supply functions for a product are $p = 5000 - 20q - 0.7q^2$ and $p = 500 + 10q + 0.3q^2$, respectively, find the tax per unit t that will maximize the tax revenue T.

3.5 | APPLICATIONS OF MAXIMA AND MINIMA

OBJECTIVE

- To apply the procedures for finding maxima and minima to solve problems from management, life, and social sciences

Some of the most important applications of calculus require the use of the derivative for finding maxima and minima. As managers, workers, or consumers, we may be interested in such things as maximum revenue, maximum profit, minimum cost, maximum medical dosage, maximum utilization of resources, and so on. If we have functions that model cost, revenue, or population growth, for example, we can apply the methods of this chapter to find the maxima and minima of the functions.

EXAMPLE 1

Suppose that a new company begins production in 1992 with eight employees and the growth of the company over the next 10 years is predicted by

$$N = N(t) = 8\left(1 + \frac{160\,t}{t^2 + 16}\right), \qquad 0 \le t \le 10,$$

where N is the number of employees t years after 1992.

(a) In what year will the number of employees in the company be maximized?

(b) What will be the maximum number of employees?

Solution This function will have a relative maximum when $N'(t) = 0$.

$$N'(t) = 8\left[\frac{(t^2 + 16)(160) - (160t)(2t)}{(t^2 + 16)^2}\right]$$

$$= 8\left[\frac{160t^2 + 2560 - 320t^2}{(t^2 + 16)^2}\right]$$

$$= 8\left[\frac{2560 - 160t^2}{(t^2 + 16)^2}\right]$$

Now, $N'(t) = 0$ when its numerator is 0 (note that the denominator is never 0), so we must solve

$$2560 - 160t^2 = 0$$
$$160\,(4 + t)(4 - t) = 0,$$

so

$$t = -4 \quad \text{or} \quad t = 4.$$

We are only interested in positive t-values, so we test $t = 4$.

$$N'(0) = 8\left[\frac{2560}{256}\right] > 0$$
$$N'(10) = 8\left[\frac{-13{,}440}{(116)^2}\right] < 0$$
$$\Biggr\} \Rightarrow \text{relative maximum}$$

The relative maximum is

$$N(4) = 8\left(1 + \frac{640}{32}\right) = 168.$$

At $t = 0$, the number of employees is $N(0) = 8$, and it increases to $N(4) = 168$. After $t = 4$, $N(t)$ decreases to $N(10) = 118$ (approximately), so $N(4) = 168$ is the maximum number of employees.

Sometimes we must develop the function we need from the statement of the problem. In this case, it is important to understand what is to be maximized or minimized and to express that quantity as a function of *one* variable.

EXAMPLE 2   A farmer needs to enclose a rectangular pasture containing 1,600,000 square feet so that there will be enough grass for his herd. Suppose that along the road adjoining his property he wants to use a more expensive fence and that he needs no fence on one side perpendicular to the road because a river bounds his property on that side. If the fence costs $15 per foot along the road and $10 per foot along the two remaining sides that must be fenced, what dimensions of his rectangular field will minimize his cost? (See Figure 3.36.)

FIGURE 3.36

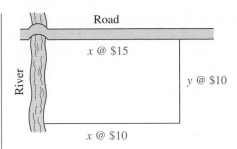

Solution In Figure 3.36, x represents the length of the pasture along the road (and parallel to the road) and y represents the width. The cost function for the fence used is

$$C = 15x + 10y + 10x = 25x + 10y.$$

We cannot use a derivative to find where C is minimized unless we write C as a function of x or y only. Because the area of the rectangular field must be 1,600,000 square feet, we have

$$A = xy = 1,600,000.$$

Solving for y in terms of x and substituting gives

$$y = \frac{1,600,000}{x},$$
$$C = 25x + 10\left(\frac{1,600,000}{x}\right) = 25x + \frac{16,000,000}{x}.$$

The derivative of C with respect to x is

$$C'(x) = 25 - \frac{16,000,000}{x^2},$$

and we find the relative minimum of C as follows:

$$0 = 25 - \frac{16,000,000}{x^2}$$
$$0 = 25x^2 - 16,000,000$$
$$25x^2 = 16,000,000$$
$$x^2 = 640,000$$
$$x = 800 \text{ feet}.$$

Testing to see if $x = 800$ gives the minimum cost, we find

$$C''(x) = \frac{32,000,000}{x^3}.$$

$C''(x) > 0$ for $x > 0$, so $C(x)$ is concave up for all positive x. Thus $x = 800$ gives the absolute minimum, and $C(800)$ is the minimum cost. The other dimension of the regular field is $y = 1,600,000/800 = 2000$ feet.

EXAMPLE 3

Postal restrictions limit the size of packages sent through the mail. If the restrictions are that the length plus the girth may not exceed 108 in., find the volume of the largest box with square cross section that can be mailed.

Solution Let l equal the length of the box and s equal a side of the square end. See Figure 3.37. The volume we seek to maximize is given by

$$V = s^2 l.$$

We can use the restriction that girth plus length equals 108,

$$4s + l = 108,$$

to express V as a function of s or l. Since $l = 108 - 4s$, the equation for V becomes

$$V = s^2(108 - 4s)$$

or

$$V = 108s^2 - 4s^3.$$

Thus we can use dV/ds to find the critical values.

$$\frac{dV}{ds} = 216s - 12s^2$$
$$0 = s(216 - 12s)$$

Critical values are $s = 0$, $s = \frac{216}{12} = 18$. The critical value $s = 0$ will not maximize the volume for, in this case, $V = 0$. Testing to the left and right of $s = 18$ gives

$$V'(17) > 0 \quad \text{and} \quad V'(19) < 0.$$

Thus $s = 18$ in. and $l = 108 - 4(18) = 36$ in. yield a maximum volume of 11,664 cubic inches.

FIGURE 3.37

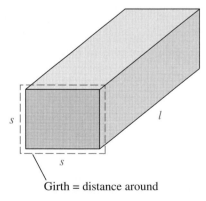

Girth = distance around

CHECKPOINT

Suppose that we want to find the minimum value of $C = 5x + 2y$ and we know that x and y must be positive and that $xy = 1000$. Answer the following:

1. What equation do we differentiate to solve this problem?

2. Find the critical values.

3. Find the minimum value of C.

Manufacturers make production runs to restock their inventories. Since there are costs associated with both the production of items and their storage (placement into inventory), a typical question in these **inventory cost models** is "How many items should be produced in each production run to minimize the total costs of production and storage?" If x items are produced in each run, and items are removed from inventory at a fixed constant rate, then the number of units in storage changes with time and is illustrated in Figure 3.38.

To see how these models work, consider the following example.

FIGURE 3.38

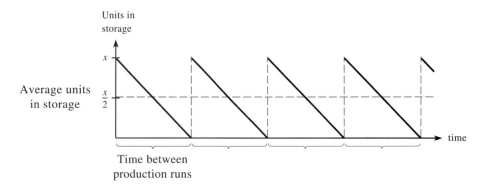

EXAMPLE 4

Suppose that a company needs 1,000,000 items during a year and that preparation costs are $800 for each production run. Suppose further that it costs the company $6 to produce each item and $1 to store an item for up to one year. If each production run consists of x items, find x so that the total costs of production and storage are minimized.

Solution The total production costs are given by

$$\begin{pmatrix} \text{No. of} \\ \text{runs} \end{pmatrix} \begin{pmatrix} \text{cost} \\ \text{per run} \end{pmatrix} + \begin{pmatrix} \text{no. of} \\ \text{items} \end{pmatrix} \begin{pmatrix} \text{cost} \\ \text{per item} \end{pmatrix} = \left(\frac{1,000,000}{x} \right) (\$800) + (1,000,000)(\$6).$$

The total storage costs are

$$\begin{pmatrix} \text{Average} \\ \text{no. stored} \end{pmatrix} \begin{pmatrix} \text{storage cost} \\ \text{per item} \end{pmatrix} = \left(\frac{x}{2} \right) (\$1).$$

Thus the total costs of production and storage are

$$C = \left(\frac{1,000,000}{x} \right) (800) + 6,000,000 + \frac{x}{2}.$$

We wish to find x so that C is minimized.

$$C' = \frac{-800,000,000}{x^2} + \frac{1}{2}$$

If $x > 0$, critical values occur when $C' = 0$.

$$0 = \frac{-800,000,000}{x^2} + \frac{1}{2}$$

$$\frac{800,000,000}{x^2} = \frac{1}{2}$$

$$1,600,000,000 = x^2$$

$$x = \pm\, 40,000$$

Because x must be positive, we use the second derivative test with $x = 40,000$.

$$C''(x) = \frac{1,600,000,000}{x^3}, \quad \text{so} \quad C''(40,000) > 0.$$

Note $x = 40,000$ yields an absolute minimum value for C, because $C'' > 0$ for all $x > 0$. That is, production runs of 40,000 items yield minimum total costs for production and storage.

TECHNOLOGY CORNER

We can use a graph to solve applied problems like the one in Example 3.

1. The equation $V = s^2(108 - 4s)$ gives the volume of a package with square cross section. Graph this and then find the maximum volume and the value of x where it occurs. Does this agree with our solution in Example 3?

2. Suppose that the package were a tube, so that cross sections were circles. Modify the equation of V to account for this and then use a graph to determine the maximum value of V.

3. Experiment with cross sections that are equilateral triangles or rectangles that are twice as wide as they are high to see if either of these designs exceeds the maximum volume for square or circular cross sections.

CHECKPOINT
SOLUTIONS

1. We must differentiate C, but first C must be expressed as a function of one variable: $xy = 1000$ means that $y = 1000/x$. If we substitute $1000/x$ for y in $C = 5x + 2y$, we get

$$C(x) = 5x + 2\left(\frac{1000}{x}\right) = 5x + \frac{2000}{x}.$$

Find $C'(x)$ to solve the problem.

2. $C'(x) = 5 - 2000/x^2$, so $C'(x) = 0$ when

$$5 - \frac{2000}{x^2} = 0 \quad \text{or} \quad x = \pm 20.$$

Since x must be positive, the only critical value is $x = 20$.

3. $C''(x) = 4000/x^3$, so $C''(x) > 0$ for all $x > 0$. Thus $x = 20$ yields the minimum value. Also, when $x = 20$, we have $y = 50$, so the minimum value of C is $C = 5(20) + 2(50) = 200$.

EXERCISE 3.5

1. **Return to sales** The manufacturer of GRIP-PER tires modeled its return on sales from television advertising expenditures in two regions, as follows:

Region 1: $S_1 = 30 + 20x_1 - 0.4x_1{}^2$
Region 2: $S_2 = 20 + 36x_2 - 0.6x_2{}^2$

where S_1 and S_2 are the sales in millions of dollars and x_1 and x_2 are millions of dollars of expenditures for television advertising. (a) What advertising expenditures would maximize sales in each district? (b) How much money will be needed to maximize sales in both districts?

2. **Projectiles** A ball thrown into the air from a building 100 ft high travels along a path described by

$$y = \frac{-x^2}{110} + x + 100,$$

where y is its height and x is the horizontal dis-

tance from the building. What is the maximum height the ball will reach?

3. **Sensitivity to a drug** Sensitivity to a drug depends on the dosage size x according to the equation

$$S = 1000x - x^2.$$

Find the dosage that maximizes sensitivity.

4. **Efficiency of a muscle** The efficiency E of a muscle performing a maximal contraction is a function of the time of the contraction t, and has been found to satisfy the following equation:

$$E = \frac{1 - 0.24t}{2 + t}.$$

Find the maximum efficiency.

5. **Profit** The profit from a grove of orange trees is given by $x(800 - x)$, where x is the number

of orange trees per acre. How many trees per acre will maximize the profit?

6. **Reaction rates** The velocity v of an autocatalytic reaction can be represented by the equation

$$v = x(a - x),$$

where a is the amount of material originally present and x is the amount that has been decomposed at any given time. Find the maximum velocity of the reaction.

7. **Productivity** Analysis of daily output of a factory shows that the hourly number of units y produced after t hours of production is

$$y = 70t + \tfrac{1}{2}t^2 - t^3, \qquad 0 \leq t \leq 8.$$

(a) After how many hours will the hourly number of units be maximized?

(b) What is the maximum hourly output?

8. **Productivity** A time study showed that, on average, the productivity of a worker after t hours on the job can be modeled by

$$P = 27t + 6t - t^3, \qquad 0 \leq t \leq 8,$$

where P is the number of units produced per hour. After how many hours will productivity be maximized? What is the maximum productivity?

9. **Consumer expenditure** Suppose that the demand x for a product is $x = 10{,}000 - 100p$, where p dollars is the market price per unit. Then the consumer expenditure for the product is

$$E = px = 10{,}000p - 100p^2.$$

For what market price will expenditure be greatest?

10. **Production costs** Suppose that the monthly cost of mining a certain ore is related to the number of pieces of equipment purchased, according to

$$C = 25{,}000x + \frac{870{,}000}{x}, \qquad x > 0,$$

where x is the number of pieces of equipment

used. Using how many pieces of equipment will minimize the cost?

11. **Advertising and sales** An inferior product with a large advertising budget sells well when it is introduced, but sales fall as people discontinue use of the product. Suppose that the weekly sales S are given by

$$S = \frac{200t}{(t + 1)^2}, \qquad t \geq 0,$$

where S is in millions of dollars and t is in weeks. After how many weeks will sales be maximized?

12. **Revenue** A newly released film has its weekly revenue given by

$$R(t) = \frac{50t}{t^2 + 36}, \qquad t \geq 0,$$

where R is in millions of dollars and t is in weeks.

(a) After how many weeks will weekly revenue be maximized?

(b) What is the maximum weekly revenue?

13. **News impact** Suppose that the percentage p (as a decimal) of people who could correctly identify 2 of 8 defendants in a drug case t days after their trial began is given by

$$p(t) = \frac{6.4t}{t^2 + 64} + 0.05.$$

Find the number of days before the percentage is maximized, and find the maximum percentage.

14. **Candidate recognition** Suppose that in an election year the proportion p of voters that recognize a certain candidate's name t months after the campaign started is given by

$$p(t) = \frac{7.2t}{t^2 + 36} + 0.2.$$

After how many months is the proportion maximized?

15. **Minimum fence** Two equal rectangular lots are enclosed by fencing the perimeter of a rectangular lot and then putting a fence across its middle. If each lot is to contain 1200 square feet, what is the minimum amount of fence needed to enclose the lots (include the fence across the middle)?

16. **Minimum fence** The running yard for a dog kennel must contain at least 900 square feet. If a 20-foot side of the kennel is used as part of one side of a rectangular yard with 900 square feet, what dimensions will require the least amount of fencing?

17. **Minimum cost** A rectangular field with one side along a river is to be fenced. Suppose that no fence is needed along the river, the fence on the side opposite the river costs $20 per foot, and the fence on the other sides costs $5 per foot. If the field must contain 45,000 square feet, what dimensions will minimize costs?

18. **Minimum cost** From a tract of land a developer plans to fence a rectangular region and then divide it into two identical rectangular lots by putting a fence down the middle. Suppose that the fence for the outside boundary costs $5 per foot and the fence for the middle costs $2 per foot. If each lot contains 13,500 square feet, find the dimensions of each lot that yield the minimum cost for the fence.

19. **Optimization at a fixed cost** A rectangular area is to be enclosed and divided into thirds. The family has $800 to spend for the fencing material. The outside fence costs $10 per running foot installed, and the dividers cost $20 per running foot installed. What are the dimensions that will maximize the area enclosed? (Answer has a fraction.)

20. **Minimum cost** A kennel of 640 square feet is to be constructed as shown in Figure 3.39. The cost is $4 per running foot for the sides and $1 per running foot for the ends and dividers. What are the dimensions of the kennel that will minimize the cost?

FIGURE 3.39

21. **Minimum cost** The base of a rectangular box is to be twice as long as it is wide. The volume of the box is 256 cubic inches. Material for the top costs $0.10 per square inch and the material for the sides and bottom costs $0.05 per square inch. Find the dimensions that will make the cost a minimum.

22. **Velocity of air during a cough** According to B. F. Visser, the velocity v of air in the trachea during a cough is related to the radius r of the trachea according to

$$v = ar^2(r_0 - r),$$

where a is a constant and r_0 is the radius of the trachea in a relaxed state. Find the radius r that produces the maximum velocity of air in the trachea during a cough.

23. **Inventory-cost model** Suppose that a company needs 1,500,000 items during a year and that preparation for each production run costs $600. Suppose also that it costs $15 to produce each item and $2 per year to store an item. Use the inventory-cost model to find the number of items in each production run so that the total costs of production and storage are minimized.

24. **Inventory-cost model** Suppose that a company needs 60,000 items during a year and that preparation for each production run costs $400. Suppose further that it costs $4 to produce each item and $0.75 to store each one for one year. Use the inventory-cost model to find the number of items in each production run that will minimize the total costs of production and storage.

25. **Inventory-cost model** A company needs 150,000 items per year. It costs the company $360 to prepare a production run of these items and $7 to produce each item. If it also costs the company $0.75 per year for each item stored, find the number of items that should

be produced in each run so that the total costs of production and storage are minimized.

26. **Inventory-cost model** A company needs 450,000 items per year. Production costs are $500 to prepare for a production run and $10 for each item produced. Inventory costs are $2 per item per year. Find the number of items that should be produced in each run so that the total costs of production and storage are minimized.

27. **Volume** A rectangular box with a square base is to be formed from a square piece of metal with 12-inch sides. If a square piece with side x is cut from the corners of the metal and the sides are folded up to form an open box, the volume of the box is $V = (12 - 2x)^2 x$ (see Figure 3.40). What value of x will maximize the volume of the box?

FIGURE 3.40

```
        12
      ┌──────────┐
      │ x    x   │
    x │          │ x
 12   │          │  12
    x │          │ x
      │ x    x   │
      └──────────┘
        12
```

28. **Volume** A square piece of cardboard 36 cm on a side is to be formed into a rectangular box by cutting squares with length x from each corner and folding up the sides. What is the maximum volume possible for the box?

29. **Revenue** The owner of an orange grove must decide when to pick one variety of oranges. She can sell them for $8 a bushel if she sells them now, with each tree yielding an average of 5 bushels. The yield increases by one half bushel per week for the next 5 weeks, but the price per bushel decreases by $0.50 per bushel each week. When should the oranges be picked for maximum return?

30. **Minimum material** A box with an open top and a square base is to be constructed to contain 4000 cubic inches. Find the dimensions

that will require the minimum amount of material to construct the box.

31. **Minimum cost** A printer has a contract to print 100,000 posters for a political candidate. He can run the posters by using any number of plates from 1 to 30 on his press. If he uses x metal plates, they will produce x copies of the poster with each impression of the press. The metal plates cost $2.00 to prepare, and it costs $12.50 per hour to run the press. If the press can make 1000 impressions per hour, how many metal plates should he make to minimize costs?

32. **Shortest time** A vacationer on an island 8 miles offshore from a point that is 48 miles from town must travel to town occasionally. (See Figure 3.41.) The vacationer has a boat capable of traveling 30 mph and can go by auto along the coast at 55 mph. At what point should the car be left to minimize the time it takes to get to town?

FIGURE 3.41

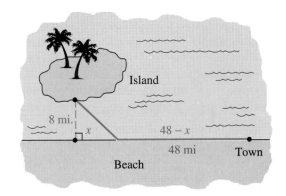

33. **Utility installation costs** A homeowner has to pay for utility line installation to her house from a transformer on the street at the corner of her property. Because of local restrictions the lines must be underground on her property. Suppose that the costs are $5/foot along the street and $10/foot underground. How far from the transformer should she enter the property to minimize installation costs? See Figure 3.42.

FIGURE 3.42

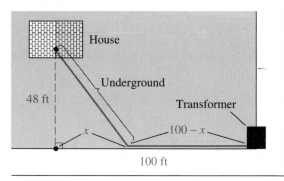

100 ft

34. **Shortest time** A boat is 1 mile offshore from a point B that is 10 miles from a town. If the line from the boat to B is perpendicular to the line from B to town, and if the person in the boat can row at 3 mph and walk at 5 mph, find the point A so that rowing to A and walking from there to town minimizes the time it takes to get to town.

3.6 | DIFFERENTIALS

OBJECTIVES

- To find differentials
- To find approximations by using differentials

There are occasions when we are given $y = f(x)$ and we wish to know how y changes when a small change is made in x. We have already used marginal revenue, $R'(x)$, to estimate the change in revenue when x is increased by 1 unit (say 1 ton). But to approximate how the revenue is changed by a very small change in x (say by 0.1 tons), we use **differentials.**

Suppose that for the function $y = f(x)$, we use Δx to represent a small change in x. Then the change in y, as x changes from x to $x + \Delta x$, is

$$\Delta y = f(x + \Delta x) - f(x).$$

EXAMPLE 1

If $y = x^3$ gives the volume of a cube that is x units on a side, by how much will y increase if each side is 10 in. and each side is increased by $\Delta x = 0.2$ in.?

Solution The increase in y is

$$\begin{aligned} \Delta y = f(x + \Delta x) - f(x) &= (10 + 0.2)^3 - 10^3 \\ &= 1061.208 - 1000 \\ &= 61.208 \quad \text{(cubic inches)}. \end{aligned}$$

Because $\Delta y = f(x + \Delta x) - f(x)$, we have

$$\frac{\Delta y}{\Delta x} = \frac{f(x + \Delta x) - f(x)}{\Delta x}$$

and

$$\lim_{\Delta x \to 0} \frac{\Delta y}{\Delta x} = \lim_{\Delta x \to 0} \frac{f(x + \Delta x) - f(x)}{\Delta x}.$$

By our definition of derivative, the expression above is the derivative of $y = f(x)$ (with $\Delta x = h$):

$$f'(x) = \lim_{\Delta x \to 0} \frac{\Delta y}{\Delta x}.$$

Thus when Δx is very small, but not 0, $f'(x)$ is approximated by $\Delta y / \Delta x$:

$$f'(x) \approx \frac{\Delta y}{\Delta x}.$$

This means that for small values of Δx we can approximate the change in y by

$$\Delta y \approx f'(x) \Delta x.$$

If we represent the change in x, Δx, by the **differential of x, dx,** we can *approximate* the change in y, Δy, by the **differential of y, dy,** where

$$dy = f'(x) dx.$$

Differentials	Let $f'(x)$ be the derivative of the differentiable function $y = f(x)$. The **differential of x** is $dx = \Delta x$, when $\Delta x \neq 0$.

The **differential of y** is

$$dy = f'(x) dx.$$

and $\Delta y \approx dy$ when $dx \approx 0$.

Figure 3.43 shows that dy/dx represents the slope of the tangent line to the curve at a point on the curve. Thus a change of dx in the x direction results in a vertical change of dy on the tangent line and a vertical change of Δy on the graph of the function. If Δx is small, it is clear (see Figure 3.43) that dy approximates Δy.

FIGURE 3.43

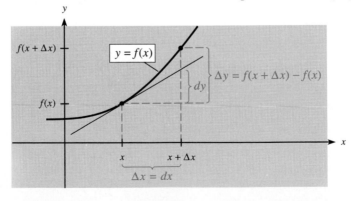

EXAMPLE 2

Find the differential dy for the following functions.

(a) $y = x^3 - 4x^2$ (b) $f(x) = \sqrt[3]{x^3 - 5}$

Solution

(a) $dy = f'(x)dx = (3x^2 - 8x)dx$

(b) $f'(x) = \dfrac{1}{3}(x^3 - 5)^{-2/3}\, 3x^2 = \dfrac{x^2}{(x^3 - 5)^{2/3}}$

$\quad\quad dy = f'(x)dx = \dfrac{x^2}{(x^3 - 5)^{2/3}}\, dx$

EXAMPLE 3

If $y = x^3$ gives the volume of a cube that is x units on a side, use differentials to approximate the change in volume if each side is increased from 10 in. to 10.2 in.

Solution The change in y, Δy, is approximated by dy. For any value of x,

$$dy = f'(x)dx = 3x^2 \cdot dx.$$

If x increases from 10 to 10.2, we use $x = 10$ and $dx = 0.2$ to approximate the change in volume.

$$dy = 3(10)^2(0.2) = 60 \quad \text{(cubic inches)}$$

This value approximates the true change in volume, $\Delta y = 61.208$ cubic inches, found in Example 1.

If we are given a revenue function $R(x)$, we have used $\overline{MR} = R'(x)$ to approximate the change in revenue that results from a change of one unit in x. This relates to differential approximations as follows.

$$dR = R'(x)dx = \overline{MR}\, dx$$

When $dx = 1$, dR equals the marginal revenue. When the change in x is different from 1, we can use $dR = R'(x)dx$ to approximate the corresponding change in $R(x)$.

EXAMPLE 4

Suppose that the revenue function for the sale of x thousand units of a new calculator is given by

$$R(x) = 60{,}000x + \frac{40{,}000}{x + 10} - 4000.$$

(a) Find the revenue from the sale of 30,000 units.

(b) Approximate the change in revenue that results when the number of units sold changes from 30,000 to 30,500.

Solution

(a) Because x represents the number of thousands of units, $x = 30$ when 30,000 units are sold. Thus the revenue is

$$R(30) = 60,000(30) + \frac{40,000}{30 + 10} - 4000$$
$$= 1,800,000 + 1000 - 4000 = 1,797,000.$$

(b) The approximate change in revenue is given by the value of the differential when $x = 30$ and $dx = 0.5$.

$$dR = R'(x)dx$$
$$= [60,000 - 40,000(x + 10)^{-2}]dx$$
$$= \left[60,000 - \frac{40,000}{(x + 10)^2} \right] dx$$

When $x = 30$ and $dx = 0.5$, we have

$$dR = \left[60,000 - \frac{40,000}{(40)^2} \right] (0.5)$$
$$= (60,000 - 25)(0.5)$$
$$= 30,000 - 12.5 = \$29,987.50.$$

Thus if the number of units sold increases from 30 thousand to 30.5 thousand, the revenue would increase by approximately \$29,987.50.

CHECKPOINT

1. True or false:
   (a) If $y = x^4$, then $dy = 4x^3$.
   (b) If $y = x^4 - 4x + 1$, then $dy = 4(x^3 - 1)dx$.

2. Let $y = (x^2 + 1)^5$ and complete the following.
   (a) Find dy.   (b) Find dy when $x = 1$ and $dx = 0.2$.
   (c) Find dy when $x = 1$ and $dx = -0.1$.

TECHNOLOGY CORNER

1. Consider $f(x) = x^2$. Then we have

$$\Delta f = f(x + \Delta x) - f(x)$$
$$= (x + \Delta x)^2 - x^2 = 2x\Delta x + (\Delta x)^2.$$

Since $\Delta x = dx$, by definition,

$$\Delta f = 2xdx + (dx)^2 \quad \text{and} \quad df = 2xdx.$$

(a) Fix $x = 1$ and graph $\Delta f = 2dx + (dx)^2$ and $df = 2dx$. Treat dx as the independent variable.

(b) What do you notice about Δf and df when dx is close to 0? When dx is not close to 0, is df a good approximation to Δf?

(c) Form $y = \Delta f - df$ and graph it. Does its graph support your conclusions from (b)?

2. (a) Fix $x = 4$ and graph $\Delta f = 8dx + (dx)^2$ and $df = 8dx$.

(b), (c) Use these graphs and repeat parts (b) and (c) above.

3. Consider $f(x) = x^3$.

(a) Find Δf and df.

(b) Fix $x = 1$ and graph both Δf and df.

(c) Fix $x = 4$ and graph both Δf and df.

(d) When is df approximately the same as Δf?

CHECKPOINT

SOLUTIONS

1. (a) False, $dy = 4x^3 dx$

(b) True

2. (a) $dy = 5(x^2 + 1)^4(2x)dx = 10x(x^2 + 1)^4 dx$

(b) $dy = 10(1)(1^2 + 1)^4(0.2) = 10(16)(0.2) = 32$

(c) $dy = 10(1)(1^2 + 1)^4(-0.1) = 10(16)(-0.1) = -16$

EXERCISE 3.6

For each function in problems 1–4, find Δy for each given x and Δx.

1. $y = 3x^2 + 1$ $x = 10, \Delta x = 1$

2. $y = x^2 - 4$ $x = 2, \Delta x = 0.5$

3. $f(x) = \dfrac{1}{x^3}$ $x = 2, \Delta x = -0.5$

4. $f(x) = \sqrt{4 - 5x}$ $x = 0, \Delta x = -1$

Find dy for each function given in problems 5–14.

5. $y = 8x^2 - x$

6. $y = 4 + x - 7x^2$

7. $f(r) = \dfrac{x^4}{4} - \dfrac{4x^3}{3} + 11$

8. $g(x) = 1 - 5x^4$

9. $y = \dfrac{1}{x^2} - \dfrac{2}{x}$

10. $y = 6\sqrt{x} + \dfrac{4}{x^4} - 1$

11. $f(x) = \dfrac{3x^4}{3x^4 + 5}$

12. $f(x) = \dfrac{1 - 2x^2}{1 + x - 2x^2}$

13. $g(x) = \dfrac{\sqrt{4 - 3x^4}}{6}$

14. $g(x) = \dfrac{(1 - 2x^5)^{10}}{100}$

15. If $u = x^2 + 2x + 1$, express $u^{10}du$ in terms of x and dx.

16. If $u = 1 - 2x$, express $u^{1/2}du$ in terms of x and dx.

For each function in problems 17–20, use $x = 4$ and $\Delta x = 0.5$ to find Δy, dy, and dx.

17. $f(x) = x^2 + 5x$

18. $f(x) = 1 - 4x^2$

19. $y = 3\sqrt{x} - 1$

20. $y = x^2 - \dfrac{16}{x^2}$

21. When a croquet ball is painted, the thickness of the paint causes a small change in the volume. Approximate the change in volume if the radius of the ball is 2 inches, the thickness of the paint is 0.02 inches, and the formula for the volume of the ball is $V = \frac{4}{3}\pi r^3$.

22. The area of a rectangular plate that is twice as long as it is wide is given by $A = 2x^2$, where x is the width. If such a plate has a width of 2 inches and expands when it is heated so that its area increases by 1.2 square inches, approximate the change in x.

If $y = f(x)$, we have seen that dy is the approximate change in y that results when x changes by dx. For each of these quantities, we can also find percentage changes:

for y: $\left(\dfrac{dy}{y}\right)(100\%)$ for x: $\left(\dfrac{dx}{x}\right)(100\%)$

In problems 23–26, find the percentage change in y caused by each percentage change in x.

23. $y = 6x^2$;   3% change in x from $x = 10$.

24. $y = \dfrac{4}{3}\pi x^3$;   1% change in x from $x = 100$.

25. $y = 4x^{3/4}$;   4% change in x from $x = 16$.

26. $y = \dfrac{2}{\sqrt{x}}$;   3% change in x from $x = 25$.

APPLICATIONS

27. Demand The demand q for a product depends on its price p (in dollars) according to

$$q = \dfrac{1000}{\sqrt{p}} - 1 \quad \text{for} \quad p > 0.$$

Approximate the change in demand if price changes (a) from \$25 to \$25.50 and (b) from \$25 to \$24.20.

28. Output and capital investment The monthly output Q in thousands of units of a product is given by

$$Q(x) = 800x^{5/2},$$

where x is the capital investment in millions of dollars. Approximate the change in output if capital investment changes (a) from \$1 million to \$1.2 million and (b) from \$1 million to \$0.9 million.

29. Pollution The number of tons of pollutants p entering a stream near an industrial site is given by

$$p = \dfrac{t^{7/4}}{1050},$$

where t is the number of weeks after manufacture of a new product begins. Approximate the *daily* change in the tons of pollutants after (a) 1 week and (b) 4 weeks. *Note:* a daily change means that $dt = 1/7$.

30. Bacterial populations The number of organisms of a certain bacteria present at time t (in hours) is

$$N(t) = 2500(1 + 2t^2).$$

Approximate the change in the number of organisms between $t = 1$ and $t = 1.25$.

31. Cost-benefit models Suppose that the cost C of removing p percent of the particulate pollution from the exhaust gases of a factory is given by

$$C(p) = \dfrac{8100p}{100 - p}.$$

Approximate the increased cost associated with increasing p from 98 to 98.5.

32. Sales from advertising For a certain product, suppose that sales y (in millions of dollars) are related to advertising expenditures x (in millions of dollars) according to

$$y = \dfrac{300x}{x + 10}.$$

Approximate the change in sales if advertising expenditures increase from \$5 million to \$5.3 million.

33. **IRA investments** If an IRA is a fixed rate investment for 5-year intervals at a rate $r\%$ per year, compounded monthly, then the amount A that accumulates from an initial investment of \$2000 is

$$A = 2000\left[1 + \left(\frac{0.01r}{12}\right)\right]^{60}.$$

If, just before the investment is made, the rate changes from 7% to 7.2%, approximate the change in A.

34. **Populations of microorganisms** Suppose that the population P of a certain microorganism at time t (in minutes) is given by

$$P = 1000 - 9900(t + 10)^{-1}.$$

Find the population when $t = 0$ and approxi-mate the change in the population over the next 30 seconds.

35. **Revenue** The monthly revenue in thousands of dollars from the sale of x thousand units of a product is

$$R(x) = 15(3x + 5)^{-1} + 50x - 3.$$

Approximate the change in revenue if sales fall from 15,000 units per month to 14,750 units per month.

36. **Pricing and sales volume** Suppose that the weekly sales volume y (in thousands of units) for a product is given by

$$y = \frac{32}{(p + 8)^{2/5}},$$

where p is the price in dollars per unit. Approximate the effect on sales volume if the price is (a) raised from \$24 to \$24.50 and (b) lowered from \$24 to \$23.75.

3.7 | IMPLICIT DIFFERENTIATION; ELASTICITY OF DEMAND

OBJECTIVES
- To find derivatives by using implicit differentiation
- To find slopes of tangents by using implicit differentiation
- To find elasticity of demand

IMPLICIT DIFFERENTIATION

Up to this point, we have taken derivatives of functions of the form $y = f(x)$. Some functions are given in equations of the form $F(x, y) = 0$. For example, the equa-tion $xy - 4x + 1 = 0$ is in the form $F(x, y) = 0$, but we can solve for y to write the equation in the form $y = (4x - 1)/x$. We can say that $xy - 4x + 1 = 0$ defines y **implicitly** as a function of x, while $y = (4x - 1)/x$ defines the function explicitly.

The equation $x^2 + y^2 - 9 = 0$ has a circle as its graph. If we solve the equation for y, we get $y = \pm\sqrt{9 - x^2}$, which indicates that y is not a function of x. We can, however, consider the equation as defining *two* functions, $y = \sqrt{9 - x^2}$ and

$y = -\sqrt{9 - x^2}$ (see Figure 3.44). We say that the equation $x^2 + y^2 - 9 = 0$ defines the two functions implicitly.

Even though an equation like $\ln xy + xe^y + x - 3 = 0$ may be difficult or even impossible to solve for y, and even though the equation may not represent y as a single function of x, we can use a technique called **implicit differentiation** to find the derivative of y with respect to x. The word *implicit* means that we are implying that y is a function of x without verifying it. We simply take the derivatives of both sides of $f(x, y) = 0$ and then solve algebraically for dy/dx.

FIGURE 3.44

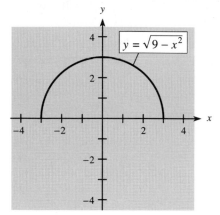
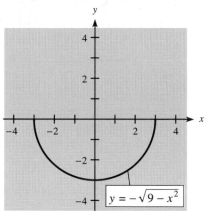

For example, we can find the derivative dy/dx from $x^2 + y^2 - 9 = 0$ by taking the derivatives of both sides of the equation.

$$\frac{d}{dx}(x^2 + y^2 - 9) = \frac{d}{dx}(0)$$

$$\frac{d}{dx}(x^2) + \frac{d}{dx}(y^2) + \frac{d}{dx}(-9) = \frac{d}{dx}(0)$$

We have assumed that y is a function of x; the derivative of y^2 is treated like the derivative of u^n, where u is a function of x. Thus the derivatives indicated above give

$$2x + 2y^1 \cdot \frac{dy}{dx} + 0 = 0.$$

Solving for dy/dx gives

$$\frac{dy}{dx} = -\frac{2x}{2y} = -\frac{x}{y}.$$

Let us now compare this derivative with the derivatives of the two functions $y = \sqrt{9 - x^2}$ and $y = -\sqrt{9 - x^2}$. The derivative of $y = \sqrt{9 - x^2}$ is

$$\frac{dy}{dx} = \frac{1}{2}(9 - x^2)^{-1/2}(-2x) = \frac{-x}{\sqrt{9 - x^2}}$$

and the derivative of $y = -\sqrt{9 - x^2}$ is

$$\frac{dy}{dx} = -\frac{1}{2}(9 - x^2)^{-1/2}(-2x) = \frac{x}{\sqrt{9 - x^2}}.$$

Note that if we substitute $\sqrt{9 - x^2}$ and $-\sqrt{9 - x^2}$, respectively, for y in our "implicit" derivative, we get the two derivatives that were derived from the "explicit" functions.

EXAMPLE 1　Find the slope of the tangent to the graph of $x^2 + y^2 - 9 = 0$ at $(\sqrt{5}, 2)$.

Solution　The slope of the tangent to the curve is the derivative of the equation, evaluated at the given point. As we saw above, taking the derivative implicitly gives us $dy/dx = -x/y$. Evaluating the derivative at $(\sqrt{5}, 2)$ gives the slope of the tangent as $-\sqrt{5}/2$.

We also found the derivative of $x^2 + y^2 - 9 = 0$ by solving for y explicitly. The function whose graph contains $(\sqrt{5}, 2)$ is $y = \sqrt{9 - x^2}$, and its derivative is

$$\frac{dy}{dx} = \frac{-x}{\sqrt{9 - x^2}}.$$

Evaluating the derivative at $(\sqrt{5}, 2)$, we get the slope of the tangent: $-\sqrt{5}/2$.

Thus we see that both methods give us the same slope for the tangent, but that the implicit method is easier to use.

EXAMPLE 2　Find dy/dx if $x^2 + 4x - 3y^2 + 4y = 0$.

Solution　Taking the derivative implicitly gives

$$\frac{d}{dx}(x^2) + \frac{d}{dx}(4x) + \frac{d}{dx}(-3y^2) + \frac{d}{dx}(4y) = \frac{d}{dx}(0).$$

Now,

$$\frac{d}{dx}(x^2) - 2x$$

$$\frac{d}{dx}(4x) = 4$$

$$\frac{d}{dx}(-3y^2) = -3(2y)\frac{dy}{dx} = -6y\frac{dy}{dx}$$

$$\frac{d}{dx}(4y) = 4\frac{dy}{dx}$$

and

$$\frac{d}{dx}(0) = 0.$$

So

$$2x + 4 - 6y\frac{dy}{dx} + 4\frac{dy}{dx} = 0$$

$$(-6y + 4)\frac{dy}{dx} = -2x - 4$$

$$\frac{dy}{dx} = \frac{-2x - 4}{-6y + 4}$$

$$\frac{dy}{dx} = \frac{x + 2}{3y - 2}$$

EXAMPLE 3 Write the equation of the tangent to the graph of $x^3 + xy + 4 = 0$ at the point $(-2, -2)$.

Solution Taking the derivative implicitly gives

$$\frac{d}{dx}(x^3) + \frac{d}{dx}(xy) + \frac{d}{dx}(4) = \frac{d}{dx}(0).$$

The $\frac{d}{dx}(xy)$ indicates that we should take the derivative of the *product* of x and y. Since we are assuming that y is a function of x and since x is a function of x, we must use the Product Rule to find $\frac{d}{dx}(xy)$.

$$\frac{d}{dx}(xy) = x \cdot 1\frac{dy}{dx} + y \cdot 1 = x\frac{dy}{dx} + y$$

Thus we have

$$3x^2 + \left(x\frac{dy}{dx} + y\right) + 0 = 0.$$

Solving for dy/dx gives

$$\frac{dy}{dx} = \frac{-3x^2 - y}{x}.$$

The slope of the tangent to the curve at $x = -2$, $y = -2$ is

$$m = \frac{-3(-2)^2 - (-2)}{-2} = 5.$$

The equation of the tangent line is

$$y - (-2) = 5[x - (-2)], \quad \text{or} \quad y = 5x + 8.$$

EXAMPLE 4

At what point(s) does $x^2 + 4y^2 - 2x + 4y - 2 = 0$ have a horizontal tangent? At what point(s) does it have a vertical tangent?

Solution First we find the derivative implicitly:

$$2x + 8y \cdot y' - 2 + 4y' - 0 \doteq 0$$
$$(8y + 4)y' = 2 - 2x$$
$$y' = \frac{2 - 2x}{8y + 4} = \frac{1 - x}{4y + 2}$$

Horizontal tangents will occur where $y' = 0$; that is, where $x = 1$. We can now find the corresponding y value(s) by substituting 1 for x in the original equation and solving.

$$1 + 4y^2 - 2 + 4y - 2 = 0$$
$$4y^2 + 4y - 3 = 0$$
$$(2y - 1)(2y + 3) = 0$$
$$y = \tfrac{1}{2}, \qquad y = -\tfrac{3}{2}$$

Thus horizontal tangents occur at $(1, \tfrac{1}{2})$, and $(1, -\tfrac{3}{2})$ (see Figure 3.45).

FIGURE 3.45

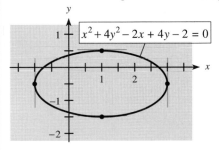

Vertical tangents will occur where the derivative is undefined; that is, where $y = -\tfrac{1}{2}$. To find the corresponding x value(s), we substitute $-\tfrac{1}{2}$ for y in the original equation and solve for x.

$$x^2 + 4(-\tfrac{1}{2})^2 - 2x + 4(-\tfrac{1}{2}) - 2 = 0$$
$$x^2 - 2x - 3 = 0$$
$$(x \quad 3)(x \mid 1) = 0$$
$$x = 3, \qquad x = -1$$

Thus vertical tangents occur at $(3, -\tfrac{1}{2})$ and $(-1, -\tfrac{1}{2})$ (see Figure 3.45).

CHECKPOINT

1. Find the following:

   (a) $\dfrac{d}{dx}(x^3)$ (b) $\dfrac{d}{dx}(y^4)$ (c) $\dfrac{d}{dx}(x^2y^5)$

2. Find $\dfrac{dy}{dx}$ for $x^3 + y^4 = x^2y^5$.

ELASTICITY OF DEMAND

We know from the law of demand that consumers will respond to changes in prices; if prices increase, the quantity demanded will decrease. But the degree of responsiveness of the consumers to price changes will vary widely for different products. For example, a price increase in insulin will not decrease greatly the demand for it by diabetics, but a price increase in clothes may cause consumers to buy considerably less and wear their old clothes longer. When the response to price changes is considerable, we say that the demand is **elastic.** When price changes cause relatively small changes in demand for a product, the demand is said to be **inelastic** for that product.

The **elasticity of demand** is measured by economists by dividing the rate of change in demand by the rate of change in price. We may write this as

$$E_d = -\frac{\text{change in quantity demanded}}{\text{original quantity demanded}} \div \frac{\text{change in price}}{\text{original price}}$$

or

$$E_d = -\frac{\Delta q}{q} \div \frac{\Delta p}{p}.$$

The demand curve usually has a negative slope, so we have introduced a negative sign into the formula to give us a positive elasticity.

We can write the equation for elasticity as

$$E_d = -\frac{p}{q} \cdot \frac{\Delta q}{\Delta p},$$

and define the **point elasticity of demand** as

$$\eta = \lim_{\Delta p \to 0} \left(-\frac{p}{q} \cdot \frac{\Delta q}{\Delta p} \right) = -\frac{p}{q} \cdot \frac{dq}{dp}.$$

Elasticity of Demand

The **point elasticity of demand** at the point (q_A, p_A) is

$$\eta = -\frac{p}{q} \cdot \frac{dq}{dp} \bigg|_{(q_A, p_A)}$$

EXAMPLE 5

If a commodity has a demand curve given by $p + 5q = 100$, find the point elasticity of demand at $q = 8$, $p = 60$.

Solution We can find dq/dp by using implicit differentiation with respect to p.

$$1 + 5\frac{dq}{dp} = 0$$

$$\frac{dq}{dp} = -\frac{1}{5}.$$

Thus

$$\eta = -\frac{p}{q}\left(-\frac{1}{5}\right)\bigg|_{(8,\,60)} = -\frac{60}{8}\left(-\frac{1}{5}\right) = \frac{3}{2}.$$

In the next example, we will see that the derivative dq/dp for $p + 5q = 100$ is also $-\frac{1}{5}$ when it is found by first solving for q.

EXAMPLE 6

Find the point elasticity of the demand function $p + 5q = 100$ at $(10, 50)$.

Solution Solving the demand function for q gives $q = 20 - \frac{1}{5}p$. Then $dq/dp = -\frac{1}{5}$, and

$$\eta = -\frac{p}{q}\left(-\frac{1}{5}\right)\bigg|_{(10,\,50)} = -\frac{50}{10}\left(-\frac{1}{5}\right) = 1.$$

Note that in Examples 5 and 6 the demand equation was $p + 5q = 100$, so the demand "curve" is a straight line, with slope $m = -5$. But the elasticity was $\eta = 3/2$ at $(8, 60)$ and $\eta = 1$ at $(10, 50)$. The elasticity for this same demand curve is $\eta = 2/3$ at $(12, 40)$. This illustrates that the elasticity of demand may be different at different points on the demand curve, even though the slope of the demand "curve" is constant. (See Figure 3.46.)

FIGURE 3.46

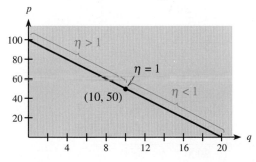

These examples show that the elasticity of demand is more than just the slope of the demand curve, which is the rate at which the demand is changing. Recall that the elasticity measures the consumers' degree of responsiveness to a price change.

We can look at the relation between elasticity and a firm's total revenue as follows:

1. If $\eta > 1$, the demand is **elastic,** and an increase in price will result in a decrease in total revenue. On the other hand, a decrease in price will increase total revenue.

2. If $\eta < 1$, the demand is **inelastic,** and an increase in price will result in an increase in total revenue. A decrease in price will lead to a decrease in revenue.

3. If $\eta = 1$, the demand is **unitary elastic,** and neither an increase nor a decrease in price will change total revenue. That is, $\eta = 1$ means that $dR/dp = 0$ (see problem 49) and, in fact, revenue is at a maximum when $\eta = 1$.

EXAMPLE 7

The demand for a certain product is given by

$$p = \frac{1000}{(q + 1)^2},$$

where p is the price per unit in dollars and q is demand in units of the product. Find the elasticity of demand with respect to price when $q = 19$.

Solution To find the elasticity, we need to find dq/dp. Using implicit differentiation, we get the following:

$$\frac{d}{dp}(p) = \frac{d}{dp}[1000(q + 1)^{-2}]$$

$$1 = 1000\left[-2(q + 1)^{-3}\frac{dq}{dp}\right]$$

$$1 = \frac{-2000}{(q + 1)^3}\frac{dq}{dp}$$

$$\frac{(q + 1)^3}{-2000} = \frac{dq}{dp}.$$

When $q = 19$, we have $p = 1000/(19 + 1)^2 = 1000/400 = 5/2$ and

$$\frac{dq}{dp}\bigg|_{(q=19)} = \frac{(19 + 1)^3}{-2000} = \frac{8000}{-2000} = -4.$$

The elasticity of demand when $q = 19$ is

$$\eta = \frac{-p}{q} \cdot \frac{dq}{dp} = -\frac{(5/2)}{19} \cdot (-4) = \frac{10}{19} < 1.$$

Thus the demand for this product is inelastic, so an increase in price would result in an increase in total revenue.

CHECKPOINT

3. Write the formula for point elasticity, η.

4. (a) If $\eta > 1$, the demand is called _____.
   (b) If $\eta < 1$, the demand is called _____.
   (c) If $\eta = 1$, the demand is called _____.

5. Find the elasticity of demand for $q = \dfrac{100}{p} - 1$ when $p = 10$ and $q = 9$. ■

TECHNOLOGY CORNER

Consider the demand function $p = 100 - 0.5q$.

1. Find the elasticity as a function of q; that is, find $\eta = \eta(q)$.
2. Graph the function $f(q) = \eta - 1 = \eta(q) - 1$.
3. The q-intercept of the graph of $f(q)$ marks the quantity where the demand for this product has unitary elasticity. For what values of q is the demand elastic? For what values is it inelastic?
4. We know that revenue equals price times quantity sold, so

   $$R(q) = p \cdot q = (100 - 0.5q)q.$$

Graph $R(q)$.

5. Find the q-value where maximum revenue occurs.
6. Find intervals where R is increasing and where it is decreasing.
7. Compare the values and intervals found in parts (c) and (d) with those from parts (e) and (f). What do you notice? Do your findings support the conclusions from this section about elasticity and revenue?

CHECKPOINT

SOLUTIONS

1. (a) $\dfrac{d}{dx}(x^3) = 3x^2$ (b) $\dfrac{d}{dx}(y^4) = 4y^3\dfrac{dy}{dx}$

   (c) $\dfrac{d}{dx}(x^2y^5) = x^2\left(5y^4\dfrac{dy}{dx}\right) + y^5(2x)$ (by the Product Rule)

2. For $x^3 + y^4 = x^2 y^5$, we can use the answers to question (1) to obtain

$$3x^2 + 4y^3 \frac{dy}{dx} = x^2 \left(5y^4 \frac{dy}{dx} \right) + y^5 (2x)$$

$$3x^2 + 4y^3 \frac{dy}{dx} = 5x^2 y^4 \frac{dy}{dx} + 2xy^5$$

$$3x^2 - 2xy^5 = (5x^2 y^4 - 4y^3) \frac{dy}{dx}$$

$$\frac{3x^2 - 2xy^5}{5x^2 y^4 - 4y^3} = \frac{dy}{dx}$$

3. $\eta = \dfrac{-p}{q} \cdot \dfrac{dq}{dp}$

4. (a) elastic (b) inelastic (c) unitary elastic

5. $\dfrac{dq}{dp} = \dfrac{-100}{p^2}$ and $\dfrac{dq}{dp} = -1$ when $p = 10, q = 9$

$$\eta = \frac{-10}{9}(-1) = \frac{10}{9} \quad \text{(elastic)}$$

EXERCISE 3.7

Find dy/dx for the functions in problems 1–4.

1. $x^2 + 2y^2 - 4 = 0$
2. $x + y^2 - 4y + 6 = 0$
3. $x^2 + 4x + y^2 - 3y + 1 = 0$
4. $x^2 - 5x + y^3 - 3y - 3 = 0$
5. If $x^2 + y^2 = 4$, find y'.
6. If $p^2 + 4p - q = 4$, find dp/dq.
7. If $x^2 + 3xy = 4$, find y'.
8. If $xy^2 - y^2 = 1$, find y'.
9. If $pq = 4$, find dp/dq.
10. If $pq = 4p - 2$, find dp/dq.
11. If $x^2 - 3y^4 = 2x^5 + 7y^3 - 5$, find dy/dx.
12. If $3x^5 - 5y^3 = 5x^2 + 3y^5$, find dy/dx.

13. If $x^2 + 3x^2 y^4 = y + 8$, find dy/dx.
14. If $x^4 + 2x^3 y^2 = x - y^3$, find dy/dx.
15. If $(x + y)^2 = 5x^4 y^3$, find dy/dx.
16. If $x^{1/3} + y^{1/3} = xy$, find y'.
17. Find dy/dx for $x^4 + 3x^3 y^2 - 2y^5 = (2x + 3y)^2$.
18. Find y' for $2x + 2y = \sqrt{x^2 + y^2}$.

For problems 19–22, find the slope of the tangent to the curve.

19. $x^2 + 4x + y^2 + 2y - 4 = 0$ at $(1, -1)$
20. $x^2 - 4x + 2y^2 - 4 = 0$ at $(2, 2)$
21. $x^2 + 2xy + 3 = 0$ at $(-1, 2)$
22. $y + x^2 = 4$ at $(0, 4)$

For problems 23–26, write the equation of the tangent to the curve.

23. $x^2 - 2y^2 + 4 = 0$ at $(2, 2)$

24. $x^2 + y^2 + 2x - 3 = 0$ at $(-1, 2)$

25. $4x^2 + 3y^2 - 4y - 3 = 0$ at $(-1, 1)$

26. $xy + y = 0$ at $(3, 0)$

27. At what points does the curve defined by $x^2 + 4y^2 - 4x - 4 = 0$ have
    (a) horizontal tangents?
    (b) vertical tangents?

28. At what points does the curve defined by $x^2 + 4y^2 - 4 = 0$ have
    (a) horizontal tangents?
    (b) vertical tangents?

29. In problem 5, the derivative was found to be

$$y' = \frac{-x}{y}.$$

Take the implicit derivatives of both sides of this equation to show that

$$y'' = \frac{-y + xy'}{y^2}.$$

30. Find y' implicitly for $x^3 - y^3 = 8$. Then, by taking derivatives implicitly, use it to show that

$$y'' = \frac{2x(y - xy')}{y^3}.$$

31. Use the result of problem 29 to answer the questions in parts (a) and (b) below.
    (a) Substitute $-x/y$ for y' in the expression for y'' and simplify to show that

$$y'' = -\frac{(x^2 + y^2)}{y^3}.$$

    (b) Does $y'' = -4/y^3$? Why or why not?

32. Use the result of problem 30.
    (a) Substitute x^2/y^2 for y' in the expression for y'' and simplify to show that

$$y'' = \frac{2x(y^3 - x^3)}{y^5}.$$

    (b) Does $y'' = -16x/y^5$? Why or why not?

33. Find y'' for $\sqrt{x} + \sqrt{y} = 1$, and simplify.

34. Find y'' for $\dfrac{1}{x} - \dfrac{1}{y} = 1$.

APPLICATIONS

35. **Advertising and sales** Suppose that a company's sales volume y (in thousands of dollars) is related to its advertising expenditures x (in thousands of dollars) according to

$$xy - 20x + 10y = 0.$$

Find the rate of change of sales volume with respect to advertising expenditures when $x = 10$ (thousand dollars).

36. **Insect control** Suppose that the number of mosquitoes N (in thousands) in a certain swampy area near a community is related to the number of pounds of insecticide x sprayed on the nesting areas according to

$$Nx - 10x + N = 300.$$

Find the rate of change of N with respect to x when 49 lb of insecticide are used.

37. **Production** Suppose that a company can produce 12,000 units when the number of hours of skilled labor y and unskilled labor x satisfy

$$384 = (x + 1)^{3/4}(y + 2)^{1/3}.$$

Find the rate of change of skilled labor hours with respect to unskilled labor hours when $x = 255$ and $y = 214$. This can be used to approximate the change in skilled labor hours required to maintain the same production level when unskilled labor hours are increased by one hour.

38. **Production** Suppose that production of 10,000 units of a certain agricultural crop is related to the number of hours of labor x and

the number of acres of the crop y according to

$$300x + 30{,}000y = 11xy - 0.0002x^2 - 5y.$$

Find the rate of change of the number of hours with respect to the number of acres.

39. **Demand** If the demand function for a product is given by

$$p(q + 1)^2 = 200{,}000,$$

find the rate of change of quantity with respect to price when $p = \$80$. Interpret this result.

40. **Demand** If the demand function for a commodity is given by

$$p^2(2q + 1) = 100{,}000,$$

find the rate of change of quantity with respect to price when $p = \$50$. Interpret this result.

ELASTICITY OF DEMAND

41. (a) Find the point elasticity of the demand function $p + 4q = 80$ at $(10, 40)$.
    (b) How will a price increase affect total revenue?

42. (a) Find the point elasticity of the demand function $2p + 3q = 150$ at the price $p = 15$.
    (b) How will a price increase affect total revenue?

43. (a) Find the point elasticity of the demand function $p^2 + 2p + q = 49$ at $p = 6$.
    (b) How will a price increase affect total revenue?

44. (a) Find the point elasticity of the demand function $pq = 81$ at $p = 3$.
    (b) How will a price increase affect total revenue?

45. Suppose that the demand for a product is given by $pq + p = 5000$.
    (a) Find the elasticity when $p = \$50$ and $q = 99$.
    (b) Tell what type of elasticity this is: unitary, elastic, or inelastic.
    (c) How would revenue be affected by a price increase?

46. Suppose that the demand for a product is given by $2p^2q = 10{,}000 + 9000p^2$.
    (a) Find the elasticity when $p = \$50$ and $q = 4502$.
    (b) Tell what type of elasticity this is: unitary, elastic, or inelastic.
    (c) How would revenue be affected by a price increase?

47. Suppose that the demand for a product is given by $pq + p + 100q = 50{,}000$.
    (a) Find the elasticity when $p = \$401$.
    (b) Tell what type of elasticity this is.
    (c) How would a price increase affect revenue?

48. Suppose that the demand for a product is given by

$$(p + 1)\sqrt{q + 1} = 1000.$$

    (a) Find the elasticity when $p = \$39$.
    (b) Tell what type of elasticity this is.
    (c) How would a price increase affect revenue?

49. We have stated that when

$$\eta = -\frac{p}{q} \cdot \frac{dq}{dp} = 1,$$

the total revenue is unchanged as price increases. Given the total revenue function

$$R = p \cdot q, \quad \text{with} \quad q = f(p),$$

use implicit differentiation with respect to p to show that R is unchanged $(dR/dp = 0)$ when $\eta = 1$.

50. We have stated that when

$$\eta = -\frac{p}{q} \cdot \frac{dq}{dp} > 1,$$

the total revenue decreases as price increases. Given the total revenue function

$$R = p \cdot q, \quad \text{with} \quad q = f(p),$$

use implicit differentiation with respect to p to show that R is decreasing $(dR/dp < 0)$ when $\eta > 1$.

51. Show that $R = p \cdot q$ is increasing $(dR/dp > 0)$ when $\eta < 1$.

3.8 | RELATED RATES

OBJECTIVE

- To use implicit differentiation to solve problems involving related rates

We have seen that the derivative represents the instantaneous rate of change of one variable with respect to another. When the derivative is taken with respect to time, it represents the rate at which that variable is changing with respect to time (or the velocity). For example, if distance x is measured in miles and time t in hours, then dx/dt is measured in miles per hour, and would measure how fast x is changing. Similarly, if V represents the volume of water (in cubic feet) in a swimming pool and t is time (in minutes), then dV/dt is measured in cubic feet per minute (ft^3/min) and might measure the rate at which the pool is being filled with water or being emptied.

Sometimes, two (or more) quantities that depend on time are also related to each other. For example, the height of a tree h (in feet) is related to the radius r (in inches) of its trunk and this relationship can be modeled by

$$h = kr^{2/3},$$

where k is a constant.* Of course, both h and r are also related to time, and hence, the rates of change dh/dt and dr/dt are related to each other. Thus they are called **related rates.**

The specific relationship between dh/dt and dr/dt can be found by differentiating $h = kr^{2/3}$ implicitly with respect to time t.

EXAMPLE 1

Suppose that for a certain type of tree the height of the tree (in feet) is related to the radius of its trunk (in inches) by

$$h = 15r^{2/3}.$$

Suppose that the rate of change of r is $\frac{3}{4}$ inch per year. Find how fast the height is changing when the radius is 8 inches.

Solution To find how the rates dh/dt and dr/dt are related, we differentiate $h = 15r^{2/3}$ implicitly with respect to time t.

$$\frac{dh}{dt} = 10r^{-1/3}\frac{dr}{dt}$$

*T. McMahon, "Size and Shape in Biology," *Science* 179 (1979): 1201.

Using $r = 8$ inches and $dr/dt = \frac{3}{4}$ inch per year gives

$$\frac{dh}{dt} = 10(8)^{-1/3}(3/4) = \frac{15}{4} = 3\frac{3}{4} \text{ feet per year.}$$

While the work in Example 1 shows how to obtain related rates, the different units (feet per year) and (inches per year) may be somewhat difficult to interpret. For this reason, many applications in the life sciences deal with percentage rates of change.

EXAMPLE 2

According to Poiseuille's law, the flow of blood F is related to the radius r of the vessel according to

$$F = kr^4$$

where k is a constant. When the radius of a blood vessel is restricted, such as by cholesterol deposits, the flow of blood is also restricted. To increase the flow of blood, drugs can be administered that will increase the radius of the blood vessel. Find the percentage rate of change in the flow of blood that corresponds to the percentage rate of change in the radius of a blood vessel caused by the drug.

Solution We seek the percentage rate of change of flow, $(dF/dt)/F$, that results from a given percentage rate of change of the radius $(dr/dt)/r$. We first find the related rates of change by differentiating

$$F = kr^4$$

implicitly with respect to time.

$$\frac{dF}{dt} = k\left(4r^3\frac{dr}{dt}\right)$$

Then the percentage rate of change of flow can be found by dividing both sides of the equation by F.

$$\frac{\frac{dF}{dt}}{F} = \frac{4kr^3\frac{dr}{dt}}{F}$$

If we replace F on the right side of the equation with kr^4 and reduce, we get

$$\frac{\frac{dF}{dt}}{F} = \frac{4kr^3\frac{dr}{dt}}{kr^4} = 4\frac{\frac{dr}{dt}}{r}.$$

Thus we see that the percentage rate of change of the flow of blood is 4 times the corresponding percentage rate of change of the radius of the blood vessel. This means that a drug that would cause a 12% increase in the radius of a blood vessel at a certain time would produce a corresponding 48% increase in blood flow through that vessel at that time.

In the examples considered so far, the equation relating the time-dependent variables has been given. For some problems, the original equation relating the variables must first be developed from the statement of the problem. These problems can be solved with the aid of the following procedure.

SOLVING RELATED RATES PROBLEMS

PROCEDURE	EXAMPLE
To solve related rates problems:	Sand falls at a rate of 5 ft³/min on a conical pile, with the diameter always equal to the height of the pile. At what rate is the height increasing when it is 10 ft?
1. Use geometric and/or physical conditions to write an equation that relates the time-dependent variables.	1. The conical pile has its volume given by $$V = \frac{1}{3}\pi r^2 h.$$
2. Substitute values or relationships that are true *at all times* into the equation.	2. The radius $r = \frac{1}{2}h$ at all times, so $$V = \frac{1}{3}\pi\left(\frac{1}{4}h^2\right)h = \frac{\pi}{12}h^3.$$
3. Differentiate both sides of the equation implicitly with respect to time. This equation is valid for all times.	3. $\dfrac{dV}{dt} = \dfrac{\pi}{12}\left(3h^2\dfrac{dh}{dt}\right)$
4. Substitute the values that are known at the instant specified.	4. $\dfrac{dV}{dt} = 5$ at all times, so when $h = 10$, $$5 = \frac{\pi}{4}(10^2)\frac{dh}{dt}.$$
5. Solve for the specified quantity at the given time.	5. $\dfrac{dh}{dt} = \dfrac{20}{100\pi} = \dfrac{1}{5\pi}$ (ft/min) when $h = 10$ ft.

Note that you should *not* substitute numerical values for any quantity that is varying with time until after the derivative is taken.

EXAMPLE 3   A hot air balloon has a velocity of 50 ft/min and is flying at a constant height of 500 ft. An observer on the ground is watching the balloon approach. How fast is the distance between the balloon and the observer changing when the balloon is 1000 ft from the observer?

Solution If we let r be the distance between the balloon and the observer and x be the horizontal distance from the balloon to a point directly above the observer, then we see that these quantities are related by the equation

$$x^2 + 500^2 = r^2. \quad \text{(See Figure 3.47.)}$$

FIGURE 3.47

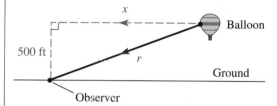

Because the distance x is decreasing, we know that dx/dt must be negative. Thus we are given that $dx/dt = -50$ at all times, and we need to find dr/dt when $r = 1000$. Taking the derivative with respect to t of both sides of the equation $x^2 + 500^2 = r^2$ gives

$$2x\frac{dx}{dt} + 0 = 2r\frac{dr}{dt}.$$

Using $dx/dt = -50$ and $r = 1000$, we get

$$2x(-50) = 2000\,\frac{dr}{dt}$$

$$\frac{dr}{dt} = \frac{-100x}{2000} = \frac{-x}{20}.$$

Using $r = 1000$ in $x^2 + 500^2 = r^2$ gives $x^2 = 750{,}000$. So $x = 500\sqrt{3}$, and

$$\frac{dr}{dt} = \frac{-500\sqrt{3}}{20} = -25\sqrt{3} \text{ ft/min.}$$

CHECKPOINT

1. If V represents volume, write a mathematical symbol that represents "the rate of change of volume with respect to time."

2. (a) Differentiate $x^2 + 64 = y^2$ implicitly with respect to time.

   (b) Suppose that we know that y is increasing at 2 units per minute. Use part (a) to find the rate of change of x at the instant when $x = 6$ and $y = 10$.

   (c) True or false: In solving a related rates problem, we substitute all numerical values into the equation before we take derivatives.

EXAMPLE 4 | Suppose that oil is spreading in a circular pattern from a leak at an offshore rig. If the rate at which the radius of the oil slick is growing is 1 ft/min, at what rate is the area of the oil slick growing when the radius is 600 ft?

Solution The area of the circular oil slick is given by

$$A = \pi r^2,$$

where r is the radius. The rate at which the area is changing is

$$\frac{dA}{dt} = 2\pi r \frac{dr}{dt}.$$

Using $r = 600$ ft and $dr/dt = 1$ ft/min gives

$$\frac{dA}{dt} = 2\pi(600 \text{ ft})(1 \text{ ft/min}) = 1200\pi \text{ ft}^2/\text{min}.$$

Thus when the radius of the oil slick is 600 ft, the area is growing at the rate of 1200π ft^2/min, or approximately 3770 ft^2/min.

CHECKPOINT
SOLUTIONS

1. dV/dt

2. (a) $2x\dfrac{dx}{dt} + 0 = 2y\dfrac{dy}{dt}$

   $x\dfrac{dx}{dt} = y\dfrac{dy}{dt}$

   (b) Use $\dfrac{dy}{dt} = 2$, $x = 6$ and $y = 10$ in part (a)

   to obtain $6\dfrac{dx}{dt} = 10(2)$ or $\dfrac{dx}{dt} = \dfrac{20}{6} = \dfrac{10}{3}$.

3. False. The numerical values for any quantity that is varying with time should not be substituted until after the derivative is taken.

EXERCISE 3.8

In problems 1–4, assume that x and y are differentiable functions of t. In each case, find dx/dt given that $x = 5$, $y = 12$, and $dy/dt = 2$.

1. $x^2 + y^2 = 169$ 2. $y^2 - x^2 = 119$
3. $y^2 = 2xy + 24$
4. $x^2(y - 6) = 12y + 6$
5. If $x^2 + y^2 = z^2$, find dy/dt when $x = 3$, $y = 4$, $dx/dt = 10$, and $dz/dt = 2$.

6. If $s = 2\pi r(r + h)$, find dr/dt when $r = 2$, $h = 8$, $dh/dt = 3$, and $ds/dt = 10\pi$.

7. A point is moving along the graph of the equation $y = -4x^2$. At what rate is y changing when $x = 5$ and is changing at a rate of 2 units/sec?

8. A point is moving along the graph of the equation $y = 5x^3 - 2x$. At what rate is y changing

when $x = 4$ and is changing at a rate of 3 units per sec?

9. The radius of a circle is increasing at a rate of 2 ft/min. At what rate is its area changing when the radius is 3 ft? (Recall that for a circle, $A = \pi r^2$.)

10. The area of a circle is changing at a rate of 1 in²/sec. At what rate is its radius changing when the radius is 2 in.?

11. The volume of a cube is increasing at a rate of 64 in³/sec. At what rate is the length of each edge of the cube changing when the edges are 6 in. long? (Recall that for a cube, $V = x^3$.)

12. The lengths of the edges of a cube are increasing at a rate of 8 ft/min. At what rate is the surface area changing when the edges are 24 ft long? (Recall that for a cube, $S = 6x^2$.)

APPLICATIONS

13. **Cell growth** A bacterial cell has a spherical shape. If the volume of the cell is increasing at a rate of 4 cubic micrometers per day, at what rate is the radius of the cell increasing when it is 2 micrometers? (Recall that for a sphere, $V = \frac{4}{3}\pi r^3$.)

14. **Volume and radius** Suppose that air is being pumped into a spherical balloon at a rate of 5 in³/min. At what rate is the radius of the balloon increasing when the radius is 5 in.?

Tumor growth For problems 15 and 16, suppose that a tumor in a person's body has a spherical shape, and that treatment is causing the radius of the tumor to decrease at a rate of 1 millimeter per month.

15. At what rate is the volume decreasing when the radius is 3 millimeters?

16. At what rate is the surface area of the tumor decreasing? (Recall that for a sphere, $S = 4\pi r^2$.)

17. **Allometric relationships—fish** For many species of fish, the allometric relationship between the weight W and the length L is approximately $W = kL^3$, where k is a constant. Find the percentage rate of change of the weight as a corresponding percentage rate of change of the length.

18. **Blood flow** The resistance R of a blood vessel to the flow of blood is a function of the radius r of the blood vessel and is given by

$$R = \frac{k}{r^4},$$

where k is a constant. Find the percentage rate of change of the resistance of a blood vessel in terms of the percentage rate of change in the radius of the blood vessel.

19. **Allometric relationships—crabs** For fiddler crabs, data gathered by Thompson* show that the allometric relationship between the weight C of the claw and the weight W of the body is given by

$$C = 0.11W^{1.54}.$$

Find the percentage rate of change in the claw weight in terms of the percentage rate of change in the body weight for fiddler crabs.

20. **Body weight and surface area** For human beings, the surface area S of the body is related to the body's weight W according to

$$S = kW^{2/3},$$

where k is a constant. Find the percentage rate of change in the body's surface area in terms of the percentage rate of change in the body's weight.

21. **Profit** Suppose that the daily profit (in dollars) from the production and sale of x units of

*d'Arcy Thompson, *On Growth and Form* (Cambridge: Cambridge University Press, 1961).

a product is given by

$$P = 180x - \frac{x^2}{1000} - 2000.$$

At what rate is the profit changing when the number of units produced and sold is 100 and is increasing at a rate of 10 units per day?

22. **Profit** Suppose that the monthly revenue and cost (in dollars) for x units of a product are

$$R = 400x - \frac{x^2}{20} \quad \text{and} \quad C = 5000 + 70x.$$

At what rate is the profit changing if the number of units produced and sold is 100 and is increasing at a rate of 10 units per month?

23. **Demand** Suppose that the price p (in dollars) of a product is given by the demand function

$$p = \frac{1000 - 10x}{400 - x},$$

where x represents the quantity demanded. If the daily demand is *decreasing* at a rate of 20 units per day, at what rate is the price changing when the demand is 20 units?

24. **Supply** The supply function for a product is given by $p = 40 + 100\sqrt{2x + 9}$, where x is the number of units supplied and p is the price in dollars. If the price is increasing at a rate of $1 per month, at what rate is the supply changing when $x = 20$?

25. **Capital investment and production** Suppose that the number of units x of a product that is produced per month depends on the number of thousands of dollars y invested, with $x = 30y + 20y^2$. At what rate will production increase if $10,000 is invested and if the investment capital is increasing at a rate of $1000 per month?

26. **Boyle's law** Boyle's law for enclosed gases states that at a constant temperature, the pressure is related to the volume by the equation

$$P = \frac{k}{V},$$

where k is a constant. If the volume is increasing at a rate of 5 cubic inches per hour, at what rate is the pressure changing when the volume is 30 cubic inches and $k = 2$ inch-pounds?

27. **Boat docking** Suppose that a boat is being pulled toward a dock by a winch that is 5 ft above the level of the boat deck. If the winch is pulling the cable at a rate of 3 ft/min, at what rate is the boat approaching the dock when it is 12 ft from the dock? Use Figure 3.48.

FIGURE 3.48

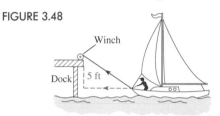

MISCELLANEOUS APPLICATIONS

28. A 30-ft ladder is leaning against a wall. If the bottom is pulled away from the wall at a rate of 1 ft/sec, at what rate is the top of the ladder sliding down the wall when the bottom is 18 ft from the wall?

29. A kite is 30 ft high and is moving horizontally at a rate 10 ft/min. If the kite string is taut, at what rate is the string being played out when 50 ft of string is out?

30. A plane is flying at a constant altitude of 1 mile and a speed of 300 mph. If it is flying toward an observer on the ground, how fast is the plane approaching the observer when it is 5 miles from the observer?

31. Two boats leave the same port at the same time, with boat A traveling north at 15 knots and boat B traveling east at 20 knots. How fast

is the distance between them changing when boat A is 30 nautical miles from port?

32. Two cars are approaching an intersection on roads that are perpendicular to each other. Car A is north of the intersection and traveling south at 40 mph. Car B is east of the intersection and traveling west at 55 mph. How fast is the distance between the cars changing when car A is 15 miles from the intersection and car B is 8 miles from the intersection?

33. Water is flowing into a barrel in the shape of a right circular cylinder at the rate of 200 in^3/min. If the radius of the barrel is 18 in., at what rate is the depth of the water changing when the water is 30 in. deep?

34. Suppose that water is being pumped into a rectangular swimming pool of uniform depth at 10 ft^3/hr. If the pool is 10 ft wide and 25 ft long, at what rate is the water rising when it is 4 ft deep?

KEY TERMS
& FORMULAS

SECTION	KEY TERM	FORMULA
3.1	Increasing	$f'(x) > 0$
	Decreasing	$f'(x) < 0$
	Critical points	$f'(x) = 0$ or $f'(x)$ undefined
	Maxima and minima	
	Sign diagram for $f'(x)$	
	First-derivative test	
	Horizontal point of inflection	
3.2	Concave up	$f''(x) > 0$
	Concave down	$f''(x) < 0$
	Point of inflection	May occur where $f''(x) = 0$ or $f''(x)$ undefined
	Sign diagram for $f''(x)$	
	Second-derivative test	
3.3	Asymptotes	
	Horizontal: $y = b$	$\lim_{x \to +\infty} f(x) = b$ or $\lim_{x \to -\infty} f(x) = b$

SECTION	KEY TERM	FORMULA
	Vertical: $x = c$ for rational function $y = f(x)/g(x)$	y unbounded near $x = c$ if $g(c) = 0$ and $f(c) \neq 0$
3.4	Average cost	$\overline{C}(x) = C(x)/x$
	Profit maximization	
	Competitive market	$R(x) = p \cdot x$ where p = equilibrium price
	Monopolistic market	$R(x) = p \cdot x$ where $p = f(x)$ is the demand function
	Taxation in competitive market	New supply: $p = f(q) + t$
3.5	Inventory cost models	
3.6	Differential	$dy = f'(x)dx$
3.7	Implicit differentiation	
	Elasticity of demand	$\eta = \dfrac{-p}{q} \cdot \dfrac{dq}{dp}$
	Elastic	$\eta > 1$
	Inelastic	$\eta < 1$
	Unitary elastic	$\eta = 1$
3.8	Related rates	
	Percentage rate of change	

REVIEW EXERCISES

3.1   In problems 1–4, find all critical points and determine whether they are relative maxima, relative minima, or horizontal points of inflection. Do not sketch.

1. $y = -x^2$

2. $p = q^2 - 4q - 5$

3. $f(x) = 1 - 3x + 3x^2 - x^3$

4. $f(x) = \dfrac{3x}{x^2 + 1}$

In problems 5–10,
(a) find all critical values, including those where $f'(x)$ is undefined.
(b) find the relative maxima and minima, if any exist.
(c) find the horizontal points of inflection, if any exist.
(d) sketch the graph.

5. $y = x^3 + x^2 - x - 1$ 6. $f(x) = 4x^3 - x^4$

7. $f(x) = x^3 - \dfrac{15}{2}x^2 - 18x + \dfrac{3}{2}$ 8. $y = 5x^7 - 7x^5 - 1$

9. $y = x^{2/3} - 1$ 10. $y = x^{2/3}(x - 4)^2$

3.2

11. Is the graph of $y = x^4 - 3x^3 + 2x - 1$ concave up or concave down at $x = 2$?

12. Find the points of inflection of the graph of $y = x^4 - 2x^3 - 12x^2 + 6$.

13. Find the relative maxima, relative minima, and points of inflection of the graph of $y = x^3 - 3x^2 - 9x + 10$.

In problems 14 and 15, find any relative maxima, relative minima, points of inflection, and sketch each graph.

14. $y = x^3 - 12x$

15. $y = 2 + 5x^3 - 3x^5$

3.3

In problems 16 and 17, use the graphs to find the following:
(a) vertical asymptotes   (b) horizontal asymptotes
(c) $\lim\limits_{x \to +\infty} f(x)$ (d) $\lim\limits_{x \to -\infty} f(x)$

16.
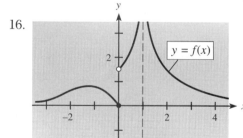

17.
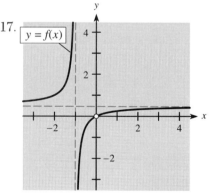

In problems 18 and 19, find any horizontal asymptotes and any vertical asymptotes.

18. $y = \dfrac{3x + 2}{2x - 4}$ 19. $y = \dfrac{x^2}{1 - x^2}$

In problems 20–22,
(a) find any horizontal and vertical asymptotes.
(b) find any relative maxima and minima.
(c) sketch each graph.

20. $y = \dfrac{3x}{x + 2}$ 21. $y = \dfrac{8(x - 2)}{x^2}$ 22. $y = \dfrac{x^2}{x - 1}$

3.4

23. Given $R = 280x - x^2$, find the absolute maximum and minimum for R when
(a) $0 \le x \le 200$ and (b) $0 \le x \le 100$.

24. Given $y = 6400x - 18x^2 - \dfrac{x^3}{3}$, find the absolute maximum and minimum for y when
(a) $0 \le x \le 50$ and (b) $0 \le x \le 100$.

3.6

25. Find dy for $y = \dfrac{x^2}{1 - x^2}$.

26. Find dy for $y = \dfrac{1}{8}(3x + 4)^8$

27. Let $y = 500x - 0.1x^2$. Approximate the change in y when x changes from 100 to 100.5.

28. Let $y = \dfrac{10}{\sqrt{6x + 1}}$. Approximate the change in y when x changes from 4 to 3.8.

3.7

29. Find dy/dx for $y^2 = 4x - 1$.
30. Find dy/dx if $x^2 + 3y^2 + 2x - 3y + 2 = 0$.
31. Find dy/dx for $3x^2 + 2x^3y^2 - y^5 = 7$.
32. Find the second derivative of $x^2 + y^2 = 1$.
33. Find the slope of the tangent to the curve $x^2 + 4x - 3y^2 + 6 = 0$ at $(3, 3)$.
34. Find the points where tangents to the graph of the equation in problem 33 are horizontal.

3.8

35. Suppose that $3x^2 - 2y^3 = 10y$, where x and y are differentiable functions of t. If $dx/dt = 2$, find dy/dt when $x = 10$ and $y = 5$.

36. A right triangle with legs of lengths x and y has its area given by

$$A = \tfrac{1}{2}xy.$$

If the rate of change of x is 2 units per minute and the rate of change of y is 5 units per minute, find the rate of change of the area when $x = 4$ and $y = 1$.

APPLICATIONS

3.4

37. **Cost** If the total cost function for a product is

$$C(x) = 3x^2 + 15x + 75,$$

how many units will minimize the average cost? Find the minimum average cost.

38. **Revenue** If the total revenue function for a product is given by

$$R(x) = 32x - 0.01x^2,$$

how many units will maximize the total revenue? Find the maximum revenue.

39. **Profit** Suppose that the profit function for a product is given by

$$P(x) = 1080x + 9.6x^2 - 0.1x^3 - 50,000.$$

Find the maximum profit.

40. **Profit** If $R(x) = 46x - x^2$ and $C(x) = 5x^2 + 10x + 3$, how many units (x) will maximize profit?

41. **Profit** A product can be produced at a total cost $C(x) = 800 + 4x$, where x is the number produced. If the total revenue is given by $R(x) = 80x - \frac{1}{4}x^2$, determine the level of production that will maximize the profit.

42. **Average cost** The total cost function for a product is $C = 2x^2 + 54x + 98$. Producing how many units will minimize average cost?

43. **Revenue** McRobert's TV Shop sells 200 sets per month at a price of $400 per unit. Market research indicates that they can sell one additional set for each $1 they reduce the price. At what selling price will they maximize revenue?

44. **Profit** If, in problem 43, the sets cost the shop $250 each, when will profit be maximized?

45. **Profit** Suppose that for a product in a competitive market the demand function is $p = 1200 - 2x$ and that the supply function is $p = 200 + 2x$, where x is the number of units. If a firm's average cost function for this product is

$$\overline{C}(x) = \frac{12,000}{x} + 50 + x,$$

find the maximum profit. *Hint:* First find the equilibrium price.

46. **Profit** The monthly demand function for a product sold by a monopoly is $p = 800 - x$, and its average cost is $\overline{C} = 200 + x$. Determine
    (a) the quantity that will maximize profit.
    (b) the selling price at the optimal quantity.

47. **Profit** Suppose that in a monopolistic market the demand function for a commodity is

$$p = 7000 - 10x - \frac{x^2}{3}.$$

If a company's average cost function for this commodity is

$$\overline{C}(x) = \frac{40,000}{x} + 600 + 8x,$$

find the maximum profit.

48. **Taxation** Can increasing the tax per unit sold actually lead to a decrease in tax revenues?

49. **Taxation** If the demand and supply functions for a product are

$$p = 2800 - 8q - \frac{q^2}{3} \quad \text{and} \quad p = 400 + 2q,$$

respectively, find the tax per unit t that will maximize the tax revenue T.

50. **Taxation** If the supply and demand functions for a product are

$$p = 40 + 20q \quad \text{and} \quad p = \frac{5000}{q + 1},$$

respectively, find the tax t that maximizes tax revenue T.

3.5

51. **Reaction to a drug** The reaction R to an injection of a drug is related to the dosage x according to

$$R(x) = x^2 \left(500 - \frac{x}{3} \right).$$

Find the dosage that yields the maximum reaction.

52. **Productivity** The number of parts produced per hour by a worker is given by

$$N = 4 + 3t^2 - t^3,$$

where t is the number of hours on the job without a break. If the worker starts at 8 A.M., when will she be at maximum production during the morning?

53. **Population** Population estimates show that the equation $P = 300 + 10t - t^2$ represents the size of the graduating class of a high school, with t representing the number of years after 1990, $0 \le t \le 10$. What will be the largest graduating class in the decade?

54. **Night brightness** Suppose that an observatory is to be built between cities A and B that are 30 miles apart. For the best viewing, the observatory should be located where the night brightness from these cities is minimum. If the night brightness of city A is 8 times that of city B, then the night brightness b between the two cities and x miles from A is given by

$$b = \frac{8k}{x^2} + \frac{k}{(30 - x)^2},$$

where k is a constant. Find the best location for the observatory; that is, find x that minimizes b.

55. **Product design** A playpen manufacturer wants to make a rectangular enclosure with maximum play area. To remain competitive, he wants the perimeter of the base to be only 16 feet. What dimensions should the playpen have?

56. **Printing design** A printed page is to contain 56 square inches and have a $\frac{3}{4}$-inch margin at

the bottom and 1-inch margins at the top and on both sides. Find the dimensions that minimize the size of the page (and hence the costs for paper).

57. **Drug sensitivity** The reaction R to an injection of a drug is related to the dosage x according to

$$R(x) = x^2\left(500 - \frac{x}{3}\right).$$

The sensitivity to the drug is defined by dR/dx. Find the dosage that maximizes sensitivity.

58. **Photosynthesis** The amount of photosynthesis that takes place in a certain plant depends on the intensity of light x according to the equation

$$f(x) = 145x^2 - 30x^3.$$

The rate of change of the amount of photosynthesis with respect to the intensity is $f'(x)$. Find the intensity that maximizes the rate of change.

59. **Inventory-cost model** A company needs 288,000 items per year. Production costs are $1500 to prepare for a production run and $30 for each item produced. Inventory costs are $1.50 per year for each item stored. Find the number of items that should be produced in each run so that the total costs of production and storage are minimum.

3.6

60. **Job training and productivity** During a new salesperson's first four months of employment, his monthly sales S (in thousands of dollars) are related to the number of hours of training, as follows:

$$S(x) = \frac{9}{x} + 10 + \frac{x}{4}, \quad \text{with} \quad x \geq 4.$$

(a) Find the change in sales if training is increased from 10 hours to 12 hours.
(b) Use differentials to approximate the same change.

61. **Revenue** Suppose that the revenue (in millions of dollars) from the sale of x million units of a product is given by

$$R(x) = \frac{900,000x}{(x + 250)^2}.$$

Approximate the change in revenue if the number of units sold increases from 50.0 million to 50.3 million.

3.7

62. **Elasticity of demand**
(a) Find the point elasticity of the demand function $pq = 27$ at $(9, 3)$.
(b) How will a price increase affect total revenue?

63. **Elasticity of demand** Suppose that the demand for a product is given by

$$p^2(2q + 1) = 10,000.$$

Find the elasticity of demand when $p = \$20$.

64. **Evaporation rates** A spherical droplet of water evaporates at a rate of 1 mm³/min. Find the rate of change of the radius when the droplet has a radius of 2.5 mm.

65. **Miscellaneous** A sign is being lowered over the side of a building at the rate of 2 ft/min. A worker handling a guide line is 7 ft away from a spot directly below the sign. How fast is the worker taking in the guide line at the instant the sign is 25 ft from the worker's hands? See Figure 3.49.

FIGURE 3.49

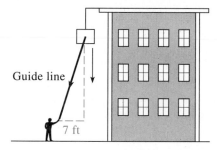

Guide line

7 ft

66. **Species habitats** Suppose that in a study of water birds, the relationship between the area (in square miles) of wetlands A and the number of different species S of birds found in the area was found to be

$S = kA^{1/3}$

where k is a constant. Find the percentage rate of change in the number of species in terms of the percentage rate of change of the area.

PRODUCTION MANAGEMENT

Metal Containers, Inc. is reviewing the way in which it submits bids on U.S. Army contracts. Several times each month, the company has the opportunity to submit a bid for boxes of different sizes and specifications. The army often requests open-top boxes, with square bases and of specified volumes. The army also specifies the materials for the boxes, with the base of the box usually made of a different material than the sides. The box is put together by riveting a bracket at each of the eight corners. For Metal Containers, the total cost of producing a box is the sum of the cost of the materials for the box and the labor costs associated with affixing each bracket.

Instead of estimating each job separately, the company wants to develop an overall approach that will allow it to cost out proposals more easily. To accomplish this they need you to devise a formula for the total cost of producing each box and determine the dimensions that allow a box of specified volume to be produced at minimum cost. Use the following notation to help you solve this problem.

Cost of the material for the base = A per square unit
Cost of the material for the sides = B per square unit
Cost of each bracket = C
Cost to affix each bracket = D
Length of the sides of the base = x
Height of the box = h
Volume specified by the army = V

1. Write an expression for the company's total cost in terms of these quantities.

2. At the time an order is received for boxes of a specified volume, the costs of the materials and labor will be fixed and only the dimensions will vary. Find a formula for each of the dimensions of the box so that the total cost is a minimum.

3. The army requests bids on boxes of 48 cubic feet with base material costing the container company $12 per square foot and side material costing $8 per square foot. Each bracket costs $5, and the associated labor cost is $1 per bracket. Use your formulas to find the dimensions of the box that meets the army's requirements at a minimum cost. What is this cost?

Metal Containers asks you to help them determine how best to order the brackets they use on their boxes. You are able to obtain the following information: They use approximately 100,000 brackets a year and the purchase price of each is $5. They buy the same number of brackets (say, n) each time they place an order with their supplier, and it costs $60 to process each order. Metal Containers also has additional costs associated with storing, insuring, and financing their inventory of brackets. These carrying costs amount to 15% of the average value of inventory annually. The brackets are used steadily and deliveries are made just as inventory reaches zero, so that inventory fluctuates between zero and n brackets.

4. If the total annual cost associated with the bracket supply is the sum of the annual purchasing cost and the annual carrying costs, what order size n would minimize the total cost?

5. In the general case of the bracket ordering problem, the order size n that minimizes the total cost of the bracket supply is called the Economic Order Quantity or EOQ. Use the following notations to determine a general formula for the EOQ.

Fixed cost per order $= F$
Quantity purchased per year $= P$
Unit cost $= C$
Carrying cost (as a decimal rate) $= r$

PREREQUISITE PROBLEM TYPE	REVIEW SECTION/ANSWER
SECTIONS 4.1, 4.2, 4.3, 4.5 Write the following with positive exponents: (a) x^{-3} (b) $\dfrac{1}{x^{-2}}$ (c) $\sqrt{x^2 - 1}$	Sections 0.2, 0.3, Exponents and radicals (a) $\dfrac{1}{x^3}$ (b) x^2 (c) $(x^2 - 1)^{1/2}$
SECTIONS 4.1, 4.2, 4.5 Simplify: (a) 2^0 (b) x^0 $(x \neq 0)$ (c) $49^{1/2}$ (d) 10^{-2}	Sections 0.2, 0.3, Exponents (a) 1 (b) 1 (c) 7 (d) $\frac{1}{100}$
SECTIONS 4.1, 4.2 Answer true or false. (a) $(\frac{1}{2})^x = 2^{-x}$ (b) $\sqrt{50} = 50^{1/2}$ (c) If $8 = 2^y$, then $y = 4$. (d) If $x^3 = 8$, then $x = 2$.	Sections 0.2, 0.3, Exponents and radicals (a) True (b) True (c) False; $y = 3$ (d) True
SECTION 4.3 Simplify: $\dfrac{1}{(3x)^{1/2}} \cdot \dfrac{1}{2}(3x)^{-1/2} \cdot 3$	Section 0.3, Rational exponents $\dfrac{1}{2x}$
SECTIONS 4.1, 4.2, 4.5 (a) If $f(x) = 2^{-2x}$, what is $f(-2)$? (b) If $f(x) = 2^{-2x}$, what is $f(1)$? (c) If $f(t) = (1 + 0.02)^t$, what is $f(0)$? (d) If $f(t) = 100(0.03)^{0.02t}$, what is $f(0)$?	Section 1.1, Functional notation (a) 16 (b) $\frac{1}{4}$ (c) 1 (d) 3

4 | EXPONENTIAL AND LOGARITHMIC FUNCTIONS

In this chapter we study exponential and logarithmic functions, which provide models for many applications that at first seem remote and unrelated. For example, a business manager uses these functions to study the growth of money or corporations or the decay of new sales volume. A social scientist uses exponential and logarithmic functions to study the growth of organizations or populations or the dating of fossilized remains. And a biologist uses these functions to study the growth of microorganisms in a laboratory culture, the spread of disease, the measurement of pH, or the decay of radioactive material.

In our study of exponential and logarithmic functions and their derivatives, we will examine their descriptions, their properties, their graphs, and the special inverse relationship between these two functions. We will see how these functions are applied to some of the concerns of social scientists, business managers, and life scientists. In these applications, the inverse relationship of the exponential and logarithmic functions is used to solve some of the equations that arise. The work with these functions will be much easier if you have a calculator that computes powers of e and logarithms to the base e (denoted e^x and $\ln x$, respectively), but tables have been provided in the appendix in case you do not have such a calculator.

4.1 | EXPONENTIAL FUNCTIONS

OBJECTIVE

• To graph exponential functions

Suppose that we observe a culture of bacteria to have the characteristic that each minute, every microorganism present splits into two new organisms. Then we can describe the number of bacteria present in the culture as a function of time. That is, if we begin the culture with just one microorganism, then we know that after one minute we will have two organisms, after two minutes, four, and so on. Table 4.1 gives a few of the values that describe this growth.

TABLE 4.1

Minutes passed	Number of organisms
0	1
1	2
2	4
3	8
4	16

If x represents the number of minutes that have passed and y represents the number of organisms, the points (x, y) lie on the graph of the function with equation

$$y = 2^x.$$

This equation is an example of a special group of functions called **exponential functions.** In general, we define these functions as follows:

Exponential Functions

If a is a positive real number and $a \neq 1$, then the function

$$f(x) = a^x$$

is an **exponential function.**

A table of some values satisfying $y = 2^x$ and the graph of this function are given in Figure 4.1. This function is said to model the growth of the number of organisms in the discussion above even though some points on the graph do not correspond to a time and a number of organisms. For example, time x could not be negative, and the number of organisms y could not be fractional.

We have defined rational powers of x in terms of radicals in Chapter 0, so 2^x makes sense for any rational power x. It can also be shown that the laws of exponents apply for irrational numbers. We will assume that if we graphed $y = 2^x$ for irrational values of x, those points would lie on the curve in Figure 4.1. Thus in general, we can graph an exponential function by plotting easily calculated points, such as those in the table in Figure 4.1, and drawing a smooth curve through the points.

FIGURE 4.1

x	$y = 2^x$
-3	$2^{-3} = \frac{1}{8}$
-2	$2^{-2} = \frac{1}{4}$
-1	$2^{-1} = \frac{1}{2}$
0	$2^0 = 1$
1	$2^1 = 2$
2	$2^2 = 4$
3	$2^3 = 8$

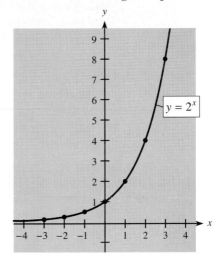

EXAMPLE 1

Graph $y = 10^x$.

Solution A table of values and the graph are given in Figure 4.2.

FIGURE 4.2

x	y
-3	$10^{-3} = 1/1000$
-2	$10^{-2} = 1/100$
-1	$10^{-1} = 1/10$
0	$10^0 = 1$
1	$10^1 = 10$
2	$10^2 = 100$
3	$10^3 - 1000$

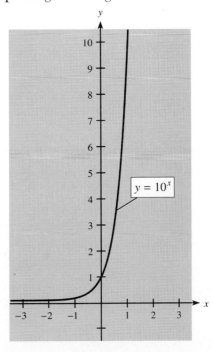

Note that the graphs of $y = 2^x$ (Figure 4.1) and $y = 10^x$ (Figure 4.2) are very similar. In each case there is no x-value that makes 2^x or 10^x less than or equal to zero. Each graph approaches, but never touches, the x-axis on the left. (We call the x-axis an **asymptote** for these curves.) The domain of each function contains all real numbers, and the range contains all positive real numbers. Both graphs pass through the point $(0, 1)$. In fact, the only difference between the graphs of $y = 2^x$ and $y = 10^x$ is that $y = 10^x$ rises more rapidly than $y = 2^x$.

The shapes of the graphs of equations of the form $y = a^x$, with $a > 1$, are similar to those for $y = 2^x$ and $y = 10^x$. Exponentials of this type model growth in diverse applications, and their graphs have the following basic shape:

Graphs of Exponential Functions

Equation: $y = a^x$ $(a > 1)$
y-intercept: $(0, 1)$
Domain: All reals
Range: All positive reals
Asymptote: x-axis (negative half)

Basic shape

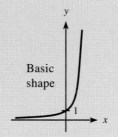

CHECKPOINT

1. Can any value of x give a negative value for y if $y = a^x$ and $a > 1$?

2. What asymptote does the graph of $y = a^x$ approach?

A special function that occurs frequently in economics and biology is $y = e^x$, where e is a fixed irrational number (approximately $2.71828 \ldots$). The number e is defined by either of the following limits:

$$e = \lim_{m \to \infty} \left(1 + \frac{1}{m} \right)^m$$

$$e = \lim_{a \to 0} (1 + a)^{1/a}$$

In Section 4.5, we will see how these limits arise when we discuss interest that is compounded continuously.

Since $e > 1$, the graph of $y = e^x$ will have the same basic shape as other growth exponentials. We can calculate the y-coordinate for points on the graph of this function with a calculator or Table I in the appendix. A table of some values (with y-values rounded to two places) and the graph are shown in Figure 4.3.

FIGURE 4.3

x	$y = e^x$
-2	0.14
-1	0.37
0	1.00
1	2.72
2	7.39

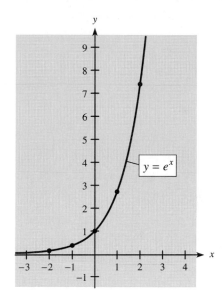

Exponential functions with base e often arise in natural ways. As we will see in Section 4.5, the growth of money that is compounded continuously is given by $S = Pe^{rt}$, where P is the original principal, r the annual interest rate, and t the time in years. Certain populations (of insects, for example) grow exponentially, and the number of individuals can be closely approximated by the equation $y = P_0 e^{ht}$, where P_0 is the original population size, h is a constant that depends on the type of population, and y is the population size at any instant t. These are both examples of exponential growth with base e.

Exponentials whose bases are between 0 and 1, such as $y = (\frac{1}{2})^x$, have graphs different from those of the exponentials just discussed. Using the properties of exponents, we have

$$y = \left(\frac{1}{2}\right)^x = (2^{-1})^x = 2^{-x}.$$

This suggests that exponentials of the form $y = b^x$, where $0 < b < 1$, can be rewritten in the form $y = a^{-x}$, where $a > 1$.

EXAMPLE 2 Graph $y = 2^{-x}$.

Solution A table of values and the graph are given in Figure 4.4.

FIGURE 4.4

x	$y = 2^{-x}$
-3	$2^3 = 8$
-2	$2^2 = 4$
-1	$2^1 = 2$
0	$2^0 = 1$
1	$2^{-1} = \frac{1}{2}$
2	$2^{-2} = \frac{1}{4}$
3	$2^{-3} = \frac{1}{8}$

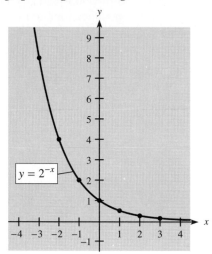

EXAMPLE 3 Graph $y = e^{-2x}$.

Solution Using a calculator or Table I in the appendix to find the values of powers of e (to two decimal places), we get the graph shown in Figure 4.5.

FIGURE 4.5

x	y
-3	$e^6 = 403.43$
-2	$e^4 = 54.60$
-1	$e^2 = 7.39$
0	$e^0 = 1.00$
1	$e^{-2} = 0.14$
2	$e^{-4} = 0.02$

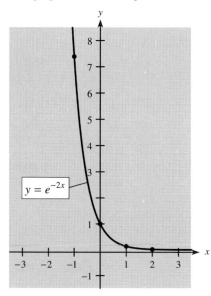

Exponential functions of the form $y = a^{-x}$, where $a > 1$, all have a similar basic shape. They fall rapidly to the right, approaching but not touching the positive x-axis. Functions of this type model decay for various phenomena. For example, the number of atoms y of a radioactive element at an instant in time t is given by

$$y = w_0 e^{-h(t - t_0)},$$

where w_0 is the number of atoms at time t_0 and h is a constant that depends on the element.

There are some important exponential functions that use base e, but whose graphs are different from those we have discussed. For example, the standard normal probability curve (often referred to as a bell-shaped curve) is the graph of an exponential function with base e (see Figure 4.6).

FIGURE 4.6

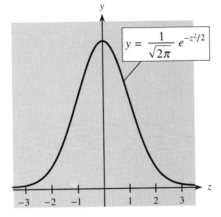

$$y = \frac{1}{\sqrt{2\pi}}\, e^{-z^2/2}$$

Standard normal probability curve

Later in this chapter we will study other exponential functions that model growth, but whose graphs are also different from those discussed previously.

CHECKPOINT

3. True or false: The graph of $y = \left(\dfrac{1}{a}\right)^x$, with $a > 1$, is the same as the graph of $y = a^{-x}$.

4. True or false: The graph of $y = a^{-x}$, with $a > 1$, approaches the x-axis as an asymptote as $x \to \infty$.

5. True or false: The graph of $y = 2^{-x}$ is the graph of $y = 2^x$ reflected about the y-axis.

TECHNOLOGY CORNER

1. (a) Graph $f(x) = me^x$ for $m = \pm 1$ and $m = \pm 4$.

   (b) What effect does m have on the graph? In particular, does the domain change? Does the range change? Does the asymptote change? Does the intercept change? Does the general shape change?

2. (a) Graph $f(x) = e^{ax}$ for $a = 0.5$, 1, and 10.

   (b) What effect does a have on the graphs of $f(x)$?

   (c) For different values of a, what is similar about the graphs of $f(x)$? Pay attention to items such as those mentioned in 1(b).

3. Suppose that sales are related to advertising expenditures according to one of the following two models, where S_1 and S_n are sales and x is advertising, all in millions of dollars.

$$S_1 = 30 + 20x - 0.4x^2$$
$$S_n = 24.58 + 325.18(1 - e^{-x/14})$$

   (a) Graph both of these functions on the same set of axes.

   (b) Do these two functions give approximately the same sales per million dollars of advertising for $0 \le x \le 20$?

   (c) How do these functions differ for $x > 20$? Which more realistically represents the relationship between sales and advertising expenditures after $20 million is spent on advertising? Why?

CHECKPOINT
SOLUTIONS

1. No, all values of y are positive.

2. The left side of the x-axis $(y = 0)$

3. True.

4. True.

5. True.

⊞ In problems 1–10, use a calculator or table to evaluate each expression.

1. $10^{0.5}$ 2. $10^{3.6}$

3. $5^{-2.7}$ 4. $8^{-2.6}$

5. $3^{1/3}$ 6. $2^{11/6}$

7. e^2 8. e^5

9. e^{-3} 10. $e^{-1.5}$

In problems 11–22, graph each function.

11. $y = 4^x$ 12. $y = 8^x$

13. $y = 2(x^3)$ 14. $y = 3(2^x)$

15. $y = 5^x$ 16. $y = 3^{x-1}$

17. $y = e^x$ 18. $y = 2e^x$

19. $y = 3^{-x}$ 20. $y = 3^{-2x}$

21. $y = e^{-x}$ 22. $y = \frac{1}{3}e^x$

In problems 23–28, use the graph of $y = 2^x$ (see Figure 4.1) to sketch each graph.

23. $y = 2^{x+1}$ 24. $y = 2^{x-2}$

25. $y = 3(2^x)$ 26. $y = \frac{1}{4}(2^x)$

27. $y + 1 = 2^x$ 28. $y - 1 = 2^x$

29. Graph $y = 1 + e^x$ 30. Graph $y = 2 + e^{-x}$

31. How does the graph in problem 29 differ from the graph of $y = e^x$?

32. How does the graph in problem 30 differ from the graph of $y = e^{-x}$?

APPLICATIONS

Population growth For problems 33–36, consider that world population is growing according to the equation

$$N = N_0(1 + r)^t$$

where N_0 is the number of individuals at time $t = 0$, r is the yearly rate of growth, and t is the number of years.

33. Sketch the graph for $t = 0$ to $t = 10$ when the growth rate is 2% and N_0 is 4.1 billion.

34. Sketch the graph for $t = 0$ to $t = 10$ when the growth rate is 3% and N_0 is 4.1 billion.

35. Sketch the graph for $t = 0$ to $t = 10$ when the growth rate is 5% and N_0 is 4.1 billion.

36. Sketch the graph for $t = 0$ to $t = 10$ when the growth rate is 7% and N_0 is 4.1 billion.

37. The number of molecules of a certain substance that have enough energy to activate a reaction is given by

$$y = 100,000\, e^{-1/x},$$

where y is the number of molecules and x is the (absolute) temperature of the substance. Plot the graph of this equation for $x > 0$.

38. **Newton's law of cooling** When a body is moved from one medium to another, its temperature T changes according to the equation

$$T = T_0 + Ce^{kt},$$

where T_0 is the temperature of the new medium, C the temperature difference between the mediums (old–new), t the time in the new medium, and k a constant. Given that $T_0 = 70$, $C = 23$, and $k = -0.2$, sketch the graph for $t \geq 0$.

39. **Compound interest** If P is invested for t years at 10% compounded continuously, the total amount returned on the investment is given by

$$S = Pe^{0.1t}.$$

Use $P = 1000$ and graph this function for $0 \leq t \leq 20$.

40. **Bacterial growth** A single bacterium splits into two bacteria every half hour, so that the number of bacteria in a culture quadruples every hour. Thus the equation by which a colony of 10 bacteria multiplies in t hours is

given by

$$y = 10(4^t).$$

Graph this equation for $0 \le t \le 8$.

41. **Drug in the bloodstream** The concentration y of a certain drug in the bloodstream at any time t is given by the equation

$$y = 100(1 - e^{-0.462t}).$$

Graph this equation for $0 \le t \le 10$.

42. **Product reliability** A statistical study shows that the fraction of television sets of a certain brand that are still in service after x years is given by $f = e^{-0.15x}$. Graph this equation for $0 \le x \le 10$.

43. **Atmospheric pressure** The atmospheric pressure P (in lb/sq in.) is given by

$$P = 14.7e^{-0.2x},$$

where x is the number of miles above sea level. Graph this equation for $0 \le x \le 20$.

44. **Dow Jones Industrial Average** The following table shows the high values achieved by the Dow Jones Industrial Average for the years from 1979 to 1989. Assume that the high h can be modeled with the function $h(x) = 1933.27 - 69.1e^{x/20} + 0.93e^{x/10}$, where x is the number of years past 1900. This function and the data points are graphed in the figure below.

Year	Dow Jones High
1979	897
1980	1000
1981	1024
1982	1070
1983	1287
1984	1286
1985	1553
1986	1955
1987	2722
1988	2183
1989	2791

Source: *World Almanac*, 1991.

(a) Find the actual change in the high for the Dow Jones Industrial Average from 1979 to 1989.

(b) Find the change predicted by the model $h(x)$ from 1979 to 1989.

(c) Find the actual average rate of change in the high for the Dow Jones Industrial Average from 1979 to 1989.

(d) Find the average rate of change predicted by the model $h(x)$ from 1979 to 1989.

$$h(x) = 1933.27 - 69.1e^{x/20} + 0.93e^{x/10}$$

Year

4.2 | LOGARITHMIC FUNCTIONS AND THEIR PROPERTIES

OBJECTIVES

- To convert equations for logarithmic functions from logarithmic to exponential form and vice versa
- To evaluate some special logarithms
- To graph logarithmic functions
- To use properties of logarithmic functions to simplify expressions involving logarithms

LOGARITHMIC FUNCTIONS AND GRAPHS

Before the development and easy availability of calculators and computers, certain arithmetic computations, such as $(1.37)^{13}$ and $\sqrt[16]{3.09}$, were difficult to perform. The computations could be performed relatively easily using **logarithms,** which were developed in the seventeenth century by John Napier, or by using a slide rule, which is based on logarithms. The use of logarithms as a computing technique has all but disappeared today, but the study of **logarithmic functions** is still very important because of the many applications of these functions.

For example, let us again consider the culture of bacteria described at the beginning of Section 4.1. If we know that the culture is begun with one microorganism and that each minute every microorganism present splits into two new ones, then we can find the number of minutes it takes until there are 1024 organisms by solving

$$1024 = 2^y.$$

The solution of this equation may be written in the form

$$y = \log_2 1024,$$

which is read "y equals the logarithm of 1024 to the base 2."

In general, we may express the equation $x = a^y$ $(a > 0,\ a \neq 1)$ in the form $y = f(x)$ by defining a **logarithmic function.**

Logarithmic Function

For $a > 0$ and $a \neq 1$, the **logarithmic function**

$$y = \log_a x \qquad \text{(logarithmic form)}$$

has domain $x > 0$, and is defined by

$$a^y = x \qquad \text{(exponential form)}.$$

The a is called the **base** in both $\log_a x = y$ and $a^y = x$, and y is the *logarithm* in $\log_a x = y$ and the *exponent* in $a^y = x$. Thus **a logarithm is an exponent.**

Table 4.2 shows some logarithmic equations and their equivalent exponential forms.

TABLE 4.2

Logarithmic form	*Exponential form*
$\log_{10} 100 = 2$	$10^2 = 100$
$\log_{10} 0.1 = -1$	$10^{-1} = 0.1$
$\log_2 x = y$	$2^y = x$
$\log_a 1 = 0 \quad (a > 0)$	$a^0 = 1$
$\log_a a = 1 \quad (a > 0)$	$a^1 = a$

EXAMPLE 1

(a) Write $64 = 4^3$ in logarithmic form.

(b) Write $\log_4 \left(\frac{1}{64}\right) = -3$ in exponential form.

(c) If $4 = \log_2 x$, find x.

Solution

(a) $64 = 4^3$ is equivalent to $3 = \log_4 64$.

(b) $\log_4 \left(\frac{1}{64}\right) = -3$ is equivalent to $4^{-3} = \frac{1}{64}$.

(c) If $4 = \log_2 x$, then $2^4 = x$ and $x = 16$.

EXAMPLE 2

Evaluate: (a) $\log_2 8$ (b) $\log_3 9$ (c) $\log_5 \left(\frac{1}{25}\right)$.

Solution

(a) If $y = \log_2 8$, then $8 = 2^y$. Since $2^3 = 8$, $\log_2 8 = 3$.

(b) If $y = \log_3 9$, then $9 = 3^y$. Since $3^2 = 9$, $\log_3 9 = 2$.

(c) If $y = \log_5 \left(\frac{1}{25}\right)$, then $\frac{1}{25} = 5^y$. Since $5^{-2} = \frac{1}{25}$, $\log_5 \left(\frac{1}{25}\right) = -2$.

We can use the exponential form of a logarithmic equation to sketch its graph.

EXAMPLE 3

Graph $y = \log_2 x$.

Solution We may graph $y = \log_2 x$ by graphing $x = 2^y$. The table of values (found by substituting values for y and calculating x) and the graph are shown in Figure 4.7.

FIGURE 4.7

$x = 2^y$	y
$\frac{1}{8}$	-3
$\frac{1}{4}$	-2
$\frac{1}{2}$	-1
1	0
2	1
4	2
8	3

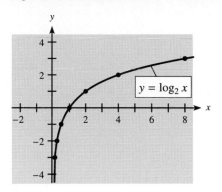

From the definition of logarithms, we see that every logarithm has a base. Most applications of logarithms involve logarithms to the base 10 (called **common logarithms**) or logarithms to the base e (called **natural logarithms**). In fact, logarithms to the base 10 and to the base e are the only ones that have function keys on scientific calculators. Thus it is important to be familiar with their names and designations.

Common and Natural Logarithms

Common logarithms: $\log x$ means $\log_{10} x$

Natural logarithms: $\ln x$ means $\log_e x$

Values of the natural logarithm function are found in Table II in the appendix.

EXAMPLE 4

Graph $y = \ln x$.

Solution   We can graph $y = \ln x$ by writing the equation in its exponential form, $x = e^y$, and then finding x for integer values of y. We can also graph by evaluating $y = \ln x$ for $x > 0$ (including some values $0 < x < 1$) with a calculator or Table II in the appendix. The graph is shown in Figure 4.8 on the following page.

y	$x = e^y$		x	$y = \ln x$
-3	0.050		0.05	-3.000
-2	0.135		0.10	-2.303
-1	0.368		0.50	-0.693
0	1.000		1	0.000
1	2.718		2	0.693
2	7.389		3	1.099
3	20.086		5	1.609
			10	2.303

FIGURE 4.8

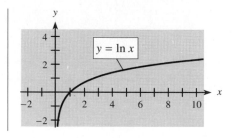

Note that the graphs of $y = \log_2 x$ (Figure 4.7) and $y = \ln x$ (Figure 4.8) are very similar. The shapes of graphs of equations of the form $y = \log_a x$ with $a > 1$ are similar to these two graphs.

Graphs of Logarithmic Functions	Equation: $y = \log_a x$ $(a > 1)$ x-intercept: $(1, 0)$ Domain: All positive reals Range: All reals Asymptote: y-axis (negative half)	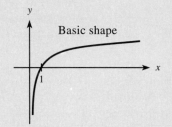

CHECKPOINT

1. What asymptote does the graph of $y = \log_a x$ approach when $a > 1$?

2. For $a > 1$, does the equation $y = \log_a x$ represent the same function as the equation $x = a^y$?

3. For what values of x is $y = \log_a x$, $a > 0$, $a \neq 1$, defined?

The definition of the logarithmic function and the previous examples suggest a special relationship between the logarithmic function $y = \log_a x$ and the exponential function $y = a^x$ $(a > 0, a \neq 1)$. Since we can write $y = \log_a x$ in exponential form as $x = a^y$, we see that the connection between

$$y = \log_a x \quad \text{and} \quad y = a^x$$

is that x and y have been interchanged from one function to the other. This is true for the functional description and hence for the ordered pairs that satisfy these functions. This is illustrated in Table 4.3 for the functions $y = \log_{10} x$ and $y = 10^x$.

TABLE 4.3

$y = \log_{10} x$		$y = 10^x$	
Coordinates	Justification	Coordinates	Justification
$(1000, 3)$	$3 = \log_{10} 1000$	$(3, 1000)$	$1000 = 10^3$
$(100, 2)$	$2 = \log_{10} 100$	$(2, 100)$	$100 = 10^2$
$(\frac{1}{10}, -1)$	$-1 = \log_{10} \frac{1}{10}$	$(-1, \frac{1}{10})$	$\frac{1}{10} = 10^{-1}$

In general, we say that $y = f(x)$ and $y = g(x)$ are **inverse functions** if, whenever the pair (a, b) satisfies $y = f(x)$, the pair (b, a) satisfies $y = g(x)$. Furthermore, because the values of the x and y coordinates are interchanged for inverse functions, their graphs are reflections of each other about the line $y = x$.

Thus for $a > 0$ and $a \neq 1$, the logarithmic function $y = \log_a x$ (also written $x = a^y$) and the exponential function $y = a^x$ are inverse functions.

The logarithmic function $y = \log x$ is the inverse of the exponential function $y = 10^x$. Thus the graphs $y = \log_{10} x$ and $y = 10^x$ are reflections of each other about the line $y = x$. Some values of x and y for these functions are given in Table 4.3, and their graphs are shown in Figure 4.9.

FIGURE 4.9

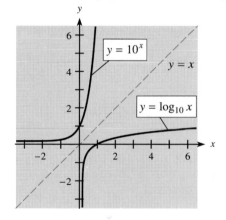

Logarithm Properties

As we stated previously, if $y = \log_a x$, then $x = a^y$. This means that the logarithm y is an exponent. For example, $\log_3 81 = 4$ because $3^4 = 81$. In this case the logarithm 4 was the exponent to which we had to raise the base to obtain 81. In general, if $y = \log_a x$, then y is the exponent to which the base a must be raised to obtain x.

Since logarithms are exponents, the properties of logarithms can be derived from the properties of exponents. (The properties of exponents are discussed in Chapter 0.) The following properties of logarithms are useful in simplifying expressions containing logarithms.

Logarithm Property I

If $a > 0$, $a \neq 1$, then $\log_a a^x = x$, for any real number x.

To prove this result, note that the exponential form of $y = \log_a a^x$ is $a^y = a^x$, so $y = x$. That is, $\log_a a^x = x$.

EXAMPLE 5

Use Property I to simplify each of the following.
(a) $\log_4 4^3$ (b) $\log_e e^x$

Solution
(a) $\log_4 4^3 = 3$

CHECK: The exponential form is $4^3 = 4^3$.

(b) $\log_e e^x = x$

CHECK: The exponential form is $e^x = e^x$.

We note that two special cases of Property I are used frequently; these are when $x = 1$ and $x = 0$.

Special Cases of Logarithm Property I

Since $a^1 = a$,   we have $\log_a a = 1$.
Since $a^0 = 1$,   we have $\log_a 1 = 0$.

The logarithmic form of $y = a^{\log_a x}$ is $\log_a y = \log_a x$, so $y = x$. This means that $a^{\log_a x} = x$ and proves Property II.

Logarithm Property II

If $a > 0$, $a \neq 1$, then $a^{\log_a x} = x$, for any positive real number x.

EXAMPLE 6

Use Property II to simplify each of the following.
(a) $2^{\log_2 4}$ (b) $e^{\ln x}$

Solution
(a) $2^{\log_2 4} = 4$

CHECK: The logarithmic form is $\log_2 4 = \log_2 4$.

(b) $e^{\ln x} = x$

CHECK: The logarithmic form is $\log_e x = \ln x$.

If $u = \log_a M$ and $v = \log_a N$, then the exponential forms are $a^u = M$ and $a^v = N$. Thus

$$\log_a (MN) = \log_a (a^u \cdot a^v) = \log_a (a^{u + v}) = u + v = \log_a M + \log_a N,$$

and Property III is established.

Logarithm Property III	If $a > 0$, $a \neq 1$, and M and N are positive real numbers, then $$\log_a (MN) = \log_a M + \log_a N.$$

EXAMPLE 7

(a) Find $\log_2 (4 \cdot 16)$, if $\log_2 4 = 2$ and $\log_2 16 = 4$.

(b) Find $\log_{10} (4 \cdot 5)$ if $\log_{10} 4 = 0.6021$ and $\log_{10} 5 = 0.6990$ (to four decimal places).

Solution

(a) $\log_2 (4 \cdot 16) = \log_2 4 + \log_2 16 = 2 + 4 = 6$

CHECK: $\log_2 (4 \cdot 16) = \log_2 (64) = 6$, because $2^6 = 64$.

(b) $\log_{10} (4 \cdot 5) = \log_{10} 4 + \log_{10} 5 = 0.6021 + 0.6990 = 1.3011$

CHECK: Using a calculator, we can see that $10^{1.3011} = 20 = 4 \cdot 5$.

Logarithm Property IV	If $a > 0$, $a \neq 1$, and M and N are positive real numbers, then $$\log_a (M/N) = \log_a M - \log_a N.$$

The proof of this property is left to the student in problem 56 of the exercises.

EXAMPLE 8

(a) Evaluate $\log_3 \left(\frac{9}{27}\right)$.

(b) Find $\log_{10} \left(\frac{16}{5}\right)$, if $\log_{10} 16 = 1.2041$ and $\log_{10} 5 = 0.6990$ (to 4 decimal places).

Solution

(a) $\log_3 \left(\frac{9}{27}\right) = \log_3 9 - \log_3 27 = 2 - 3 = -1$

CHECK: $\log_3 \left(\frac{1}{3}\right) = -1$ because $3^{-1} = \frac{1}{3}$.

(b) $\log_{10} \left(\frac{16}{5}\right) = \log_{10} 16 - \log_{10} 5 = 1.2041 - 0.6990 = 0.5051$

CHECK: Using a calculator, we can see that $10^{0.5051} = 3.2 = \frac{16}{5}$.

Logarithm Property V	If $a > 0$, $a \neq 1$, M is a positive real number, and N is any real number, then $$\log_a (M^N) = N \log_a M.$$

The proof of this property is left to the student in problem 57 of the exercises.

EXAMPLE 9

(a) Simplify $\log_3 (9^2)$.

(b) Simplify $\ln 8^{-4}$, if $\ln 8 = 2.0794$ (to 4 decimal places).

Solution

(a) $\log_3 (9^2) = 2 \log_3 9 = 2 \cdot 2 = 4$

CHECK: $\log_3 81 = 4$ because $3^4 = 81$.

(b) $\ln 8^{-4} = -4 \ln 8 = -4(2.0794) = -8.3176$

CHECK: Using a calculator, we can see that $8^{-4} \approx 0.000244$ and $\ln(0.000244) \approx -8.3176$.

CHECKPOINT

4. Simplify:

(a) $6^{\log_6 x}$

(b) $\log_7 7^3$

(c) $\ln \left(\dfrac{1}{e^2} \right)$

(d) $\log 1$

By using a calculator we can directly evaluate only those logarithms with base 10 or base e. Yet we can evaluate logarithms with other bases, such as $\log_b a$, by using properties of logarithms. In general, if we write

$$y = \log_b x \quad \text{in the form} \quad b^y = x$$

and take the base a logarithms of both sides, we have

$$\log_a b^y = \log_a x$$
$$y \log_a b = \log_a x$$
$$y = \frac{\log_a x}{\log_a b}.$$

This gives us the **change of base formula** from base b to base a.

Change of Base Formula

If $a \neq 1, b \neq 1, a > 0, b > 0$, then

$$\log_b x = \frac{\log_a x}{\log_a b}.$$

EXAMPLE 10

Evaluate $\log_7 15$ by using (a) natural logarithms and (b) common logarithms.

Solution

(a) $\log_7 15 = \dfrac{\ln 15}{\ln 7} = \dfrac{2.70805}{1.94591} = 1.39166$ (approximately)

(b) $\log_7 15 = \dfrac{\log 15}{\log 7} = \dfrac{1.17609}{0.84510} = 1.39166$ (approximately)

Natural logarithms, $y = \ln x$ (and the inverse exponential with base e), have many practical applications, some of which are considered in Section 4.5. Common logarithms, $y = \log x$, were widely used for computation before computers and calculators became popular. They also have several applications to scaling variables, where the purpose is to reduce the scale of variation when a natural physical variable covers a wide range.

EXAMPLE 11

The Richter scale is used to measure the intensity of an earthquake. The magnitude on the Richter scale of an earthquake of intensity I is given by

$$R = \log (I/I_0),$$

where I_0 is a certain minimum intensity used for comparison.

(a) Find R if I is 3,160,000 times as great as I_0.

(b) The 1964 Alaskan earthquake measured 8.5 on the Richter scale. Find the intensity of the 1964 Alaskan earthquake.

Solution

(a) With $I = 3{,}160{,}000\, I_0$, then $I/I_0 = 3{,}160{,}000$. Hence

$$R = \log (3{,}160{,}000)$$
$$= 6.5 \quad \text{(approximated to one decimal place).}$$

(b) For $R = 8.5$, it follows that

$$8.5 = \log (I/I_0).$$

Rewriting this in exponential form gives

$$10^{8.5} = I/I_0,$$

and from a calculator we obtain

$$I/I_0 = 316{,}000{,}000 \quad \text{(approximately).}$$

Thus the intensity is 316,000,000 times I_0.

Notice that a Richter scale measurement that is 2 units larger means that the intensity is $10^2 = 100$ *times* greater.

TECHNOLOGY CORNER

1. (a) Graph $f(x) = \log x$ and $g(x) = \ln x$.

   (b) What are the domains of $f(x)$ and $g(x)$?

   (c) Where do these two graphs intersect? Would you expect a logarithmic function with a base different from 10 or e to contain this point?

   (d) Which of the graphs in (a) lies above the other when $x = 4$? When $x > 1$? When $x < 1$?

   (e) For $x > 1$, where would you expect the graph of $y = \log_2 x$ to be in relation to the graphs of $f(x)$ and $g(x)$? What about the graph of $y = \log_7 x$? What about $y = \log_{15} x$?

2. (a) Graph $f(x) = \ln (x - c)$ for $c = 0, \pm 2$.

   (b) Each graph has a vertical asymptote. Where is it?

   (c) For each c, what are the domains of $f(x)$?

   (d) If you graphed $h(x) = \log (x - c)$ for $c = 2$ and $c = -2$, would the domain and vertical asymptote be the same as those for $f(x)$?

3. By the change of base formula, we know that

   $$\log_a x = \frac{\ln x}{\ln a} = \frac{1}{\ln a} \cdot \ln x.$$

   (a) Use this formula to graph $f(x) = \log_a x$ for $a = 2, 5,$ and 15.

   (b) Do the graphs in (a) appear to be "stretched" versions of the graph of $y = \ln x$, with the same domain, x-intercept, and vertical asymptote? Explain.

CHECKPOINT
SOLUTIONS

1. the (negative) y-axis

2. Yes.

3. $x > 0$ is the domain of $\log_a x$.

4. (a) x, by Property II

   (b) 3, by Property I

   (c) $\ln\left(\frac{1}{e^2}\right) = \ln(e^{-2}) = -2$, by Property I

   (d) 0, because $\log_a 1 = 0$ for any base a

EXERCISE 4.2

change

In problems 1–4, write each equation in exponential form.

1. $4 = \log_2 16$
2. $4 = \log_3 81$
3. $\frac{1}{2} = \log_4 2$
4. $-2 = \log_3 \left(\frac{1}{9}\right)$

In problems 5–8, solve for x by writing the equations in exponential form.

5. $\log_2 x = 3$
6. $\log_4 x = -2$
7. $\log_8 x = -\frac{1}{3}$
8. $\log_{25} x = \frac{1}{2}$

In problems 9–12, write each equation in logarithmic form.

9. $2^5 = 32$
10. $5^3 = 125$
11. $4^{-1} = \frac{1}{4}$
12. $9^{1/2} = 3$

In problems 13–18, graph the functions.

13. $y = \log_3 x$
14. $y = \log_4 x$
15. $y = \ln x$
16. $y = \log_9 x$
17. $y = \log_2 (-x)$
18. $y = \ln (-x)$

Evaluate the following: *change of base theorem*

19. $\log_3 27 \, 3$
20. $\log_4 16$ $\dfrac{\log 16}{\log 4}$
21. $\log_9 3$
22. $\log_5 \left(\frac{1}{5}\right)$
23. $\log_3 3^4$
24. $\log_5 5^{2/3}$
25. $\ln e^x$
26. $\ln e^5$
27. $\log 10$
28. $\ln e$
29. $\log 100$
30. $\ln \sqrt{e}$
31. $3^{\log_3 x}$
32. $4^{\log_4 5}$
33. $10^{\log 2}$
34. $e^{\ln 3}$

35. Find $\log (3 \cdot 4)$, if $\log 3 = 0.4771$ and $\log 4 = 0.6021$ (to 4 decimal places).
36. Find $\log (12 \cdot 43)$, if $\log 12 = 1.0792$ and $\log 43 = 1.6335$ (to 4 decimal places).
37. Find $\log \left(\frac{13}{4}\right)$, if $\log 13 = 1.1139$ and $\log 4 = 0.6021$ (to 4 decimal places).

38. Find $\log_3 \left(\frac{27}{9}\right)$, if $\log_3 27 = 3$ and $\log_3 9 = 2$. Does the answer equal $\log_3 3$?
39. Find $\log (16^{-2})$, given that $\log 16 = 1.2041$ (to 4 decimal places).
40. Find $\log \sqrt{351}$, given that $\log 351 = 2.5453$ (to 4 decimal places).
41. Find $\ln 16^3$, if $\ln 16 = 2.7723$ (to 4 decimal places).
42. Find $\ln \sqrt{50}$, if $\ln 50 = 3.912$ (to 3 decimal places).

Write each expression in problems 43–46 as the sum or difference of two logarithmic functions containing no exponents.

43. $\log \left(\dfrac{x}{x + 1}\right)$
44. $\ln[(x + 1)(4x + 5)]$
45. $\log_7 (x \sqrt[3]{x + 4})$
46. $\log_5 \left(\dfrac{x^2}{\sqrt{x + 4}}\right)$

Use the properties of logarithms to write each expression in problems 47–50 as a single logarithm.

47. $\ln x - \ln y$
48. $\log_3 (x + 1) + \log_3 (x - 1)$
49. $\log_7 (x + 1) + \frac{1}{2} \log_7 x$
50. $\log (2x + 1) - \frac{1}{3} \log (x + 1)$

In problems 51–55, use the change of base formula to evaluate each logarithm.

51. $\log_2 17$
52. $\log_3 12$
53. $\log_3 16$
54. $\log_5 37$
55. $\log_2 0.01$
56. Prove logarithm Property IV.
57. Prove logarithm Property V.

58. **Demand** If the demand function for a product is $p = 100/\ln(q + 1)$,
    (a) what will be the price if 19 units are demanded?
    (b) how many units, to the nearest unit, will be demanded if the price is $29.40? *Hint:* Find p for $q = 28$, 29, and 30.

59. **Supply** If the supply function for a product is given by $p = 100 \ln(q + 1)$,
    (a) at what price will 9 items be supplied?
    (b) how many units, to the nearest unit, will be supplied if the price is $346.57? *Hint:* Find p for q between 30 and 35.

Richter scale Use the formula $R = \log(I/I_0)$ in problems 60–65.

60. Find the Richter scale reading of an earthquake with intensity 20,000 times I_0.

61. Find the Richter scale reading of an earthquake with intensity 800,000 times I_0.

62. In May 1983, an earthquake measuring 7.7 on the Richter scale occurred in Japan. This was the first major earthquake in Japan since 1948, when one registered 7.3 on the Richter scale. How many times more severe was the 1983 shock?

63. The strongest earthquake ever to strike Japan occurred in 1933 and measured 8.9 on the Richter scale. How many times more severe was this 1933 quake than the one in May 1983? (See problem 62.)

64. The San Francisco earthquake of 1906 measured 8.25 on the Richter scale, and the San Francisco earthquake of 1989 measured 7.1. How much more intense was the 1906 quake?

65. The largest earthquakes ever recorded measured 8.9 on the Richter scale; the San Francisco earthquake of 1906 measured 8.25. Calculate the ratio of their intensities. (These readings correspond to devastating quakes.)

Decibel readings Problems 66–69. The loudness of sound (in decibels) perceived by the human ear depends upon intensity levels according to

$$L = 10 \log(I/I_0),$$

where I_0 is the threshold of hearing for the average human ear.

66. Find the loudness when I is 10,000 times I_0. This is the intensity level of the average voice.

67. A sound that causes pain has intensity about 10^{14} times I_0. Find the decibel reading for this threshold.

68. Graph the equation for loudness. Use I/I_0 as the independent variable.

69. A relatively quiet room has a background noise level of about $L_1 = 32$ decibels, and a heated argument has a decibel level of about $L_2 = 66$. Find the ratio I_2/I_1 of the associated intensities.

pH levels Problems 70–74. Chemists use the pH (hydrogen potential) of a solution to measure its acidity or basicity. The pH is given by the formula

$$\text{pH} = -\log[\text{H}^+],$$

where $[\text{H}^+]$ is the concentration of hydrogen ions in moles per liter.

70. Most common solutions have a pH range between 1 and 14. What values of H^+ are associated with these extremes?

71. Find the approximate pH of each of the following.
    (a) blood: $[\text{H}^+] = 3.98 \times 10^{-8}$
       $= 0.0000000398$
    (b) beer: $[\text{H}^+] = 6.31 \times 10^{-5} = 0.0000631$
    (c) vinegar: $[\text{H}^+] = 6.3 \times 10^{-3} = 0.0063$

72. Sometimes pH is defined as the logarithm of the reciprocal of the concentration of hydrogen ions. Write an equation that represents this sentence, and explain how it and the equation given above can both represent pH.

73. Find the approximate hydrogen ion concentration $[H^+]$ for each of the following.
    (a) apples: pH = 3.0
    (b) eggs: pH = 7.79
    (c) water (neutral): pH = 7.0

74. A solution is considered acidic if $[H^+] > 10^{-7}$ or basic if $[H^+] < 10^{-7}$. What pH values correspond to acids and what values correspond to bases?

4.3 | DERIVATIVES OF LOGARITHMIC FUNCTIONS

OBJECTIVE

• To find derivatives of logarithmic functions

Although logarithmic functions can involve logarithms of any base, most of the problems in calculus and most of the applications to management, life, and social sciences involve logarithms with base e, called **natural logarithms.** The formula for the derivative of $y = \ln x$ follows.

Derivative of $y = \ln x$

If $y = \ln x$, then

$$\frac{dy}{dx} = \frac{1}{x}.$$

The proof uses the definition of the derivative and logarithmic properties. If $y = f(x) = \ln x$,

$$\frac{dy}{dx} = \lim_{h \to 0} \frac{f(x + h) - f(x)}{h}$$

$$= \lim_{h \to 0} \frac{\ln(x + h) - \ln x}{h}$$

$$= \lim_{h \to 0} \frac{\ln\left(\dfrac{x + h}{x}\right)}{h}. \qquad \text{(Property IV)}$$

$$= \lim_{h \to 0} \frac{x}{x} \cdot \frac{1}{h} \ln\left(\frac{x + h}{x}\right) \qquad \left(\text{introduce } \frac{x}{x}\right)$$

$$= \lim_{h \to 0} \frac{1}{x} \cdot \frac{x}{h} \ln\left(1 + \frac{h}{x}\right).$$

$$= \lim_{h \to 0} \frac{1}{x} \ln\left(1 + \frac{h}{x}\right)^{x/h}. \qquad \text{(Property V)}$$

The natural logarithmic function is continuous when it is defined, so

$$\frac{dy}{dx} = \frac{1}{x} \ln \left[\lim_{h \to 0} \left(1 + \frac{h}{x} \right)^{x/h} \right].$$

We have seen in Section 4.1 that

$$\lim_{a \to 0} (1 + a)^{1/a} = e.$$

Because

$$\lim_{h \to 0} \left(1 + \frac{h}{x} \right)^{x/h}$$

has this form, we have

$$\frac{dy}{dx} = \frac{1}{x} \ln e = \frac{1}{x}.$$

EXAMPLE 1   If $y = x^3 + 3 \ln x$, find dy/dx.

Solution

$$\frac{dy}{dx} = 3x^2 + 3\left(\frac{1}{x}\right) = 3x^2 + \frac{3}{x}$$

EXAMPLE 2   If $y = x^2 \ln x$, find y'.

Solution By the Product Rule,

$$y' = x^2 \cdot \frac{1}{x} + (\ln x)(2x) = x + 2x \ln x.$$

We can use the Chain Rule to find the formula for the derivatives of $y = \ln u$, where $u = f(x)$.

Derivatives of Natural Logarithmic Functions

If $y = \ln u$, where u is a differentiable function of x, then

$$\frac{dy}{dx} = \frac{1}{u} \cdot \frac{du}{dx}.$$

EXAMPLE 3   (a) Find $f'(x)$ if $f(x) = \frac{1}{3} \ln(2x^6 - 3x + 2)$.

(b) Find $g'(x)$ if $g(x) = \dfrac{\ln(2x + 1)}{2x + 1}$.

Solution

(a) $f'(x) = \dfrac{1}{3} \cdot \dfrac{1}{2x^6 - 3x + 2}(12x^5 - 3)$

$= \dfrac{4x^5 - 1}{2x^6 - 3x + 2}$

(b) By the Quotient Rule,

$g'(x) = \dfrac{(2x + 1)\dfrac{1}{2x + 1}(2) - [\ln(2x + 1)]2}{(2x + 1)^2}$

$= \dfrac{2 - 2\ln(2x + 1)}{(2x + 1)^2}$

EXAMPLE 4   Use logarithm properties to find dy/dx when

$y = \ln[x(x^5 - 2)^{10}]$.

Solution   We use logarithm Properties III and IV to rewrite the function:

$y = \ln x + \ln(x^5 - 2)^{10}$ (Property III)
$y = \ln x + 10\ln(x^5 - 2)$ (Property IV)

We now take the derivative:

$\dfrac{dy}{dx} = \dfrac{1}{x} + 10 \cdot \dfrac{1}{x^5 - 2} \cdot 5x^4$

$= \dfrac{1}{x} + \dfrac{50x^4}{x^5 - 2}.$

CHECKPOINT

1. If $y = \ln(3x^2 + 2)$, find y'.

2. If $y = \ln x^6$, find y'.

3. If $y = \ln \sqrt[3]{x^2 + 1}$, find y'.

The change of base formula, introduced in Section 4.2, can be used to express logarithms with base a as natural logarithms (that is, logarithms with base e):

$\log_a x = \dfrac{\ln x}{\ln a}.$

We can apply this change of base formula to find the derivative of a logarithm with any base, as the following example illustrates.

EXAMPLE 5

If $y = \log_4(x^3 + 1)$, find dy/dx.

Solution By using the change of base formula, we have

$$y = \log_4(x^3 + 1) = \frac{\ln(x^3 + 1)}{\ln 4}$$

$$= \frac{1}{\ln 4} \cdot \ln(x^3 + 1).$$

Thus

$$\frac{dy}{dx} = \frac{1}{\ln 4} \cdot \frac{1}{x^3 + 1} \cdot 3x^2$$

$$= \frac{3x^2}{(x^3 + 1)\ln 4}.$$

TECHNOLOGY CORNER

Graph $g(x) = x \ln x$ and use the graph to complete exercises 1–4.

1. What is the domain of $g(x)$?

2. Find $\lim\limits_{x \to 0^+} g(x)$.

3. Find the x-intercepts, if any.

4. Estimate the x-values where $g(x)$ has any relative maximum points or relative minimum points.

5. If it is known that $f(x)$ satisfies $f'(x) = g(x)$, sketch a possible graph for $f(x)$ from the graph of $g(x)$.

6. Show that a possibility for $f(x)$ is $f(x) = \dfrac{x^2}{2} \ln x - \dfrac{x^2}{4}$, by calculating $f'(x)$.

7. Check your sketch from (5) by graphing $f(x)$ from (6).

CHECKPOINT
SOLUTIONS

1. $y' = \dfrac{6x}{3x^2 + 2}$

2. $y = 6 \ln x$, so $y' = 6\left(\dfrac{1}{x}\right) = \dfrac{6}{x}$

3. $y = \ln[(x^2 + 1)^{1/3}] = \dfrac{1}{3} \ln (x^2 + 1)$

$y' = \dfrac{1}{3}\left(\dfrac{2x}{x^2 + 1}\right) = \dfrac{2x}{3(x^2 + 1)}$

(handwritten)
19) $\dfrac{dy}{dx} = x \cdot \dfrac{1}{x} + \ln x \cdot 1 - 1$

$\dfrac{dy}{dx}$ $1 + \ln x - 1$ ■

$\dfrac{dy}{dx} = \boxed{\ln x}$

(handwritten)
23) $y = 2\ln (x^4 + 3)$

$y' = 2 \cdot \dfrac{1}{x^4 + 3}\left(4x^3\right) = \dfrac{8x^3}{(x^4 + 3)}$

$\dfrac{1}{u} \quad y' \text{ of } u$

EXERCISE 4.3

Find the derivatives of the functions in problems 1–18.

1. (a) $y = \ln x^4$ (b) $y = 4 \ln x$
2. (a) $y = \ln x^3$ (b) $y = 3 \ln x$

3. (a) $y = \ln \dfrac{x}{x - 1}$
   (b) $y = \ln x - \ln(x - 1)$
4. (a) $y = \ln[(x - 1)(2x + 1)]$
   (b) $y = \ln(x - 1) + \ln (2x + 1)$
5. (a) $y = \ln \sqrt[3]{x^2 - 1}$
   (b) $y = \frac{1}{3}\ln(x^2 - 1)$
6. (a) $y = \ln(x^4 - 1)^3$
   (b) $y = 3 \ln(x^4 - 1)$

7. (a) $y = \ln\left(\dfrac{4x - 1}{x^3}\right)$
   (b) $y = \ln(4x - 1) - 3 \ln x$

8. (a) $y = \ln\left(\dfrac{x^3}{x + 1}\right)$
   (b) $y = 3 \ln x - \ln(x + 1)$
9. (a) $y = \ln(x^3\sqrt{x + 1})$ *(handwritten: $\ln(x)^3 + \ln \sqrt[3]{x + 1} \cdots$)*
   (b) $y = 3 \ln x + \frac{1}{2}\ln (x + 1)$
10. (a) $y = \ln[x^2(x^4 - x + 1)]$
    (b) $y = 2 \ln x + \ln(x^4 - x + 1)$
11. $y = \ln \sqrt{2}$ 12. $y = \ln \sqrt{e}$
13. Find dp/dq if $p = \ln(q^2 + 1)$.

14. Find $\dfrac{ds}{dq}$ if $s = \ln\left(\dfrac{q^2}{4} + 1\right)$.

15. Find $\dfrac{dp}{dq}$ if $p = \ln\left(\dfrac{q^2 - 1}{q}\right)$.

16. Find $\dfrac{ds}{dt}$ if $s = \ln[t^3(t^2 - 1)]$.

17. Find $\dfrac{dy}{dt}$ if $y = \ln\left(\dfrac{t^2 + 3}{\sqrt{1 - t}}\right)$.

18. Find $\dfrac{dy}{dx}$ if $y = \ln\left(\dfrac{3x + 2}{x^2 - 5}\right)^{1/4}$.

In problems 19–32, find dy/dx.

19. $y = x \ln x - x$ 20. $y = x^2 \ln(2x + 3)$

21. $y = \dfrac{\ln x}{x}$ 22. $y = \dfrac{1 + \ln x}{x^2}$

23. $y = \ln(x^4 + 3)^2$ 24. $y = \ln(3x + 1)^{1/2}$
25. $y = (\ln x)^4$ 26. $y = (\ln x)^{-1}$
27. $y = [\ln (x^4 + 3)]^2$ 28. $y = \sqrt{\ln (3x + 1)}$
29. $y = \log_4 x$ 30. $y = \log_5 x$
31. $y = \log_6(x^4 - 4x^3 + 1)$
32. $y = \log_2(1 - x - x^2)$

APPLICATIONS

33. **Marginal cost** Suppose that the total cost (in dollars) for a product is given by

$$C(x) = 1500 + 200 \ln(2x + 1),$$

where x is the number of units produced.
(a) Find the marginal cost function.
(b) Find the marginal cost when 200 units are produced, and interpret your result.

34. **Marginal revenue** The total revenue from

the sale of x units of a product is given by

$$R(x) = \frac{2500x}{\ln(10x + 10)}.$$

(a) Find the marginal revenue function.
(b) Find the marginal revenue when 100 units are sold, and interpret your result.

35. **Supply** Suppose that the supply of q units of a product at price x dollars is given by

$$q = 10 + 50 \ln(3x + 1).$$

Find the rate of change of supply with respect to price.

36. **Demand** The demand function for a product is given by $p = 4000/\ln(x + 10)$, where p is the price per unit when x units are demanded.
(a) Find the rate of change of price with respect to the number of units sold when 40 units are sold.
(b) Find the rate of change of price with respect to the number of units sold when 90 units are sold.
(c) Find the second derivative to see if the rate at which the price is changing at 40 units is increasing or decreasing.

37. **pH level** If the pH of a solution is given by

$$pH = -\log[H^+],$$

where $[H^+]$ is the concentration of hydrogen ions (in gram atoms per liter), what is the rate of change of pH with respect to $[H^+]$?

38. **Reynolds number** If the Reynolds number relating to the flow of blood exceeds R, where

$$R = A \ln(r - Br),$$

and r is the radius of the aorta and A and B are positive constants, the blood flow becomes turbulent. What is the radius r that makes R a maximum?

39. **Expected life span** The following table shows the expected life span at birth of people born in certain years in the United States. Assume that for these years, the expected life span

at birth can be modeled with the function $l(x) = 11.7 + 14.1 \ln x$, where x is the number of years past 1900. The graph of this function and the data points are shown in the figure.

Year	Life span (in years)
1920	54.1
1930	59.7
1940	62.9
1950	68.2
1960	69.7
1970	70.8
1975	72.6
1980	73.7
1987	75.0
1988	74.9
1989	75.2

Source: *World Almanac*, 1991.

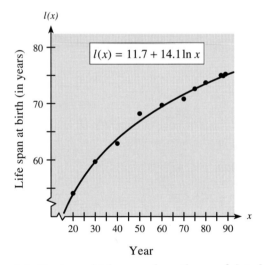

(a) During which year does the model indicate that the rate of growth in expected life span was equal to 1?
(b) Does $l(x)$ have a maximum value for $x > 0$?
(c) Evaluate $\lim_{x \to +\infty} l'(x)$.
(d) What do (b) and (c) tell us about the increase in life span?

4.4 | DERIVATIVES OF EXPONENTIAL FUNCTIONS

OBJECTIVE

- To find derivatives of exponential functions

In the previous section we found derivatives of logarithmic functions. In this section we turn our attention to exponential functions. The formula for the derivative of $y = e^x$ is developed as follows.

From Property I of logarithms, we know that

$$\ln e^x = x.$$

Taking the derivative, with respect to x, of both sides of this equation, we have

$$\frac{d}{dx} \ln e^x = \frac{d}{dx}x.$$

Using the Chain Rule for logarithms gives

$$\frac{1}{e^x} \cdot \frac{d}{dx} e^x = 1,$$

and solving for $\dfrac{d}{dx} e^x$ gives

$$\frac{d}{dx} e^x = e^x.$$

Thus we can conclude the following.

Derivative of $y = e^x$	If $y = e^x$, then $$\frac{dy}{dx} = e^x.$$

EXAMPLE 1   If $p = e^q$, find dp/dq.

Solution $\dfrac{dp}{dq} = e^q$

As with the logarithmic functions, the Chain Rule will permit us to expand our derivative formulas.

| **Derivatives of Exponential Functions** | If $y = e^u$, where u is a differentiable function of x, then $$\frac{dy}{dx} = e^u \cdot \frac{du}{dx}.$$ |

EXAMPLE 2

If $f(x) = e^{4x^3}$, find $f'(x)$.

Solution

$$f'(x) = e^{4x^3} \cdot 12x^2 = 12x^2 e^{4x^3}$$

EXAMPLE 3

If $p = qe^{5q}$, find dp/dq.

Solution

$$\frac{dp}{dq} = (q \cdot e^{5q} \cdot 5) + (e^{5q} \cdot 1)$$

$$= 5qe^{5q} + e^{5q}$$

EXAMPLE 4

If $s = 3te^{3t^2 + 5t}$, find ds/dt.

Solution

$$\frac{ds}{dt} = 3t \cdot e^{3t^2 + 5t}(6t + 5) + e^{3t^2 + 5t} \cdot 3$$

$$= (18t^2 + 15t)e^{3t^2 + 5t} + 3e^{3t^2 + 5t}$$

EXAMPLE 5

If $y = e^{\ln x^2}$, find y'.

Solution

$$y' = e^{\ln x^2} \cdot \frac{1}{x^2} \cdot 2x = \frac{2}{x} e^{\ln x^2}$$

By Property II of logarithms (Section 4.2), $e^{\ln u} = u$, and we can simplify the derivative to

$$y' = \frac{2}{x} \cdot x^2 = 2x.$$

Note that if we had used this property *before* taking the derivative, we would have had

$$y = e^{\ln x^2} = x^2.$$

The derivative is $y' = 2x$.

EXAMPLE 6 | If $u = w/e^{3w}$, find u'.

Solution The function is a quotient, with the denominator equal to e^{3w}. Using the Quotient Rule gives

$$u' = \frac{e^{3w} \cdot 1 - w \cdot e^{3w} \cdot 3}{(e^{3w})^2}$$

$$= \frac{e^{3w} - 3we^{3w}}{e^{6w}}$$

$$= \frac{1 - 3w}{e^{3w}}.$$

CHECKPOINT

1. If $y = 2e^{4x}$, find y'.
2. If $y = e^{x^2 + 6x}$, find y'.
3. If $s = te^{t^2}$, find ds/dt.

EXAMPLE 7 | If $q = e^{-p}$ describes the demand for a product, find dq/dp.

Solution

$$\frac{dq}{dp} = e^{-p}(-1) = -e^{-p}$$

In a manner similar to that used to find the derivative of $y = e^x$, we can develop a formula for the derivative of $y = a^x$ for any base a.

Derivative of $y = a^u$

If $y = a^x$, then

$$\frac{dy}{dx} = a^x \ln a.$$

If $y = a^u$, where u is a differentiable function of x, then

$$\frac{dy}{dx} = a^u \frac{du}{dx} \ln a.$$

EXAMPLE 8 | If $y = 4^x$, find dy/dx.

Solution

$$\frac{dy}{dx} = 4^x \ln 4$$

EXAMPLE 9 | If $y = 10^{x^2}$, find dy/dx.

Solution

$$\frac{dy}{dx} = 2x \cdot 10^{x^2} \ln 10.$$

TECHNOLOGY CORNER

Consider $y_1 = 5e^{-x}(x - 2)$, $y_2 = 5xe^{-x}$, and $y_3 = 5e^{-x}(1 - x)$.

1. Graph these three functions.

2. It is a fact that these three graphs are the graphs of f, f', and f'' for some function f. Use the graphs of y_1, y_2, and y_3 to decide which of these are f, f', and f''.

3. Check your results in (b) by calculating derivatives of y_1, y_2, and y_3.

CHECKPOINT
SOLUTIONS

1. $y' = 2e^{4x}(4) = 8e^{4x}$

2. $y' = (2x + 6)e^{x^2 + 6x}$

3. By the Product Rule, $\dfrac{ds}{dt} = e^{t^2}(1) + t[e^{t^2}(2t)] = e^{t^2} + 2t^2e^{t^2}$

EXERCISE 4.4

Find the derivatives of the functions in problems 1–30.

1. $y = e^{x^3}$

2. $y = e^{x^2 - 1}$

3. $y = 6e^{3x^2}$

4. $y = 1 - 2e^{-x^3}$

5. $y = e^{-1/x}$

6. $y = 2e^{\sqrt{x}}$

7. $y = 2e^{(x^2 + 1)^3}$

8. $y = e^{\sqrt{x^2 - 9}}$

9. $y = e^{-1/x^2} + e^{-x^2}$

10. $y = \dfrac{2}{e^{2x}} + \dfrac{e^{2x}}{2}$

11. $s = t^2e^t$

12. $p = 4qe^{q^3}$

13. $y = e^3 + e^{\ln x}$

14. $s = x \ln e^{x^3}$

15. $y = 2\sqrt{e^x} + e^{\sqrt{x}}$

16. $y = e^{x^4} - (e^x)^4$

17. $y = 4(e^x)^3 - 4e^{x^3}$

18. $y = 3e^{2x^2} - 5(e^{2x})^2$

19. $y = \ln(e^{2x} + 1)$

20. $y = \ln(e^{4x} + 2)$

21. $y = e^{-3x} \ln(2x)$

22. $y = e^{2x^2} \ln(4x)$

23. $y = \dfrac{1 + e^{5x}}{e^{3x}}$

24. $y = \dfrac{x}{1 + e^{2x}}$

25. $y = (e^{3x} + 4)^{10}$

26. $y = \dfrac{e^x - e^{-x}}{e^x + e^{-x}}$

27. $y = 6^x$

28. $y = 3^x$

29. $y = 4^{x^2}$

30. $y = 5^{x-1}$

31. Write the equation of the line tangent to the graph of $y = xe^{-x}$ at $x = 1$.

32. Write the equation of the line tangent to the graph of $y = e^{-x}/(1 + e^{-x})$ at $x = 0$.

33. The equation for the standard normal probability distribution is

$$y = \frac{1}{\sqrt{2\pi}} e^{-z^2/2}.$$

At what value of z will the curve be at its highest point?

34. (a) Find the mode of the normal distribution* given by

$$y = \frac{1}{\sqrt{2\pi}} e^{-(x-10)^2/2}.$$

(b) What is the mean of this normal distribution?

35. Figure 4.10 shows the graph of the standard normal probability distribution,

$$y = \frac{1}{\sqrt{2\pi}} e^{-z^2/2}.$$

FIGURE 4.10

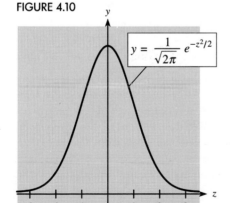

$$y = \frac{1}{\sqrt{2\pi}} e^{-z^2/2}$$

Standard normal probability curve

*The mode occurs at the highest point on normal curves and equals the mean.

At what values of z does the curve have points of inflection?

36. The normal probability distribution with mean 10 and standard deviation 2 has equation

$$y = \frac{1}{2\sqrt{2\pi}} e^{-(x-10)^2/8}.$$

At what values of x will the graph of this equation have points of inflection?

Applications

37. **Compound amount** The compound amount that accrues when $100 is invested at 8%, compounded continuously, is $S(t) = 100e^{0.08t}$, where t is the number of years. At what rate is the money in this account growing when
   (a) $t = 1$?
   (b) $t = 10$?

38. **World population** Suppose that world population can be considered as growing according to the equation $N = N_0(1 + r)^t$, where N_0 and r are constants. Find the rate of change of N with respect to t.

39. **Sales decay** After the end of an advertising campaign, the sales of a product are given by

$$S = 100,000e^{-0.5t},$$

where S is weekly sales and t is the number of weeks since the end of the campaign. Find the rate of change of S (that is, the rate of *sales decay*).

40. **Sales decay** The sales decay for a product is given by

$$S = 50,000e^{-0.8t},$$

where S is the daily sales and t is the number of days since the end of a promotional campaign. Find the rate of sales decay.

41. **Chemical reaction** The number of molecules of a certain substance that have enough energy to activate a reaction is given by $y = 100,000e^{-1/x}$, where y is the number of molecules and x is the (absolute) temperature

of the substance. What is the rate of change of y with respect to temperature?

42. **Newton's law of cooling** When a body is moved from one medium to another, its temperature T will change according to the equation

$$T = T_0 + Ce^{kt},$$

where T_0 is the temperature of the new medium, C the temperature difference between the mediums (old–new), t the time in the new medium, and k a constant. If T_0, C, and k are held constant, what is the rate of change of T with respect to time?

43. **Compound amount** If \$$P$ is invested for n years at 10%, compounded continuously, the compound amount is given by the function

$$S = Pe^{0.1n}.$$

(a) At what rate is the compound amount growing at any time (for any n)?
(b) At what rate is the compound amount growing after 1 year ($n = 1$)?
(c) Is the rate of growth of the compound amount after 1 year greater than 10%? Why?

44. **Blood pressure** Medical research has shown that between heartbeats the pressure in the aorta of a normal adult is a function of time and can be modeled by the equation

$$P = 95e^{-0.491t}.$$

(a) Use the derivative to find the rate at which the pressure changes at any time t.
(b) Use the derivative to find the rate at which the pressure changes after 0.1 seconds.
(c) Is the pressure increasing or decreasing?

45. **Drugs in a bloodstream** The concentration y of a certain drug in the bloodstream at any time t (in hours) is given by $y = 100(1 - e^{-0.462t})$. Find the rate of change of the concentration after one hour. Give your answer to 3 decimal places.

46. **Radioactive decay** The amount of the radioactive isotope thorium-234 present at

time t is given by

$$Q(t) = 100e^{-0.02828t}.$$

Find the rate of radioactive decay of the isotope.

47. **Marginal cost** Suppose that the total cost in dollars of producing x units of a product is given by

$$C(x) = 10{,}000 + 600xe^{x/600}.$$

Find the marginal cost when 600 units are produced.

48. **Marginal revenue** Suppose that the revenue in dollars from the sale of x units of a product is given by

$$R(x) = 1000xe^{-x/50}.$$

Find the marginal revenue function.

49. **Spread of a rumor** The number of people $N(t)$ in a community who are reached by a particular rumor at time t (in days) is given by

$$N(t) = \frac{50{,}500}{1 + 100e^{-0.7t}}.$$

Find the rate of change of $N(t)$.

50. **Spread of disease** Suppose that the spread of a disease through the student body at an isolated college campus can be modeled by

$$y = \frac{10{,}000}{1 + 9999e^{-0.99t}},$$

where y is the total number affected at time t (in days). Find the rate of change of y.

51. **U.S. debt** The following table shows the U.S. national debt and percentage of federal expenditures devoted to payment of the interest on this debt for selected years from 1900 to 1989. Assume that the amount of the national debt (in billions of dollars) can be modeled by the function

$$d(x) = 1956.16 + 29x - 2018.91e^{x/100} + 0.44e^{x/10},$$

where x is the number of years past 1900. This function and the data points are graphed in the following figure.

Year	U.S. debt (in billions)	Percentage to interest
1900	$1.2	0.0
1910	1.1	0.0
1920	24.2	0.0
1930	16.1	0.0
1940	43.0	10.5
1945	258.7	4.1
1955	272.8	9.4
1965	313.8	9.6
1975	533.2	9.8
1985	1823.1	18.9
1987	2350.3	19.5
1989	2857.4	25.0

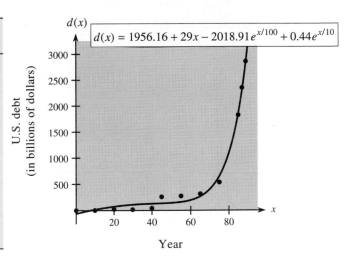

$$d(x) = 1956.16 + 29x - 2018.91\,e^{x/100} + 0.44e^{x/10}$$

Source: *World Almanac*, 1991.

(a) What function describes how fast the national debt is changing?

(b) Find the instantaneous rate of change of the national debt model $d(x)$ in 1940 and 1985.

(c) The Gramm-Rudman Balanced Budget Act (passed in 1985) was designed to limit the growth of the national debt and hence change the function that modeled it. Why was this necessary?

4.5 | APPLICATIONS OF EXPONENTIAL AND LOGARITHMIC FUNCTIONS

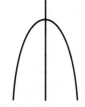

OBJECTIVES

- To find the compound amount and compound interest of money invested where interest is compounded at regular intervals

- To find the compound amount and compound interest on money where interest is compounded continuously

- To solve exponential growth or decay equations when sufficient data are known

- To solve exponential and logarithmic equations representing demand, supply, total revenue, or total cost when sufficient data are known.

COMPOUND INTEREST

An understanding of compound interest is important not only for people planning careers with financial institutions, but also for anyone planning to invest money. The tables that bankers use to compute the compound amount on deposits are developed with the following exponential function.

Compound Amount

If $\$P$ is invested for t years at a nominal interest rate, r (as a decimal), compounded m times per year, then the total number of compounding periods is

$$n = mt,$$

the interest rate per compounding period is

$$i = \frac{r}{m},$$

and the compound amount is

$$S = P(1 + i)^n = P\left(1 + \frac{r}{m}\right)^{mt}.$$

EXAMPLE 1

If $8000 is invested for 6 years at 8%, compounded quarterly, find
(a) the compound amount.
(b) the compound interest.

Solution

(a) Compounding quarterly gives four compounding periods per year, so the compound amount is

$$S = (\$8000)\left(1 + \frac{0.08}{4}\right)^{4 \cdot 6} = (\$8000)(1.02)^{24} \approx \$12{,}867.50.$$

(b) The compound interest is given by the amount S minus the original principal P, or $\$12{,}867.50 - \$8000.00 = \$4867.50$.

In Example 1, if the interest had been compounded monthly (12 times per year), then the compound amount would be larger.

$$S = (\$8000)\left(1 + \frac{0.08}{12}\right)^{12 \cdot 6} = (\$8000)(1.613502) \approx \$12{,}908.02.$$

It is reasonable to assume that the more frequently the interest is compounded, the larger the compound amount will become. In order to determine the interest that results from *continuous* compounding (compounding every instant), consider an investment of $1 for 1 year at a 100% interest rate. If the interest is compounded m times per year, the compound amount is given by

$$S = \left(1 + \frac{1}{m}\right)^m.$$

Table 4.4 shows the compound amount that results as the number of compounding periods increases.

TABLE 4.4	*Compounded*	*Number of periods per year*	*Compound amount*
	Annually	1	$(1 + \frac{1}{1})^1 = 2$
	Monthly	12	$(1 + \frac{1}{12})^{12} = 2.6130 \ldots$
	Daily	360 (business year)	$(1 + \frac{1}{360})^{360} = 2.7145 \ldots$
	Hourly	8640	$(1 + \frac{1}{8640})^{8640} = 2.71812 \ldots$
	Each minute	518,400	$(1 + \frac{1}{518,400})^{518,400} = 2.71827 \ldots$

As Table 4.4 shows, as m increases in size, the limiting value of S is the special number

$$e \approx 2.71828.$$

In fact, this limit defines the number e. That is,

The Number e $e = \lim\limits_{m \to \infty} \left(1 + \frac{1}{m}\right)^m$ (by definition)

We also note (by using $a = 1/m$) that e can be expressed equivalently by

$$e = \lim\limits_{a \to 0} (1 + a)^{1/a},$$

which is sometimes taken as the definition.

When interest is compounded continuously, the compound amount is an exponential function with base e.

Continuous Compounding   If interest is compounded continuously for t years at a rate of r per year (as a decimal), the compound amount resulting from an investment of P is given by

$$S = Pe^{rt}.$$

EXAMPLE 2   Find the compound amount if $8000 is invested for 6 years at 8%, compounded continuously.

Solution The amount is

$$S = \$8000e^{(0.08)(6)} = \$8000e^{0.48}$$
$$\approx \$8000(1.616074) \approx \$12{,}928.60.$$

Note that compound amounts calculated in Examples 1 and 2 were on the same investment, except for the compounding. Clearly, compounding continuously yields a larger compound amount than compounding quarterly.

CHECKPOINT

1. Find the compound amount if $1000 is invested for 10 years at (a) 9% compounded monthly and (b) 9% compounded continuously.

GROWTH AND DECAY

If the function modeling some situation is given by an equation of the form $f(x) = ma^{-x}$, with $a > 1$ and $m > 0$, we say that the function represents **exponential decay.** We have already mentioned that radioactive decay has this form, as do the demand curves discussed later. Another example of this phenomenon occurs in the life sciences when the valves to the aorta are closed, and blood flows into the heart. During this period of time, the blood pressure in the aorta falls exponentially. This is illustrated in the following example.

EXAMPLE 3

Medical research has shown that over short periods of time when the valves to the aorta of a normal adult close, the pressure in the aorta is a function of time and can be modeled by the equation

$$P = 95e^{-0.491t},$$

where t is in seconds.

(a) What is the aortic pressure when the valves are first closed ($t = 0$)?

(b) What is the aortic pressure after 0.1 seconds?

(c) How long will it be before the pressure reaches 80?

Solution

(a) If $t = 0$, the pressure is given by

$$P = 95e^0 = 95.$$

(b) If $t = 0.1$, the pressure is given by

$$P = 95e^{-0.491(.01)}$$
$$= 95e^{-0.0491}$$
$$= 95(0.952)$$
$$= 90.44.$$

(c) Setting $P = 80$ and solving for t will give us the length of time before the pressure reaches 80.

$$80 = 95e^{-0.491t}$$

To solve this equation for t, we must rewrite it so that t is not in an exponent. We first isolate the exponential containing t by dividing both sides by 95.

$$\frac{80}{95} = e^{-0.491t}$$

Rewriting this equation in logarithmic form gives

$$\ln\left(\frac{80}{95}\right) = -0.491t.$$

Using tables or a calculator, we have $-0.172 = -0.491t$. Thus

$$\frac{-0.172}{-0.491} = t$$

$$t = 0.35 \text{ seconds} \qquad \text{(approximately)}.$$

Note that in Example 1 we could have solved

$$\frac{80}{95} = e^{-0.491t}$$

for t by taking the logarithm, base e, of both sides and then using properties of logarithms.

$$\ln\left(\frac{80}{95}\right) = \ln e^{-0.491t}$$

By logarithm Property I, we have

$$\ln\left(\frac{80}{95}\right) = -0.491t.$$

Note that taking the natural logarithm of both sides gives the same result as writing $80/95 = e^{-0.491t}$ in logarithmic form.

The advantage of taking the natural logarithm (or the common logarithm) of both sides of an exponential equation to solve the equation becomes apparent when the base of the exponential is not e (or 10).

To solve an exponential equation, we must be able to rewrite the equation so that the variable is not in an exponent. For equations involving a single exponential, we solve for that exponential. (That is, we isolate the exponential expression on one side of the equation.)

$$Na^X = M \quad \text{yields} \quad a^X = \frac{M}{N}.$$

Then taking the logarithm (base 10 or base e) of both sides of the equation, using logarithm Property V, and using algebraic methods, we can solve the equation. Part (b) of the following example illustrates this solution method.

EXAMPLE 4

A company finds that its daily sales begin to fall after the end of an advertising campaign, and the decline is such that the number of sales is $S = 2000(2^{-0.1x})$, where x is the number of days after the end of the campaign.

(a) How many sales will be made 10 days after the end of the campaign?

(b) If they do not want sales to drop below 500 per day, when should they start a new campaign?

Solution

(a) If $x = 10$, sales are given by $S = 2000(2^{-1}) = 1000$.

(b) Setting $S = 500$ and solving for x will give us the number of days after the end of the campaign when sales will reach 500.

$$500 = 2000(2^{-0.1x})$$
$$\frac{500}{2000} = 2^{-0.1x} \qquad \text{(Isolate the exponential.)}$$
$$0.25 = 2^{-0.1x}$$

Since the base of this exponential is 2 rather than e or 10, we choose to take the logarithm, base 10, of both sides of the equation instead of rewriting in logarithmic form. (*Note:* taking logarithms base e would also work.)

$$\log(0.25) = \log(2^{-0.1x})$$
$$\log(0.25) = (-0.1x)(\log 2) \qquad \text{(Property V)}$$
$$\frac{\log(0.25)}{\log 2} = -0.1x$$
$$\frac{-0.6021}{0.3021} = -0.1x$$
$$-1.993 = -0.1x$$
$$x = 20 \qquad \text{(approximately)}$$

Thus sales will be 500 on the 20th day after the end of the campaign. If a new campaign isn't begun on or before the 21st day, sales will drop below 500. (See Figure 4.11.)

FIGURE 4.11

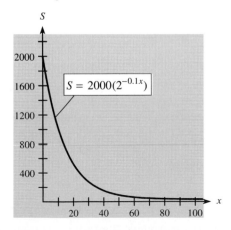

$S = 2000(2^{-0.1x})$

CHECKPOINT

2. If the sales of a product are given by $S = 1000e^{-0.2x}$, where x is the number of days after the end of an advertising campaign, what is the rate of decline in sales 20 days after the end of the campaign? ■

Example 4 is typical of many exponential decay models. In particular, once some action is completed, such as an advertising campaign, its effect on sales volume diminishes, or decays, with time.

For a given quantity or substance, if the formula that models its growth (or decay) is of the form

$$f(t) = Ce^{kt},$$

then the rate of growth (or decay) is proportional to the amount present. In fact,

$$f'(t) = (Ce^{kt})(k) = kf(t).$$

For example, the function in Example 3,

$$P = 95e^{-0.491t},$$

describes the decay of blood pressure in the aorta. The rate of decay is

$$\frac{dP}{dt} = 95e^{-0.491t}(-0.491)$$
$$= P(-0.491).$$

This shows that the rate of decay of pressure is proportional to the amount of pressure, and the constant of proportionality is $k = -0.491$.

In business, economics, biology, and the social sciences, the growth of money, bacteria, or population is frequently of interest. If growth can be described by a function of the form

$$f(x) = ma^x,$$

with $a > 0$ and $m > 0$, the growth is called **exponential growth.**

The curve that models the growth of some populations is given by $y = P_0e^{ht}$, where P_0 is the population size at a particular time t, h is a constant that depends on the population involved, and y is the total population at time t. This function may be used to model population growth for humans, insects, or bacteria.

EXAMPLE 5

The population of a certain city was 30,000 in 1980 and 40,500 in 1990. If the formula $y = P_0e^{ht}$ applies to the growth of the city's population, what should the population be in the year 2010?

Solution We can first use the data from 1980 and 1990 to find the value of h in the formula. Letting $P_0 = 30,000$ and $t = 10$, we get

$$40,500 = 30,000e^{h(10)}$$
$$1.35 = e^{10h}. \quad \text{(Isolate the exponential.)}$$

Taking the natural logarithm of both sides gives

$$\ln 1.35 = \ln e^{10h} = 10h(\ln e)$$
$$\ln 1.35 = 10h, \quad \text{since} \quad \ln e = 1$$
$$0.3001 = 10h$$
$$h = 0.0300 \quad \text{(approximately)}.$$

Thus the formula for this population is $y = P_0e^{0.03t}$. To predict the population for the year 2010, we use $P_0 = 40,500$ (for 1990) and $t = 20$. This gives

$$y = 40,500e^{0.03(20)}$$
$$= 40,500e^{0.6}$$
$$= 40,500(1.8221)$$
$$= 73,795 \quad \text{(approximately)}.$$

EXAMPLE 6

In Example 5, the population of a city was found to be given by

$$y = 40,500e^{0.03t},$$

where t is the number of years after 1990. At what rate is the population expected to be growing in 2000?

Solution The rate of growth of the population is

$$\frac{dy}{dt} = 40,500e^{0.03t} (0.03) = 1215e^{0.03t}.$$

In 2000 ($t = 10$), the rate of growth is expected to be

$$\frac{dy}{dt}\bigg|_{t=10} = 1640.08 \quad \text{(to 2 decimal places)}.$$

One family of curves that has been used to describe human growth and development, the growth of organisms in a limited environment, and the growth of many types of organizations is the family of **Gompertz curves.** These curves are graphs of equations of the form

$$N = Ca^{R^t},$$

where t represents the time, R $(0 < R < 1)$ is a constant depending on the population, a represents the proportion of initial growth, C is the maximum possible number of individuals, and N is the number of individuals at a given time t.

For example, the equation $N = 100(0.03)^{0.2t}$ could be used to predict the size of a deer herd introduced onto a small island. Here the maximum number of deer C would be 100, the proportion of the initial growth a is 0.03, and R is 0.2. For this example, t represents time, measured in decades. The graph of this equation is given in Figure 4.12.

FIGURE 4.12

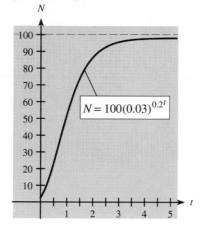

$$N = 100(0.03)^{0.2t}$$

EXAMPLE 7

A hospital administrator predicts that the growth in the number of hospital employees will follow the Gompertz equation

$$N = 2000(0.6)^{0.5t},$$

where t represents the number of years after the opening of a new facility.

(a) What is the number of employees when the facility opens ($t = 0$)?

(b) How many employees are predicted after one year of operation ($t = 1$)?

(c) Graph the curve.

(d) What is the maximum value for N that the curve will approach?

Solution

(a) If $t = 0$, $N = 2000(0.6)^1 = 1200$.

(b) If $t = 1$, $N = 2000(0.6)^{0.5} = 2000\sqrt{0.6} = 1549$ (approximately).

(c) The graph is shown in Figure 4.13 on the following page.

(d) From the graph we can see that as larger values of t are substituted in the function, the values of N approach, but never reach, 2000. We say that the line $N = 2000$ (dashed) is an **asymptote** for this curve, and that 2000 is the maximum possible value.

FIGURE 4.13

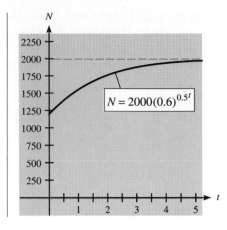

EXAMPLE 8

The Gompertz equation

$$N = 100(0.03)^{0.2^t}$$

predicts the size of a deer herd on a small island t decades from now. During what year will the deer population reach or exceed 70?

Solution We solve the equation with $N = 70$.

$$70 = 100(0.03)^{0.2^t}$$

$$0.7 = 0.03^{0.2^t} \qquad \text{(Isolate the exponential.)}$$

$$\ln 0.7 = \ln 0.03^{0.2^t} = 0.2^t \ln 0.03$$

$$\frac{\ln 0.7}{\ln 0.03} = 0.2^t \qquad \text{(Again, isolate the exponential.)}$$

$$\ln\left(\frac{\ln 0.7}{\ln 0.03}\right) = \ln (0.2)^t = t \ln 0.2$$

$$\ln (0.10172) = t(-1.6094)$$

$$\frac{-2.2855}{-1.6094} = t$$

$$t = 1.42 \text{ decades} \qquad \text{(approximately)}$$

The population will exceed 70 in just over 14 years, or during the 15th year.

ECONOMIC AND MANAGEMENT APPLICATIONS

In previous sections of this text, we have discussed both linear and quadratic cost, revenue, demand, and supply functions. But cost, revenue, demand, and supply may also be modeled by exponential or logarithmic equations. For example, suppose that the demand for a product is given by $p = 30(3^{-q/2})$, where q is the number of units (in tons) demanded at a price of p dollars per unit. Then the graph of the demand curve is as given in Figure 4.14.

FIGURE 4.14

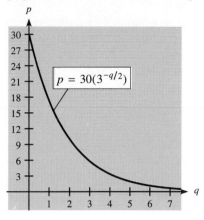

$$p = 30(3^{-q/2})$$

EXAMPLE 9

If the demand function for a certain commodity is given by $p = 30(3^{-q/2})$,

(a) at what price per unit will the demand equal 4 units (tons)?

(b) how many units, to the nearest unit, will be demanded if the price is $17.32?

Solution

(a) If $q = 4$, then $p = 30(3^{-4/2})$

$$= 30(0.1111)$$

$$= 3.33 \text{ dollars} \quad \text{(approximately)}.$$

(b) If $p = 17.32$, then $17.32 = 30(3^{-q/2})$

$$0.5773 = 3^{-q/2} \quad \text{(Isolate the exponential.)}$$

$$\ln 0.5773 = \ln 3^{-q/2}$$

$$\ln 0.5773 = \frac{q}{2} \ln 3$$

$$\frac{-2 \ln 0.5773}{\ln 3} = q$$

$$1 = q \quad \text{(approximately)}.$$

The number of tons demanded would be 1, to the nearest ton.

EXAMPLE 10

If the demand function for a commodity is given by $p = 100e^{-x/10}$, where p is the price per unit when x units are sold,

(a) what is the total revenue function for the commodity?

(b) what would be the total revenue if 30 units were demanded and supplied?

(c) what is the marginal revenue?

Solution

(a) The total revenue can be computed by multiplying the quantity sold times the price per unit. Since the demand function gives the price per unit when x units are sold, the total revenue for x units is $x \cdot p = x(100e^{-x/10})$. Thus the total revenue function is $R(x) = 100xe^{-x/10}$.

(b) If 30 units are sold, the total revenue is

$$R(30) = 100(30)e^{-30/10} = 100(30)(0.0498) = 149.40 \text{ (dollars) (approximately)}.$$

(c) The marginal revenue is

$$\overline{MR} = R'(x) = 100x[e^{-x/10}(-\tfrac{1}{10})] + e^{-x/10}(100)$$
$$= 10e^{-x/10}[10 - x].$$

TECHNOLOGY CORNER

We have seen in this section that if P dollars is invested for t years at a nominal interest rate, r, compounded m times per year, then the compound amount S that results is

$$S = P\left(1 + \frac{r}{m}\right)^{mt}.$$

We also saw that if P dollars is invested for t years at a nominal rate, r, compounded continuously, the compound amount is given by

$$S = Pe^{rt}.$$

Note that if interest is compounded continuously, the number of compounding periods approaches ∞, and we can find the compound amount by evaluating

$$\lim_{m \to \infty} P\left(1 + \frac{r}{m}\right)^{mt}.$$

To better understand the effect of compounding periods on an investment, consider an investment with a return of 10%. Then the function $f(t) = 100(1 + \frac{0.10}{m})^{mt}$ gives the return on $100 for t years if the investment is compounded m times per year.

1. For each of the following values of m, graph $f(t)$ for $19 \leq t \leq 47.5$ and $100 \leq y \leq 10{,}000$.

(a) $m = 1$ (compounded annually)

(b) $m = 4$ (compounded quarterly)

(c) $m = 365$ (compounded daily)

2. What do you notice about the graphs? In particular, which graph lies above the others? What conclusions can you draw from this observation?

3. (a) Graph $g(t) = 100e^{0.10t}$ on the same axis with $f(t)$ from 1(c) with $m = 365$.

(b) Is it easy to see a difference between these graphs? Are they, in fact, the same graph? Explain.

(c) Is it reasonable to conclude that

$$\lim_{m \to \infty} P\left(1 + \frac{r}{m}\right)^{mt} = Pe^{rt}?$$

CHECKPOINT

SOLUTIONS

1. (a) $S = \$1000(1 + \frac{0.09}{12})^{(10)(12)}$

$= \$1000(1.0075)^{120} \approx \$2451.36$

(b) $S = \$1000e^{(0.09)(10)}$

$= \$1000e^{0.9} \approx \$2459.60$

2. The rate of decline is given by dS/dx.

$$\frac{dS}{dx} = 1000e^{-0.2x}(-0.2) = -200e^{-0.2x}$$

$$\left.\frac{dS}{dx}\right|_{x=20} = -200e^{(-0.2)(20)}$$

$$= -200e^{-4} \approx -3.663 \text{ sales/day.}$$

EXERCISE 4.5

COMPOUND INTEREST

1. Find the amount that will result if $5000 is invested for 3 years at 10%, compounded annually.

2. Find the amount that will result if $10,000 is invested for 8 years at 8%, compounded annually.

3. What amount will result if $8600 is invested for 8 years at 10%, compounded semiannually?

4. What interest will be earned if $3200 is invested for 5 years at 8%, compounded quarterly?

5. What amount will result if $6300 is invested for 3 years at 12%, compounded continuously?

6. Find the interest that will be earned if $8600 is invested for 6 years at 10%, compounded continuously.

7. Find the interest that will result if $8000 is invested at 7%, compounded continuously, for 8 years.

8. Find the amount that will result if $5100 is invested for 4 years at 9%, compounded continuously.

9. Suppose that $5000 is invested at 9% per year compounded monthly.
   (a) What is the amount after 1 year?
   (b) How long before the investment doubles?

10. Suppose that $1000 is invested at 10% compounded continuously.
    (a) What is the amount after 1 year?
    (b) How long before the investment doubles?

11. Suppose that $5000 is invested at 13.5% compounded continuously.
    (a) What is the amount after 9 months?
    (b) How long before the investment doubles?

12. Suppose that $10,000 is invested at 12% compounded monthly.
    (a) What is the amount after $1\frac{1}{2}$ years?
    (b) How long before the investment doubles?

GROWTH AND DECAY

13. **Sales decay** The sales decay for a product is given by $S = 50,000e^{-0.8x}$, where S is the monthly sales and x is the number of months that have passed since the end of a promotional campaign.
    (a) What will be the sales 4 months after the end of the campaign?
    (b) How many months after the end of the campaign will sales drop below 1000, if no new campaign is initiated?

14. **Sales decay** The sales of a product decline after the end of an advertising campaign, with the sales decay given by $S = 100,000e^{-0.5x}$, where S represents the weekly sales and x rep-

resents the number of weeks since the end of the campaign.
    (a) What will be the sales for the tenth week after the end of the campaign?
    (b) During what week after the end of the campaign will sales drop below 400?

15. **Radioactive decay** Radioactive carbon-14 can be used to determine the age of fossils. Carbon-14 decays according to the equation

    $$y = y_0 e^{-0.00012378t},$$

    where y is the amount of carbon-14 at time t, in years, and y_0 is the original amount.
    (a) How much of the original amount would be left after 3000 years?
    (b) If a fossil is found to have $\frac{1}{100}$ the original amount of carbon-14, how old is the fossil?

16. **Product reliability** A statistical study shows that the fraction of television sets of a certain brand that are still in service after x years is given by $f(x) = e^{-0.15x}$.
    (a) What fraction of the sets are still in service after 5 years?
    (b) What fraction can be expected to be replaced in the sixth year? Use $f'(x)$.

17. **Radioactive half-life** An initial amount of 100 g of the radioactive isotope thorium-234 decays according to

    $$Q(t) = 100e^{-0.02828t},$$

    where t is in years. How long before half the initial amount has disintegrated? This time is called the half-life of this isotope.

18. **Radioactive half-life** A breeder reactor converts stable uranium-238 into the isotope plutonium-239. The decay of this isotope is given by

    $$A(t) = A_0 e^{-0.00002876t},$$

    where $A(t)$ is the amount of the isotope at time t, in years, and A_0 is the original amount.
    (a) If $A_0 = 500$ lb, how much will be left after a human lifetime (use $t = 70$ years)?
    (b) Find the half-life of this isotope.

19. **Population growth** If the population of a certain county was 100,000 in 1970 and 110,517 in 1980, and if the formula $y = P_0e^{ht}$ applies to the growth of the county's population, estimate the population of the county in 1995.

20. **Population growth** The population of a certain city grows according to the formula $y = P_0e^{0.03t}$. If the population was 250,000 in 1980, estimate the population in the year 2100.

21. **Sales growth** The president of a company predicts that sales will increase after she assumes office, and that the number of monthly sales will follow the curve given by $N = 3000(0.2)^{0.6t}$, where t represents the months since she assumed office.
    (a) What will be the sales when she assumes office?
    (b) What will be the sales after three months?
    (c) What is the expected upper limit on sales?
    (d) Graph the curve.

22. **Organizational growth** Because of a new market opening, the number of employees of a firm is expected to increase according to the equation $N = 1400(0.5)^{0.3t}$, where t represents the number of years after the new market opens.
    (a) What is the level of employment when the new market opens?
    (b) How many employees should be working at the end of two years?
    (c) What is the expected upper limit on the number of employees?
    (d) Graph the curve.

23. **Organizational growth** Suppose that the equation $N = 500(0.02)^{0.7t}$ represents the number of employees working t years after a company begins operations.
    (a) How many employees are there when the company opens (at $t = 0$)?
    (b) After how many years will at least 100 employees be working?

24. **Sales growth** A firm predicts that sales will increase during a promotional campaign, and that the number of daily sales will be given by $N = 200(0.01)^{0.8t}$, where t represents the num-

ber of days after the campaign begins. How many days after the beginning of the campaign would the firm expect to sell at least 60 units per day?

Gompertz curves describe situations in which growth is limited. There are other equations that describe this phenomenon under different assumptions. Two examples are

(a) $y = c(1 - e^{-ax})$, $a > 0$

(b) $y = \dfrac{A}{1 + ce^{-ax}}$, $a > 0$ (logistic curve)

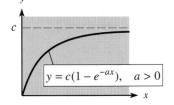

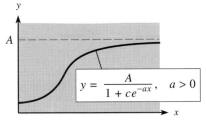

These equations have many applications. In general, both (a) and (b) can be used to describe learning, sales of new products, and population growth, and (b) can be used to describe the spread of epidemics. Problems 25–28 illustrate applications.

25. **Drugs in the bloodstream** The concentration y of a certain drug after t hours in the bloodstream (with $0 \le t \le 15$) is given by the equation

    $$y = 100(1 - e^{-0.462t}).$$

    (a) What is y after one hour ($t = 1$)?
    (b) How long does it take for y to reach 50?

26. **Population growth** Suppose that the size y of a deer herd t years after being introduced onto an island is given by

    $$y = 2500 - 2490e^{-0.1t}.$$

(a) Find the population when the herd was introduced (at $t = 0$).

(b) How long before the herd numbers 1500?

27. **Spread of disease** On a college campus of 10,000 students, a single student returned to campus infected by a disease. The spread of the disease through the student body is given by

$$y = \frac{10,000}{1 + 9999e^{-0.99t}},$$

where y is the total number infected at time t (in days).

(a) How many are infected after 4 days?

(b) If the school will shut down if 50% of the students are ill, during what day will it close?

28. **Spread of a rumor** The number of people $N(t)$ in a community who are reached by a particular rumor at time t is given by the equation

$$N(t) = \frac{50,500}{1 + 100e^{-0.7t}}.$$

(a) Find $N(0)$.

(b) What is the upper limit on the number of people affected?

(c) How long before 75% of the upper limit is reached?

ECONOMIC AND MANAGEMENT APPLICATIONS

29. **Demand** If the demand function for a certain commodity is given by $p = 100e^{-q/2}$,

(a) at what price per unit will the quantity demanded equal 6 units?

(b) if the price is $1.83 per unit, how many units will be demanded, to the nearest unit?

30. **Demand** If the demand function for a product is given by $p = 3000e^{-q/3}$,

(a) at what price per unit will the quantity demanded equal 6 units?

(b) if the price is $149.40 per unit, how many units will be demanded, to the nearest unit?

31. **Supply** If the supply function for a product is given by $p = 100e^q/(q + 1)$, where q represents the number of hundreds of units, what will be the price when the producers are willing to supply 300 units?

32. **Supply** If the supply function for a product is given by $p = 200(2^q)$, where q represents the number of hundreds of units, what will be the price when the producers are willing to supply 500 units?

33. **Total cost** If the total cost function for a product is $C(x) = e^{0.1x} + 400$, where x is the number of items produced, what is the total cost of producing 30 units?

34. **Total cost** If the total cost for a product is given by $C(x) = 400 \ln (x + 10) + 100$, what is the total cost of producing 100 units?

35. **Total revenue** If the demand function for a product is given by $p = 200e^{-0.02x}$, where p is the price per unit when x units are demanded, then what is the total revenue when 100 units are demanded and supplied?

36. **Total revenue** If the demand function for a product is given by $p = 4000/\ln (x + 10)$, where p is the price per unit when x units are demanded, then what is total revenue when 40 units are demanded and supplied?

37. **Market share** Suppose that the market share y (as a percent) that a company expects t months after a new product is introduced is given by $y = 40 - 40e^{-0.05t}$.

(a) What is the market share after the first month (to the nearest percent)?

(b) How long (to the nearest month) before their market share is 25%?

38. **Advertising** An advertising agency has found that when it promotes a new product in a certain market of 350,000, then the number of people x who are aware of the product t days after initiating the ad campaign is given by

$$x = 350,000(1 - e^{-0.077t}).$$

(a) How many people (to the nearest thousand) are aware after 1 week?

(b) How long (to the nearest day) before 300,000 are aware of the new product?

ADDITIONAL APPLICATIONS

39. **Pollution** Pollution levels in Lake Erie have been modeled* by the equation

$$x = 0.05 + 0.18e^{-0.38t},$$

where x is the volume of pollutants (in cubic kilometers) and t is the time (in years).

(a) Find the initial pollution levels; that is, find x when $t = 0$.

(b) How long before x is 30% of that initial level?

40. **Fish length** Suppose that the length x (in centimeters) of an individual of a certain species of fish is given by

$$x = 50 - 40e^{-0.05t},$$

where t is its age in months.

(a) Find the length after 1 year.

(b) How long (to the nearest month) until the length is 45 cm?

41. **Chemical reaction** When two chemicals, A and B, react to form another chemical C (such as in the digestive process), this is a special case of the **law of mass action,** which is fundamental to studying chemical reaction rates.

Suppose that chemical C is formed from A and B according to

$$x = \frac{120\,[1 - (0.6)^{3t}]}{4 - (0.6)^{3t}},$$

where x is the number of pounds of C formed in t minutes.

(a) How much of C is present when the reaction begins?

(b) How much of C is formed in 4 minutes?

(c) How long does it take to form 10 lb of C?

42. **Newton's law of cooling** A certain object at 90°F that is allowed to cool in a room where the temperature is 20°F has its temperature T given as a function of time t (in minutes) according to

$$T = 20 + 70e^{-0.056t}.$$

(a) Find the temperature of the object 30 seconds after it is in the room.

(b) How long does it take before the temperature of the object is 20.5°F?

43. **Ventilation** The ventilation system in a building operates when the concentration of carbon dioxide (CO_2) reaches a certain level. Suppose that when the ventilation system operates, the cubic feet of CO_2, x, in an 8000 cu ft room depends on time t (in minutes) according to

$$x = 4.8 + 11.2e^{-t/4}.$$

(a) Find the initial amount of CO_2 in the room, and find the concentration of CO_2 (as a percent) at this time.

(b) How long does it take to have a concentration of 0.07% CO_2?

(c) The steady-state or equilibrium concentration is what would result if the ventilation system were left on indefinitely. Find x as $t \to +\infty$ to determine the steady state concentration.

*Adapted from R. H. Rainey, *Science* 155 (1967), pp. 1242–1243.

SECTION	KEY TERM	FORMULA
4.1	Exponential function	$f(x) = a^x$
	e	$e = \lim\limits_{a \to 0} (1 + a)^{1/a}$
4.2	Logarithmic function	$y = \log_a x$, defined by $x = a^y$
	Common logarithm	$\log x = \log_{10} x$
	Natural logarithm	$\ln x = \log_e x$
	Inverse functions	
	Logarithmic Properties I–V	$\log_a a^x = x; \quad a^{\log_a x} = x;$
		$\log_a (MN) = \log_a M + \log_a N;$
		$\log_a (M/N) = \log_a M - \log_a N;$
		$\log_a (M^N) = N(\log_a M)$
	Change of base formula	$\log_b x = \dfrac{\log_a x}{\log_a b}$
4.3	Derivatives of logarithmic functions	$\dfrac{d}{dx} (\ln x) = \dfrac{1}{x}$
		$\dfrac{d}{dx} (\ln u) = \dfrac{1}{u} \cdot \dfrac{du}{dx}$
4.4	Derivatives of exponential functions	$\dfrac{d}{dx} (e^x) = e^x$
		$\dfrac{d}{dx} e^u = e^u \dfrac{du}{dx}$
		$\dfrac{d}{dx} a^u = a^u \dfrac{du}{dx} \ln a$
4.5	Compound amount	$S = P\left(1 + \dfrac{r}{m}\right)^{mt}$
	After continuous compounding	$S = Pe^{rt}$
	Exponential growth and decay	$f(x) = ma^x \quad \text{and} \quad f(x) = ma^{-x}$
	Gompertz curves	$N = Ca^{R^t}$

4.1, 4.2   1. Write each statement in logarithmic form.
  (a) $2^x = y$ (b) $3^y = 2x$

2. Write each statement in exponential form.
   (a) $\log_7(\frac{1}{49}) = -2$ (b) $\log_4 x = -1$

Graph the following functions.

3. $y = e^x$ 4. $y = e^{-x}$ 5. $y = \log_2 x$

6. $y = 2^x$ 7. $y = 4^x$ 8. $y = \ln x$

9. $y = \log_4 x$ 10. $y = 3^{-2x}$ 11. $y = \log x$

12. $y = \log(x + 2)$ 13. $y = \ln(x - 3)$ 14. $y = 10(2^{-x})$

In problems 15–22 evaluate each logarithm without using a calculator.

15. $\log_5 1$ 16. $\log_8 64$ 17. $\log_{25} 5$ 18. $\log_3(\frac{1}{3})$

19. $\log_3 3^8$ 20. $\ln e$ 21. $e^{\ln 5}$ 20. $10^{\log 3.15}$

If $\log 16 = 1.2041$ and $\log 4 = 0.6021$ (to 4 decimal places), find each of the following by using the properties of logarithms.

23. $\log(16 \div 4)$ 24. $\log \sqrt{16}$ 25. $\log(16 \cdot 4)$ 26. $\log 4^3$

In problems 27–28, use the properties of logarithms to write each expression as the sum or difference of two logarithmic functions containing no exponents.

27. $\log(yz)$ 28. $\ln \sqrt{\dfrac{x + 1}{x}}$

4.3, 4.4   In problems 29–40, find the derivative of each function.

29. If $y = x^2 e^x$, find dy/dx.   30. If $y = \ln e^{x^2}$, find y'.

31. If $p = \ln\left(\dfrac{q}{q^2 - 1}\right)$, find $\dfrac{dp}{dq}$.   32. If $y = e^{x^2}$, find dy/dx.

33. If $y = 3^{3x-4}$, find dy/dx.   34. If $y = (1 + \ln x)^{10}$, find dy/dx.

35. If $y = \dfrac{\ln x}{x}$, find $\dfrac{dy}{dx}$.   36. If $y = \dfrac{1 + e^{-x}}{1 - e^{-x}}$, find $\dfrac{dy}{dx}$.

37. If $y = \dfrac{\ln(2x + 1)}{2x + 1}$, find $\dfrac{dy}{dx}$.   38. If $x = e^t(t^2 + 4)^2$, find $\dfrac{dx}{dt}$.

39. If $y \ln x = 5$, find $\dfrac{dy}{dx}$.   40. Find $\dfrac{dy}{dx}$ for $e^{xy} = y$.

APPLICATIONS

4.2   41. ***Stellar magnitude*** The stellar magnitude M of a star is related to its brightness B as seen from Earth according to $M = -\frac{5}{2}\log(B/B_0)$, where B_0 is a minimum level of brightness.
   (a) Find the magnitude of Venus if its brightness is 36.3 times B_0.
   (b) Find the brightness of the North Star if its magnitude is 2.1 (as a multiple of B_0).
   (c) If the faintest stars have magnitude 6, find their brightness (as a multiple of B_0).
   (d) Is a star with magnitude -1.0 brighter than a star with magnitude $+1.0$?

42. ***Compound amount*** If the compound amount of $1000 invested for t years at 12%, compounded continuously, is given by $S = 1000e^{0.12t}$, find the rate at which the compounded amount is growing after 1 year.

43. ***Compound amount***
    (a) In problem 42, find the rate of growth of the compounded amount after 2 years.
    (b) How much faster is the compound amount growing at the end of 2 years than after 1 year?

44. ***Radioactive decay*** A breeder reactor converts stable uranium-238 into the isotope plutonium-239. The decay of this isotope is given by $A(t) = A_0e^{-0.00002876t}$, where $A(t)$ is the amount of isotope at time t, in years, and A_0 is the original amount. This isotope has a half-life of 24,101 years (that is, half of it will decay away in 24,101 years).
    (a) At what rate is $A(t)$ decaying its half-life?
    (b) At what rate is $A(t)$ decaying after 1 year?
    (c) Is the rate of decay at its half-life greater or less than after 1 year?

45. ***Marginal cost*** The average cost of producing a product is $\overline{C} = 600e^{x/600}$. What is the marginal cost when 600 units are produced?

46. ***Compound amount*** If $8000 is invested at 12%, compounded annually, for 3 years, what is the compound amount at the end of the 3 years?

47. ***Compound amount*** If $1000 is invested for 4 years at 8%, compounded quarterly, how much interest will be earned?

48. ***Compound amount*** What is the compound amount if $1000 is invested for 6 years at 8%, compounded continuously?

49. ***Compound amount*** How long (in years) would $700 have to be invested at 11.9%, compounded continuously, to earn $300 interest?

50. ***Compound amount*** How long (in years) would $600 have to be invested at 8%, compounded continuously, to amount to $970?

51. ***Sales growth*** Because of a new advertising campaign, a company predicts that sales will increase, and that the yearly sales will be given by the equation $N = 10,000(0.3)^{0.5^t}$, where t represents the number of years after the start of the campaign. What are the
    (a) sales when the campaign begins?
    (b) predicted sales for the third year?
    (c) maximum predicted sales?

52. ***Sales decay*** The sales decay for a product is given by $S = 50,000e^{-0.1t}$, where S is the weekly sales and t is the number of weeks that have passed since the end of an advertising campaign.
    (a) What will sales be 6 weeks after the end of the campaign?
    (b) How many weeks will pass before sales drop below 15,000?

53. ***Sales decay*** The sales decay for a product is given by $S = 50,000e^{-0.6t}$, where S is the monthly sales and t is the number of months that have passed since the end of an advertising campaign. What will sales be 6 months after the end of the campaign?

PROFIT REINVESTMENT

T.C. Hardware Store wants to construct a new building at a cost of $250,000. The owners plan to invest $1000 per month of their profits in order to make the 20% down payment that is required. They can put their money into an annuity account that pays 9%, compounded monthly, but they are concerned about the 6% average annual inflation rate in the construction industry. They would like you to give them some projections about how long it will take them to accrue the necessary down payment. They are interested in projections that ignore as well as include the 6% inflation in new construction costs.

To help you address the owners' questions and prepare your report to them, answer the following.

1. How long will it take to get the down payment if we ignore the inflation rate?

   HINT: The sum S of an annuity is

   $$S = R\frac{(1 + i)^n - 1}{i},$$

   where R is the size of each payment, i is the monthly interest rate, and n is the number of months.

2. At what rate will the money in the account be growing at the end of 2 years?

3. If the 6% annual inflation is compounded monthly, how long will it take to get the down payment?

   HINT: The down payment necessary will be 20% of

   $$250,000 \left(1 + \frac{0.06}{12}\right)^n,$$

   and thus you must find n so that this amount equals the sum of the owners' annuity. That is, you need to solve

   $$0.20 \, (250{,}000)(1.005)^n = 1000\left[\frac{(1.0075)^n - 1}{0.0075}\right]$$

   for n. One way to solve this equation is to graph each side as a function, and find the point of intersection of the graphs.

4. Suppose that the 6% inflation rate in new construction is accurate, but that the owners would like to begin construction within 4 years. How much would they have to contribute each month to meet this schedule?

PREREQUISITE PROBLEM TYPE	REVIEW SECTION/ANSWER
SECTIONS 5.1–5.4 Write as a power: (a) $\sqrt{x}$ (b) $\sqrt{x^2 - 9}$	Section 0.3, Radicals (a) $x^{1/2}$ (b) $(x^2 - 9)^{1/2}$
SECTION 5.2 Expand $(x^2 + 4)^2$.	Section 0.4, Special powers $x^4 + 8x^2 + 16$
SECTION 5.3 Divide $x^4 - 2x^3 + 4x^2 - 7x - 1$ by $x^2 - 2x$.	Section 0.6, Division $x^2 + 4 + \dfrac{x - 1}{x^2 - 2x}$
SECTIONS 5.1, 5.2, 5.3 Find the derivative of (a) $f(x) = 2x^{1/2}$ (b) $u = x^3 - 3x$	Section 2.4, Derivatives (a) $f'(x) = x^{-1/2}$ (b) $u' = 3x^2 - 3$
SECTION 5.2 If $y = \dfrac{(x^2 + 4)^6}{6}$, what is y'?	Section 2.6, Derivatives $(x^2 + 4)^5 2x$
SECTION 5.3 (a) If $y = \ln u$, what is y'? (b) If $y = e^u$, what is y'?	Sections 4.3, 4.4, Derivatives (a) $y' = \dfrac{1}{u} \cdot u'$ (b) $y' = e^u \cdot u'$
SECTION 5.2 If $u = x^2 + 4$, what is du?	Section 3.6, Differentials $2x \, dx$

5 | INDEFINITE INTEGRALS

If the marginal cost for a product is $36 at all levels of production, we know that the total cost function is a linear function. In particular, $C(x) = 36x + FC$, where FC is the fixed cost. But if the marginal cost changes at different levels of production, the total cost function cannot be linear. In this chapter we will use integration to find total cost functions, given information about marginal costs and fixed costs.

Accountants can use linear regression to translate information about marginal cost into a linear equation defining (approximately) the marginal cost function. By integrating this marginal cost function, it is possible to find an (approximate) function that defines the total cost.

We can also use integration to find total revenue functions from marginal revenue functions, to optimize profit from information about marginal cost and marginal revenue, and to find national consumption functions from information about marginal propensity to consume.

5.1 | THE INDEFINITE INTEGRAL

OBJECTIVE

• To find certain indefinite integrals

We have discussed methods for finding derivatives of functions in the previous chapters. We will now turn our attention to reversing the operation of differentiation. Given the derivative of a function, we can find the function. This process is called **antidifferentiation.** For example, if the derivative of a function is $2x$, we know that the function could be $f(x) = x^2$ because $\dfrac{d}{dx}(x^2) = 2x$. But the function could also be $f(x) = x^2 + 4$ because $\dfrac{d}{dx}(x^2 + 4) = 2x$. It is clear that any function of the form $f(x) = x^2 + C$, where C is a constant, will have $f'(x) = 2x$ as its derivative. Thus we say that the **antiderivative** of $f'(x) = 2x$ is $f(x) = x^2 + C$, where C is an arbitrary constant.

Antiderivative   A function F is called an **antiderivative** of a function f if, for every x in the domain of f, $F'(x) = f(x)$.

EXAMPLE 1   If $f'(x) = 3x^2$, what is $f(x)$?

Solution   The derivative of the function $f(x) = x^3$ is $f'(x) = 3x^2$. But other functions also have this derivative. They will all be of the form $f(x) = x^3 + C$, where C is a constant. Thus we say that $f(x) = x^3 + C$ is the antiderivative of $f'(x) = 3x^2$.

EXAMPLE 2   If $f'(x) = x^3$, what is $f(x)$?

Solution   We know that the derivative of $f(x) = x^4$ is $4x^3$, so the derivative of $f(x) = x^4/4$ is $f'(x) = x^3$. Thus any function of the form $f(x) = x^4/4 + C$ will have the derivative $f'(x) = x^3$.

It is easily seen that

$$\text{if } f'(x) = x^4, \quad \text{then } f(x) = \frac{x^5}{5} + C;$$

$$\text{if } f'(x) = x^5, \quad \text{then } f(x) = \frac{x^6}{6} + C.$$

In general, we have the following.

Antiderivative of $f(x) = x^n$	If $f'(x) = x^n$, then $f(x) = \dfrac{x^{n+1}}{n+1} + C$, for $n \neq -1$.

We can see that this general formula applies for any $n \neq -1$ by noting that the derivative of

$$f(x) = \frac{x^{n+1}}{n+1} + C \quad \text{is} \quad f'(x) = \frac{(n+1)x^n}{n+1} + 0 = x^n.$$

Later, we will discuss the case when $n = -1$.

EXAMPLE 3

What is the antiderivative of $f'(x) = x^{-1/2}$?

Solution Using the formula, we get

$$f(x) = \frac{x^{1/2}}{1/2} + C = 2x^{1/2} + C.$$

We can check by noting that the derivative of $2x^{1/2} + C$ is $x^{-1/2}$.

The process of finding an antiderivative is called **integration.** The function that results when integration takes place is called an **indefinite integral,** or more simply, an **integral.** We can denote the indefinite integral (that is, the antiderivative) of a function $f(x)$ by $\int f(x)\, dx$. Thus we can write $\int x^2\, dx$ to indicate the antiderivative of the function $f(x) = x^2$. The expression is read as "the integral of x^2 with respect to x." In this case, x^2 is called the **integrand.** The **integral sign,** $\int$, indicates the process of integration, and the dx indicates that the integral is to be taken with respect to x. Since the antiderivative of x^2 is $x^3/3 + C$, we can write

$$\int x^2\, dx = \frac{x^3}{3} + C.$$

Note that integration results in a function (actually a number of functions, one for each value of C).

We can now use the integral sign and rewrite the formula for integrating powers of x.

Powers of x Formula	$\displaystyle \int x^n\, dx = \frac{x^{n+1}}{n+1} + C \qquad \text{(for } n \neq -1)$

EXAMPLE 4 Find (a) $\int \sqrt[3]{x}\, dx$ and (b) $\int \frac{1}{x^2}\, dx$.

Solution

(a) $\int \sqrt[3]{x}\, dx = \int x^{1/3}\, dx = \frac{x^{4/3}}{4/3} + C$

$= \frac{3}{4}x^{4/3} + C = \frac{3}{4}\sqrt[3]{x^4} + C.$

(b) We write the power of x in the numerator so the integral has the form in the formula above.

$$\int \frac{1}{x^2}\, dx = \int x^{-2}\, dx = \frac{x^{-2+1}}{-2+1} + C = \frac{x^{-1}}{-1} + C = \frac{-1}{x} + C$$

Other formulas will be useful in evaluating integrals. The following table shows how some new integration formulas result from differentiation formulas.

INTEGRATION FORMULAS

DERIVATIVE	RESULTING INTEGRAL
$\frac{d}{dx}(x) = 1$	$\int 1\, dx = \int dx = x + C$
$\frac{d}{dx}[c \cdot u(x)] = c \cdot \frac{d}{dx}u(x)$	$\int c\, u(x)\, dx = c \int u(x)\, dx$
$\frac{d}{dx}[u(x) \pm v(x)] = \frac{d}{dx}u(x) \pm \frac{d}{dx}v(x)$	$\int [u(x) \pm v(x)]\, dx = \int u(x)\, dx \pm \int v(x)\, dx$

The formulas above indicate that we can integrate functions term-by-term just as we were able to take derivatives term-by-term.

EXAMPLE 5 Evaluate $\int 4\, dx$.

Solution

$$\int 4\, dx = 4 \int dx = 4(x + C_1) = 4x + C$$

(Since C_1 is an unknown constant, we can write $4C_1$ as the unknown constant C.)

EXAMPLE 6   Evaluate $\int 8x^5 \, dx$.

Solution

$$\int 8x^5 \, dx = 8 \int x^5 \, dx = 8\left(\frac{x^6}{6} + C_1\right) = \frac{4x^6}{3} + C$$

EXAMPLE 7   Evaluate $\int (x^3 + 4x) \, dx$.

Solution

$$\int (x^3 + 4x) \, dx = \int x^3 \, dx + \int 4x \, dx$$
$$= \left(\frac{x^4}{4} + C_1\right) + \left(4 \cdot \frac{x^2}{2} + C_2\right)$$
$$= \frac{x^4}{4} + 2x^2 + C_1 + C_2$$
$$= \frac{x^4}{4} + 2x^2 + C$$

Note that we need only one constant because the sum of C_1 and C_2 is just a new constant.

EXAMPLE 8   Evaluate $\int (x^2 - 4)^2 \, dx$.

Solution   We expand $(x^2 - 4)^2$ so the integrand is in a form that fits the basic integration formulas.

$$\int (x^2 - 4)^2 \, dx = \int (x^4 - 8x^2 + 16) \, dx = \frac{x^5}{5} - \frac{8x^3}{3} + 16x + C$$

CHECKPOINT   1. True or false:

(a) $\int (4x^3 - 2x) \, dx = \int 4x^3 \, dx - \int 2x \, dx = (x^4 + C) - (x^2 + C) = x^4 - x^2$

(b) $\int \frac{1}{3x^2} \, dx = \frac{1}{3(x^3/3)} + C = \frac{1}{x^3} + C$

2. Evaluate $\int (2x^3 + x^{-1/2} - 4x^{-5}) \, dx$.

EXAMPLE 9   Sales records show that the rate of change of the revenue (that is, the marginal revenue) for a product is $\overline{MR} = 300 - 0.2x$, where x represents the quantity sold. Find the total revenue function for the product.

Solution We know that the marginal revenue can be found by differentiating the total revenue function. That is,

$$R'(x) = 300 - 0.2x.$$

Thus integrating the marginal revenue function will give the total revenue function.

$$R(x) = \int (300 - 0.2x)\, dx = 300x - 0.1x^2 + K*$$

We can use the fact that there is no revenue when no units are sold to evaluate K. Setting $x = 0$ and $R = 0$ gives $0 = 300(0) - 0.1(0)^2 + K$, so $K = 0$. Thus the total revenue function is

$$R(x) = 300x - 0.1x^2.$$

TECHNOLOGY CORNER

To investigate why the antiderivative of a function contains a constant C, consider the following.

1. For $f'(x) = 4x$, find a description for all functions $f(x)$.

2. Sketch graphs of $f(x)$ for $C = -2, -1, 0, 1,$ and 2. How would you describe the differences among these graphs?

3. For each $f(x)$ sketched, write the equation of the tangent line to $f(x)$ at $x = -1$.

4. Sketch the graph of each tangent line with the particular $f(x)$ to which it belongs.

5. What do the tangent lines have in common?

CHECKPOINT
SOLUTIONS

1. (a) False, $\int (4x^3 - 2x)\, dx = \int 4x^3\, dx - \int 2x\, dx = (x^4 + C_1) - (x^2 + C_2)$
$$= x^4 - x^2 + C$$

---

*We are using K rather than C here to represent the constant of integration to avoid confusion between the constant C and the cost function $C = C(x)$.

(b) False, $\displaystyle\int \frac{1}{3x^2}\,dx = \int \frac{1}{3}\cdot\frac{1}{x^2}\,dx = \frac{1}{3}\int x^{-2}\,dx$

$$= \frac{1}{3}\cdot\frac{x^{-1}}{-1} + C = \frac{-1}{3x} + C$$

2. $\displaystyle\int(2x^3 + x^{-1/2} - 4x^{-5})\,dx = \frac{2x^4}{4} + \frac{x^{1/2}}{1/2} - \frac{4x^{-4}}{-4} + C = \frac{x^4}{2} + 2x^{1/2} + x^{-4} + C$ ∎

EXERCISE 5.1

1. If $f'(x) = 4x^3$, what is $f(x)$?
2. If $f'(x) = 5x^4$, what is $f(x)$?
3. If $f'(x) = x^6$, what is $f(x)$?
4. If $g'(x) = x^4$, what is $g(x)$?

Evaluate the following integrals.

5. $\int x^7\,dx$
6. $\int x^5\,dx$
7. $\int 5x^3\,dx$
8. $\int 4x^5\,dx$
9. $\int 8x^5\,dx$
10. $\int 16x^9\,dx$
11. $\int(3^3 + x^3)\,dx$
12. $\int(5^2 + x^5)\,dx$
13. $\int x^{3/2}\,dx$
14. $\int x^{2/3}\,dx$
15. $\int(x^4 - 3x^2)\,dx$
16. $\int(3x^2 - 4x)\,dx$
17. $\int\sqrt{x}\,dx$
18. $\int\sqrt{x^3}\,dx$
19. $\int 6\sqrt[4]{x}\,dx$
20. $\int 3\sqrt[3]{x^2}\,dx$
21. $\displaystyle\int \frac{5}{x^4}\,dx$
22. $\displaystyle\int \frac{6}{x^5}\,dx$
23. $\displaystyle\int \frac{dx}{2\sqrt[3]{x^2}}$
24. $\displaystyle\int \frac{2\,dx}{5\sqrt{x^3}}$
25. $\displaystyle\int\left(x^3 - 4 + \frac{5}{x^6}\right)dx$
26. $\displaystyle\int\left(x^3 - 7 - \frac{3}{x^4}\right)dx$
27. $\displaystyle\int\left(x^9 - \frac{1}{x^3} + \frac{2}{\sqrt[3]{x}}\right)dx$
28. $\displaystyle\int\left(3x^8 + \frac{4}{x^8} - \frac{5}{\sqrt[5]{x}}\right)dx$

In problems 29–34, use algebra to rewrite the integrands, integrate, and simplify.

29. $\int(x + 5)^2 x\,dx$
30. $\int(2x + 1)^2 x\,dx$
31. $\int(4x^2 - 1)^2\,dx$
32. $\int(x^3 + 1)^2\,dx$
33. $\displaystyle\int \frac{x + 1}{x^3}\,dx$
34. $\displaystyle\int \frac{x - 3}{\sqrt{x}}\,dx$

Applications

35. **Revenue** If the marginal revenue for a month for a commodity is $\overline{MR} = 3$, what is the total revenue function?

36. **Revenue** If the marginal revenue for a month for a commodity is $\overline{MR} = 5$, what is the total revenue function?

37. **Revenue** If the marginal revenue for a month for a commodity is $\overline{MR} = 4x + 3$, find the total revenue function.

38. **Revenue** If the marginal revenue for a month for a commodity is $\overline{MR} = 5x + 2$, find the total revenue function.

39. **Revenue** If the marginal revenue for a month is given by $\overline{MR} = 3x + 1$, what is the total revenue from the production and sale of 50 units?

40. **Revenue** If the marginal revenue for a month is given by $\overline{MR} = 5x + 3$, find the total revenue from the sale of 75 units.

41. **Stimulus-response** Suppose that when a sense organ receives a stimulus at time t, the

total number of action potentials is $P(t)$. If the rate at which action potentials are produced is $t^3 + 4t^2 + 6$, and if there are 0 action potentials when $t = 0$, find the formula for $P(t)$.

42. **Projectiles** Suppose that a particle has been shot into the air in such a way that the rate at which its height is changing is $v = 320 - 32t$, in feet per second, and suppose that it is 1600 feet high when $t = 10$. Write the equation that describes the height of the particle at any time t.

43. **Pollution** A factory is dumping pollutants into a river at a rate given by $dx/dt = t^{3/4}/600$ tons per week, where t is the time in weeks since the dumping began and x is the number of tons of pollutants.
    (a) Find the equation for total tons of pollutants dumped.
    (b) How many tons were dumped during the first year?

44. **Spread of an oil spill** The rate at which the radius of an oil slick is spreading from an off-shore oil well is 4 feet per hour. If the radius is 100 feet when $t = 25$ hours, write the radius of the oil slick as a function of time.

45. **Average cost** The DeWitt Company has found that the rate of change of its average cost for a product is

$$\overline{C}'(x) = \frac{1}{4} - \frac{100}{x^2},$$

in dollars, where x is the number of units. If the average cost of producing 20 units is $40.00, find
    (a) the average cost function for the product.
    (b) the average cost of 100 units of the product.

46. **Population growth** The rate of growth of the population of a city is predicted to be

$$\frac{dp}{dt} = 1000t^{1.08},$$

where p is the population at time t, and t is measured in years from the present. Suppose that the current population is 100,000. What is the predicted
    (a) rate of growth 5 years from the present?
    (b) population 5 years from the present?

47. **Oil leakage** An oil tanker hits a reef and begins to leak. The efforts of the workers repairing the leak cause the rate at which the oil is leaking to decrease. If the oil was leaking at a rate of 31 barrels per hour at the end of the first hour after the accident, and if the rate is decreasing at a rate of one barrel per hour,
    (a) what function describes the rate of loss?
    (b) how many barrels of oil will leak in the first 6 hours?
    (c) when will the oil leak be stopped? How much will have leaked altogether?

5.2 | THE POWER RULE

OBJECTIVE

- To evaluate integrals of the form $\int u^n \cdot u' \, dx$ if $n \neq -1$

Our goal in this section is to extend the formula

$$\int x^n \, dx = \frac{x^{n+1}}{n+1} + C \qquad (n \neq -1)$$

to powers of a function of x. In order to do this, we must understand the importance of the symbol dx.

Recall that the derivative of $y = f(x)$ with respect to x can be denoted by dy/dx. Recall also, from Section 3.6, that dy and dx have meaning as separate quantities called the differential of y, dy, and the differential of x, dx.

Thus in terms of our goal of extending the powers of x integration formula, we would suspect that if x is replaced by a function of x, then dx should be replaced by the differential of that function. Let's see if this is true.

Recall that if $y = [u(x)]^n$, the derivative of y is

$$\frac{dy}{dx} = n[u(x)]^{n-1} \cdot u'(x).$$

Using this formula for derivatives, we can see that

$$\int n[u(x)]^{n-1} \cdot u'(x)\, dx = [u(x)]^n + C.$$

It is easy to see that this formula is equivalent to the following formula, called the **Power Rule for Integration.**

Power Rule for Integration

$$\int [u(x)]^n \cdot u'(x)\, dx = \frac{[u(x)]^{n+1}}{n+1} + C, \qquad \text{if } n \neq -1$$

Using the fact that

$$du = u'(x)\, dx \quad \text{or} \quad du = u'\, dx,$$

we can write the Power Rule in the alternate form below.

Power Rule (Alternate Form)

$$\int u^n\, du = \frac{u^{n+1}}{n+1} + C, \qquad n \neq -1$$

Note that this formula has the same form as the formula

$$\int x^n\, dx = \frac{x^{n+1}}{n+1} + C, \qquad n \neq -1,$$

with the function u *substituted for x and du substituted for dx.*

EXAMPLE 1

Evaluate $\int (x^2 + 4)^5 \cdot 2x \, dx$.

Solution To use the Power Rule, we must be sure that we have the function $u(x)$, its derivative $u'(x)$, and n.

$$u = x^2 + 4, \quad n = 5$$
$$u' = 2x$$

All required parts are present, so the integral is of the form

$$\int (x^2 + 4)^5 2x \, dx = \int u^5 \cdot u' \, dx = \int u^5 \, du$$

$$= \frac{u^6}{6} + C = \frac{(x^2 + 4)^6}{6} + C.$$

We can check the integration by noting that the derivative of

$$\frac{(x^2 + 4)^6}{6} + C \quad \text{is} \quad (x^2 + 4)^5 \cdot 2x.$$

EXAMPLE 2

Evaluate $\int \sqrt{2x + 3} \cdot 2 \, dx$.

Solution If we let $u = 2x + 3$, then $u' = 2$, and so we have

$$\int \sqrt{2x + 3} \cdot 2 \, dx = \int \sqrt{u} \, u' \, dx = \int \sqrt{u} \, du$$

$$= \int u^{1/2} \, du$$

$$= \frac{u^{3/2}}{3/2} + C.$$

Since $u = 2x + 3$, we have

$$\int \sqrt{2x + 3} \cdot 2 \, dx = \frac{2}{3}(2x + 3)^{3/2} + C.$$

CHECK: The derivative of $\frac{2}{3}(2x + 3)^{3/2} + C$ is $(2x + 3)^{1/2} \cdot 2$.

EXAMPLE 3

Evaluate $\int (x^2 + 4)^4 \cdot x \, dx$.

Solution If we let $u = x^2 + 4$, then $u' = 2x$. Thus we do not have an integral of the form $\int u^n \cdot u' \, dx$, as we had in Example 1; the factor 2 is not in the integrand. To get the integrand in the correct form, we can multiply by 2 and divide it out as follows:

$$\int (x^2 + 4)^4 \cdot x \, dx = \int (x^2 + 4)^4 \cdot \frac{1}{2}(2x) \, dx.$$

Because $\frac{1}{2}$ is a constant factor, we can factor it outside the integral sign, getting

$\frac{1}{2}\int(x^2 + 4)^4 \cdot 2x\, dx.$

Now the integral is in the form $\frac{1}{2}\int u^4 \cdot u'\, dx$. Thus

$$\int (x^2 + 4)^4 \cdot x\, dx = \frac{1}{2}\int(x^2 + 4)^4 \cdot 2x\, dx$$
$$= \frac{1}{2}\frac{(x^2 + 4)^5}{5} + C$$
$$= \frac{1}{10}(x^2 + 4)^5 + C.$$

EXAMPLE 4

Evaluate $\int\sqrt{x^3 - 4} \cdot 5x^2\, dx.$

Solution If we let $u = x^3 - 4$, then $u' = 3x^2$. Thus we need the factor 3, rather than 5, in the integrand. If we multiply by the constant factor 3 (and divide it out), we have

$$\int\sqrt{x^3 - 4} \cdot 5x^2\, dx = \int\sqrt{x^3 - 4} \cdot \frac{5}{3}(3x^2)\, dx$$
$$= \frac{5}{3}\int(x^3 - 4)^{1/2} \cdot 3x^2\, dx.$$

This integral is of the form $\frac{5}{3}\int u^{1/2} \cdot u'\, dx$, resulting in

$$\frac{5}{3}\cdot\frac{u^{3/2}}{3/2} + C = \frac{5}{3}\cdot\frac{(x^3 - 4)^{3/2}}{3/2} + C$$
$$= \frac{10}{9}(x^3 - 4)^{3/2} + C.$$

Note that we can factor a constant outside the integral sign to obtain the integrand in the form we seek, but if the integral requires the introduction of a variable to obtain the form $u^n \cdot u'\, dx$, we *cannot* use this form, and must try something else.

EXAMPLE 5

Evaluate $\int(x^2 + 4)^2\, dx.$

Solution If we let $u = x^2 + 4$, then $u' = 2x$. Since we would have to introduce a variable to get u' in the integral, we cannot solve this problem by using the Power Rule. We must find another method. We can evaluate this integral by squaring and then integrating term-by-term.

$$\int(x^2 + 4)^2\, dx = \int(x^4 + 8x^2 + 16)\, dx$$
$$= \frac{x^5}{5} + \frac{8x^3}{3} + 16x + C$$

Note that if we had tried to introduce the factor $2x$ into the integral of Example 5, we would get

$$\int (x^2 + 4)^2 \, dx = \int (x^2 + 4)^2 \cdot \frac{1}{2x} (2x) \, dx$$

$$= \frac{1}{2} \int (x^2 + 4)^2 \cdot \frac{1}{x} (2x) \, dx.$$

But we cannot factor the $1/x$ outside the integral, so we do not have the proper form. Again, we can only introduce *a constant factor* to get an integral in the proper form.

EXAMPLE 6

Evaluate $\int (2x^2 - 4x)^2 (x - 1) \, dx$.

Solution If we want to treat this as an integral of the form $\int u^n u' \, dx$, we will have to let $u = 2x^2 - 4x$. Then u' will be $4x - 4$. Multiplying and dividing by 4 will give us this form, as follows.

$$\int (2x^2 - 4x)^2 (x - 1) \, dx = \int (2x^2 - 4x)^2 \cdot \frac{1}{4} \cdot 4(x - 1) \, dx$$

$$= \frac{1}{4} \int (2x^2 - 4x)^2 (4x - 4) \, dx$$

$$= \frac{1}{4} \int u^2 u' \, dx = \frac{1}{4} \cdot \frac{u^3}{3} + C$$

$$= \frac{1}{4} \frac{(2x^2 - 4x)^3}{3} + C$$

$$= \frac{1}{12} (2x^2 - 4x)^3 + C$$

EXAMPLE 7

Evaluate $\int \frac{x^2 - 1}{(x^3 - 3x)^3} \, dx$.

Solution This integral can be treated as $\int u^{-3} u' \, dx$ if we let $u = x^3 - 3x$. Then we can multiply (and divide) by 3 to get $u' = 3(x^2 - 1)$.

$$\int \frac{x^2 - 1}{(x^3 - 3x)^3} \, dx = \int (x^3 - 3x)^{-3} \cdot \frac{1}{3} \cdot 3(x^2 - 1) \, dx$$

$$= \frac{1}{3} \int (x^3 - 3x)^{-3} (3x^2 - 3) \, dx$$

$$= \frac{1}{3} \left[\frac{(x^3 - 3x)^{-2}}{-2} \right] + C$$

$$= \frac{-1}{6(x^3 - 3x)^2} + C$$

CHECKPOINT

1. Which of the following can be evaluated with the Power Rule?
   (a) $\int(4x^2 + 1)^{10}(8x\,dx)$
   (b) $\int(4x^2 + 1)^{10}(x\,dx)$
   (c) $\int(4x^2 + 1)^{10}(8\,dx)$
   (d) $\int(4x^2 + 1)^{10}\,dx$

2. Which of the following is equal to $\int(2x^3 + 5)^{-2}\,(6x^2\,dx)$?

   (a) $\dfrac{[(2x^4)/4 + 5x]^{-1}}{-1} \cdot \dfrac{6x^3}{3} + C$ (b) $\dfrac{(2x^3 + 5)^{-1}}{-1} \cdot \dfrac{6x^3}{3} + C$

   (c) $\dfrac{(2x^3 + 5)^{-1}}{-1} + C$

3. True or false: Constants can be factored outside the integral sign.

4. Evaluate:
   (a) $\int(x^3 + 9)^5(3x^2\,dx)$
   (b) $\int(x^3 + 9)^{15}(x^2\,dx)$
   (c) $\int(x^3 + 9)^2(x\,dx)$

EXAMPLE 8

Suppose that the marginal revenue for a product is given by

$$\overline{MR} = \frac{600}{\sqrt{3x + 1}} + 2.$$

Find the total revenue function.

Solution

$$
\begin{aligned}
R(x) &= \int \overline{MR}\,dx \\
&= \int \left[\frac{600}{(3x + 1)^{1/2}} + 2 \right] dx \\
&= \int 600(3x + 1)^{-1/2}\,dx + \int 2\,dx \\
&= 600\left(\frac{1}{3}\right)\int (3x + 1)^{-1/2}(3\,dx) + 2\int dx \\
&= 200\,\frac{(3x + 1)^{1/2}}{1/2} + 2x + K \\
&= 400\,\sqrt{3x + 1} + 2x + K
\end{aligned}
$$

We know that $R(0) = 0$, so we have

$$0 = 400\,\sqrt{1} + 0 + K \quad \text{or} \quad K = -400.$$

Thus the total revenue function is

$$R(x) = 400\,\sqrt{3x + 1} + 2x - 400.$$

Notice in Example 8 that even though $R(0) = 0$, the constant of integration K was *not* 0. This is because $x = 0$ does not necessarily mean that $u(x)$ will also be 0.

TECHNOLOGY CORNER

1. Graph $f'(x) = \dfrac{-x}{\sqrt{4 - x^2}}$ and determine where it is undefined.

2. Find all possible functions $f(x)$ for which $f'(x) = \dfrac{-x}{\sqrt{4 - x^2}}$ by integrating $f'(x)$.

3. Sketch the graph of $f(x)$ when $C = 4$, 0, and -4. What is the same about these three graphs? What is different about these three graphs?

4. Are there any values of x where $f'(x)$ is undefined and $f(x)$ is defined? What happens at these values of x?

CHECKPOINT
SOLUTIONS

1. Expressions (a) and (b) can be evaluated with the Power Rule. For (a), we let $u = 4x^2 + 1$ so that the integral becomes

$$\int u^{10} u' \, dx = \int u^{10} \, du.$$

For (b), we let $u = 4x^2 + 1$ again, and the integral becomes

$$\frac{1}{8} \int u^{10} u' \, dx = \frac{1}{8} \int u^{10} \, du.$$

Expressions (c) and (d) do not fit the format of the Power Rule, because neither integral has an x with the dx, outside the power.

2. $u = 2x^3 + 5$, so $u' = 6x^2$

$$\int (2x^3 + 5)^{-2}(6x^2) \, dx = \int u^{-2} u' \, dx = \int u^{-2} \, du$$
$$= -u^{-1} + C = -(2x^3 + 5)^{-1} + C$$

Thus (c) is the correct choice.

3. True

4. (a) $\int (x^3 + 9)^5 (3x^2) \, dx = \int u^5 u' \, dx = \dfrac{u^6}{6} + C$
$$= \dfrac{(x^3 + 9)^6}{6} + C$$

(b) $\int (x^3 + 9)^{15}(x^2\, dx) = \dfrac{1}{3} \int (x^3 + 9)^{15}(3x^2\, dx)$

$$= \dfrac{1}{3} \cdot \dfrac{(x^3 + 9)^{16}}{16} + C = \dfrac{(x^3 + 9)^{16}}{48} + C$$

(c) The Power Rule does not fit, so we expand the integrand.

$$\int (x^3 + 9)^2(x\, dx) = \int (x^6 + 18x^3 + 81)\, x\, dx$$

$$= \int (x^7 + 18x^4 + 81x)\, dx$$

$$= \dfrac{x^8}{8} + \dfrac{18x^5}{5} + \dfrac{81x^2}{2} + C$$

EXERCISE 5.2

Evaluate the following integrals.

1. $\int (x^2 + 3)^3 2x\, dx$
2. $\int (3x^3 + 1)^4 9x^2\, dx$
3. $\int (15x^2 + 10)^4(30x)\, dx$
4. $\int (8x^4 + 5)^3(32x^3)\, dx$
5. $\int (3x - x^3)^2(3 - 3x^2)\, dx$
6. $\int (4x^2 - 3x)^4(8x - 3)\, dx$
7. $\int (x^2 + 5)^3 x\, dx$
8. $\int (3x^2 - 4)^6 x\, dx$
9. $\int 7\sqrt{x^4 + 6}\, x^3\, dx$
10. $\int 3\sqrt{5 - x^2}\, x\, dx$
11. $\int (3 - x^2)^2\, dx$
12. $\int (x^2 - 5)^2\, dx$
13. $\int (4x - 1)^6\, 7\, dx$
14. $\int (5 - x)^{-3}\, 3\, dx$
15. $\int (x^2 + 1)^{-3}\, x\, dx$
16. $\int (x^2 - 3)^3\, dx$
17. $\int (x^2 - 2x)^4(x - 1)\, dx$
18. $\int \sqrt{x^3 - 3x}(x^2 - 1)\, dx$
19. $\int (x + 1)\sqrt[3]{x^2 + 2x}\, dx$
20. $\int (x^4 - x^2)^6(2x^3 - x)\, dx$

21. $\displaystyle\int \dfrac{x^2}{(x^3 - 1)^2}\, dx$
22. $\displaystyle\int \dfrac{x}{(x^2 - 1)^3}\, dx$
23. $\displaystyle\int \dfrac{x^2}{(x^3 - 5)^4}\, dx$
24. $\displaystyle\int \dfrac{x^3}{\sqrt[3]{x^4 + 5}}\, dx$
25. $\displaystyle\int \dfrac{x^2 - 4x}{\sqrt{x^3 - 6x^2}}\, dx$
26. $\displaystyle\int \dfrac{3x^5 - 2x^3}{(x^6 - x^4)^5}\, dx$
27. $\displaystyle\int \dfrac{8x^2}{(x^3 - 4)^2}\, dx$
28. $\displaystyle\int \dfrac{5x^3}{(x^4 - 8)^3}\, dx$
29. $\displaystyle\int \dfrac{x^3 - 1}{(x^4 - 4x)^3}\, dx$
30. $\displaystyle\int \dfrac{x^2 + 1}{\sqrt{x^3 + 3x}}\, dx$

APPLICATIONS

31. **Physical productivity** The total physical output of a number of machines or workers is called *physical productivity*, and is a function of the number of machines or workers. If $P = f(x)$ is the productivity, dP/dx is the marginal physical productivity. If the marginal physical productivity for bricklayers is $dP/dx = 90(x + 1)^2$, where P is the number of bricks laid per day, find the physical productivity of 4 bricklayers. *Note:* $P = 0$ when $x = 0$.

32. **Revenue** Suppose that the marginal revenue for a product is given by

$$\overline{MR} = \dfrac{-30}{(2x + 1)^2} + 30.$$

Find the total revenue.

33. **Revenue** The marginal revenue for a new calculator is given by

$$\overline{MR} = 60{,}000 - \dfrac{40{,}000}{(10 + x)^2},$$

where x represents hundreds of calculators. Find the total revenue function for these calculators.

34. **Production** The rate of production of a new line of products is given by

$$\dfrac{dx}{dt} = 200\left[1 + \dfrac{400}{(t + 40)^2} \right],$$

where x is the number of items and t is the number of weeks the product has been in production.

(a) Assuming that $x = 0$ when $t = 0$, find the total number of items produced as a function of time t.

(b) How many items were produced in the 5th week?

35. **Typing speed** The rate of change in typing speed of the average student is $ds/dx = 5(x + 1)^{-1/2}$, where x is the number of typing lessons the student has had.

(a) Find the typing speed as a function of the number of lessons if the average student can type 10 words per minute with no lessons ($x = 0$).

(b) How many words per minute can the average student type after 24 lessons?

36. **Productivity** Because a new employee must learn an assigned task, production will increase with time. Suppose that for the average new employee, the rate of performance is given by

$$\frac{dN}{dt} = \frac{1}{2\sqrt{t + 1}}$$

where N is the number of units completed t hours after beginning a new task. If 2 units are completed after 3 hours, how many units are completed after 8 hours?

37. **Film attendance** An excellent film with a very small advertising budget must depend largely on word-of-mouth advertising. In this case, the rate at which weekly attendance might grow can be given by

$$\frac{dA}{dt} = \frac{-100}{(t + 10)^2} + \frac{2000}{(t + 10)^3},$$

where t is the time in weeks since release and A is attendance in millions.

(a) Find the function that describes weekly attendance at this film.

(b) Find the attendance at this film in the 10th week.

38. **Product quality and advertising** An inferior product with a large advertising budget does well when it is introduced, but sales decline as people discontinue use of the product. Suppose that the rate of weekly sales is given by

$$S'(t) = \frac{400}{(t + 1)^3} - \frac{200}{(t + 1)^2},$$

where S is sales in millions and t is time in weeks.

(a) Find the function that describes the weekly sales.

(b) Find the sales for the first week and for the 9th week.

39. **Demographics** Because of the decline of the steel industry, a western Pennsylvania town predicts that its public school population will decrease at the rate

$$\frac{dN}{dx} = \frac{-300}{\sqrt{x + 9}},$$

where x is the number of years and N is the total school population. If the present population ($x = 0$) is 8000, what population size is planned for in 7 years?

40. **Franchise growth** A new fast-food firm predicts that the number of franchises for its products will grow at the rate

$$\frac{dn}{dt} = 9\sqrt{t + 1},$$

where t is the number of years, $0 \le t \le 10$. If there is one franchise ($n = 1$) at present ($t = 0$), how many franchises are predicted for 8 years from now?

5.3 | INTEGRALS INVOLVING LOGARITHMIC AND EXPONENTIAL FUNCTIONS

OBJECTIVES

- To evaluate integrals of the form $\int \dfrac{u'}{u}\, dx$
- To evaluate integrals of the form $\int e^u\, u'\, dx$

Recall that the Power Rule for integrals applies only if $n \neq -1$. That is,

$$\int u^n\, u'\, dx = \frac{u^{n+1}}{n+1} + C \qquad \text{if } n \neq -1.$$

The following formula applies when $n = -1$.

Logarithmic Formula If u is a function of x,

$$\int u^{-1}\, u'\, dx = \int \frac{u'}{u}\, dx = \int \frac{du}{u} = \ln |u| + C$$

This formula is a direct result of the fact that

$$\frac{d}{dx}(\ln u) = \frac{1}{u} \cdot u'.$$

The absolute value is used with the natural logarithm because u may be positive or negative, but the logarithm is defined only when the quantity is positive.

EXAMPLE 1   Evaluate $\displaystyle\int \frac{4}{4x+1}\, dx.$

Solution This integral is of the form

$$\int \frac{u'}{u}\, dx, = \ln |u| + C$$

with $u = 4x + 1$ and $u' = 4$. Thus

$$\int \frac{4}{4x+1}\, dx = \ln |4x + 1| + C.$$

EXAMPLE 2

Evaluate $\int \dfrac{x-3}{x^2 - 6x + 1}\, dx$.

Solution This integral is of the form $\int (u'/u)\, dx$, *almost*. If we let $u = x^2 - 6x + 1$, then $u' = 2x - 6$. If we multiply (and divide) the numerator by 2, we get

$$
\begin{aligned}
\int \frac{x-3}{x^2 - 6x + 1}\, dx &= \frac{1}{2}\int \frac{2(x-3)}{x^2 - 6x + 1}\, dx \\
&= \frac{1}{2}\int \frac{2x - 6}{x^2 - 6x + 1}\, dx \\
&= \frac{1}{2}\int \frac{u'}{u}\, dx = \frac{1}{2}\ln |u| + C \\
&= \frac{1}{2}\ln |x^2 - 6x + 1| + C.
\end{aligned}
$$

If an integral contains a fraction in which the degree of the numerator is equal to or greater than that of the denominator, we should divide the denominator into the numerator as a first step.

EXAMPLE 3

Evaluate $\int \dfrac{x^4 - 2x^3 + 4x^2 - 7x - 1}{x^2 - 2x}\, dx$.

Solution Since the numerator is of higher degree than the denominator, we begin by dividing $x^2 - 2x$ into the numerator.

$$
\begin{array}{r}
x^2 + 4 \\
x^2 - 2x \overline{)\, x^4 - 2x^3 + 4x^2 - 7x - 1\,} \\
\underline{x^4 - 2x^3 } \\
4x^2 - 7x - 1 \\
\underline{4x^2 - 8x } \\
x - 1
\end{array}
$$

Thus

$$
\begin{aligned}
\int \frac{x^4 - 2x^3 + 4x^2 - 7x - 1}{x^2 - 2x}\, dx &= \int \left(x^2 + 4 + \frac{x-1}{x^2 - 2x} \right) dx \\
&= \int (x^2 + 4)\, dx + \frac{1}{2}\int \frac{2(x-1)\, dx}{x^2 - 2x} \\
&= \frac{x^3}{3} + 4x + \frac{1}{2}\ln |x^2 - 2x| + C.
\end{aligned}
$$

CHECKPOINT

1. True or false:

(a) $\displaystyle\int \frac{3x^2\, dx}{x^3 + 4} = \ln |x^3 + 4| + C$

(b) $\displaystyle\int \frac{2x\,dx}{\sqrt{x^2+1}} = \ln|\sqrt{x^2+1}| + C$ (c) $\displaystyle\int \frac{2}{x}\,dx = 2\ln|x| + C$

(d) $\displaystyle\int \frac{x}{x+1}\,dx = x\int \frac{1}{x+1}\,dx = x\ln|x+1| + C$

(e) To evaluate $\displaystyle\int \frac{4x}{4x+1}\,dx$, our first step is to divide $4x+1$ into $4x$.

2. (a) Divide $4x+1$ into $4x$.

 (b) Evaluate $\displaystyle\int \frac{4x}{4x+1}\,dx$.

We know that

$$\frac{d}{dx}(e^u) = e^u \cdot u'.$$

The corresponding integral is given by the following.

Exponential Formula   If u is a function of x,

$$\int e^u \cdot u'\,dx = \int e^u\,du = e^u + C.$$

EXAMPLE 4   Evaluate $\int 5e^x\,dx$.

Solution $\int 5e^x\,dx = 5\int e^x\,dx = 5e^x + C$

EXAMPLE 5   Evaluate $\int 2xe^{x^2}\,dx$.

Solution   Letting $u = x^2$ implies that $u' = 2x$, and the integral is of the form $\int e^u \cdot u'\,dx$. Thus

$$\int 2xe^{x^2}\,dx = \int e^{x^2}(2x)\,dx$$

$$= \int e^u \cdot u'\,dx = e^u + C$$

$$= e^{x^2} + C.$$

EXAMPLE 6   Evaluate $\displaystyle\int \frac{x^2\,dx}{e^{x^3}}$.

Solution   In order to use $\int e^u \cdot u'\,dx$, we write the exponential in the numerator. Thus

$$\int \frac{x^2\,dx}{e^{x^3}} = \int e^{-x^3}(x^2\,dx).$$

This is *almost* of the form $\int e^u \cdot u'\, dx$. Letting $u = -x^3$ gives $u' = -3x^2$. Thus

$$\int e^{-x^3}(x^2\, dx) = -\frac{1}{3}\int e^{-x^3}(-3x^2\, dx) = -\frac{1}{3}\,e^{-x^3} + C = \frac{-1}{3e^{x^3}} + C.$$

CHECKPOINT

3. True or false:

(a) $\int e^{x^2}(2x\, dx) = e^{x^2} \cdot x^2 + C$

(b) $\int e^{-3x}\, dx = -\frac{1}{3}e^{-3x} + C$

(c) $\int \dfrac{dx}{e^{3x}} = \dfrac{1}{3}\left(\dfrac{1}{e^{3x}}\right) + C$

(d) $\int e^{3x+1}(3\, dx) = \dfrac{e^{3x+2}}{3x+2} + C$

TECHNOLOGY CORNER

1. (a) Graph $f'(x) = -xe^{-x^2}$ and $f(x) = \int(-xe^{-x^2})\, dx$, with $C = 0$.

   (b) Determine the intervals where $f'(x) > 0$ and see that they correspond to where $f(x)$ is increasing.

   (c) From the graph of $f'(x)$, determine where $f(x)$ has critical values.

   (d) Do the inflection points of $f(x)$ correspond to relative extremes of $f'(x)$?

2. We have seen that if $f'(x) = 1/x$, then $f(x) = \ln|x| + C$. To see why we need the absolute value, consider the following.

   (a) We know that differentiability implies continuity, so that wherever $f'(x)$ is defined, $f(x)$ must be continuous. Graph $f(x) = \ln x$ and observe all values where it is continuous.

   (b) Now graph $f(x) = \ln|x|$ and observe all values of x where it is continuous.

   (c) Graph $f'(x) = \dfrac{1}{x}$ and determine whether $f(x) = \ln x$ or $f(x) = \ln|x|$ is continuous where $f'(x)$ exists.

CHECKPOINT
SOLUTIONS

1. (a) True

(b) False: $\int \dfrac{2x\,dx}{\sqrt{x^2+1}} = \int (x^2+1)^{-1/2}(2x\,dx)$

$$= \dfrac{(x^2+1)^{1/2}}{1/2} + C = 2\,(x^2+1)^{1/2} + C$$

(c) True

(d) False. We cannot factor the variable x outside the integral sign.

(e) True

2. (a) $4x + 1\,)\,\overline{\begin{array}{l}1 \\ 4x\end{array}}$
$$\underline{4x+1} \\ -1$$

so $\dfrac{4x}{4x+1} = 1 - \dfrac{1}{4x+1}$.

(b) $\int \dfrac{4x\,dx}{4x+1} = \int\left(1 - \dfrac{1}{4x+1}\right)dx = x - \dfrac{1}{4}\ln|4x+1| + C$

3. (a) False. The correct solution is $e^{x^2} + C$ (see Example 5).

(b) True

(c) False; $\int \dfrac{dx}{e^{3x}} = \int e^{-3x}\,dx = -\dfrac{1}{3}e^{-3x} + C = \dfrac{-1}{3e^{3x}} + C$

(d) False; $\int e^{3x+1}\,(3\,dx) = e^{3x+1} + C$

EXERCISE 5.3

Evaluate the following integrals.

1. $\displaystyle\int \dfrac{3x^2}{x^3+4}\,dx$

2. $\displaystyle\int \dfrac{8x^7}{x^8-1}\,dx$

3. $\displaystyle\int \dfrac{3x^2-2}{x^3-2x}\,dx$

4. $\displaystyle\int \dfrac{4x^3+2x}{x^4+x^2}\,dx$

5. $\displaystyle\int \dfrac{x^3}{x^4+1}\,dx$

6. $\displaystyle\int \dfrac{x^2}{x^3-9}\,dx$

7. $\displaystyle\int \dfrac{4x}{x^2-4}\,dx$

8. $\displaystyle\int \dfrac{5x^2}{x^3-1}\,dx$

9. $\displaystyle\int \dfrac{dz}{4z+1}$

10. $\displaystyle\int \dfrac{y}{y^2+1}\,dy$

11. $\displaystyle\int \dfrac{z^2+1}{z^3+3z}\,dz$

12. $\displaystyle\int \dfrac{x+2}{x^2+4x}\,dx$

13. $\displaystyle\int \dfrac{x^3-x^2+1}{x-1}\,dx$

14. $\displaystyle\int \dfrac{2x^3+x^2+2x+3}{2x+1}\,dx$

15. $\displaystyle\int \dfrac{x^2+x+3}{x^2+3}\,dx$

16. $\displaystyle\int \dfrac{x^4-2x^2+x}{x^2-2}\,dx$

17. $\displaystyle\int 3e^{3x}\,dx$

18. $\displaystyle\int 4e^{4x}\,dx$

19. $\displaystyle\int e^{-x}\,dx$

20. $\displaystyle\int e^{2x}\,dx$

21. $\displaystyle\int x^3 e^{3x^4}\,dx$

22. $\displaystyle\int xe^{2x^2}\,dx$

23. $\displaystyle\int \dfrac{3}{e^{2x}}\,dx$

24. $\displaystyle\int \dfrac{4}{e^{1-2x}}\,dx$

25. $\displaystyle\int \dfrac{x^5}{e^{2-3x^6}}\,dx$

26. $\displaystyle\int \dfrac{x^3}{e^{4x^4}}\,dx$

27. $\int \left(e^{4x} - \dfrac{3}{e^{x/2}} \right) dx$

28. $\int \left(xe^{3x^2} - \dfrac{5}{e^{x/3}} \right) dx$

APPLICATIONS

29. **Revenue** Suppose that the marginal revenue from the sale of a product is $\overline{MR} = R'(x) = 6e^{0.01x}$. What is the revenue on the sale of 100 units of the product?

30. **Concentration of a drug** Suppose that the rate at which the concentration of a drug in the blood changes with respect to time t is given by

$$C'(t) = \dfrac{c}{b - a} (be^{-bt} - ae^{-at}), \qquad t \geq 0,$$

where a, b, and c are constants depending on the drug administered, with $b > a$. Assuming that $C(t) = 0$ when $t = 0$, find the formula for the concentration of the drug in the blood at any time t.

31. **Radioactive decay** The rate of disintegration of a radioactive substance can be described by

$$\dfrac{dn}{dt} = n_0(-K)e^{-Kt},$$

where n_0 is the number of radioactive atoms present when time t is 0, and K is a positive constant that depends on the substance involved. Using the fact that the constant of integration is 0, integrate dn/dt to find the number of atoms n that are still radioactive after time t.

32. **World population** Since the world contains only about 10 billion acres of arable land, world population is limited. Suppose that the world population is limited to 40 billion people and that the rate of population growth is proportional to how close the world is to this upper limit. Then the rate of growth would be $dP/dt = K(40 - P)$, where K is a positive con-

stant. This means that

$$t = \dfrac{1}{K} \int \dfrac{1}{40 - P} \, dP.$$

(a) Evaluate this integral to find an expression relating P and t.
(b) Use the properties relating logarithms and exponential functions to write P as a function of t.

33. **Memorization** The rate of vocabulary memorization of the average student in a foreign language is given by

$$\dfrac{dv}{dt} = \dfrac{40}{t + 1},$$

where t is the number of continuous hours of study, $0 < t \leq 4$. How many words would the average student memorize in 3 hours?

34. **Population growth** The rate of growth of world population can be modeled by

$$\dfrac{dn}{dt} = N_0(1 + r)^t \ln (1 + r), \qquad r < 1,$$

where t is the time in years from the present and N_0 and r are constants. What function describes world population if the present population is N_0? Use the formula $\int (a^u \ln a) u' \, dx = a^u + C$.

35. **Compound interest** If $\$P$ are invested for n years at 10%, compounded continuously, the rate at which the compound amount is growing is

$$\dfrac{dS}{dn} = 0.1Pe^{0.1n}.$$

(a) What function describes the compound amount at the end of n years?
(b) In how many years will the compound amount double?

36. **Temperature changes** When an object is moved from one environment to another, its temperature T changes at a rate given by

$$\dfrac{dT}{dt} = kCe^{kt},$$

where t is the time in the new environment (in hours), C is the temperature difference (old–new) between the two environments, and k is a constant. If the temperature of the body (and the old environment) is 70°F, and $C = -10°F$, what function describes the temperature T of the object t hours after it is moved?

37. **Blood pressure in the aorta** The rate at which blood pressure decreases in the aorta of a normal adult after a heartbeat is

$$\frac{dp}{dt} = -46.645e^{-0.491t},$$

where t is time in seconds.
  (a) What function describes the blood pressure in the aorta if $p = 95$ when $t = 0$?

(b) What is the blood pressure 0.1 second after a heartbeat?

38. **Sales and advertising** A store finds that its sales decline after the end of an advertising campaign, with its daily sales for the period declining at the rate $S'(t) = -147.78e^{-0.2t}$, $0 \le t \le 100$, where t is the number of days since the end of the campaign. Suppose that $S = 7389$ when $t = 0$.
  (a) Find the function that describes the number of daily sales t days after the end of the campaign.
  (b) Find the total number of sales 10 days after the end of the advertising campaign.

5.4 APPLICATIONS OF THE INDEFINITE INTEGRAL IN BUSINESS AND ECONOMICS

OBJECTIVES

- To use integration to find total cost functions from information involving marginal cost
- To optimize profit, given information regarding marginal cost and marginal revenue
- To use integration to find national consumption functions from information about marginal propensity to consume and marginal propensity to save

We turn our attention to applications involving cost, profit, and consumption. A thorough understanding of these concepts is imperative for success in any study of economics and business.

TOTAL COST AND PROFIT

We can use integration to derive total cost and profit functions from the marginal cost and marginal revenue functions. One of the reasons for the marginal approach in economics is that firms can observe marginal changes in real life. If they know the marginal cost and the total cost when a given quantity is sold, they can develop their total cost function.

We know that the marginal cost for a commodity is $\overline{MC} = C'(x)$, where $C(x)$ is the total cost function. Thus if we have the marginal cost function, we can integrate to find the total cost. That is, $C(x) = \int \overline{MC}\, dx$.

If, for example, the marginal cost is $\overline{MC} = 4x + 3$, the total cost is given by

$$C(x) = \int \overline{MC}\, dx$$
$$= \int (4x + 3)\, dx$$
$$= 2x^2 + 3x + K,$$

where K represents the constant of integration. Now, we know that the total revenue is 0 if no items are produced, but the total cost may not be 0 if nothing is produced. The fixed costs accrue whether goods are produced or not. Thus the value for the constant of integration depends on the fixed costs FC of production.

Thus we cannot determine the total cost function from the marginal cost unless additional information is available to help us determine the fixed costs.

EXAMPLE 1

If the marginal cost function for a month for a certain product is $\overline{MC} = 3x + 50$, and if the fixed costs related to the product amount to $100 per month, find the total cost function for the month.

Solution The total cost function is

$$C(x) = \int (3x + 50)\, dx$$
$$= \frac{3x^2}{2} + 50x + K.$$

But the constant of integration K is found by using the fact that $C(0) = FC = 100$. Thus

$$3(0)^2 + 50(0) + K = 100, \qquad \text{so } K = 100.$$

Thus the total cost for the month is given by

$$C(x) = \frac{3x^2}{2} + 50x + 100.$$

EXAMPLE 2

If the monthly records show that the rate of change of the cost (that is, the marginal cost) for a product is $\overline{MC} = 10x + 40$, and that the total cost of producing 100 items in the month is $60,000, what would be the total cost of producing 400 items per month?

Solution We can integrate the marginal cost to find the total cost function.

$$C(x) = \int \overline{MC}\, dx = \int (10x + 40)\, dx$$
$$= 5x^2 + 40x + K$$

We can find K by using the fact that the cost for 100 items is \$60,000.

$$C(100) = 60{,}000 = 5(100)^2 + 40(100) + K,$$

so

$$K = 6000$$

Thus the total cost function is $C(x) = 5x^2 + 40x + 6000$, and the cost of producing 400 items is

$$C(400) = 800{,}000 + 16{,}000 + 6000$$
$$= 822{,}000 \quad \text{(dollars)}.$$

It can be shown that the profit is usually maximized when $\overline{MR} = \overline{MC}$. To see that this does not always give us a maximum *positive* profit, consider the following facts concerning the manufacture of widgets over the period of a month:

(a) The marginal revenue is $\overline{MR} = 400 - 30x$.

(b) The marginal cost is $\overline{MC} = 20x + 50$.

(c) When 5 widgets are produced and sold, the total cost is \$1750. The profit *should* be maximized when $\overline{MR} = \overline{MC}$, or when $400 - 30x = 20x + 50$. Solving for x gives $x = 7$. To see if our profit is maximized when 7 units are produced and sold, let us examine the profit function.

The profit function is given by $P(x) = R(x) - C(x)$, where

$$R(x) = \int \overline{MR}\, dx \quad \text{and} \quad C(x) = \int \overline{MC}\, dx.$$

Integrating, we get

$$R(x) = \int (400 - 30x)\, dx = 400x - 15x^2 + K,$$

but $K = 0$ for this total revenue function, so

$$R(x) = 400x - 15x^2.$$

The total cost function is

$$C(x) = \int (20x + 50)\, dx = 10x^2 + 50x + K.$$

The value of fixed cost can be determined by using the fact that 5 widgets cost \$1750. This tells us $C(5) = 1750 = 250 + 250 + K$, so $K = 1250$.

Thus the total cost is $C(x) = 10x^2 + 50x + 1250$. Now, the profit is

$$P(x) = R(x) - C(x),$$

or

$$P(x) = (400x - 15x^2) - (10x^2 + 50x + 1250).$$

Simplifying gives

$$P(x) = 350x - 25x^2 - 1250.$$

We have found that $\overline{MR} = \overline{MC}$ if $x = 7$, and the graph of $P(x)$ is a parabola that opens downward, so profit is maximized at $x = 7$. But if $x = 7$, profit is

$$P(7) = 2450 - 1225 - 1250 = -25.$$

That is, the production and sale of 7 items result in a loss of $25.

The preceding discussion indicates that, although setting $\overline{MR} = \overline{MC}$ may optimize profit, it does not indicate the level of profit or loss, as forming the profit function does.

If the widget firm is in a competitive market, and its optimal level of production results in a loss, it has two options. It can continue to produce at the optimal level in the short run until it can lower or eliminate its fixed costs, even though it is losing money; or it can take a larger loss (its fixed cost) by stopping production. Producing 7 units causes a loss of $25 per month, and ceasing production results in a loss of $1250 (the fixed cost) per month. If this firm and many others like it cease production, the supply will be reduced, causing an eventual increase in price. The firm can resume production when the price increase indicates that it can make a profit.

EXAMPLE 3

Given that $\overline{MR} = 200 - 4x$, $\overline{MC} = 50 + 2x$, and the total cost of producing 10 Wagbats is $700, at what level should the Wagbat firm hold production in order to maximize the profits?

Solution Setting $\overline{MR} = \overline{MC}$, we can solve for the production level that maximizes profit.

$$200 - 4x = 50 + 2x$$
$$150 = 6x$$
$$25 = x$$

The level of production that should optimize profit is 25 units. To see whether 25 units maximizes profits or minimizes the losses (in the short run), we must find the total revenue and total cost functions.

$$R(x) = \int (200 - 4x)\, dx = 200x - 2x^2 + K$$
$$= 200x - 2x^2, \quad \text{since } K = 0$$

$$C(x) = \int (50 + 2x)\, dx = 50x + x^2 + K$$

We find K by noting $C(x) = 700$ when $x = 10$.

$$700 = 50(10) + (10)^2 + K,$$

so $K = 100$.

Thus the cost is given by $C = C(x) = 50x + x^2 + 100$.

At $x = 25$, $R = R(25) = 200(25) - 2(25)^2 = \$3750$
and $C = C(25) = 50(25) + (25)^2 + 100 = \$1975$.

We see that the total revenue is greater than the total cost, so production should be held at 25 units, which results in a maximum profit.

CHECKPOINT

1. True or false:
   (a) If $C(x) = \int \overline{MC}\, dx$, then the constant of integration equals the fixed costs.
   (b) If $R(x) = \int \overline{MR}\, dx$, then the constant of integration equals 0.

2. Find $C(x)$ if $\overline{MC} = \dfrac{100}{\sqrt{x+1}}$ and fixed costs are \$8000.

National Consumption and Savings

The consumption function is one of the basic ingredients in a larger discussion of how an economy can have persistent high unemployment or persistent high inflation. This study is often called **Keynesian analysis,** after its founder John Maynard Keynes.

If C represents national consumption (in billions of dollars), then a **national consumption function** has the form $C = f(y)$, where y is disposable national income (also in billions of dollars). The **marginal propensity to consume** is the derivative of the national consumption function with respect to y, or $dC/dy = f'(y)$. For example, suppose that

$$C = f(y) = 0.8y + 6$$

is a national consumption function; then the marginal propensity to consume is $f'(y) = 0.8$.

If we know the marginal propensity to consume, we can integrate with respect to y to find national consumption:

$$C = \int f'(y)\, dy = f(y) + K.$$

We can find the unique national consumption function if we have additional information to help us determine the value of K, the constant of integration.

EXAMPLE 4

If consumption is \$6 billion when disposable income is 0, and if the marginal propensity to consume is $dC/dy = 0.3 + 0.4/\sqrt{y}$ (in billions of dollars), then find the national consumption function.

Solution If

$$\frac{dC}{dy} = 0.3 + \frac{0.4}{\sqrt{y}},$$

then

$$C = \int \left(0.3 + \frac{0.4}{\sqrt{y}} \right) dy = 0.3y + 0.8y^{1/2} + K.$$

Now, if $C = 6$ when $y = 0$, then $6 = 0.3(0) + 0.8\sqrt{0} + K$. Thus the constant of integration is $K = 6$, and the consumption function is

$$C = 0.3y + 0.8\sqrt{y} + 6 \qquad \text{(billions of dollars)}.$$

If S represents national savings, we can assume that the disposable national income is given by $y = C + S$, or $S = y - C$. Then the **marginal propensity to save** is $dS/dy = 1 - dC/dy$.

EXAMPLE 5

If the consumption is \$9 billion when income is 0, and if the marginal propensity to save is 0.25, find the consumption function.

Solution If $dS/dy = 0.25$, then $0.25 = 1 - dC/dy$, or $dC/dy = 0.75$. Thus

$$C = \int 0.75 \, dy = 0.75y + K.$$

If $C = 9$ when $y = 0$, then $9 = 0.75(0) + K$, or $K = 9$. Then the consumption function is $C = 0.75y + 9$ (billions of dollars).

CHECKPOINT

3. If the marginal propensity to save is

$$\frac{dS}{dy} = 0.7 - \frac{0.4}{\sqrt{y}},$$

find the marginal propensity to consume.

4. Find the national consumption function if the marginal propensity to consume is

$$\frac{dC}{dy} = \frac{1}{\sqrt{y + 4}} + 0.2$$

and national consumption is \$6.8 billion when disposable income is 0.

TECHNOLOGY CORNER

Suppose that $\overline{MC} = 1.01(x + 190)^{0.01}$ and $\overline{MR} = (1/\sqrt{2x + 1}) + 2$, where x is the number of thousands of units and both revenue and cost are in thousands of dollars. Suppose further that fixed costs are \$200,236 and that production is limited to at most 180 thousand units.

1. Determine $C(x)$ and $R(x)$ and graph them to determine whether a profit can be made.

2. If cost-cutting measures result in fixed costs being reduced by \$100 (thousand), graph $R(x)$ and the new $C(x)$ to determine whether a profit can be made.

3. Estimate the break-even point for the functions described in problem 2.

4. For $R(x)$ and $C(x)$ described in problem 2, graph $P(x)$ and estimate the level of production that yields maximum profit. Determine the maximum profit.

CHECKPOINT
SOLUTIONS

1. (a) False. $C(0)$ equals the fixed costs. It may or may not be the constant of integration. [In Self-Check problem 2, $C(0) = 8000$, but $K = 7800$.]

   (b) False. We use $R(0) = 0$ to determine the constant of integration, but it may be nonzero. See Example 8 in Section 5.2.

2. $C(x) = 100 \int (x + 1)^{-1/2} \, dx = 100 \left[\dfrac{(x + 1)^{1/2}}{1/2} \right] + K$

   $C(x) = 200\sqrt{x + 1} + K$
   When $x = 0$, $C(x) = 8000$.
   So

   $8000 = 200\sqrt{1} + K$
   $7800 = K$
   $C(x) = 200\sqrt{x + 1} + 7800.$

3. $\dfrac{dC}{dy} = 1 - \dfrac{dS}{dy} = 1 - \left(0.7 - \dfrac{0.4}{\sqrt{y}} \right) = 0.3 + \dfrac{0.4}{\sqrt{y}}$

4. $C(y) = \int \left(\dfrac{1}{\sqrt{y+4}} + 0.2 \right) dy$

$\qquad = \int [(y+4)^{-1/2} + 0.2]\, dy$

$\qquad = \dfrac{(y+4)^{1/2}}{1/2} + 0.2y + K$

$C(y) = 2\sqrt{y+4} + 0.2y + K$

Using $C(0) = 6.8$ gives $6.8 = 2\sqrt{4} + 0 + K$, or $K = 2.8$.

Thus $C(y) = 2\sqrt{y+4} + 0.2y + 2.8$. ∎

EXERCISE 5.4

TOTAL COST AND PROFIT

1. If the monthly marginal cost for a product is $\overline{MC} = 2x + 100$, with fixed costs amounting to $200, find the total cost function for the month.

2. If the monthly marginal cost for a product is $\overline{MC} = x + 30$, and the related fixed costs are $50, find the total cost function for the month.

3. If the marginal cost for a product is $\overline{MC} = 4x + 2$, and the production of 10 units results in a total cost of $300, find the total cost function.

4. If the marginal cost for a product is $\overline{MC} = 3x + 50$, and the total cost of producing 20 units is $2000, what will be the total cost function?

5. If the marginal cost for a product is $\overline{MC} = 4x + 40$, and the total cost of producing 25 units is $3000, what will be the cost of producing 30 units?

6. If the marginal cost for producing a product is $\overline{MC} = 5x + 10$, with a fixed cost of $800, what will be the cost of producing 20 units?

7. A firm knows that its marginal cost for a product is $\overline{MC} = 3x + 20$, that its marginal revenue is $\overline{MR} = 44 - 5x$, and that the cost of production and sale of 80 units is $11,400.

Given this information, find the
(a) optimal level of production.
(b) profit function.
(c) profit or loss at the optimal level.

8. A certain firm's marginal cost for a product is $\overline{MC} = 6x + 60$, its marginal revenue is $\overline{MR} = 180 - 2x$, and its total cost of production of 10 items is $1000. Given this information,
(a) find the optimal level of production.
(b) find the profit function.
(c) find the profit or loss at the optimal level of production.
(d) should production be continued for the short run?
(e) should production be continued for the long run?

9. Suppose that the marginal revenue for a product is $\overline{MR} = 900$ and the marginal cost is $\overline{MC} = 30\sqrt{x+4}$, with a fixed cost of $1000.
(a) Find the profit or loss from the production and sale of 5 units.
(b) How many units will result in a maximum profit?

10. Suppose that the marginal cost for a product is $\overline{MC} = 60\sqrt{x+1}$ and its fixed cost is $340.00. If the marginal revenue for it is $\overline{MR} = 80x$, find the profit or loss from production and

sale of:
(a) 3 units.
(b) 8 units.

11. If the average cost of a product changes at the rate

$$\overline{C}'(x) = -6x^{-2} + 1/6,$$

and if the average cost of 10 units is $20.00, find the
(a) average cost function.
(b) average cost of 20 units.

12. If the average cost of a product changes at the rate

$$\overline{C}'(x) = \frac{-10}{x^2} + \frac{1}{10},$$

and if the average cost of 10 units is $20.00, find the
(a) average cost function.
(b) average cost of 20 units.

NATIONAL CONSUMPTION AND SAVINGS

13. If consumption is $5 billion when disposable income is 0, and if the marginal propensity to consume is

$$\frac{dC}{dy} = 0.4 + \frac{0.3}{\sqrt{y}} \qquad \text{(in billions of dollars)},$$

find the national consumption function.

14. If consumption is $7 billion when disposable income is 0, and if the marginal propensity to consume is 0.80, find the national consumption function (in billions of dollars).

15. If consumption is $8 billion when income is 0, and if the marginal propensity to consume is

$$\frac{dC}{dy} = 0.3 + \frac{0.2}{\sqrt{y}} \qquad \text{(in billions of dollars)},$$

find the national consumption function.

16. If national consumption is $9 billion when income is 0, and if the marginal propensity to consume is 0.30, what is consumption when disposable income is $20 billion?

17. If consumption is $6 billion when disposable income is 0, and if the marginal propensity to consume is

$$\frac{dC}{dy} = \frac{1}{\sqrt{y + 1}} + 0.4 \qquad \text{(in billions of dollars)},$$

find the national consumption function.

18. If consumption is $5.8 billion when disposable income is 0, and if the marginal propensity to consume is

$$\frac{dC}{dy} = \frac{1}{\sqrt{2y + 9}} + 0.8 \qquad \text{(in billions of dollars)},$$

find the national consumption function.

19. Suppose that the marginal propensity to consume is

$$\frac{dC}{dy} = 0.7 - e^{-2y} \qquad \text{(in billions of dollars)},$$

and that consumption is $5.65 billion when disposable income is 0. Find the national consumption function.

20. Suppose that the marginal propensity to consume is

$$\frac{dC}{dy} = 0.04 + \frac{\ln{(y + 1)}}{y + 1} \qquad \text{(in billions of dollars)},$$

and that consumption is $6.04 billion when disposable income is 0. Find the national consumption function.

21. Suppose that the marginal propensity to save is

$$\frac{dS}{dy} = 0.15 \qquad \text{(in billions of dollars)}$$

and that consumption is $5.15 billion when disposable income is 0. Find the national consumption function.

22. Suppose that the marginal propensity to save is

$$\frac{dS}{dy} = 0.22 \qquad \text{(in billions of dollars)}$$

and that consumption is $8.6 billion when disposable income is 0. Find the national consumption function.

23. Suppose that the marginal propensity to save is

$$\frac{dS}{dy} = 0.2 - \frac{1}{\sqrt{3y + 7}} \qquad \text{(in billions of dollars)}$$

and that consumption is $6 billion when disposable income is 0. Find the national consumption function.

24. If consumption is $3 billion when disposable income is 0, and if the marginal propensity to save is

$$\frac{dS}{dy} = 0.2 + e^{-1.5y} \qquad \text{(in billions of dollars)},$$

find the national consumption function.

KEY TERMS
& FORMULAS

SECTION	KEY TERM	FORMULA
5.1	Antiderivative of $f'(x)$	$f(x) + C$
	Integral	$\int f(x)\,dx$
	Powers of x Formula	$\int x^n\,dx = \dfrac{x^{n+1}}{n+1} + C \quad (n \neq -1)$
	Integration Formulas	$\int dx = x + C$
		$\int c\,u(x)\,dx = c\int u(x)\,dx; \ \ c = \text{a constant}$
		$\int [u(x) \pm v(x)]dx = \int u(x)\,dx \pm \int v(x)dx$
5.2	Power Rule	$\int [u(x)]^n u'(x)dx = \dfrac{[u(x)]^{n+1}}{n+1} + C \quad (n \neq -1)$
5.3	Logarithmic Formula	$\int \dfrac{u'}{u}\,dx = \int \dfrac{du}{u} = \ln|u| + C$
	Exponential Formula	$\int e^u u'\,dx = \int e^u\,du = e^u + C$
5.4	Total cost	$C(x) = \int \overline{MC}\,dx$
	Total revenue	$R(x) = \int \overline{MR}\,dx$
	Profit	$P(x) = R(x) - C(x)$
	Marginal propensity to consume	$\dfrac{dC}{dy}$
	Marginal propensity to save	$\dfrac{dS}{dy} = 1 - \dfrac{dC}{dy}$
	National consumption	$C(y) = \int \left(\dfrac{dC}{dy}\right)dy$

5.1–5.3 Evaluate the following integrals.

1. $\int x^6 \, dx$

2. $\int x^{1/2} \, dx$

3. $\int (x^3 - 3x^2 + 4x + 5) \, dx$

4. $\int (x^2 - 1)^2 \, dx$

5. $\int (x^2 - 1)^2 x \, dx$

6. $\int (x^3 - 3x^2)(x^2 - 2x) \, dx$

7. $\int (x^3 + 4)^2 x \, dx$

8. $\int (x^3 + 4)^6 x^2 \, dx$

9. $\int \frac{x^2}{x^3 + 1} \, dx$

10. $\int \frac{x^2}{(x^3 + 1)^2} \, dx$

11. $\int \frac{x^2 \, dx}{\sqrt[3]{x^3 - 4}}$

12. $\int \frac{x^2 \, dx}{x^3 - 4}$

13. $\int \frac{x^3 + 1}{x^2} \, dx$

14. $\int \frac{x^3 - 3x + 1}{x - 1} \, dx$

15. $\int y^2 e^{y^3} \, dy$

16. $\int (x - 1)^2 \, dx$

17. $\int \frac{3x^2}{2x^3 - 7} \, dx$

18. $\int \frac{5 \, dx}{e^{4x}}$

19. $\int (x^3 - e^{3x}) \, dx$

20. $\int x e^{1 + x^2} \, dx$

21. $\int \frac{6x^2}{(x^3 + 1)^2} \, dx$

22. $\int \frac{7x^3}{\sqrt{1 - x^4}} \, dx$

23. $\int \left(\frac{e^{2x}}{2} + \frac{2}{e^{2x}} \right) dx$

24. $\int \left(x - \frac{1}{(x + 1)^2} \right) dx$

25. (a) $\int (x^2 - 1)^4 x \, dx$ (b) $\int (x^2 - 1)^{10} x \, dx$ (c) $\int (x^2 - 1)^7 3x \, dx$ (d) $\int (x^2 - 1)^{-2/3} x \, dx$

26. (a) $\int \frac{2x \, dx}{x^2 - 1}$ (b) $\int \frac{2x \, dx}{(x^2 - 1)^2}$ (c) $\int \frac{3x \, dx}{\sqrt{x^2 - 1}}$ (d) $\int \frac{3x \, dx}{x^2 - 1}$

APPLICATIONS

5.1

27. **Revenue** If the marginal revenue for a month for a product is $\overline{MR} = 6x - 12$, find the total revenue from the sale of 4 units of the product.

28. **Productivity** Suppose that the rate of change of production of the average worker at a factory is given by

$$\frac{dp}{dt} = 27 + 24t - 3t^2, \qquad 0 \le t \le 8,$$

where p is the number of units produced by the worker in t hours. How many units will the average worker produce in an 8-hour shift? (Assume that $p = 0$ when $t = 0$.)

5.2

29. **Oxygen levels in water** The rate of change of the oxygen level in a body of water after an oil spill is given by

$$P'(t) = 400 \left[\frac{5}{(t + 5)^2} - \frac{50}{(t + 5)^3} \right],$$

where t is the number of months since the spill. What function gives the oxygen level P at any time t if $P = 400$ when $t = 0$?

30. **Bacterial growth** A population of bacteria grows at the rate

$$r = \frac{100{,}000}{(t + 100)^2},$$

where t is time. If the population is 1000 when $t = 1$, write the equation that gives the size of the population at any time t.

31. **Market share** The rate of change of the market share (as a percentage) a firm expects for a new product is

$$\frac{dy}{dt} = 2.4e^{-0.4t},$$

where t is the number of months after the product is introduced.
(a) Write the equation that gives the expected market share y at any time t. (Note that $y = 0$ when $t = 0$.)
(b) What market share does the firm expect after one year?

32. **Revenue** If the marginal revenue for a product is $\overline{MR} = \dfrac{800}{x + 1}$, find the total revenue function.

33. **Cost** If the marginal cost for a product is $\overline{MC} = 6x + 4$ and the cost of producing 100 items is $31,400,
(a) find the fixed costs.
(b) find the total cost function.

34. **Profit** Suppose that a product has a daily marginal revenue $\overline{MR} = 46$ and a daily marginal cost $\overline{MC} = 30 + \frac{1}{5}x$. If the daily fixed cost is $200.00, how many units will give maximum profit and what is the maximum profit?

35. **National consumption** If consumption is $8.5 billion when disposable income is 0, and if the marginal propensity to consume is

$$\frac{dC}{dy} = \frac{1}{\sqrt{2y + 16}} + 0.6 \qquad \text{(in billions of dollars)},$$

find the national consumption function.

36. **National consumption** Suppose that the marginal propensity to save is

$$\frac{dS}{dy} = 0.2 - 0.1e^{-2y} \qquad \text{(in billions of dollars)}$$

and consumption is $7.8 billion when disposable income is 0. Find the national consumption function.

EMPLOYEE PRODUCTION RATE

The manager of a plant has been instructed to hire and train additional employees to manufacture a new product. She must hire a sufficient number of new employees so that within 30 days they will be producing 2500 units of the product each day.

Because a new employee must learn an assigned task, production will increase with training. Suppose that research on similar projects indicates that production increases with training according to the learning curve, so that for the average employee, the rate of production per day is given by

$$\frac{dN}{dt} = be^{-at},$$

where N is the number of units produced per day after t days of training. Because of experience with a very similar project, the manager expects the rate for this project to be

$$\frac{dN}{dt} = 2.5e^{-0.05t}$$

The manager tested her training program with 5 employees and learned that the average employee could produce 11 units per day after 5 days of training. Based on this information, she must decide how many employees to hire and begin to train so that a month from now they will be producing 2500 units of the product per day. She estimates that it will take her 10 days to hire the employees, and thus she will have 15 days remaining to train them. She also expects a 10% attrition rate during this peroid.

How may employees would you advise the plant manager to hire? Check your advice by answering the following questions.

1. Use the expected rate of production and the results of the manager's test to find the function relating N and t, that is, $N = N(t)$.

2. Find the number of units the average employee can produce after 15 days of training. How many such employees would be needed to maintain a production rate of 2500 units per day?

3. Explain how you would revise this last result to account for the expected 10% attrition rate. How many new employees should the manager hire?

PREREQUISITE PROBLEM TYPE	REVIEW SECTION/ANSWER
SECTION 6.1 Simplify: $$\frac{1}{n^3}\left[\frac{n(n+1)(2n+1)}{6} - \frac{2n(n+1)}{2} + n\right]$$	Section 0.6, Fractions $$\frac{2n^2 - 3n + 1}{6n^2}$$
SECTIONS 6.2, 6.5, 6.8 (a) If $F(x) = \dfrac{x^4}{4} + 4x + C$, what is $F(4) - F(2)$? (b) If $F(x) = -\dfrac{1}{9}\ln\dfrac{9 + \sqrt{81 - 9x^2}}{3x}$, what is $F(3) - F(2)$?	Section 1.1, Functional notation (a) 68 (b) $\dfrac{1}{9}\ln\left(\dfrac{3 + \sqrt{5}}{2}\right)$
SECTIONS 6.1, 6.7 Find the limit: (a) $\displaystyle\lim_{n\to+\infty}\frac{n^2 + n}{2n^2}$ (b) $\displaystyle\lim_{n\to+\infty}\frac{2n^2 - 3n + 1}{6n^2}$ (c) $\displaystyle\lim_{b\to\infty}\left(1 - \frac{1}{b}\right)$ (d) $\displaystyle\lim_{b\to\infty}\left(\frac{-100,000}{e^{0.10b}} + 100,000\right)$	Section 2.2, Limits at infinity (a) $\frac{1}{2}$ (b) $\frac{1}{3}$ (c) 1 (d) 100,000
SECTION 6.6 Find the derivative of $y = \ln x$.	Section 4.3, Derivatives of logarithmic functions $\dfrac{1}{x}$
SECTIONS 6.2–6.7 Integrate (a) $\displaystyle\int (x^3 + 4)\,dx$ (b) $\displaystyle\int x\sqrt{x^2 - 9}\,dx$ (c) $\displaystyle\int e^{2x}\,dx$	Sections 5.1, 5.2, 5.3, Integration (a) $\dfrac{x^4}{4} + 4x + C$ (b) $\frac{1}{3}(x^2 - 9)^{3/2} + C$ (c) $\frac{1}{2}e^{2x} + C$

WARM UP

6 | DEFINITE INTEGRALS

We have seen some applications of the indefinite integral in Chapter 5. In this chapter we define the definite integral and discuss a theorem that is useful for evaluating it. We will also see how it can be used to find the areas under certain curves. The definite integral is used to solve many interesting types of problems from economics, finance, and probability.

Some consumers are willing to pay more than the market equilibrium price, and some producers are willing to sell for less than this price. The savings are called **consumer's surplus** and **producer's surplus,** respectively, and areas under the demand and supply curves are used to calculate them.

Definite integrals can be used to approximate the total value and the **present value** of a **continuous income stream.** Improper integrals can be used to find the **capital values** of continuous income streams.

Evaluation of improper integrals is one of three new techniques of integration introduced in this chapter. The other two are use of integral tables and use of integration by parts.

In this chapter we will also discuss the Trapezoidal Rule and Simpson's Rule, two numerical methods that can be used to integrate functions that cannot be integrated with a formula.

6.1 | AREA UNDER A CURVE

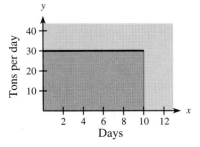

OBJECTIVES

- To use the sum of areas of rectangles to approximate the area under a curve
- To use Σ notation to denote sums
- To find exact area under a curve

One way to find the accumulated production (such as the production of ore from a mine) over a period of time is to graph the rate of production as a function of time, and find the area under the resulting curve over a specified time interval. For example, if a coal mine produces at a rate of 30 tons per day, the production over 10 days ($30 \cdot 10 = 300$) could be represented by the area under the line $y = 30$ between $x = 0$ and $x = 10$ (see Figure 6.1).

FIGURE 6.1

Although we did not need area to find the total production in this case, using area to determine the accumulated production is very useful when the rate of production function varies at different points in time. For example, if the rate of production is represented by

$$y = 100e^{-0.1x},$$

where x represents the number of days, then the area under the curve (and above the x-axis) from $x = 0$ to $x = 10$ represents the total production over the 10-day period [see Figure 6.2(a)].

FIGURE 6.2

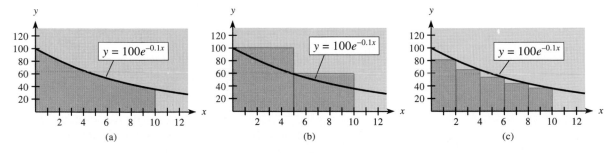

(a) (b) (c)

In order to determine the accumulated production and solve other types of problems, we need a method for finding areas under curves. We can find a rough approximation of the area under this curve by fitting two rectangles to the curve as shown in Figure 6.2(b). The area of the first rectangle is $5 \cdot 100 = 500$ square units, and the area of the second rectangle is $(10 - 5)[100e^{-0.1(5)}] \approx 5(60.65) = 303.25$ square units, so this rough approximation is 803.25 square units. This approximation is clearly larger than the exact area under the curve. Why?

EXAMPLE 1

Fit five rectangles with equal bases inside the area under the curve $y = 100e^{-0.1x}$, and use them to approximate the area under the curve from $x = 0$ to $x = 10$ [see Figure 6.2(c)].

Solution Each of the five rectangles has base 2, and the height of each rectangle is the value of the function at the right-hand endpoint of the interval forming its base. Thus the areas of the rectangles are as follows:

Rectangle	Base	Height	Area = base × height
1	2	$100e^{-0.1(2)} \approx 81.87$	$2(81.87) = 163.74$
2	2	$100e^{-0.1(4)} \approx 67.03$	$2(67.03) = 134.06$
3	2	$100e^{-0.1(6)} \approx 54.88$	$2(54.88) = 109.76$
4	2	$100e^{-0.1(8)} \approx 44.93$	$2(44.93) = 89.86$
5	2	$100e^{-0.1(10)} \approx 36.79$	$2(36.79) = 73.58$

The area under the curve is approximately equal to

$$163.74 + 134.06 + 109.76 + 89.86 + 73.58 = 571.$$

The area is actually 632.12, to two decimal places, so this approximation is much better than the one we obtained with just two rectangles. In general, if we use bases of equal width, the approximation of the area under a curve will improve when more rectangles are used.

Suppose that we wish to find the area between the curve $y = x$ and the x-axis from $x = 0$ to $x = 1$ (see Figure 6.3 on the following page). One way to approximate this area is to use the areas of rectangles whose bases are on the x-axis and whose heights are the vertical distances from points on their bases to the curve. We can divide the interval $[0, 1]$ into n equal subintervals and use them as the bases of n rectangles whose heights are determined by the curve (see Figure 6.4). The width of each of these rectangles is $1/n$. Using the functional value at the right-hand endpoint of each subinterval as the height of the rectangle, we get n rectangles as shown in Figure 6.4. Because part of each rectangle lies above the curve, the sum of the areas of the rectangles will overestimate the area.

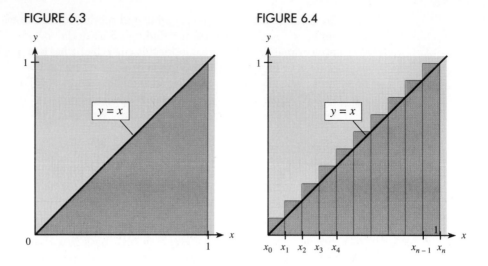

FIGURE 6.3

FIGURE 6.4

Then, with $y = f(x) = x$ and subinterval width $1/n$, the areas of the rectangles are as follows:

Rectangle	Base	Endpoint	Height	Area = base × height
1	$\dfrac{1}{n}$	$x_1 = \dfrac{1}{n}$	$f(x_1) = \dfrac{1}{n}$	$\dfrac{1}{n} \cdot \dfrac{1}{n} = \dfrac{1}{n^2}$
2	$\dfrac{1}{n}$	$x_2 = \dfrac{2}{n}$	$f(x_2) = \dfrac{2}{n}$	$\dfrac{1}{n} \cdot \dfrac{2}{n} = \dfrac{2}{n^2}$
3	$\dfrac{1}{n}$	$x_3 = \dfrac{3}{n}$	$f(x_3) = \dfrac{3}{n}$	$\dfrac{1}{n} \cdot \dfrac{3}{n} = \dfrac{3}{n^2}$
$\vdots$				
i	$\dfrac{1}{n}$	$x_i = \dfrac{i}{n}$	$f(x_i) = \dfrac{i}{n}$	$\dfrac{1}{n} \cdot \dfrac{i}{n} = \dfrac{i}{n^2}$
$\vdots$				
n	$\dfrac{1}{n}$	$x_n = \dfrac{n}{n}$	$f(x_n) = \dfrac{n}{n}$	$\dfrac{1}{n} \cdot \dfrac{n}{n} = \dfrac{n}{n^2}$

Note that i/n^2 gives the area of the ith rectangle of *any* value of i. Thus for any value of n, this area can be approximated by the sum

$$A \approx \frac{1}{n^2} + \frac{2}{n^2} + \frac{3}{n^2} + \cdots + \frac{i}{n^2} + \cdots + \frac{n}{n^2}.$$

In particular, we have the following approximations of this area for specific values of n (the number of rectangles).

$$n = 5: \quad A \approx \frac{1}{25} + \frac{2}{25} + \frac{3}{25} + \frac{4}{25} + \frac{5}{25} = \frac{15}{25} = 0.60$$

$$n = 10: \quad A \approx \frac{1}{100} + \frac{2}{100} + \frac{3}{100} + \cdots + \frac{10}{100} = \frac{55}{100} = 0.55$$

$$n = 100: A \approx \frac{1}{10{,}000} + \frac{2}{10{,}000} + \frac{3}{10{,}000} + \cdots + \frac{100}{10{,}000} = \frac{5050}{10{,}000} = 0.505$$

We can find this sum for any n more easily if we observe that the common denominator is n^2 and that the numerator is the sum of the first n terms of an arithmetic sequence with first term 1 and last term n. As you may recall from an algebra course, the first n terms of this arithmetic sequence add to $(n + 1)/2$. Thus the area is approximated by

$$A \approx \frac{1 + 2 + 3 + \cdots + n}{n^2} = \frac{n(n + 1)/2}{n^2} = \frac{n + 1}{2n}.$$

Using this formula, we see the following.

$$n = 5: \quad A \approx \frac{5 + 1}{2(5)} = \frac{6}{10} = 0.60$$

$$n = 10: \quad A \approx \frac{10 + 1}{2(10)} = \frac{11}{20} = 0.55$$

$$n = 100: A \approx \frac{100 + 1}{2(100)} = \frac{101}{200} = 0.505$$

Note that as n gets larger, the number of rectangles increases, the area of each rectangle decreases, and the approximation becomes more accurate. If we let n increase without bound, the approximation approaches the exact area.

$$A = \lim_{n \to +\infty} \frac{n + 1}{2n} = \lim_{n \to +\infty} \frac{1 + 1/n}{2} = \frac{1}{2}.$$

We can see that this area is correct, for we are computing the area of a triangle with base 1 and height 1. The formula for the area of a triangle gives

$$A = \frac{1}{2}bh = \frac{1}{2} \cdot 1 \cdot 1 = \frac{1}{2}.$$

A special notation exists that uses the Greek letter Σ (sigma) to express the sum of numbers or expressions. For example, we may indicate the sum of the n numbers $a_1, a_2, a_3, a_4, \ldots, a_n$ by

$$\sum_{i=1}^{n} a_i = a_1 + a_2 + a_3 + \cdots + a_n.$$

This may be read as "The sum of a_i as i goes from 1 to n." The subscript i in a_i is replaced, first by 1, then by 2, then by 3, $\ldots$, until it reaches the value above the sigma. The i is called the **index of summation,** and it starts with the lower limit, 1, and ends with the upper limit, n. For example, if $x_1 = 2$, $x_2 = 3$, $x_3 = -1$, and $x_4 = -2$, then

$$\sum_{i=1}^{4} x_i = x_1 + x_2 + x_3 + x_4 = 2 + 3 + (-1) + (-2) = 2.$$

The area of the triangle under $y = x$ that we discussed above was approximated by

$$A \approx \frac{1}{n^2} + \frac{2}{n^2} + \frac{3}{n^2} + \cdots + \frac{i}{n^2} + \cdots + \frac{n}{n^2}.$$

Using **sigma notation,** we can write this sum as

$$A \approx \sum_{i=1}^{n} \left(\frac{i}{n^2} \right).$$

Sigma notation allows us to represent the sums of the areas of the rectangles in an abbreviated fashion. Some formulas that simplify computations involving sums follow.

Sum Formulas

I. $\displaystyle\sum_{i=1}^{n} 1 = n$

II. $\displaystyle\sum_{i=1}^{n} cx_i = c \sum_{i=1}^{n} x_i \qquad (c = \text{constant})$

III. $\displaystyle\sum_{i=1}^{n} (x_i + y_i) = \sum_{i=1}^{n} x_i + \sum_{i=1}^{n} y_i$

IV. $\displaystyle\sum_{i=1}^{n} i = \frac{n(n + 1)}{2}$

V. $\displaystyle\sum_{i=1}^{n} i^2 = \frac{n(n + 1)(2n + 1)}{6}$

We have found that the area of the triangle discussed above was approximated by

$$A \approx \sum_{i=1}^{n} \frac{i}{n^2}.$$

We can use these formulas to simplify this sum as follows.

$$\sum_{i=1}^{n} \frac{i}{n^2} = \frac{1}{n^2} \sum_{i=1}^{n} i \qquad \text{(Formula II)}$$

$$= \frac{1}{n^2} \left[\frac{n(n + 1)}{2} \right] \qquad \text{(Formula IV)}$$

$$= \frac{n + 1}{2n}$$

Note that this is the same formula we obtained previously using other methods.

The following example shows that we can find the area by evaluating the function at the left-hand endpoints of the subintervals.

EXAMPLE 2

Use rectangles to find the area under $y = x^2$ (and above the x-axis) from $x = 0$ to $x = 1$.

Solution   We again divide the interval $[0, 1]$ into n equal subintervals of length $1/n$. If we evaluate the function at the left-hand endpoints of these subintervals to determine the heights of the rectangles, the sum of the areas of the rectangles will underestimate the area (see Figure 6.5).

FIGURE 6.5

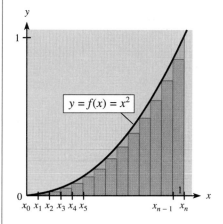

Thus we have the following:

Rectangle	Base	Endpoint	Height	Area = base × height
1	$\dfrac{1}{n}$	$x_0 = 0$	$f(x_0) = 0$	$\dfrac{1}{n} \cdot 0 = 0$
2	$\dfrac{1}{n}$	$x_1 = \dfrac{1}{n}$	$f(x_1) = \dfrac{1}{n^2}$	$\dfrac{1}{n} \cdot \dfrac{1}{n^2} = \dfrac{1}{n^3}$
3	$\dfrac{1}{n}$	$x_2 = \dfrac{2}{n}$	$f(x_2) = \dfrac{4}{n^2}$	$\dfrac{1}{n} \cdot \dfrac{4}{n^2} = \dfrac{4}{n^3}$
4	$\dfrac{1}{n}$	$x_3 = \dfrac{3}{n}$	$f(x_3) = \dfrac{9}{n^2}$	$\dfrac{1}{n} \cdot \dfrac{9}{n^2} = \dfrac{9}{n^3}$
$\vdots$				
i	$\dfrac{1}{n}$	$x_{i-1} = \dfrac{i-1}{n}$	$\dfrac{(i-1)^2}{n}$	$\dfrac{(i-1)^2}{n^3}$
$\vdots$				
n	$\dfrac{1}{n}$	$x_{n-1} = \dfrac{n-1}{n}$	$\dfrac{(n-1)^2}{n^2}$	$\dfrac{(n-1)^2}{n^3}$

Note that $(i - 1)^2/n^3 = (i^2 - 2i + 1)/n^3$ gives the area of the ith rectangle for *any* value of i.

The sum of these areas may be written as

$$S = \sum_{i=1}^{n} \frac{i^2 - 2i + 1}{n^3} = \frac{1}{n^3}\left(\sum_{i=1}^{n} i^2 - 2\sum_{i=1}^{n} i + \sum_{i=1}^{n} 1\right) \qquad \text{(Formulas II and III)}$$

$$= \frac{1}{n^3}\left[\frac{n(n+1)(2n+1)}{6} - \frac{2n(n+1)}{2} + n\right] \qquad \text{(Formulas V, IV, and I)}$$

$$= \frac{2n^3 + 3n^2 + n}{6n^3} - \frac{n^2 + n}{n^3} + \frac{n}{n^3}$$

$$= \frac{2n^2 - 3n + 1}{6n^2}.$$

If n is large, there will be a large number of smaller rectangles and the approximation of the area under the curve will be good; the larger n, the better the approximation. For example, if $n = 10$, the area approximation is

$$S(10) = \frac{200 - 30 + 1}{600} = 0.285,$$

whereas if $n = 100$,

$$S(100) = \frac{20,000 - 300 + 1}{60,000} = 0.328.$$

If we let n increase without bound, we find the exact area.

$$A = \lim_{n\to\infty}\left(\frac{2n^2 - 3n + 1}{6n^2}\right)$$

$$= \lim_{n\to\infty}\left(\frac{2 - \dfrac{3}{n} + \dfrac{1}{n^2}}{6}\right) = \frac{1}{3}.$$

Note that the approximations with $n = 10$ and $n = 100$ were less than $\frac{1}{3}$. This is because all the rectangles were *under* the curve (see Figure 6.5).

Thus we see that we can determine the area under a curve $y = f(x)$ from $x = a$ to $x = b$ by dividing the interval $[a, b]$ into n equal subintervals of width $(b - a)/n$ and evaluating

$$A = \lim_{n\to\infty} S_R = \lim_{n\to\infty}\sum_{i=1}^{n} f(x_i)\left(\frac{b - a}{n}\right) \qquad \text{(using right-hand endpoints)}$$

or

$$A = \lim_{n\to\infty} S_L = \lim_{n\to\infty}\sum_{i=1}^{n} f(x_{i-1})\left(\frac{b - a}{n}\right) \qquad \text{(using left-hand endpoints)}.$$

CHECKPOINT   1. For the interval $[0, 2]$, determine whether the following are true or false.

(a) For 4 subintervals, each subinterval has width $\dfrac{1}{2}$.

(b) For 200 subintervals, each subinterval has width $\dfrac{1}{100}$.

(c) For n subintervals, each subinterval has width $\dfrac{2}{n}$.

(d) For n subintervals, $x_0 = 0$, $x_1 = \dfrac{2}{n}$, $x_2 = 2\left(\dfrac{2}{n}\right)$, ... , $x_i = i\left(\dfrac{2}{n}\right)$, ...
and $x_n = 2$.

2. If $\dfrac{b - a}{n} = \dfrac{2}{n}$, $x_i = \dfrac{2i}{n}$, and $f(x) = 3x - x^2$, find:

(a) $f(x_i)$

(b) $f(x_i)\dfrac{b - a}{n}$

(c) $\displaystyle\sum_{i=1}^{n} f(x_i)\dfrac{b - a}{n}$, and simplify

(d) $\displaystyle\lim_{n \to \infty} \sum_{i=1}^{n} f(x_i)\dfrac{b - a}{n}$

TECHNOLOGY CORNER

1. Use a program on your computer or calculator to find S_L and S_R for the values of n in the table below if $f(x) = \sqrt{x}$ on the interval $[0, 4]$.

n	2	4	8	64	128
S_L					
S_R					

2. Predict $\displaystyle\lim_{n \to \infty} S_L$ and $\displaystyle\lim_{n \to \infty} S_R$ from your table.

1. All parts are true.

2. (a) $f(x_i) = f\left(\dfrac{2i}{n}\right) = 3\left(\dfrac{2i}{n}\right) - \left(\dfrac{2i}{n}\right)^2 = \dfrac{6i}{n} - \dfrac{4i^2}{n^2}$

(b) $f(x_i)\dfrac{b-a}{n} = \left(\dfrac{6i}{n} - \dfrac{4i^2}{n^2}\right)\left(\dfrac{2}{n}\right) = \dfrac{12i}{n^2} - \dfrac{8i^2}{n^3}$

(c) $\displaystyle\sum_{i=1}^{n} f(x_i)\dfrac{b-a}{n} = \sum_{i=1}^{n}\left(\dfrac{12i}{n^2} - \dfrac{8i^2}{n^3}\right)$

$\displaystyle = \sum_{i=1}^{n}\dfrac{12i}{n^2} - \sum_{i=1}^{n}\dfrac{8i^2}{n^3}$

$\displaystyle = \dfrac{12}{n^2}\sum_{i=1}^{n} i - \dfrac{8}{n^3}\sum_{i=1}^{n} i^2$

$= \dfrac{12}{n^2}\left[\dfrac{n(n+1)}{2}\right] - \dfrac{8}{n^3}\left[\dfrac{n(n+1)(2n+1)}{6}\right]$

$= \dfrac{6(n+1)}{n} - \dfrac{4(n+1)(2n+1)}{3n^2}$

(d) $\displaystyle\lim_{n\to\infty}\sum_{i=1}^{n} f(x_i)\dfrac{b-a}{n} = \lim_{n\to\infty}\left(\dfrac{6n+6}{n} - \dfrac{8n^2+12n+4}{3n^2}\right)$

$= 6 - \dfrac{8}{3} = \dfrac{10}{3}.$ ■

In problems 1–4, approximate the area under each curve over the interval specified by using the indicated number of subintervals (or rectangles) and evaluating the function at the *right-hand* endpoints of the subintervals.

1. $f(x) = 4x - x^2$ from $x = 0$ to $x = 2$;
   4 subintervals

2. $f(x) = x^3$ from $x = 0$ to $x = 3$; 6 subintervals

3. $f(x) = 9 - x^2$ from $x = 1$ to $x = 3$;
   8 subintervals

4. $f(x) = x^2 + x + 1$ from $x = -1$ to $x = 1$;
   4 subintervals

In problems 5–8, approximate the area under each curve by evaluating the function at the *left-hand* endpoints of the subintervals.

5. $f(x) = 4x - x^2$ from $x = 0$ to $x = 2$;
   4 subintervals

6. $f(x) = x^3$ from $x = 0$ to $x = 3$; 6 subintervals

7. $f(x) = 9 - x^2$ from $x = 1$ to $x = 3$;
   8 subintervals

8. $f(x) = x^2 + x + 1$ from $x = -1$ to $x = 1$;
   4 subintervals

When the area under $f(x) = x^2 + x$ from $x = 0$ to

$x = 2$ is approximated, the formulas for the sum of n rectangles using *left-hand* endpoints and *right-hand* endpoints are as follows:

Left-hand endpoints: $\quad S_L = \dfrac{14}{3} - \dfrac{6}{n} + \dfrac{4}{3n^2}$

Right-hand endpoints: $\quad S_R = \dfrac{14n^2 + 18n + 4}{3n^2}$

Use these formulas to answer problems 9–13.

9. Find $S_L(10)$ and $S_R(10)$.

10. Find $S_L(100)$ and $S_R(100)$.

11. Find $\lim\limits_{n\to\infty} S_L$ and $\lim\limits_{n\to\infty} S_R$.

12. Compare the right-hand and left-hand values by finding $S_R - S_L$ for $n = 10$, for $n = 100$, and as $n \to \infty$. (Use problems 9–11.)

13. Since $f(x) = x^2 + x$ is increasing over the interval from $x = 0$ to $x = 2$, functional values at the right-hand endpoints are maximum values for each subinterval, and functional values at the left-hand endpoints are minimum values for each subinterval. How would the approximate area using $n = 10$ and *any* other point within each subinterval compare with $S_L(10)$ and $S_R(10)$? What would happen to the area result as $n \to \infty$ if any other point in each subinterval were used?

In problems 14–23, find the value of each sum.

14. $\sum\limits_{k=1}^{3} x_k$, if $x_1 = 1, x_2 = 3, x_3 = -1, x_4 = 5$

15. $\sum\limits_{i=1}^{4} x_i$, if $x_1 = 3, x_2 = -1, x_3 = 3, x_4 = -2$

16. $\sum\limits_{i=3}^{5} (i^2 + 1)$

17. $\sum\limits_{j=2}^{5} (j^2 - 3)$

18. $\sum\limits_{i=4}^{7} \left(\dfrac{i-3}{i^2}\right)$

19. $\sum\limits_{j=0}^{4} (j^2 - 4j + 1)$

20. $\sum\limits_{k=1}^{50} 1$

21. $\sum\limits_{j=1}^{60} 3$

22. $\sum\limits_{k=1}^{50} (6k^2 + 5)$

23. $\sum\limits_{k=1}^{30} (k^2 + 4k)$

In problems 24 and 25, use the Sum Formulas I–IV to express each of the following without the summation symbol.

24. $\sum\limits_{i=1}^{n} \left(1 + \dfrac{i^2}{n^2}\right)\left(\dfrac{2}{n}\right)$

25. $\sum\limits_{i=1}^{n} \left(1 - \dfrac{2i}{n} + \dfrac{i^2}{n^2}\right)\left(\dfrac{3}{n}\right)$

Use the function $y = x$ from $x = 0$ to $x = 1$ and n equal subintervals with the function evaluated at the *left-hand* endpoint of each subinterval for problems 26–27.

26. What is the area of the
   (a) first rectangle?
   (b) second rectangle?
   (c) ith rectangle?

27. (a) Find a formula for the sum of the areas of the n rectangles (call this S), then find
   (b) $S(10)$.
   (c) $S(100)$.
   (d) $S(1000)$.
   (e) $\lim\limits_{n\to\infty} S$.

28. How do your answers to problems 27(a)–(e) compare with the corresponding calculations in the discussion (after Example 1) of the area under $y = x$ using *right-hand* endpoints?

For problems 29(a)–(e), use the function $y = x^2$ from $x = 0$ to $x = 1$ and n equal subintervals with the function evaluated at the *right-hand* endpoints.

29. (a) Find a formula for the sum of the areas of the n rectangles (call this S), then find
   (b) $S(10)$.
   (c) $S(100)$.
   (d) $S(1000)$.
   (e) $\lim\limits_{n\to\infty} S$.

30. How do your answers to problems 29(a)–(e) compare with the corresponding calculations in Example 2?

31. Use rectangles to find the area between $y = x^2 - 6x + 8$ and the x-axis from $x = 0$ to $x = 2$. Divide the interval $[0, 2]$ into n equal subintervals, so each subinterval has length $2/n$.

32. Use rectangles to find the area between $y = 4x - x^2$ and the x-axis from $x = 0$ to $x = 4$. Divide the interval $[0, 4]$ into n equal subintervals, so each subinterval has length $4/n$.

6.2 | THE DEFINITE INTEGRAL; THE FUNDAMENTAL THEOREM OF CALCULUS

OBJECTIVES

- To evaluate definite integrals using the Fundamental Theorem of Calculus
- To use definite integrals to find the area under a curve

In the previous section, we saw that we could determine the area under a curve using equal subintervals and the functional values at either the left-hand endpoints or the right-hand endpoints of the subintervals. In fact, we can use subintervals that are not of equal length, and we can use any point within each subinterval to determine the height of each rectangle. Suppose that we wish to find the area above the x-axis and under the curve $y = f(x)$ over a closed interval $[a, b]$. We can divide the interval into n subintervals (not necessarily equal), with the endpoints of these intervals at $x_0 = a, x_1, x_2, \ldots, x_n = b$. We now choose a point (*any* point) in each subinterval, and denote the points $x_1^*, x_2^*, \ldots, x_i^*, \ldots, x_n^*$. Then the ith rectangle (for any i) has height $f(x_i^*)$ and width $x_i - x_{i-1}$, so its area is $f(x_i^*)(x_i - x_{i-1})$. Then the sum of the areas of the n rectangles is

$$S = \sum_{i=1}^{n} f(x_i^*)(x_i - x_{i-1})$$

$$= \sum_{i=1}^{n} f(x_i^*)\Delta x_i, \qquad \text{where } \Delta x_i = x_i - x_{i-1}.$$

Because the points in the subinterval may be chosen anywhere in the subinterval, we cannot be sure if the rectangles will underestimate or overestimate the area under the curve. But increasing the number of subintervals (increasing n) and making sure that every interval becomes smaller (just increasing n will not guarantee this if the subintervals are unequal) will improve the estimation. Thus for any subdivision of $[a, b]$ and any x_i^*, the area is given by

$$A = \lim_{\substack{n \to \infty \\ \max \Delta x_i \to 0}} \sum_{i=1}^{n} f(x_i^*) \Delta x_i, \qquad \text{provided that this limit exists.}$$

The preceding discussion takes place in the context of finding the area under a curve. However, if f is any function (not necessarily nonnegative) defined on $[a, b]$, then for each subdivision of $[a, b]$ and each choice of x_i^*, we define the sum S above as the **Riemann sum** of f for the subdivision of $[a, b]$. In addition, the limit of the Riemann sum (as max $\Delta x_i \to 0$) has other important applications, and is called the **definite integral** of $f(x)$ over the interval $[a, b]$.

Definite Integral

If f is a function on the interval $[a, b]$, then the *definite integral* of f from a to b is

$$\int_a^b f(x)\, dx = \lim_{\substack{n \to \infty \\ \max \Delta x_i \to 0}} \sum_{i=1}^{n} f(x_i^*)\, \Delta x_i.$$

If the limit exists, then the definite integral exists and we say that f is integrable on $[a, b]$.

The obvious question is, how is this definite integral related to the indefinite integral (antiderivative) we have been studying? The answer to this question is given by the **Fundamental Theorem of Calculus.**

Fundamental Theorem of Calculus

Let f be a continuous function on the closed interval $[a, b]$; then the definite integral of f exists on this interval, and

$$\int_a^b f(x)\, dx = F(b) - F(a),$$

where F is any function such that $F'(x) = f(x)$ for all x in $[a, b]$.

Stated differently, the theorem says that if the function F is an indefinite integral of a function f that is continuous on the interval $[a, b]$, then

$$\int_a^b f(x)\, dx = F(b) - F(a).$$

We denote $F(b) - F(a)$ by $F(x)\Big|_a^b$.

EXAMPLE 1 | Evaluate $\int_2^4 (x^3 + 4)\, dx$.

Solution

$$\int_2^4 (x^3 + 4)\, dx = \frac{x^4}{4} + 4x + C \Big|_2^4$$

$$= \left[\frac{(4)^4}{4} + 4(4) + C\right] - \left[\frac{(2)^4}{4} + 4(2) + C\right]$$

$$= (64 + 16 + C) - (4 + 8 + C)$$

$$= 68 \qquad \text{(Note that the } C\text{'s subtract out)}$$

Note that the Fundamental Theorem states that F can be *any* indefinite integral of f, so we need not add the constant of integration to the integral.

EXAMPLE 2 | Evaluate $\int_1^3 (3x^2 + 6x)\, dx$.

Solution

$$\int_1^3 (3x^2 + 6x)\, dx = x^3 + 3x^2 \Big|_1^3$$

$$= (3^3 + 3 \cdot 3^2) - (1^3 + 3 \cdot 1^2)$$

$$= 54 - 4 = 50$$

The properties of definite integrals given below follow from properties of summations.

1. $\int_a^b [f(x) \pm g(x)]\, dx = \int_a^b f(x)\, dx \pm \int_a^b g(x)\, dx$

2. $\int_a^b kf(x)\, dx = k \int_a^b f(x)\, dx, \qquad$ where k is a constant

The following example uses both of these properties.

EXAMPLE 3 | Evaluate $\int_3^5 (\sqrt{x^2 - 9} + 2)x\, dx$.

Solution

$$\int_3^5 (\sqrt{x^2 - 9} + 2)x\, dx = \int_3^5 \sqrt{x^2 - 9}(x\, dx) + \int_3^5 2x\, dx$$

$$= \frac{1}{2} \int_3^5 (x^2 - 9)^{1/2}(2x\, dx) + \int_3^5 2x\, dx$$

$$= \frac{1}{2} \left[\frac{2}{3}(x^2 - 9)^{3/2}\right]\Big|_3^5 + x^2 \Big|_3^5$$

$$= \frac{1}{3}[(16)^{3/2} - (0)^{3/2}] + (25 - 9)$$

$$= \frac{64}{3} + 16$$

$$= \frac{64}{3} + \frac{48}{3} = \frac{112}{3}$$

In the integral $\int_a^b f(x)\, dx$, we call a the *lower limit* and b the *upper limit* of integration. Although we developed the definite integral with the assumption that the lower limit was less than the upper limit, the following properties permit us to evaluate the definite integral even when that is not the case.

3. $\displaystyle\int_a^a f(x)\, dx = 0$

4. If f is integrable on $[a, b]$, then

$$\int_b^a f(x)\, dx = -\int_a^b f(x)\, dx.$$

The following examples illustrate these properties.

EXAMPLE 4

Evaluate $\displaystyle\int_4^4 x^2\, dx$.

Solution

$$\int_4^4 x^2\, dx = \frac{x^3}{3}\bigg|_4^4 = \frac{4^3}{3} - \frac{4^3}{3} = 0$$

Note that because the limits of integration are the same, it is not necessary to integrate to see that the value of the integral is 0.

EXAMPLE 5

Compare $\displaystyle\int_2^4 3x^2\, dx$ and $\displaystyle\int_4^2 3x^2\, dx$.

Solution

$$\int_2^4 3x^2\, dx = x^3\bigg|_2^4 = 4^3 - 2^3 = 56$$

$$\int_4^2 3x^2\, dx = x^3\bigg|_4^2 = 2^3 - 4^3 = -56$$

Thus

$$\int_4^2 3x^2\, dx = -\int_2^4 3x^2\, dx.$$

Another property of definite integrals is called the additive property.

5. If f is continuous on some interval containing a, b, and c,* then

$$\int_a^b f(x)\, dx = \int_a^c f(x)\, dx + \int_c^b f(x)\, dx.$$

EXAMPLE 6 | Show that $\int_2^3 4x\, dx + \int_3^5 4x\, dx = \int_2^5 4x\, dx$.

Solution

$$\int_2^3 4x\, dx = 2x^2 \Big|_2^3 = 18 - 8 = 10$$

$$\int_3^5 4x\, dx = 2x^2 \Big|_3^5 = 50 - 18 = 32$$

$$\int_3^5 4x\, dx = 2x^2 \Big|_2^5 = 50 - 8 = 42$$

Thus $\int_2^3 4x\, dx + \int_3^5 4x\, dx = \int_2^5 4x\, dx$.

Let us now return to area problems, to see the relationship between the definite integral and the area under a curve. By the formula for the area of a triangle and by summing areas of rectangles, we found the area under the curve (line) $y = x$ from $x = 0$ to $x = 1$ to be $\frac{1}{2}$ [see Figure 6.6(a)]. Using the definite integral to find the area gives

$$A = \int_0^1 x\, dx = \frac{x^2}{2} \Big|_0^1 = \frac{1}{2} - 0 = \frac{1}{2}.$$

In Example 2 of Section 6.1, we used rectangles to find that the area under $y = x^2$ from $x = 0$ to $x = 1$ was $\frac{1}{3}$ [see Figure 6.6(b)]. Using the definite integral, we get

$$A = \int_0^1 x^2\, dx = \frac{x^3}{3} \Big|_0^1 = \frac{1}{3} - 0 = \frac{1}{3},$$

which agrees with the answer obtained in Example 2.

However, not every definite integral represents the area between the curve and

*Note that c need not be between a and b.

the x-axis over an integral. For example,

$$\int_0^2 (x - 2)\, dx = \frac{x^2}{2} - 2x \Big|_0^2 = (2 - 4) - (0) = -2.$$

This would indicate that the area between the curve and the x-axis is negative, but area must be positive. A look at the graph of $y = x - 2$ [see Figure 6.6(c)] shows us what is happening. The region bounded by $y = x - 2$ and the x-axis between $x = 0$ and $x = 2$ is a triangle whose base is 2 and height is 2, so its area is $\frac{1}{2}bh = \frac{1}{2}(2)(2) = 2$. The integral has value -2 because $y = x - 2$ lies below the x-axis from $x = 0$ to $x = 2$, so the functional values over the interval $[0, 2]$ are negative. Thus the value of the definite integral over *this* interval does not represent the area between the curve and the x-axis.

In general, the definite integral will give the area under the curve and above the x-axis only when $f(x) \geq 0$ for all x in $[a, b]$.

FIGURE 6.6

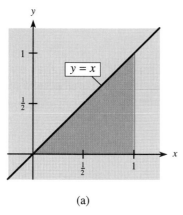

(a)

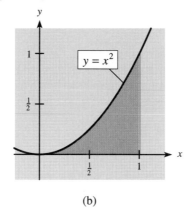

(b)

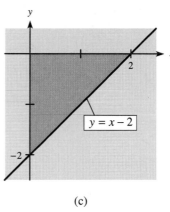

(c)

Area Under a Curve   If f is a continuous function on $[a, b]$ and $f(x) \geq 0$ on $[a, b]$, then the exact area between $y = f(x)$ and the x-axis from $x = a$ to $x = b$ is given by

$$\text{Area (shaded)} = \int_a^b f(x)\, dx.$$

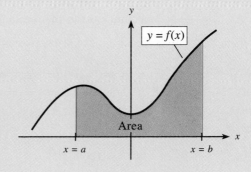

1. True or false:

   (a) For any integral, we can omit the constant of integration (i.e., the $+C$).

   (b) $-\int_{-1}^{3} f(x)\,dx = \int_{3}^{-1} f(x)\,dx,$ if f is integrable on $[-1, 3]$.

   (c) The area between $f(x)$ and the x-axis on the interval $[a, b]$ is given by
   $$\int_{a}^{b} f(x)\,dx.$$

2. Evaluate:

   (a) $\int_{0}^{3} (x^2 + 1)\,dx$

   (b) $\int_{0}^{3} (x^2 + 1)^4 x\,dx$

If the rate of growth of some function with respect to time is $f'(t)$, then the integral of that rate of growth gives the function $f(t)$. In addition, the total growth of the function during this period from $t = 0$ to $t = k$ can be found by evaluating the definite integral
$$\int_{0}^{k} f'(t)\,dt = f(t)\Big|_{0}^{k} = f(k) - f(0).$$

For nonnegative rates of growth, this definite integral (and growth) is the same as the area under the graph of $f'(t)$ from $t = 0$ to $t = k$.

EXAMPLE 7

Suppose that money flows continuously into a slot machine at a casino and grows at a rate given by
$$A' = 100e^{0.1t}$$

where t is time in hours and $0 \le t \le 10$. Find the total amount of money that accumulates in the machine during the 10-hour period if no money is paid out.

Solution The total amount is given by
$$A = \int_{0}^{10} 100e^{0.1t}\,dt$$
$$= \frac{100}{0.1}\int_{0}^{10} e^{0.1t}(0.1)\,dt$$
$$= 1000e^{0.1t}\Big|_{0}^{10}$$
$$= 1000e - 1000$$
$$\approx 1718.28 \text{ (dollars)}.$$

1. (a) False. We can omit the constant of integration $(+C)$ only for definite integrals.

   (b) True

   (c) False. Only if $f(x) \geq 0$ on $[a, b]$ is this true.

2. (a) $\displaystyle\int_0^3 (x^2 + 1)\, dx = \frac{x^3}{3} + x \Big|_0^3 = \left(\frac{27}{3} + 3\right) - (0 + 0) = 12$

   (b) $\displaystyle\int_0^3 (x^2 + 1)^4 x\, dx = \frac{1}{2}\int_0^3 (x^2 + 1)^4 (2x\, dx) = \frac{1}{2} \cdot \frac{(x^2 + 1)^5}{5} \Big|_0^3$

   $= \frac{1}{10}[(3^2 + 1)^5 - (1)^5]$

   $= \frac{1}{10}(10^5 - 1) = 9999.9$ ■

EXERCISE 6.2

Evaluate the following definite integrals.

1. $\displaystyle\int_2^4 x^3\, dx$

2. $\displaystyle\int_0^5 x^2\, dx$

3. $\displaystyle\int_{-1}^2 5x^4\, dx$

4. $\displaystyle\int_{-2}^4 4x^3\, dx$

5. $\displaystyle\int_{-2}^3 5\, dx$

6. $\displaystyle\int_{-8}^{-5} 7\, dx$

7. $\displaystyle\int_0^5 4\sqrt[3]{x^2}\, dx$

8. $\displaystyle\int_2^4 3\sqrt{x}\, dx$

9. $\displaystyle\int_2^4 (4x^3 - 6x^2 - 5x)\, dx$

10. $\displaystyle\int_0^2 (x^4 - 5x^3 + 2x)\, dx$

11. $\displaystyle\int_2^3 (x - 4)^2\, dx$

12. $\displaystyle\int_{-1}^3 (x + 2)^3\, dx$

13. $\displaystyle\int_2^4 (x^2 + 2)^3 x\, dx$

14. $\displaystyle\int_0^3 (2x - x^2)^4 (1 - x)\, dx$

15. $\displaystyle\int_{-1}^2 (x^3 - 3x^2)^3 (x^2 - 2x)\, dx$

16. $\displaystyle\int_0^4 (3x^2 - 2)^4 x\, dx$

17. $\displaystyle\int_2^3 x\sqrt{x^2 + 3}\, dx$

18. $\displaystyle\int_{-1}^2 x\sqrt[3]{x^2 - 5}\, dx$

19. $\displaystyle\int_4^4 \sqrt{x^2 - 2}\, dx$

20. $\displaystyle\int_2^2 (x^3 - 4x)\, dx$

21. $\displaystyle\int_3^6 \frac{x}{3x^2 + 4}\, dx$

22. $\displaystyle\int_0^2 \frac{x}{x^2 + 4}\, dx$

23. In Figure 6.7, which of the shaded regions A, B, C, or D has the area given by

$$\int_a^b f(x)\, dx?$$

FIGURE 6.7

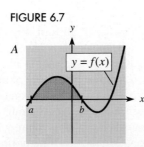

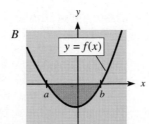

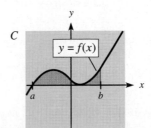

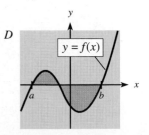

24. For which of the following functions $f(x)$ does

$$\int_0^2 f(x)\,dx$$

give the area between the graph of $f(x)$ and the x-axis from $x = 0$ to $x = 2$?
(a) $f(x) = x^2 + 1$ (b) $f(x) = -x^2$
(c) $f(x) = x - 1$

In problems 25–28,
(a) write the integral that describes the area of the shaded region.
(b) find the area.

25.

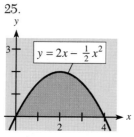

$y = 2x - \frac{1}{2}x^2$

26.

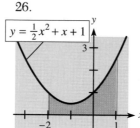

$y = \frac{1}{2}x^2 + x + 1$

27.

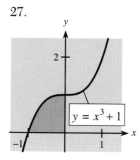

$y = x^3 + 1$

28.

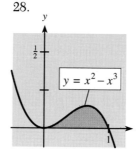

$y = x^2 - x^3$

29. Find the area between the curve $y = -x^2 + 3x - 2$ and the x-axis from $x = 1$ to $x = 2$.

30. Find the area between the curve $y = x^2 + 3x + 2$ and the x-axis from $x = -1$ to $x = 3$.

31. Find the area between the curve $y = xe^{x^2}$ and the x-axis from $x = 1$ to $x = 3$.

32. Find the area between the curve $y = e^{-x}$ and the x-axis from $x = -1$ to $x = 1$.

33. How does $\int_{-1}^{-3} x\sqrt{x^2 + 1}\,dx$ compare with $\int_{-3}^{-1} x\sqrt{x^2 + 1}\,dx$?

34. If $\int_{-1}^0 x^3\,dx = -\frac{1}{4}$ and $\int_0^1 x^3\,dx = \frac{1}{4}$, what does $\int_{-1}^1 x^3\,dx$ equal?

35. If $\int_1^2 (2x - x^2)\,dx = \frac{2}{3}$ and $\int_2^4 (2x - x^2)\,dx = -\frac{20}{3}$, what does $\int_1^4 (x^2 - 2x)\,dx$ equal?

36. If $\int_1^2 (2x - x^2)\,dx = \frac{2}{3}$, what does $\int_1^2 (12x - 6x^2)\,dx$ equal?

APPLICATIONS

37. **Total income** The income from an oil change service chain can be considered as flowing continuously at an annual rate given by

$$f(t) = 10{,}000e^{0.02t} \quad \text{(dollars)}.$$

Find the total income for this chain over the first 2 years (from $t = 0$ to $t = 2$).

38. **Total income** Suppose that a vending machine service company models its income by assuming that money flows continuously into the machines, with the annual rate of flow given by

$$f(t) = 120e^{0.01t},$$

in thousands of dollars. Find the total income from the machines over the first 3 years.

Velocity of blood In problems 39 and 40, the velocity of blood through a vessel is given by $v = K(R^2 - r^2)$, where K is the (constant) maximum velocity of the blood, R the (constant) radius of the vessel, and r the distance of the particular corpuscle from the center of the vessel. The rate of flow can be found by measuring the volume of blood that flows past a point in a given time period.

This volume, V, is given by

$$V = \int_0^R v(2\pi r \, dr).$$

39. Find the volume if $R = 0.30$ cm and $v = (0.30 - 3.33r^2)$ cm/sec.

40. Develop a general formula for V by evaluating

$$V = \int_0^R v(2\pi r \, dr)$$

using $v = K(R^2 - r^2)$.

Production In problems 41 and 42, the rate of production of a new line of products is given by

$$\frac{dx}{dt} = 200\left[1 + \frac{400}{(t + 40)^2}\right],$$

where x is the number of items produced and t is the number of weeks the products have been in production.

41. How many units were produced in the first 5 weeks?

42. How many units were produced in the 6th week?

43. **Depreciation** If the rate of depreciation of a building is given by $D'(t) = 3000(20 - t)$, $0 \leq t \leq 20$, what is the total depreciation of the building over the first 10 years ($t = 0$ to $t = 10$)?

44. **Depreciation** What is the total depreciation of the building in problem 43 during the next 10 years ($t = 10$ to $t = 20$)?

45. **Sales and advertising** A store finds that its sales change at a rate given by

$$S'(t) = -3t^2 + 300t,$$

where t is the number of days after an advertising campaign ends and $0 \leq t \leq 30$. Find
(a) the total sales for the first week after the campaign ends ($t = 0$ to $t = 7$).
(b) the total sales for the second week after the campaign ends ($t = 7$ to $t = 14$).

6.3 | AREA BETWEEN TWO CURVES

OBJECTIVES
- To find the area between two curves
- To find the average value of a function

We have used the definite integral to find the area of the region between a curve and the x-axis over an interval where the curve lies above the x-axis. We can easily extend this technique to finding the area between two curves over an interval where one curve lies above the other. (See Figure 6.8.)

FIGURE 6.8

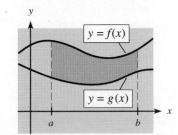

Suppose that the graphs of both $y = f(x)$ and $y = g(x)$ lie above the x-axis, and that the graph of $y = f(x)$ lies above $y = g(x)$ throughout the interval from $x = a$ to $x = b$; that is, $f(x) \geq g(x)$ on $[a, b]$.

Then $\displaystyle\int_a^b f(x)\, dx$ gives the area between the graph of $y = f(x)$ and the x-axis [see Figure 6.9(a)], and $\displaystyle\int_a^b g(x)\, dx$ gives the area between the graph of $y = g(x)$ and the x-axis [see Figure 6.9(b)]. As Figure 6.9(c) shows, the area of the region between the graphs of $y = f(x)$ and $y = g(x)$ is the difference of these two areas. That is,

FIGURE 6.9

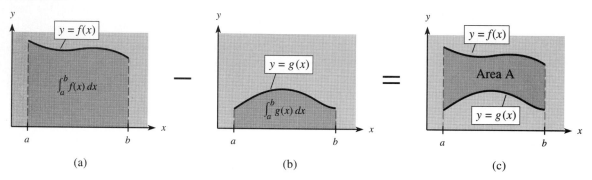

(a)   (b)   (c)

$$\text{Area between the curves} = \int_a^b f(x)\, dx - \int_a^b g(x)\, dx.$$

Although Figure 6.9(c) shows the graphs of both $y = f(x)$ and $y = g(x)$ lying above the x-axis, this difference of their integrals will always give the area between their graphs if both functions are continuous and if $f(x) \geq g(x)$ on the interval $[a, b]$.

Using the fact that

$$\int_a^b f(x)\, dx - \int_a^b g(x)\, dx = \int_a^b [f(x) - g(x)]\, dx,$$

we have the following result.

Area Between Two Curves	If f and g are continuous functions on $[a, b]$ and if $f(x) \geq g(x)$ on $[a, b]$, then the area of the region bounded by $y = f(x)$, $y = g(x)$, $x = a$, and $x = b$ is $$A = \int_a^b [f(x) - g(x)]\, dx.$$

EXAMPLE 1   Find the area of the region bounded by $y = x^2 + 4$, $y = x$, $x = 0$, and $x = 3$.

Solution We first sketch the graphs of the functions. The graph of the region is shown in Figure 6.10. Since $y = x^2 + 4$ lies above $y = x$ in the interval from $x = 0$

to $x = 3$, the area is

$$A = \int_0^3 [(x^2 + 4) - x] \, dx$$

$$= \frac{x^3}{3} + 4x - \frac{x^2}{2} \Big|_0^3$$

$$= \left(9 + 12 - \frac{9}{2}\right) - (0 + 0 - 0)$$

$$= 16\tfrac{1}{2} \text{ square units.}$$

FIGURE 6.10

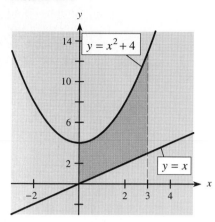

EXAMPLE 2

Find the area between $y = -x^2$ and the x-axis from $x = -1$ to $x = 1$.

Solution Graphing $y = -x^2$ gives us the region shown in Figure 6.11. Clearly $y = -x^2$ is below the x-axis $(y = 0)$. Using $f(x) = 0$ and $g(x) = -x^2$, we have $f(x) \geq g(x)$, so the area of the region from $x = -1$ to $x = 1$ is

$$A = \int_{-1}^1 [0 - (-x^2)] \, dx$$

$$= \int_{-1}^1 x^2 \, dx$$

$$= \frac{x^3}{3} \Big|_{-1}^1$$

$$= \frac{1}{3} - \left(-\frac{1}{3}\right) = \frac{2}{3} \text{ square units.}$$

FIGURE 6.11

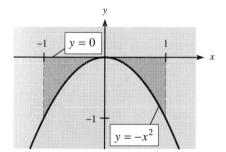

We are sometimes asked to find the area enclosed by two curves. In this case, we find the points of intersection of the curves to determine a and b.

EXAMPLE 3

Find the area enclosed by $y = x^2$ and $y = 2x + 3$.

Solution We first find a and b by finding the x-coordinates of the points of intersection of the graphs. Setting the y-values equal gives

$$x^2 = 2x + 3$$
$$x^2 - 2x - 3 = 0$$
$$(x - 3)(x + 1) = 0$$
$$x = 3, \, x = -1.$$

Thus $\quad a = -1 \quad$ and $\quad b = 3.$

We next sketch the graphs of these functions on the same set of axes. Because the graphs do not intersect on the interval $(-1, 3)$, we can determine which function is larger on this interval by evaluating $2x + 3$ and x^2 at any value c where $-1 < c < 3$. Figure 6.12 shows the region between the graphs, with $2x + 3 \geq x^2$ from $x = -1$ to $x = 3$. The area of the enclosed region is

$$A = \int_{-1}^{3} [(2x + 3) - x^2]\, dx$$

$$= x^2 + 3x - \frac{x^3}{3} \Big|_{-1}^{3}$$

$$= (9 + 9 - 9) - \left(1 - 3 + \frac{1}{3}\right)$$

$$= 10\tfrac{2}{3} \text{ square units.}$$

FIGURE 6.12

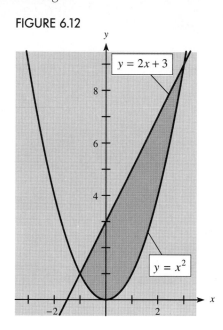

$y = 2x + 3$

$y = x^2$

Some graphs enclose two or more regions because they have more than two points of intersection.

EXAMPLE 4

Find the area of the region enclosed by the graphs of

$$y = f(x) = x^3 - x^2 \text{ and } y = g(x) = 2x.$$

Solution To find the points of intersection of the graphs, we set the y-values equal and solve for x.

$$x^3 - x^2 = 2x$$
$$x^3 - x^2 - 2x = 0$$
$$x(x - 2)(x + 1) = 0$$
$$x - 0,\ x - 2,\ x - -1$$

Graphing these functions between $x = -1$ and $x = 2$, we see that for any x-value in $(-1, 0)$, $f(x) \geq g(x)$, so $f(x) \geq g(x)$ for the region enclosed by the curves from $x = -1$ to $x = 0$. But evaluating the functions for any x-value in $(0, 2)$ shows that $f(x) \leq g(x)$ for the region enclosed by the curves from $x = 0$ to $x = 2$. See Figure 6.13.

FIGURE 6.13

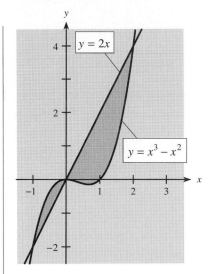

Thus we need one integral to find the area of the region from $x = -1$ to $x = 0$ and a second integral to find the area from $x = 0$ to $x = 2$. The area is found by summing these two integrals.

$$A = \int_{-1}^{0} [(x^3 - x^2) - (2x)]\, dx + \int_{0}^{2} [(2x) - (x^3 - x^2)]\, dx$$

$$= \int_{-1}^{0} (x^3 - x^2 - 2x)\, dx + \int_{0}^{2} (2x - x^3 + x^2)\, dx$$

$$= \left(\frac{x^4}{4} - \frac{x^3}{3} - x^2\right)\Big|_{-1}^{0} + \left(x^2 - \frac{x^4}{4} + \frac{x^3}{3}\right)\Big|_{0}^{2}$$

$$= \left[(0) - \left(\frac{1}{4} - \frac{-1}{3} - 1\right)\right] + \left[\left(4 - \frac{16}{4} + \frac{8}{3}\right) - (0)\right] = \frac{37}{12}$$

Thus the area between the curves is $\frac{37}{12}$ square units.

CHECKPOINT

1. True or false:
   (a) Over the interval $[a, b]$, the area between the continuous functions $f(x)$ and $g(x)$ is

   $$\int_{a}^{b} [f(x) - g(x)]\, dx.$$

   (b) If $f(x) \geq g(x)$ and the area between $f(x)$ and $g(x)$ is given by

   $$\int_{a}^{b} [f(x) - g(x)]\, dx,$$

   then $x = a$ and $x = b$ represent the left and right boundaries, respectively, of the region.

(c) To find points of intersection of $f(x)$ and $g(x)$, solve $f(x) = g(x)$.

2. Given $f(x) = x^2 + 3x - 9$ and $g(x) = \dfrac{1}{4}x^2$,

(a) find the points of intersection of $f(x)$ and $g(x)$.

(b) determine which function is greater than the other between the points found in part (a).

(c) set up the integral used to find the area between the curves in the interval between the points found in part (a).

(d) find the area.

If the graph of $y = f(x)$ lies on or above the x-axis from $x = a$ to $x = b$, then the area between the graph and the x-axis is

$$A = \int_a^b f(x)\, dx.$$

The area A is also the area of a rectangle with base equal to $b - a$ and height equal to the *average value* (or average height) of the function $y = f(x)$ (see Figure 6.14.)

FIGURE 6.14

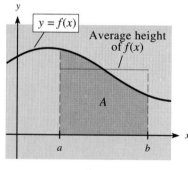

$$A = \int_a^b f(x)\, dx$$

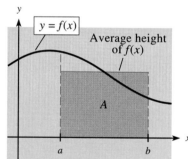

$$A = [\text{Average height of } f(x)](b - a)$$

Thus the average value of the function is

$$\frac{A}{b - a} = \frac{1}{b - a} \int_a^b f(x)\, dx.$$

Even if $f(x) \le 0$ on all or part of the interval $[a, b]$, we can find the average value by using the integral. Thus we have the following.

Average Value   The average value of a continuous function $y = f(x)$ over the interval $[a, b]$ is

$$\text{Average value} = \frac{1}{b - a} \int_a^b f(x)\, dx.$$

EXAMPLE 5

Suppose that the cost function for a product is $C(x) = 400 + x + 0.3x^2$.

(a) What is the average value of $C(x)$ for $x = 10$ to $x = 20$ units?

(b) Find the average cost per unit if 40 units are produced.

Solution

(a) The average value of $C(x)$ is

$$\frac{1}{20 - 10} \int_{10}^{20} (400 + x + 0.3x^2)\, dx = \frac{1}{10} \left(400x + \frac{x^2}{2} + 0.1x^3 \right) \Bigg|_{10}^{20}$$

$$= \frac{1}{10}[(8000 + 200 + 800) - (4000 + 50 + 100)]$$

$$= 485 \text{ (dollars)}.$$

(b) The average cost function is

$$\overline{C}(x) = \frac{C(x)}{x} = \frac{400}{x} + 1 + 0.3x.$$

The average cost per unit if 40 units are produced is

$$\overline{C}(40) = \frac{400}{40} + 1 + 0.3(40)$$

$$= 23 \text{ (dollars)}.$$

CHECKPOINT

3. Find the average value of $f(x) = x^2 - 4$ over $[-1, 3]$.

TECHNOLOGY CORNER

Consider the functions

(i) $f(x) = x - 2$ (ii) $f(x) = x^2 - 4$

(iii) $f(x) = x^3 - 4x$ (iv) $f(x) = x^4 - 4x^2$

1. Graph each function over the interval $[-2, 2]$.

2. On the graph, "eyeball" the average value (average height) of each function on $[-2, 2]$.

3. Find the average value of each function on $[-2, 2]$, and for each function sketch the graph of $y = $ (the average value). Compare this result with what you "eyeballed" in step 2.

1. (a) False. This is true only if $f(x) \geq g(x)$ over $[a, b]$.

(b) True   (c) True

2. (a) Solve $f(x) = g(x)$, or $x^2 + 3x - 9 = \frac{1}{4}x^2$.

$$\frac{3}{4}x^2 + 3x - 9 = 0$$
$$3x^2 + 12x - 36 = 0$$
$$x^2 + 4x - 12 = 0$$
$$(x + 6)(x - 2) = 0$$

$$x = -6 \quad | \quad x = 2$$

The points of intersection are $(-6, 9)$ and $(2, 1)$.

(b) Evaluating $g(x)$ and $f(x)$ at any point in the interval $(-6, 2)$ shows $g(x) > f(x)$, so $g(x) \geq f(x)$ on $[-6, 2]$.

(c) $A = \int_{-6}^{2} \left[\frac{1}{4}x^2 - (x^2 + 3x - 9) \right] dx$

(d) $A = \frac{x^3}{12} - \frac{x^3}{3} - \frac{3x^2}{2} + 9x \Big|_{-6}^{2} = 64$ square units

3. $\frac{1}{3 - (-1)} \int_{-1}^{3} (x^2 - 4)\, dx = \frac{1}{4}\left(\frac{x^3}{3} - 4x \right) \Big|_{-1}^{3}$

$$= \frac{1}{4}\left[(9 - 12) - \left(-\frac{1}{3} + 4 \right) \right]$$

$$= \frac{1}{4}\left(\frac{-20}{3} \right) = -\frac{5}{3}$$

EXERCISE 6.3

For each shaded region in problems 1–6, (a) form the integral that represents the area of the shaded region and (b) find the area of the region.

1.

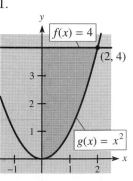

2.

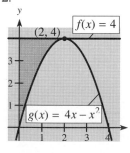

3.

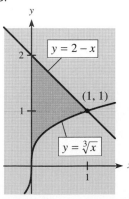

4.

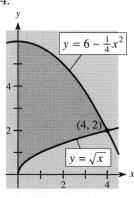

5.

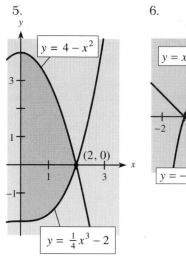

6.

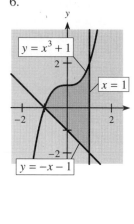

11.

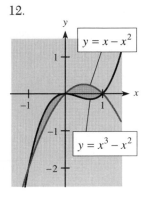

12.

For each shaded region in problems 7–12, (a) find the points of intersection of the curves, (b) form the integral that represents the area of the shaded region, and (c) find the area of the shaded region.

7.

8.

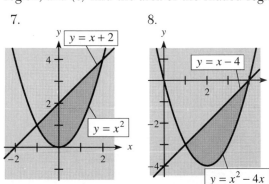

9.

10.

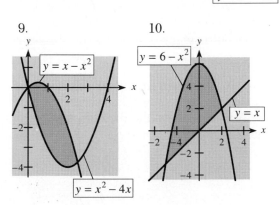

In problems 13–26, equations are given whose graphs enclose a region. In each problem, find the area of the region.

13. $f(x) = x^2 + 2$; $g(x) = -x^2$; $x = 0$; $x = 2$

14. $f(x) = x^2$; $g(x) = -\frac{1}{10}(10 + x)$; $x = 0$; $x = 3$

15. $y = x^3 - 1$; $y = x - 1$; to the right of the y-axis

16. $y = x^2 - 2x + 1$; $y = x^2 - 5x + 4$; $x = 2$

17. $y = \frac{1}{2}x^2$; $y = x^2 - 2x$

18. $y = x^2$; $y = 4x - x^2$

19. $h(x) = x^2$; $k(x) = \sqrt{x}$

20. $g(x) = 1 - x^2$; $h(x) = x^2 + x$

21. $f(x) = x^3$; $g(x) = x^2 + 2x$

22. $f(x) = x^3$; $g(x) = 2x - x^2$

23. $f(x) = \dfrac{3}{x}$; $g(x) = 4 - x$

24. $f(x) = \dfrac{6}{x}$; $g(x) = -x - 5$

25. $y = \sqrt{x + 3}$; $x = -3$; $y = 2$

26. $y = \sqrt{4 - x}$; $x = 4$; $y = 3$

In problems 27–32, find the average value of each function over the given interval.

27. $f(x) = 9 - x^2$ over $[0, 3]$

28. $f(x) = 2x - x^2$ over $[0, 2]$

29. $f(x) = x^3 - x$ over $[-1, 1]$
30. $f(x) = \frac{1}{2}x^3 + 1$ over $[-2, 0]$
31. $f(x) = \sqrt{x} - 2$ over $[1, 4]$
32. $f(x) = \sqrt[3]{x}$ over $[-8, -1]$

APPLICATIONS

33. **Cost** If the cost of producing x units of an item is $C(x) = x^2 + 400x + 2000$,
    (a) use $\overline{C}(x)$ to find the average cost of producing 1000 units.
    (b) find the average value of the cost function $C(x)$ over the interval from 0 to 1000.

34. **Inventory management** Figure 6.15 shows how an inventory of a product is depleted each quarter of a given year. What is the average inventory per month for the first 3 months for this product? [Assume that the graph is a line joining (0, 1300) and (3, 100).]

FIGURE 6.15

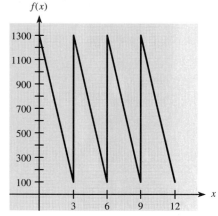

35. **Sales and advertising** The number of daily sales of a product was found to be given by
$$S = 100xe^{-x^2} + 100$$

x days after the start of an advertising campaign for this product. Find the average daily sales during the first 20 days of the campaign, that is, from $x = 0$ to $x = 20$.

36. **Sales and advertising** If no new advertising campaign is begun for the product in problem 35, what is the average number of sales per day for the next 10 days (from $x = 20$ to $x = 30$)?

37. **Demand** If the demand function for a product is given by
$$p = 500 + \frac{1000}{q + 1},$$

where p is the price and q is the number of units demanded, find the average price as demand ranges from 49 to 99 units.

38. **Total income** Suppose that the income from a slot machine in a casino flows continuously at a rate
$$f(t) = 100e^{0.1t},$$

where t is the time in hours since the casino opened. Then the total income during the first 10 hours is given by
$$\int_0^{10} 100e^{0.1t}\, dt.$$

Find the average income over the first 10 hours.

39. **Drug levels in the blood** A drug manufacturer has developed a time-release capsule with the number of milligrams of the drug in the bloodstream given by
$$S = 30x^{18/7} - 240x^{11/7} + 480x^{4/7},$$

where x is in hours and $0 \le x \le 4$. Find the average number of milligrams of the drug in the bloodstream for the first 4 hours after a capsule is taken.

6.4 | APPLICATIONS OF DEFINITE INTEGRALS IN BUSINESS AND ECONOMICS

OBJECTIVES

- To use definite integrals to find consumer's surplus
- To use definite integrals to find producer's surplus
- To use definite integrals to find total income and present value of continuous income streams

The definite integral can be used in a number of applications in business and economics, including price discrimination, revenue versus cost, consumer's surplus, and producer's surplus. In this section we will consider three applications, **consumer's surplus, producer's surplus,** and **continuous income streams.**

CONSUMER'S SURPLUS

Suppose that the demand for a product is given by $p = f(x)$, while supply of the product is described by $p = g(x)$. The price p_1 where the graphs of these functions intersect is the **equilibrium price** (see Figure 6.16). As the demand curve shows, some consumers (but not all) would be willing to pay more than $\$p_1$ for the product.

FIGURE 6.16

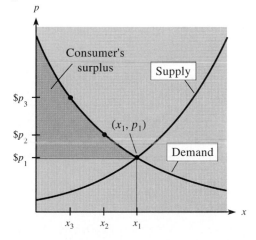

For example, some consumers would be willing to buy x_3 units if the price were $\$p_3$. Those consumers willing to pay more than $\$p_1$ are benefiting from the lower price. The total gain for all those consumers willing to pay more than $\$p_1$ is called the **consumer's surplus,** and under proper assumptions the area of the shaded region in Figure 6.16 represents this consumer's surplus.

Looking at Figure 6.17, we see that if the demand curve has equation $p = f(x)$, the consumer's surplus is given by the area between $f(x)$ and the x-axis from 0 to x_1, *minus* the area of the rectangle denoted TR:

$$CS = \int_0^{x_1} f(x)\, dx - p_1 x_1.$$

Note that $p_1 x_1$ is the area of the rectangle that represents the total revenue (see Figure 6.17).

FIGURE 6.17

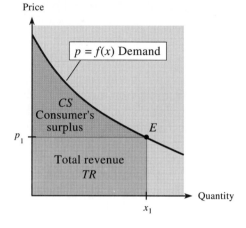

Price

$p = f(x)$ Demand

CS
Consumer's
surplus

E

P_1

Total revenue
TR

Quantity

x_1

EXAMPLE 1

The demand function for a product is $p = 100/(x + 1)$. If the equilibrium price is $20, what is the consumer's surplus?

Solution We must first find the quantity that will be purchased at this price. Letting $p = 20$, and solving for x, gives

$$20 = \frac{100}{x + 1}$$
$$20(x + 1) = 100$$
$$x + 1 = 5$$
$$x = 4.$$

Thus the equilibrium point is $(4, 20)$. The consumer's surplus is given by the formula

$$CS = \int_0^{x_1} f(x)\, dx - p_1 x_1$$

$$= \int_0^4 \frac{100}{x + 1}\, dx - 20 \cdot 4$$

$$= 100 \ln |x + 1| \Big|_0^4 - 80$$

$$= 100(\ln 5 - \ln 1) - 80$$

$$\approx 100(1.6094 - 0) - 80$$

$$= 160.94 - 80$$
$$= 80.94.$$

The consumer's surplus is $80.94.

EXAMPLE 2   The demand function for a product is $p = \sqrt{49 - 6x}$ and the supply function is $p = x + 1$. Find the equilibrium point and the consumer's surplus there.

Solution We can find the equilibrium point by solving the two equations simultaneously.

$$\sqrt{49 - 6x} = x + 1$$
$$49 - 6x = (x + 1)^2$$
$$0 = x^2 + 8x - 48$$
$$0 = (x + 12)(x - 4)$$
$$x = 4 \quad \text{or} \quad x = -12$$

Thus the equilibrium quantity is 4 and the equilibrium price is $5 (because $x = -12$ is not a solution). The graphs of the supply and demand functions are shown in Figure 6.18.

FIGURE 6.18

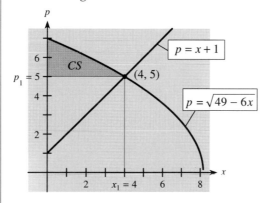

The consumer's surplus is given by

$$CS = \int_0^4 f(x)\, dx - p_1 x_1$$

$$= \int_0^4 \sqrt{49 - 6x}\, dx - 5 \cdot 4$$

$$= -\frac{1}{6} \int_0^4 \sqrt{49 - 6x}(-6\, dx) - 20$$

$$= -\frac{1}{9}(49 - 6x)^{3/2} \Big|_0^4 - 20$$

$$= -\frac{1}{9}[(25)^{3/2} - (49)^{3/2}] - 20$$

$$= -\frac{1}{9}(125 - 343) - 20$$

$$\approx 24.22 - 20 = 4.22. \qquad \text{The consumer's surplus is \$4.22.}$$

EXAMPLE 3

If a monopoly has a total cost function $C(x) = 60 + 2x^2$ for a product whose demand is given by $p = 30 - x$, find the consumer's surplus at the point where the monopoly has maximum profit.

Solution We must first find the point where the profit function is maximized. Since the demand for x units is $p = 30 - x$, the total revenue is

$$R(x) = (30 - x)x = 30x - x^2.$$

Thus the profit function is

$$P(x) = R(x) - C(x)$$
$$P(x) = 30x - x^2 - (60 + 2x^2)$$
$$P(x) = 30x - 60 - 3x^2.$$

Then $P'(x) = 30 - 6x$.
So $0 = 30 - 6x$ has solution $x = 5$.

Since $P''(5) = -6 < 0$, the profit for the monopolist is maximized when $x = 5$ units are sold at price $p = 25$.

The consumer's surplus at $x = 5$, $p = 25$ is given by

$$CS = \int_0^5 f(x)\, dx - 5 \cdot 25,$$

where $f(x)$ is the demand function.

$$CS = \int_0^5 (30 - x)\, dx - 125$$

$$= 30x - \frac{x^2}{2} \Big|_0^5 - 125$$

$$= \left(150 - \frac{25}{2} \right) - 125$$

$$= \frac{25}{2} = 12.50$$

The consumer's surplus is $12.50.

Producer's Surplus

When a product is sold at the equilibrium price, some producers will also benefit, for they would have sold the product at a lower price. The area between the line $p = p_1$ and the supply curve (from $x = 0$ to $x = x_1$) gives the producer's surplus (see Figure 6.19).

If the supply function is $p = g(x)$, the **producer's surplus** is given by the area between the graph of $p = g(x)$ and the x-axis from 0 to x_1 *subtracted from* the area

FIGURE 6.19

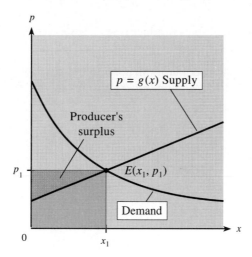

of the rectangle $0x_1Ep_1$.

$$PS = p_1x_1 - \int_0^{x_1} g(x)\, dx$$

Note that p_1x_1 represents the total revenue at the equilibrium point.

EXAMPLE 4

Suppose that the supply function for a product is $p = x^2 + x$. If the equilibrium price is \$20, what is the producer's surplus?

Solution Since $p = 20$, we can find x as follows:

$$20 = x^2 + x$$
$$0 = x^2 + x - 20$$
$$0 = (x + 5)(x - 4)$$
$$x = -5, x = 4.$$

The equilibrium point is $x = 4$, $p = 20$. The producer's surplus is given by

$$PS = 20 \cdot 4 - \int_0^4 (x^2 + x)\, dx$$

$$= 80 - \left(\frac{x^3}{3} + \frac{x^2}{2}\right)\bigg|_0^4$$

$$= 80 - \left(\frac{64}{3} + 8\right)$$

$$\approx 50.67.$$

The producer's surplus is \$50.67. See Figure 6.20.

FIGURE 6.20

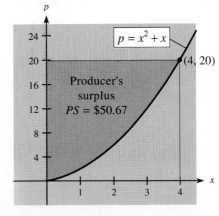

EXAMPLE 5

The demand function for a product is $p = \sqrt{49 - 6x}$ and the supply function is $p = x + 1$. Find the producer's surplus.

Solution We found the equilibrium point for these functions to be $(4, 5)$ in Example 2 (see Figure 6.18.) The producer's surplus is

$$PS = 5 \cdot 4 - \int_0^4 (x + 1)\, dx$$

$$= 20 - \left(\frac{x^2}{2} + x\right)\Bigg|_0^4$$

$$= 20 - (8 + 4) = 8.$$

The producer's surplus is $8.

CHECKPOINT

1. Suppose that for a certain product the supply function is $p = f(x)$, the demand function is $p = g(x)$, and the equilibrium point is (x_1, p_1). Decide whether the following are true or false.

(a) $CS = \int_0^{x_1} f(x)\, dx - p_1 x_1$

(b) $PS = \int_0^{x_1} f(x)\, dx - p_1 x_1$

2. If demand is $p = \dfrac{100}{x + 1}$, supply is $p = x + 1$, and the market equilibrium is $(9, 10)$, create the integral used to find the

(a) consumer's surplus.   (b) producer's surplus.

CONTINUOUS INCOME STREAMS

An oil company's profits depend upon the amount of oil that can be pumped from a well. Thus we can consider a pump at an oil field as producing a **continuous stream of income** for the owner. Since both the pump and the oil field "wear out" with time, the continuous stream of income is a function of time. Suppose $f(t)$ is the (annual) *rate* of flow of income from this pump; then we can find the total income from the rate of income by using integration. In particular, the total income for k years is given by

$$\text{Total income} = \int_0^k f(t)\, dt.$$

EXAMPLE 6

A small oil company considers the continuous pumping of oil from a well as a continuous income stream with its annual rate of flow at time t given by

$$f(t) = 600e^{-0.2t}$$

in thousands of dollars. Find an estimate of the total income from this well over the next 10 years.

Solution Total income $= \displaystyle\int_0^{10} f(t)\, dt$

$$= \int_0^{10} 600e^{-0.2t}\, dt$$

$$= \frac{600}{-0.2} e^{-0.2t} \Big|_0^{10}$$

$$= -3000(e^{-2} - 1)$$

$$\approx 2594 \text{ (to the nearest integer)}$$

Thus the total income is approximately \$2,594,000.

Besides the total income from a continuous income stream, the **present value** of the stream is also important. The present value is the value today of a continuous income stream that will be providing income in the future. The present value is useful in deciding when to replace machinery (such as the oil pump in the example) or what new equipment to select.

To find the present value of a continuous stream of income with rate of flow $f(t)$, we first graph the function $f(t)$ and divide the time interval from 0 to k into n subintervals of width Δt_i, $i = 1$ to n.

The total amount of income is the area under this curve between $t = 0$ and $t = k$. We can approximate the amount of income in each subinterval by finding the area of the rectangle in that subinterval. (See Figure 6.21.)

FIGURE 6.21

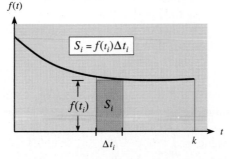

We have shown that the compound amount S that accrues if \$P is invested for t years at an annual rate r, compounded continuously, is

$$S = Pe^{rt}.$$

Thus the present value of the investment that yields the single payment of \$S after t years is

$$P = \frac{S}{e^{rt}} = Se^{-rt}.$$

The contribution to S in the ith subinterval is $S_i = f(t_i)\Delta t_i$, and the present value of this amount is

$$P_i = f(t_i)\Delta t_i e^{-rt_i}.$$

Thus the total present value of S can be approximated by

$$\sum_{i=1}^{n} f(t_i)\Delta t_i e^{-rt_i}.$$

This approximation improves as $\Delta t_i \to 0$ with the present value given by

$$\lim_{\Delta t_i \to 0} \sum_{i=1}^{n} f(t_i)\Delta t_i e^{-rt_i}.$$

This limit gives the present value as a definite integral.

Present Value of a Continuous Income Stream

If $f(t)$ is the rate of continuous income flow at interest rate r, compounded continuously, then the present value of the continuous income stream is

$$\text{Present value} = \int_0^k f(t)e^{-rt}\, dt,$$

where $t = 0$ to $t = k$ is the time interval.

EXAMPLE 7

Suppose that the oil company in Example 6 is planning to sell the well due to its remote location. Suppose further that the company wants to use the present value of the well over the next 10 years to help establish its selling price. If they determine that the annual rate of flow is

$$f(t) = 600e^{-0.2(t+5)}$$

in thousands of dollars, and if money is worth 10%, compounded continuously, find this present value.

Solution Present value $= \displaystyle\int_0^{10} f(t)e^{-rt}\, dt$

$$= \int_0^{10} 600e^{-0.2(t+5)}\, e^{-0.1t}\, dt$$

$$= \int_0^{10} 600e^{-0.3t-1}\, dt$$

$$= \frac{600}{-0.3}e^{-0.3t-1}\Big|_0^{10}$$

$$= -2000(e^{-4} - e^{-1})$$

$$\approx 699 \qquad \text{(to the nearest integer)}$$

Thus the present value is $699,000.

CHECKPOINT

3. Suppose that a continuous income stream has an annual rate of flow given by $f(t) = 5000e^{-0.01t}$, and suppose that money is worth 7% compounded continuously. Create the integral used to find the

   (a) total income for the next 5 years.

   (b) present value for the next 5 years.

TECHNOLOGY CORNER

Suppose that for a certain product the demand function is $p = 200e^{-0.01x}$ and the supply function is $p = \sqrt{200x + 49}$.

1. Graph these functions.

2. Use the graphs to find the market equilibrium.

3. Find the consumer's surplus.

4. Find the producer's surplus.

CHECKPOINT
SOLUTIONS

1. (a) False. Consumer's surplus uses the demand function, so

$$CS = \int_0^{x_1} g(x)\, dx - p_1 x_1.$$

   (b) False. Producer's surplus uses the supply function, but the formula is

$$PS = p_1 x_1 - \int_0^{x_1} f(x)\, dx.$$

2. (a) $CS = \int_0^9 \dfrac{100}{x + 1}\, dx - 90$

   (b) $PS = 90 - \int_0^9 (x + 1)\, dx$

3. (a) $\int_0^5 5000e^{-0.01t}\, dt$

   (b) $\int_0^5 (5000e^{-0.01t})(e^{-0.07t})\, dt = \int_0^5 5000e^{-0.08t}\, dt$

EXERCISE 6.4

CONSUMER'S SURPLUS

1. The demand function for a product is $p = 34 - x^2$. If the equilibrium price is $9, what is the consumer's surplus?

2. The demand function for a product is $p = 100 - 4x$. If the equilibrium price is $40, what is the consumer's surplus?

3. The demand function for a product is $p = 200/(x + 2)$. If the equilibrium quantity is 8 units, what is the consumer's surplus?

4. The demand function for a product is $p = 100/(1 + 2x)$. If the equilibrium quantity is 12 units, what is the consumer's surplus?

5. The demand function for a certain product is $p = 81 - x^2$ and the supply function is $p = x^2 + 4x + 11$. Find the equilibrium point and the consumer's surplus there.

6. The demand function for a certain product is $p = 49 - x^2$ and the supply function is $p = 4x + 4$. Find the equilibrium point and the consumer's surplus there.

7. If the demand function for a product is $p = 12/(x + 1)$ and the supply function for it is $p = 1 + 0.2x$, find the consumer's surplus under pure competition.

8. If the demand function for a good is $p = 110 - x^2$ and the supply function for it is $p = 2 - \frac{6}{5}x + \frac{1}{5}x^2$, find the consumer's surplus under pure competition.

9. A monopoly has a total cost function $C = 1000 + 120x + 6x^2$ for its product, which has demand function $p = 360 - 3x - 2x^2$. Find the consumer's surplus at the point where the monopoly has maximum profit.

10. A monopoly has a total cost function $C = 500 + 2x^2 + 10x$ for its product, which has demand function $p = -\frac{1}{3}x^2 - 2x + 30$. Find the consumer's surplus at the point where the monopoly has a maximum profit.

PRODUCER'S SURPLUS

11. Suppose that the supply function for a good is $p = 4x^2 + 2x + 2$. If the equilibrium price is $422, what is the producer's surplus there?

12. Suppose that the supply function for a good is $p = 0.1x^2 + 3x + 20$. If the equilibrium price is $36, what is the producer's surplus there?

13. If the supply function for a commodity is $p = 10e^{x/3}$, what is the producer's surplus when 15 units are sold?

14. If the supply function for a commodity is $p = 40 + 100(x + 1)^2$, what is the producer's surplus at $x = 20$?

15. Find the producer's surplus for a product if its demand function is $p = 81 - x^2$ and its supply function is $p = x^2 + 4x + 11$.

16. Find the producer's surplus for a product if its demand function is $p = 49 - x^2$ and its supply function is $p = 4x + 4$.

17. Find the producer's surplus for a product with demand function $p = 12/(x + 1)$ and supply function $p = 1 + 0.2x$.

18. Find the producer's surplus for a product with demand function $p = 110 - x^2$ and supply function $p = 2 - \frac{6}{5}x + \frac{1}{5}x^2$.

19. The demand function for a certain product is $p = 144 - 2x^2$ and the supply function is $p = x^2 + 33x + 48$. Find the producer's surplus at the equilibrium point.

20. The demand function for a product is $p = 280 - 4x - x^2$ and the supply function for it is $p = 160 + 4x + x^2$. Find the producer's surplus at the equilibrium point.

CONTINUOUS INCOME STREAMS

21. Find the total income over the next 10 years

from a continuous income stream that has an annual rate of flow at time t given by $f(t) = 12,000$ (dollars).

22. Find the total income over the next 8 years from a continuous income stream with an annual rate of flow at time t given by $f(t) = 8500$ (dollars).

23. Suppose that a steel company views the production of its continuous caster as a continuous income stream with a monthly rate of flow at time t given by

$$f(t) = 24,000e^{0.03t} \quad \text{(dollars)}.$$

Find the total income from this caster in the first year.

24. Suppose that the Quick-Fix Car Service franchise finds that the income generated by its stores can be modeled by assuming that the income is a continuous stream with a monthly rate of flow at time t given by

$$f(t) = 10,000e^{0.02t} \quad \text{(dollars)}.$$

Find the total income from a Quick-Fix store for the first 2 years of operation.

25. A small brewery considers the output of its bottling machine as a continuous income stream with an annual rate of flow at time t given by

$$f(t) = 80e^{-0.1t}$$

in thousands of dollars. Find the total income from this stream for the next 10 years.

26. A company that services a number of vending machines considers its income as a continuous stream with an annual rate of flow at time t given by

$$f(t) = 120e^{-0.4t}$$

in thousands of dollars. Find the income from this stream over the next 5 years.

27. A franchise models the profit from its store as a continuous income stream with a monthly rate of flow at time t given by

$$f(t) = 3000e^{0.004t} \quad \text{(dollars)}.$$

When a new store opens, its manager is judged against the model, with special emphasis on the second half of the first year. Find the total profit for the second 6-month period ($t = 6$ to $t = 12$).

28. The Quick-Fix Car Service franchise has a continuous income stream with a monthly rate of flow modeled by $f(t) = 10,000e^{0.02t}$ (dollars). Find the total income for years 2 through 5.

29. A continuous income stream has an annual rate of flow at time t given by

$$f(t) = 12,000e^{0.04t} \quad \text{(dollars)}.$$

If money is worth 8%, compounded continuously, find the present value of this stream for the next 8 years.

30. A continuous income stream has an annual rate of flow at time t given by

$$f(t) = 9000e^{0.12t} \quad \text{(dollars)}.$$

Find the present value of this stream for the next 10 years, if money is worth 6%, compounded continuously.

31. The income from an established chain of laundromats is a continuous stream with its annual rate of flow at time t given by $f(t) = 63,000$ (dollars). If money is worth 7%, compounded continuously, find the present value of this chain over the next 5 years.

32. The profit from an insurance agency can be considered as a continuous income stream with an annual rate of flow at time t given by $f(t) = 84,000$ (dollars). Find the present value of this agency over the next 12 years, if money is worth 8%, compounded continuously.

33. Suppose that a printing firm considers the production of its presses as a continuous income stream. If the annual rate of flow at time t is given by

$$f(t) = 97.5e^{-0.2(t+3)}$$

in thousands of dollars, and if money is worth 6%, compounded continuously, find the present value of the presses over the next 10 years.

34. Suppose that a vending machine company is considering selling some of its machines. Suppose further that the income from these particular machines is a continuous stream with an annual rate of flow at time t given by

$$f(t) = 12e^{-0.4(t+3)}$$

in thousands of dollars. Find the present value of the machines over the next 5 years if money is worth 10%, compounded continuously.

35. A 58-year old couple is considering opening a business of their own. They will purchase either an established Gift and Card Shoppe or open a new Video Rental Palace. The Gift Shoppe has a continuous income stream with

an annual rate of flow at time t given by

$$G(t) = 30,000 \quad \text{(dollars)},$$

and the Video Palace has a continuous income stream with a projected annual rate of flow at time t given by

$$V(t) = 21,600e^{0.08t} \quad \text{(dollars)}.$$

The initial investment for each business is the same, and money is worth 10%, compounded continuously. Find the present value of each business over the next 7 years (until the couple reaches age 65), to see which is the better buy.

36. If the couple in problem 35 plans to keep the business until age 70 (for the next 12 years), find each present value to see which business is the better buy in this case.

6.5 | USING TABLES OF INTEGRALS

OBJECTIVE

• To use tables of integrals to evaluate certain integrals

We have used some special integration formulas to evaluate integrals, but many integration problems require additional formulas or methods. In this section we will learn how to use a table of integration formulas already developed for us. Table 6.1 contains selected integration formulas (many more exist). Using the formulas is not quite as easy as it may sound, because finding the correct formula and using it properly may present some problems. The following examples illustrate how these formulas are used.

TABLE 6.1   Integration formulas

1. $\displaystyle\int u^n\, du = \frac{u^{n+1}}{n+1} + C,$ for $n \neq -1$

2. $\displaystyle\int \frac{du}{u} = \int u^{-1}\, du = \ln|u| + C$

3. $\displaystyle\int a^u\, du = a^u \log_a e + C = \frac{a^u}{\ln a} + C$

4. $\displaystyle\int e^u\, du = e^u + C$

5. $\displaystyle\int \frac{du}{a^2 - u^2} = \frac{1}{2a}\ln\left|\frac{a+u}{a-u}\right| + C$

6. $\displaystyle\int \sqrt{u^2 + a^2}\, du = \frac{1}{2}(u\sqrt{u^2+a^2} + a^2\ln|u + \sqrt{u^2+a^2}|) + C$

7. $\displaystyle\int \sqrt{u^2 - a^2}\, du = \frac{1}{2}(u\sqrt{u^2-a^2} - a^2\ln|u + \sqrt{u^2-a^2}|) + C$

8. $\displaystyle\int \frac{du}{\sqrt{u^2 + a^2}} = \ln|u + \sqrt{u^2+a^2}| + C$

9. $\displaystyle\int \frac{du}{u\sqrt{a^2 - u^2}} = -\frac{1}{a}\ln\left|\frac{a + \sqrt{a^2-u^2}}{u}\right| + C$

10. $\displaystyle\int \frac{du}{\sqrt{u^2 - a^2}} = \ln|u + \sqrt{u^2-a^2}| + C$

11. $\displaystyle\int \frac{du}{u\sqrt{a^2 + u^2}} = -\frac{1}{a}\ln\left|\frac{a + \sqrt{a^2+u^2}}{u}\right| + C$

12. $\displaystyle\int \frac{u\, du}{au + b} = \frac{u}{a} - \frac{b}{a^2}\ln|au + b| + C$

13. $\displaystyle\int \frac{du}{u(au + b)} = \frac{1}{b}\ln\left|\frac{u}{au+b}\right| + C$

14. $\displaystyle\int \ln u\, du = u(\ln u - 1) + C$

15. $\displaystyle\int \frac{u\, du}{(au + b)^2} = \frac{1}{a^2}\left(\ln|au + b| + \frac{b}{au+b}\right) + C$

16. $\displaystyle\int u\sqrt{au + b}\, du = \frac{2(3au - 2b)(au + b)^{3/2}}{15a^2} + C$

17. $\displaystyle\int u\, dv = uv - \int v\, du$

EXAMPLE 1   Evaluate $\displaystyle\int \frac{dx}{\sqrt{x^2 + 4}}$.

Solution We must find a formula in Table 6.1 that is of the same form as this integral. We see that formula 8 has the desired form, *if* we let $u = x$ and $a = 2$. Thus

$$\int \frac{dx}{\sqrt{x^2 + 4}} = \ln|x + \sqrt{x^2 + 4}| + C.$$

EXAMPLE 2 Evaluate $\displaystyle\int_1^2 \frac{dx}{x^2 + 2x}$.

Solution There does not appear to be any formula having exactly the same form as our integral. But if we rewrite our integral as

$$\int_1^2 \frac{dx}{x(x + 2)},$$

we see that formula 13 will work. Letting $u = x$, $a = 1$, and $b = 2$, we get

$$\int_1^2 \frac{dx}{x(x + 2)} = \frac{1}{2} \ln \left| \frac{x}{x + 2} \right|\Big\|_1^2$$

$$= \frac{1}{2} \ln \left| \frac{2}{4} \right| - \frac{1}{2} \ln \left| \frac{1}{3} \right|$$

$$= \frac{1}{2} \left(\ln \frac{1}{2} - \ln \frac{1}{3} \right)$$

$$= \frac{1}{2} \ln \frac{3}{2}$$

$$= \frac{1}{2} \ln 1.5.$$

Although the formulas in Table 6.1 are given in terms of the variable u, they may be used with any variable.

EXAMPLE 3 Evaluate $\displaystyle\int \frac{dq}{9 - q^2}$.

Solution The formula that applies in this case is formula 5, with $a = 3$, and $u = q$. Then

$$\int \frac{dq}{9 - q^2} = \frac{1}{2 \cdot 3} \ln \left| \frac{3 + q}{3 - q} \right| + C = \frac{1}{6} \ln \left| \frac{3 + q}{3 - q} \right| + C$$

EXAMPLE 4 Evaluate $\displaystyle\int \ln (2x + 1)\, dx$.

Solution This integral has the form of formula 14, with $u = 2x + 1$. But if $u = 2x + 1$, du must be represented by the differential of $2x + 1$ (that is, $2\, dx$). Thus

$$\int \ln (2x + 1)\, dx = \frac{1}{2} \int \ln (2x + 1)(2\, dx)$$

$$= \frac{1}{2}(2x + 1)[\ln (2x + 1) - 1] + C.$$

1. Can both $\displaystyle\int \frac{dx}{\sqrt{x^2 - 4}}$ and $\displaystyle -\int \frac{dx}{\sqrt{4 - x^2}}$ be evaluated with formula 10 in Table 6.1?

2. Determine the formula used to evaluate $\displaystyle\int \frac{3x}{4x - 5}\,dx$, and show how the formula would be applied.

3. True or false: To use a formula, the given integral must correspond exactly to the formula, including du.

4. True or false: $\displaystyle\int \frac{dx}{x^2(3x^2 - 7)}$ can be evaluated with formula 13.

5. True or false: $\displaystyle\int \frac{dx}{(6x + 1)^2}$ can be evaluated with either formula 1 or formula 15.

6. True or false: $\displaystyle\int \sqrt{x^2 + 4}\,dx$ can be evaluated with any one of formula 1, formula 6, or formula 16.

EXAMPLE 5

Evaluate $\displaystyle\int_2^3 \frac{dx}{x\sqrt{81 - 9x^2}}$.

Solution This integral is similar to that of formula 9 in Table 6.1. Letting $a = 9$ and $u = 3x$, and multiplying the numerator and denominator by 3, gives the proper form.

$$\int_2^3 \frac{dx}{x\sqrt{81 - 9x^2}} = \int_2^3 \frac{3dx}{3x\sqrt{81 - 9x^2}}$$

$$= -\frac{1}{9}\ln\left|\frac{9 + \sqrt{81 - 9x^2}}{3x}\right|\Bigg\|_2^3$$

$$= -\frac{1}{9}\ln\left(\frac{9 + \sqrt{0}}{9}\right) - \left[-\frac{1}{9}\ln\left(\frac{9 + \sqrt{45}}{6}\right)\right]$$

$$= \frac{1}{9}\left[\ln\left(\frac{9 + \sqrt{45}}{6}\right) - \ln(1)\right] = \frac{1}{9}\ln\left(\frac{3 + \sqrt{5}}{2}\right)$$

It should be pointed out again that the formulas given in Table 6.1 represent only a very small sample of all possible integration formulas. Additional formulas may be found in books of mathematical tables.

1. No. Although $\displaystyle\int \frac{dx}{\sqrt{x^2 - 4}}$ can be evaluated with formula 10 from Table 6.1,

$-\displaystyle\int \frac{dx}{\sqrt{4 - x^2}}$ cannot, because $\sqrt{4 - x^2}$ cannot be rewritten in the form $\sqrt{u^2 - a^2}$ as is needed to use this formula.

2. Use formula 12 with $u = x$, $a = 4$, $b = -5$, and $du = dx$.

$$\int \frac{3x}{4x - 5}\, dx = 3 \int \frac{x\, dx}{4x - 5} = 3 \int \frac{u\, du}{au + b} = 3\left(\frac{u}{a} - \frac{b}{a^2} \ln |au + b| + C\right)$$
$$= \frac{3x}{4} + \frac{15}{16} \ln |4x - 5| + C$$

3. True. An exact correspondence with the formula and du is necessary.

4. False. With $u = x^2$, we must have $du = 2x\, dx$. In this problem there is no x with dx, so the problem cannot correspond to formula 13.

5. False. The integral can be evaluated only with formula 1, not with formula 15. The correspondence is $u = 6x + 1$, $du = 6\, dx$, and $n = -2$.

6. False. The integral can be evaluated only with formula 6, with $u = x$, $du = dx$, and $a = 2$. ∎

EXERCISE 6.5

Evaluate the following integrals.

1. $\displaystyle\int \frac{dx}{16 - x^2}$

2. $\displaystyle\int \frac{dx}{x(3x + 5)}$

3. $\displaystyle\int_1^4 \frac{dx}{x\sqrt{9 + x^2}}$

4. $\displaystyle\int \frac{dx}{x\sqrt{9 - x^2}}$

5. $\displaystyle\int \ln w\, dw$

6. $\displaystyle\int \frac{dv}{v(3v + 8)}$

7. $\displaystyle\int_0^2 \frac{q\, dq}{6q + 9}$

8. $\displaystyle\int_1^5 \frac{dq}{q\sqrt{25 + q^2}}$

9. $\displaystyle\int 3^x\, dx$

10. $\displaystyle\int_0^3 \sqrt{x^2 + 16}\, dx$

11. $\displaystyle\int_5^7 \sqrt{x^2 - 25}\, dx$

12. $\displaystyle\int \frac{x\, dx}{(3x + 2)^2}$

13. $\displaystyle\int w\sqrt{4w + 5}\, dw$

14. $\displaystyle\int \frac{dy}{\sqrt{9 + y^2}}$

15. $\displaystyle\int x\, 5^{x^2}\, dx$

16. $\displaystyle\int \sqrt{9x^2 + 4}\, dx$

17. $\displaystyle\int_0^3 x\sqrt{x^2 + 4}\, dx$

18. $\displaystyle\int x\sqrt{x^4 - 36}\, dx$

19. $\displaystyle\int \frac{5\, dx}{x\sqrt{8 - x^2}}$

20. $\displaystyle\int x\, e^{x^2}\, dx$

21. $\displaystyle\int \frac{dx}{\sqrt{9x^2 - 4}}$

22. $\displaystyle\int \frac{dx}{16 - 4x^2}$

23. $\displaystyle\int_5^6 \frac{dx}{x^2 - 16}$

24. $\displaystyle\int_0^1 \frac{x\, dx}{6 - 5x}$

25. $\displaystyle\int \frac{dx}{\sqrt{(3x + 1)^2 + 1}}$

26. $\displaystyle\int \frac{dx}{9 - (2x + 3)^2}$

27. $\displaystyle\int_0^3 x\sqrt{(x^2 + 1)^2 + 9}\, dx$

28. $\displaystyle\int_1^e x \ln x^2\, dx$

29. $\displaystyle\int \frac{x\, dx}{7 - 3x^2}$

30. $\displaystyle\int_0^1 \frac{e^x}{1 + e^x}\, dx$

31. $\displaystyle\int \frac{dx}{\sqrt{4x^2 + 7}}$

32. $\displaystyle\int e^{2x}\sqrt{3e^x + 1}\, dx$

33. $\displaystyle\int \frac{e^{\sqrt{x-1}}}{\sqrt{x - 1}}\, dx$

34. $\displaystyle\int \frac{3x}{\sqrt{x^4 - 9}}\, dx$

35. $\displaystyle\int \frac{x^3 \, dx}{(4x^2 + 5)^2}$

36. $\displaystyle\int (e^x + 1)^3 \, e^x \, dx$

APPLICATIONS

37. **Producer's surplus** If the supply function for a commodity is $p = 40 + 100 \ln (x + 1)^2$, what is the producer's surplus at $x = 20$?

38. **Consumer's surplus** If the demand function for a good is $p = 5000e^{-x} + 4$, where x is the number of hundreds of bushels of wheat, what is the consumer's surplus at $x = 7$, $p = 9.10$?

39. **Cost** If the marginal cost for a good is $\overline{MC} =$

$\sqrt{x^2 + 9}$ and if the fixed cost is \$300, what is the total cost function?

40. **Total cost** What is the total cost of producing 4 units for the good in problem 39?

41. **Consumer's surplus** Suppose that the demand function for an appliance is

$$p = \frac{400q + 400}{(q + 2)^2}.$$

What is the consumer's surplus if the equilibrium price is \$19 and the equilibrium quantity is 18?

6.6 | INTEGRATION BY PARTS

OBJECTIVE

- To evaluate integrals using the method of integration by parts

Formula 17 in Table 6.1 defines a special technique for integration.

Integration by Parts	$\displaystyle\int u \, dv = uv - \int v \, du.$

This formula follows from the Product Rule for derivatives (actually differentials) as follows.

$$\frac{d}{dx}(uv) = u\frac{dv}{dx} + v\frac{du}{dx} \quad \text{so} \quad d(uv) = u \, dv + v \, du$$

Rearranging the differential form and then integrating both sides gives the following.

$$u \, dv = d(uv) - v \, du$$
$$\int u \, dv = \int d(uv) - \int v \, du$$
$$\int u \, dv = uv - \int v \, du$$

Integration by parts is very useful if the integral we seek to evaluate can be treated as the product of one function, u, and the differential dv of a second function, so that the two integrals $\int dv$ and $\int v \cdot du$ can be found. Let us consider an example using this method.

EXAMPLE 1 | Evaluate $\int xe^x \, dx$.

Solution We cannot evaluate this integral using methods we have learned. But we can "split" the integrand into two parts, setting one part equal to u and the other part equal to dv. This "split" must be done in such a way that $\int dv$ and $\int v \, du$ can be evaluated. Letting $u = x$ and $dv = e^x \, dx$ are possible choices. If we make these choices, we have

$$u = x \qquad\qquad dv = e^x \, dx$$
$$du = 1 \, dx \qquad v = \int e^x \, dx = e^x$$

Then

$$\int xe^x \, dx = u \cdot v - \int v \, du$$
$$= x \cdot e^x - \int e^x \, dx$$
$$= xe^x - e^x + C.$$

We see that choosing $u = x$ and $dv = e^x \, dx$ worked in evaluating $\int xe^x \, dx$ in Example 1. If we had chosen $u = e^x$ and $dv = x \, dx$, the results would not have been so successful.

How can we select u and dv to make integration by parts work? There are no general rules for separating the integrand into u and dv, but the goal is to select a dv that is integrable and will result in an $\int v \, du$ that is also integrable. There are usually just two reasonable choices, and it may be necessary to try both. Practice will increase your insight and lead to increasingly successful educated guesses. Consider the following examples.

EXAMPLE 2 | Evaluate $\int x \ln x \, dx$.

Solution Let $u = \ln x$ and $dv = x \, dx$. Then

$$du = \frac{1}{x} dx \quad \text{and} \quad v = \frac{x^2}{2}.$$

So

$$\int x \ln x \, dx = u \cdot v - \int v \, du$$
$$= (\ln x)\frac{x^2}{2} - \int \frac{x^2}{2} \cdot \frac{1}{x} dx$$
$$= \frac{x^2}{2} \ln x - \int \frac{x}{2} dx$$
$$= \frac{x^2}{2} \ln x - \frac{x^2}{4} + C.$$

Note that letting $dv = \ln x \, dx$ would lead to great difficulty in evaluating $\int dv$ and $\int v \, du$, so it would not be a wise choice.

EXAMPLE 3

Evaluate $\int \ln x^2 \, dx$.

Solution It is frequently good practice to let expressions involving logarithms be part of u in integrating by parts, because the derivatives of logarithmic expressions are usually simple.

In this problem, we can let $u = \ln x^2$. Thus

$$u = \ln x^2 \qquad\qquad dv = dx$$
$$du = \frac{2x}{x^2} \, dx = \frac{2}{x} \, dx \qquad\qquad v = x$$

Then,

$$\int \ln x^2 \, dx = x \ln x^2 - \int x \cdot \frac{2}{x} \, dx$$
$$= x \ln x^2 - 2x + C.$$

Note that if we write $\ln x^2$ as $2 \ln x$, we can also evaluate this integral using formula 14 in Table 6.1, so integration by parts would not be needed.

CHECKPOINT

1. True or false: In evaluating $\int u \, dv$ by parts,

   (a) the parts u and dv are selected and the parts du and v are calculated.

   (b) the differential (often dx) is always chosen as part of dv.

   (c) the parts du and v are found from u and dv as follows:

   $$du = u' \, dx \quad \text{and} \quad v = \int dv.$$

   (d) For $\int \frac{3x}{e^{2x}} \, dx$, we could choose $u = 3x$ and $dv = e^{2x} \, dx$.

2. For $\int \frac{\ln x}{x^4} \, dx$,

   (a) identify u and dv.

   (b) find du and v.

   (c) complete the evaluation of the integral.

Sometimes it is necessary to repeat the integration by parts to complete the evaluation. As before, the goal is to produce a new integral that is simpler.

EXAMPLE 4 | Evaluate $\int x^2 e^{2x}\, dx$.

Solution Let $u = x^2$ and $dv = e^{2x}\, dx$, so $du = 2x\, dx$ and $v = \frac{1}{2}e^{2x}$. Then

$$\int x^2 e^{2x}\, dx = \frac{1}{2}x^2 e^{2x} - \int xe^{2x}\, dx.$$

We cannot evaluate $\int xe^{2x}\, dx$ directly, but this new integral is simpler than the original, and a second integration by parts will be successful. Letting $u = x$ and $dv = e^{2x}\, dx$ gives $du = dx$ and $v = \frac{1}{2}e^{2x}$. So

$$\int x^2 e^{2x}\, dx = \frac{1}{2}x^2 e^{2x} - \left(\frac{1}{2}xe^{2x} - \int \frac{1}{2}e^{2x}\, dx\right)$$

$$= \frac{1}{2}x^2 e^{2x} - \frac{1}{2}xe^{2x} + \frac{1}{4}e^{2x} + C$$

$$= \frac{1}{4}e^{2x}(2x^2 - 2x + 1) + C.$$

The most obvious choices for u and dv are not always the correct ones, as the following example shows. Integration by parts still requires some trial and error.

EXAMPLE 5 | Evaluate $\int x^3 \sqrt{x^2 + 1}\, dx$.

Solution Since x^3 can be integrated easily, it may appear that the new integral would be simplified if we let $u = \sqrt{x^2 + 1}$ and $dv = x^3$. But then du would be $\frac{1}{2}(x^2 + 1)^{-1/2}\, 2x$, making $\int v\, du$ more complicated than the original integral. However, we can use $\sqrt{x^2 + 1}$ as part of dv, and we can evaluate $\int dv$ if we let $dv = x\sqrt{x^2 + 1}\, dx$. Then

$$u = x^2 \qquad dv = (x^2 + 1)^{1/2}x\, dx$$

$$du = 2x\, dx \qquad v = \int (x^2 + 1)^{1/2}(x\, dx) = \frac{1}{2}\int (x^2 + 1)^{1/2}(2x\, dx)$$

$$v = \frac{1}{2}\frac{(x^2 + 1)^{3/2}}{3/2} = \frac{1}{3}(x^2 + 1)^{3/2}$$

Then $\displaystyle \int x^3 \sqrt{x^2 + 1}\, dx = \frac{x^2}{3}(x^2 + 1)^{3/2} - \int \frac{1}{3}(x^2 + 1)^{3/2}(2x\, dx)$

$$= \frac{x^2}{3}(x^2 + 1)^{3/2} - \frac{1}{3}\frac{(x^2 + 1)^{5/2}}{5/2} + C$$

$$= \frac{x^2}{3}(x^2 + 1)^{3/2} - \frac{2}{15}(x^2 + 1)^{5/2} + C$$

$$= \frac{1}{15}(x^2 + 1)^{3/2}[5x^2 - 2(x^2 + 1)] + C$$

$$= \frac{1}{15}(x^2 + 1)^{3/2}(3x^2 - 2) + C.$$

One further note about integration by parts. It can be very useful on certain types of problems, but not on all types. Don't attempt to use integration by parts when easier methods are available.

1. (a) True   (b) True   (c) True

   (d) False. The product of u and dv must equal the original integrand. Rewrite as

$$\int \frac{3x}{e^{2x}}\,dx = \int 3xe^{-2x}\,dx,$$

then choose $u = 3x$ and $dv = e^{-2x}\,dx$.

2. (a) $u = \ln x$ and $dv = x^{-4}\,dx$

   (b) $du = \dfrac{1}{x}\,dx$ and $v = \displaystyle\int x^{-4}\,dx = \frac{x^{-3}}{-3}$

   (c) $\displaystyle\int \frac{\ln x}{x^4}\,dx = uv - \int v\,du$

$$= (\ln x)\left(\frac{x^{-3}}{-3}\right) - \int \frac{x^{-3}}{-3} \cdot \frac{1}{x}\,dx$$

$$= \frac{-\ln x}{3x^3} + \frac{1}{3}\int x^{-4}\,dx$$

$$= -\frac{\ln x}{3x^3} + \frac{1}{3}\left(\frac{x^{-3}}{-3}\right) + C$$

$$= -\frac{\ln x}{3x^3} - \frac{1}{9x^3} + C$$

Evaluate the following integrals.

1. $\displaystyle\int xe^{2x}\,dx$

2. $\displaystyle\int xe^{-x}\,dx$

3. $\displaystyle\int x^2 \ln x\,dx$

4. $\displaystyle\int x^3 \ln x\,dx$

5. $\displaystyle\int_4^6 q\sqrt{q-4}\,dq$

6. $\displaystyle\int_0^1 y(1-y)^{3/2}\,dy$

7. $\displaystyle\int_0^1 x^2 e^x\,dx$

8. $\displaystyle\int x^3 e^x\,dx$

9. $\displaystyle\int \frac{\ln x}{x^2}\,dx$

10. $\displaystyle\int \frac{\ln(x-1)}{\sqrt{x-1}}\,dx$

11. $\displaystyle\int xe^{x^2}\,dx$

12. $\displaystyle\int x^2 e^{-x}\,dx$

13. $\displaystyle\int \frac{x}{\sqrt{x-3}}\,dx$

14. $\displaystyle\int \frac{x^2}{\sqrt{x-3}}\,dx$

15. $\displaystyle\int_1^e \ln x\,dx$

16. $\displaystyle\int_0^4 \frac{t}{e^t}\,dt$

17. $\displaystyle\int x \ln(2x-3)\,dx$

18. $\displaystyle\int x \ln(4x)\,dx$

19. $\displaystyle\int q^3\sqrt{q^2-3}\,dq$

20. $\displaystyle\int \frac{x^3}{\sqrt{9-x^2}}\,dx$

21. $\displaystyle\int_0^4 x^3\sqrt{x^2+9}\,dx$

22. $\int_0^2 x^3 e^{x^2}\, dx$ (Use problem 11.)

23. $\int \sqrt{x}\,\ln x\, dx$

24. $\int_1^2 (\ln x)^2\, dx$

25. $\int x^3 \ln^2 x\, dx$

26. $\int e^{2x}\sqrt{e^x + 1}\, dx$

APPLICATIONS

27. ***Producer's surplus*** If the supply function for a commodity is $p = 30 + 50\ln (2x + 1)^2$, what is the producer's surplus at $x = 30$?

28. ***Cost*** If the marginal cost function for a product is $\overline{MC} = 1 + 3\ln (x + 1)$, and if the fixed cost is $100, find the total cost function.

29. ***Present value*** Suppose that a machine's pro-duction can be considered as a continuous income stream with annual rate of flow at time t given by

$$f(t) = 10{,}000 - 500t \qquad \text{(dollars).}$$

If money is worth 10%, compounded continu-ously, find the present value of the machine over the next 5 years.

30. ***Present value*** Suppose that the production of a machine used to mine coal is considered as a continuous income stream with annual rate of flow at time t given by

$$f(t) = 280{,}000 - 14{,}000t \qquad \text{(dollars).}$$

If money is worth 7%, compounded continu-ously, find the present value of this machine over the next 8 years.

6.7 | IMPROPER INTEGRALS AND THEIR APPLICATIONS

OBJECTIVES
- To evaluate improper integrals
- To apply improper integrals to continuous income streams

One application of calculus to business and to statistics involves finding the area of a region that extends infinitely to the left or right along the x-axis (see Figure 6.22). The areas of regions of this type can be found using **improper integrals.**

FIGURE 6.22

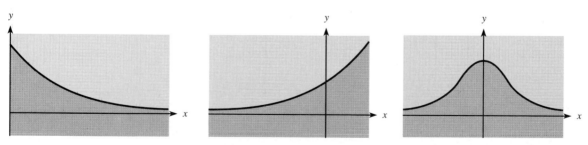

Let us consider how to find the area between the curve $y = 1/x^2$ and the x-axis to the right of $x = 1$.

To find the area under this curve from $x = 1$ to $x = b$, where b is any number greater than 1 (see Figure 6.23), we evaluate

$$A = \int_1^b \frac{1}{x^2}\,dx = \frac{-1}{x}\Big|_1^b = \frac{-1}{b} - \left(\frac{-1}{1}\right)$$
$$= 1 - \frac{1}{b}.$$

Note that the larger b is, the closer the area is to 1. If $b = 100$, $A = 99/100$; if $b = 1000$, $A = 999/1000$; and if $b = 1,000,000$, $A = 999,999/1,000,000$.

We can represent the area of the region under $1/x^2$ to the right of 1 using the notation

$$\lim_{b \to \infty} \int_1^b \frac{1}{x^2}\,dx = \lim_{b \to \infty}\left(1 - \frac{1}{b}\right),$$

FIGURE 6.23

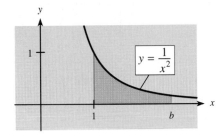

where $\lim_{b \to \infty}$ represents the limit as b gets larger without bound. Clearly

$$\lim_{b \to \infty} \frac{1}{b} = 0,$$

so

$$\lim_{b \to \infty}\left(1 - \frac{1}{b}\right) = 1.$$

Thus the area under the curve $y = 1/x^2$ to the right of $x = 1$ is 1.

In general, we define the area under a curve $y = f(x)$ to the right of $x = a$, with $f(x) \geq 0$, to be

$$\text{Area} = \lim_{b \to \infty}(\text{area from } a \text{ to } b) = \lim_{b \to \infty} \int_a^b f(x)\,dx.$$

This motivates the definition below.

| **Improper Integral** | $\int_a^\infty f(x)\,dx = \lim_{b \to \infty} \int_a^b f(x)\,dx$ |

If the limit defining the improper integral is a finite number, we say that the integral *converges;* if the limit is not a finite number, we say that the integral *diverges.*

EXAMPLE 1

Evaluate the following improper integrals, if they converge.

(a) $\displaystyle\int_1^\infty \frac{1}{x^3}\,dx$ 　　　　　　　　　　(b) $\displaystyle\int_1^\infty \frac{1}{x}\,dx$

Solution

(a) $\displaystyle\int_1^\infty \frac{1}{x^3}\,dx = \lim_{b\to\infty} \int_1^b \frac{1}{x^3}\,dx$

$\displaystyle\qquad = \lim_{b\to\infty} \left[\frac{x^{-2}}{-2}\right]_1^b$

$\displaystyle\qquad = \lim_{b\to\infty} \left[\frac{-1}{2b^2} - \left(\frac{-1}{2(1)^2}\right)\right]$

$\displaystyle\qquad = \lim_{b\to\infty} \left(\frac{-1}{2b^2} + \frac{1}{2}\right)$

Now as $b\to\infty$, $\dfrac{-1}{2b^2} \to 0$, so the limit, and the integral, converge to $\frac{1}{2}$. That is,

$\displaystyle\int_1^\infty \frac{1}{x^3}\,dx = \frac{1}{2}.$

(b) $\displaystyle\int_1^\infty \frac{1}{x}\,dx = \lim_{b\to\infty} \int_1^b \frac{1}{x}\,dx$

$\displaystyle\qquad = \lim_{b\to\infty} \left[\ln|x|\right]_1^b$

$\displaystyle\qquad = \lim_{b\to\infty} (\ln b - \ln 1)$

Now $\ln b$ increases without bound as $b\to\infty$, so the limit, and the integral, diverge. We write this as

$\displaystyle\int_1^\infty \frac{1}{x}\,dx = \infty.$

From Example 1 we can conclude that the area under the curve $y = 1/x^3$ to the right of $x = 1$ is $\frac{1}{2}$, while the corresponding area under the curve $y = 1/x$ is infinite. (We have already seen that the corresponding area under $y = 1/x^2$ is 1.)

As Figure 6.24 shows, the graphs of the curves look similar, but the graph of $1/x^2$ gets "close" to the x-axis much more rapidly than the graph of $1/x$. The area under $y = 1/x$ does not converge to a finite number because as $x \to \infty$ the graph of $1/x$ does not approach the x-axis rapidly enough.

FIGURE 6.24

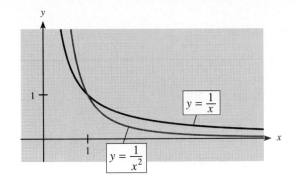

We have seen in Section 6.4 that the present value of a continuous income stream over a fixed number of years can be found using a definite integral. When this notion is extended to an infinite time interval, the result is called the **capital value** of the income stream and is given by

$$\text{Capital value} = \int_0^\infty f(t)\, e^{-rt}\, dt,$$

where $f(t)$ is the annual rate of flow at time t, and r is the annual interest rate, compounded continuously.

EXAMPLE 2

Suppose that an organization wants to establish a trust fund that will provide a continuous income stream with an annual rate of flow at time t given by $f(t) = 10,000$. If the interest rate remains at 10%, compounded continuously, find the capital value of the fund.

Solution The capital value of the fund is given by

$$\int_0^\infty 10,000e^{-0.10t}\, dt = \lim_{b \to \infty} \int_0^b 10,000e^{-0.10t}\, dt$$

$$= \lim_{b \to \infty} \left[-100,000e^{-0.10t} \right]_0^b$$

$$= \lim_{b \to \infty} \left(\frac{-100,000}{e^{0.10b}} + 100,000 \right)$$

$$= 100,000.$$

Thus the capital value of the fund is $100,000.

Another term for a fund such as the one in Example 2 is a **perpetuity.** Usually the rate of flow of a perpetuity is a constant. If the rate of flow is a constant A, it can be shown that the capital value is given by A/r (see problem 23 in the exercise set).

1. True or false:

(a) $\displaystyle\lim_{b \to +\infty} \frac{1}{b^p} = 0$ if $p > 0$

(b) $\displaystyle\lim_{b \to +\infty} b^p = +\infty$ if $p > 0$

(c) $\displaystyle\lim_{b \to +\infty} e^{-pb} = 0$ if $p > 0$

2. Evaluate the following (if they exist):

(a) $\displaystyle\int_1^\infty \frac{1}{x^{4/3}}\, dx = \lim_{b \to \infty} \int_1^b x^{-4/3}\, dx$

(b) $\displaystyle\int_0^\infty \frac{dx}{\sqrt{x+1}}$

A second improper integral has the form

$$\int_{-\infty}^b f(x)\, dx$$

and is defined by:

$$\int_{-\infty}^b f(x)\, dx = \lim_{a \to \infty} \int_{-a}^b f(x)\, dx.$$

The integral converges if the limit is finite. In addition, the improper integral

$$\int_{-\infty}^\infty f(x)\, dx$$

is defined by:

$$\int_{-\infty}^\infty f(x)\, dx = \lim_{a \to \infty} \int_{-a}^0 f(x)\, dx + \lim_{b \to \infty} \int_0^b f(x)\, dx.$$

If both limits are finite, the improper integral converges; otherwise, it diverges.

EXAMPLE 3

Evaluate the following integrals.

(a) $\displaystyle\int_{-\infty}^4 e^{3x}\, dx$

(b) $\displaystyle\int_{-\infty}^\infty \frac{x^3}{(x^4+3)^2}\, dx$

Solution

(a) $\displaystyle\int_{-\infty}^4 e^{3x}\, dx = \lim_{a \to \infty} \int_{-a}^4 e^{3x}\, dx$

$$= \lim_{a \to \infty} \left[\left(\frac{1}{3} \right) e^{3x} \right]_{-a}^4$$

$$= \lim_{a \to \infty} \left[\left(\frac{1}{3}\right)e^{12} - \left(\frac{1}{3}\right)e^{-3a} \right]$$

$$= \lim_{a \to \infty} \left[\left(\frac{1}{3}\right)e^{12} - \left(\frac{1}{3}\right)\left(\frac{1}{e^{3a}}\right) \right] \quad \text{(because } 1/e^{3a} \to 0 \quad \text{as} \quad a \to \infty\text{)}$$

$$= \frac{1}{3}e^{12}$$

(b) $\displaystyle\int_{-\infty}^{\infty} \frac{x^3}{(x^4 + 3)^2}\, dx = \lim_{a \to \infty} \int_{-a}^{0} \frac{x^3}{(x^4 + 3)^2}\, dx + \lim_{b \to \infty} \int_{0}^{b} \frac{x^3}{(x^4 + 3)^2}\, dx$

$$= \lim_{a \to \infty} \left[\frac{1}{4}\frac{(x^4 + 3)^{-1}}{-1} \right]_{-a}^{0} + \lim_{b \to \infty} \left[\frac{1}{4}\frac{(x^4 + 3)^{-1}}{-1} \right]_{0}^{b}$$

$$= \lim_{a \to \infty} \left[-\frac{1}{4}\left(\frac{1}{3} - \frac{1}{a^4 + 3}\right) \right] + \lim_{b \to \infty} \left[-\frac{1}{4}\left(\frac{1}{b^4 + 3} - \frac{1}{3}\right) \right]$$

$$= -\frac{1}{12} + 0 + 0 + \frac{1}{12} = 0$$

$$\left(\text{since } \lim_{a \to \infty} \frac{1}{a^4 + 3} = 0 \quad \text{and} \quad \lim_{b \to \infty} \frac{1}{b^4 + 3} = 0 \right)$$

TECHNOLOGY CORNER

1. Let $f(x) = \dfrac{\ln x}{x^2}$ and $F(x) = \displaystyle\int_{1}^{x} f(t)\, dt = \int_{1}^{x} \frac{\ln t}{t^2}\, dt$.

   (a) Find a formula for $F(x)$ by evaluating the integral (see Exercise 6.6, problem 9).

   (b) Graph both $f(x)$ and $F(x)$ and observe the behavior of each function as x approaches $+\infty$.

   (c) Does $\displaystyle\int_{1}^{\infty} f(t)\, dt$ exist? If so, what is it?

2. Let $f(x) = x^2 e^{-x}$ and $F(x) = \displaystyle\int_{0}^{x} f(t)\, dt = \int_{0}^{x} t^2 e^{-t}\, dt$.

   (a) Find a formula for $F(x)$.

   (b) Graph both $f(x)$ and $F(x)$ and observe the behavior of each function as x approaches $+\infty$.

   (c) Does $\displaystyle\int_{0}^{\infty} f(t)\, dt$ exist? If so, what is it?

1. (a) True   (b) True   (c) True

2. (a) $\displaystyle \lim_{b \to \infty} \int_1^b x^{-4/3}\, dx = \lim_{b \to \infty} \frac{x^{-1/3}}{-1/3}\Big|_1^b = \lim_{b \to \infty} \left(\frac{-3}{b^{1/3}} - \frac{-3}{1}\right) = 0 + 3 = 3$

   (b) $\displaystyle \lim_{b \to \infty} \int_0^b (x+1)^{-1/2}\, dx = \lim_{b \to \infty} \frac{(x+1)^{1/2}}{1/2}\Big|_0^b = \lim_{b \to \infty} 2\sqrt{x+1}\;\Big|_0^b$

$$= \lim_{b \to \infty} (2\sqrt{b+1} - 2) = \infty$$

(Integral diverges)

EXERCISE 6.7

In problems 1–16, evaluate the improper integrals where possible.

1. $\displaystyle \int_1^\infty e^{-x}\, dx$

2. $\displaystyle \int_0^\infty x^2 e^{-x^3}\, dx$

3. $\displaystyle \int_1^\infty \frac{1}{x^4}\, dx$

4. $\displaystyle \int_0^\infty e^{3x}\, dx$

5. $\displaystyle \int_1^\infty \frac{1}{\sqrt{x}}\, dx$

6. $\displaystyle \int_5^\infty \frac{dx}{(x-1)^3}$

7. $\displaystyle \int_{-\infty}^{-1} \frac{10}{x^2}\, dx$

8. $\displaystyle \int_{-\infty}^{-2} \frac{x}{\sqrt{x^2-1}}\, dx$

9. $\displaystyle \int_{-\infty}^0 x^2 e^{-x^3}\, dx$

10. $\displaystyle \int_{-\infty}^0 \frac{x}{(x^2+1)^2}\, dx$

11. $\displaystyle \int_{-\infty}^{-1} \frac{6}{x}\, dx$

12. $\displaystyle \int_{-\infty}^{-2} \frac{3x}{x^2+1}\, dx$

13. $\displaystyle \int_{-\infty}^\infty \frac{2x}{x^2+1}\, dx$

14. $\displaystyle \int_{-\infty}^\infty \frac{x}{(x^2+1)^2}\, dx$

15. $\displaystyle \int_{-\infty}^\infty x^3 e^{-x^4}\, dx$

16. $\displaystyle \int_{-\infty}^\infty x^4 e^{-x^5}\, dx$

17. For what value of c does

$$\int_0^\infty \frac{c}{e^{0.5t}}\, dt = 1?$$

18. For what value of c does

$$\int_{10}^\infty \frac{c}{x^3}\, dx = 1?$$

In problems 19–22, find the area of the region under the graph of $y = f(x)$ and to the right of $x = 1$.

19. $f(x) = \dfrac{x}{e^{x^2}}$ 20. $f(x) = \dfrac{1}{\sqrt[5]{x^3}}$

21. $f(x) = \dfrac{1}{\sqrt[3]{x^5}}$ 22. $f(x) = \dfrac{1}{x\sqrt{x}}$

APPLICATIONS

23. **Capital value** Suppose that a continuous income stream has an annual rate of flow at time t given by $f(t) = A$, where A is a constant. If the interest rate is r (as a decimal, $r > 0$), compounded continuously, show that the capital value of the stream is A/r.

24. **Capital value** Suppose that a donor wishes to provide a cash gift to a hospital that will generate a continuous income stream with an annual rate of flow at time t given by $f(t) = \$20{,}000$. If money is worth 12%, compounded continuously, find the capital value of this perpetuity.

25. **Capital value** Suppose that a business provides a continuous income stream with an annual rate of flow at time t given by $f(t) = 120e^{0.04t}$ in thousands of dollars. If the interest rate is 9%, compounded continuously, find the capital value of the business.

26. ***Capital value*** Suppose that the output of the machinery in a factory can be considered as a continuous income stream with annual rate of flow at time t given by $f(t) = 450e^{-0.09t}$ in thousands of dollars. If the annual interest rate is 6%, compounded continuously, find the capital value of the machinery.

27. ***Capital value*** A business has a continuous income stream with an annual rate of flow at time t given by $f(t) = 56,000e^{0.02t}$ (dollars). If the interest rate is 10%, compounded continuously, find the capital value of the business.

28. ***Capital value*** Suppose that a business provides a continuous income stream with an annual rate of flow at time t given by $f(t) = 10,800e^{0.06t}$ (dollars). If money is worth 12%, compounded continuously, find the capital value of the business.

29. ***Radioactive waste*** Suppose that the rate at which a nuclear power plant produces radioactive waste is proportional to the number of years it has been operating, according to $f(t) = 500t$ in pounds per year. Suppose also that the waste decays exponentially at a rate of 3% per year. Then the amount of radioactive waste that will accumulate in b years is given by

$$\int_0^b 500te^{-0.03(b-t)}\, dt.$$

(a) Evaluate this integral.
(b) How much waste will accumulate in the long run? Take the limit as $b \to \infty$ in part (a).

6.8 | NUMERICAL INTEGRATION METHODS: TRAPEZOIDAL RULE AND SIMPSON'S RULE

OBJECTIVES

- To approximate definite integrals by using the Trapezoidal Rule
- To approximate definite integrals by using Simpson's Rule

We have studied several techniques for integration and have even used tables to evaluate some integrals. Yet some functions that arise in practical problems cannot be integrated by using any formula. For any function $f(x) \geq 0$ on an interval $[a, b]$, however, we have seen that a definite integral can be viewed as an area, and that we can usually approximate the area, and hence the integral (see Figure 6.25 on the following page). One such approximation method uses rectangles, as we saw when we defined the definite integral. In this section, we consider two other **numerical integration methods** to approximate a definite integral: the **Trapezoidal Rule** and **Simpson's Rule.**

To develop the Trapezoidal Rule formula, we assume that $f(x) \geq 0$ on $[a, b]$ and we subdivide the interval $[a, b]$ into n equal pieces, each of length $(b - a)/n = h$. Then, within each subdivision, we can approximate the area by using a trapezoid. As shown in Figure 6.26, we can use the formula for the area of a trapezoid to

FIGURE 6.25

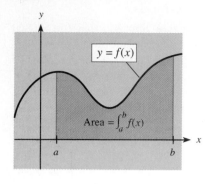

FIGURE 6.26

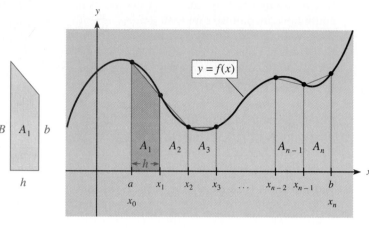

$$A_1 = \left[\frac{B+b}{2}\right]h$$

$$A_1 = \left[\frac{B+b}{2}\right]h = \left[\frac{f(x_0)+f(x_1)}{2}\right]h$$

approximate the area of the first subdivision. Continuing in this way for each trapezoid, we have

$$\int_a^b f(x)\,dx \approx A_1 + A_2 + A_3 + \ldots + A_{n-1} + A_n$$

$$= \left[\frac{f(x_0)+f(x_1)}{2}\right]h + \left[\frac{f(x_1)+f(x_2)}{2}\right]h + \left[\frac{f(x_2)+f(x_3)}{2}\right]h + \ldots + \left[\frac{f(x_{n-1})+f(x_n)}{2}\right]h$$

$$= \frac{h}{2}[f(x_0) + f(x_1) + f(x_1) + f(x_2) + f(x_2) + \ldots + f(x_{n-1}) + f(x_{n-1}) + f(x_n)].$$

This can be simplified to obtain the Trapezoidal Rule.

Trapezoidal Rule

If f is continuous on $[a, b]$, then

$$\int_a^b f(x)\,dx \approx \frac{h}{2}[f(x_0) + 2f(x_1) + 2f(x_2) + \ldots + 2f(x_{n-1}) + f(x_n)].$$

where $h = \dfrac{b-a}{n}$.

Despite the fact that we used areas to develop the Trapezoidal Rule, we can use this rule to evaluate definite integrals even if $f(x) < 0$ on all or part of $[a, b]$.

EXAMPLE 1

Use the Trapezoidal Rule to approximate $\int_1^3 \frac{1}{x}\,dx$ with

(a) $n = 4$.

(b) $n = 8$.

Solution First, we note that this integral can be evaluated directly:

$$\int_1^3 \frac{1}{x}\,dx = \ln|x| \Big|_1^3 = \ln 3 - \ln 1 = \ln 3 \approx 1.099 \qquad \text{(from a calculator)}.$$

(a) The interval $[1, 3]$ must be divided into 4 equal subintervals of width $h = \frac{3-1}{4} = \frac{2}{4} = \frac{1}{2}$ as follows.

Thus from the Trapezoidal Rule, we have

$$\int_1^3 \frac{1}{x}\,dx \approx \frac{h}{2}[f(x_0) + 2f(x_1) + 2f(x_2) + 2f(x_3) + f(x_4)]$$

$$= \frac{1/2}{2}[f(1) + 2f(1.5) + 2f(2) + 2f(2.5) + f(3)]$$

$$= \frac{1}{4}\left[1 + 2\left(\frac{1}{1.5}\right) + 2\left(\frac{1}{2}\right) + 2\left(\frac{1}{2.5}\right) + \frac{1}{3}\right]$$

$$\approx 0.25(1 + 1.333 + 1 + 0.8 + .3333)$$

$$\approx 1.117.$$

(b) In this case, the interval $[1, 3]$ is divided into 8 equal subintervals of width $h = \frac{3-1}{8} = \frac{2}{8} = \frac{1}{4}$ as follows.

Thus from the Trapezoidal Rule, we have

$$\int_1^3 \frac{1}{x}\,dx \approx \frac{h}{2}[f(x_0) + 2f(x_1) + 2f(x_2) + 2f(x_3) + 2f(x_4) + 2f(x_5)$$

$$+ 2f(x_6) + 2f(x_7) + f(x_8)]$$

$$= \frac{1/4}{2}\left[\frac{1}{1} + 2\left(\frac{1}{1.25}\right) + 2\left(\frac{1}{1.5}\right) + 2\left(\frac{1}{1.75}\right) + 2\left(\frac{1}{2}\right) + 2\left(\frac{1}{2.25}\right) + \right.$$

$$\left. 2\left(\frac{1}{2.5}\right) + 2\left(\frac{1}{2.75}\right) + \frac{1}{3}\right]$$

$$\approx 1.103.$$

In Example 1, since we know that the value of the integral is $\ln 3 \approx 1.099$, we can measure the accuracy of each approximation. We can see that a larger value of n (namely, $n = 8$) produced a more accurate approximation to $\ln 3$. In general, larger values of n produce more accurate approximations, but they also make computations more difficult.

Since the exact value of an integral is rarely available when an approximation is used, it is important to have some way to judge the accuracy of an answer. The following formula, which we state without proof, can be used to bound the error that results from using the Trapezoidal Rule.

Trapezoidal Rule Error

The error E in using the Trapezoidal Rule to approximate $\int_a^b f(x)\, dx$ satisfies

$$|E| \le \frac{(b-a)^3}{12n^2}\left[\max_{a \le x \le b} |f''(x)|\right].$$

For a numerical method to be worthwhile, there must be some way of assessing its accuracy. Hence, this formula is important. We leave its application, however, to more advanced courses.

The Trapezoidal Rule was developed by using line segments to approximate the function over each subinterval, and then using the area under that line segment to approximate the area under the curve. Another numerical method, Simpson's Rule, uses a parabola to approximate the function over each pair of subintervals (see Figure 6.27), and then uses the areas under the parabolas to approximate the area under the curve.

Simpson's Rule (n Is Even)

If $f(x)$ is continuous on $[a, b]$, and if $[a, b]$ is divided into an *even* number n of equal subdivisions, then

$$\int_a^b f(x)\, dx \approx \frac{h}{3}[f(x_0) + 4f(x_1) + 2f(x_2) + 4f(x_3) + \ldots +$$
$$2f(x_{n-2}) + 4f(x_{n-1}) + f(x_n)],$$

where $h = \dfrac{b-a}{n}$.

We leave the derivation of Simpson's Rule to more advanced courses.

FIGURE 6.27

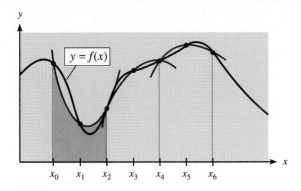

EXAMPLE 2

Use Simpson's Rule with $n = 4$ to approximate $\int_{1}^{3} \frac{1}{x} \, dx$.

Solution Since $n = 4$ is even, Simpson's Rule can be used, and the interval is divided into 4 subintervals of length $h = \frac{3-1}{4} = \frac{1}{2}$ as follows.

$$
\begin{array}{ccccc}
1 & 1.5 & 2 & 2.5 & 3 \\
\vdash & \vdash & \vdash & \vdash & \dashv \\
x_0 & x_1 & x_2 & x_3 & x_4
\end{array}
$$

$$
\begin{aligned}
\int_{1}^{3} \frac{1}{x} \, dx &\approx \frac{1/2}{3}[f(1) + 4f(1.5) + 2f(2) + 4f(2.5) + f(3)] \\
&= \frac{1}{6}\left[\frac{1}{1} + 4\left(\frac{1}{1.5}\right) + 2\left(\frac{1}{2}\right) + 4\left(\frac{1}{2.5}\right) + \frac{1}{3}\right] \\
&= 1.100
\end{aligned}
$$

Notice that the result of Example 2 is better than both the $n = 4$ and $n = 8$ Trapezoidal Rule approximations done in Example 1. In general, Simpson's Rule is more accurate than the Trapezoidal Rule for a given number of subdivisions. We can determine the accuracy of Simpson's Rule approximations by using the following formula.

Simpson's Rule Error Formula

The error E in using Simpson's Rule to approximate $\int_{a}^{b} f(x) \, dx$ satisfies

$$
|E| \le \frac{(b-a)^5}{180n^4}\left[\max_{a \le x \le b} |f^{(4)}(x)|\right]
$$

The presence of the factor $180n^4$ in the denominator indicates that the error will often be quite small for even a modest value of n. While Simpson's Rule often leads to more accurate results than the Trapezoidal Rule for a fixed choice of n, the Trapezoidal Rule is sometimes used because its error is more easily determined than that of Simpson's Rule, or, more importantly, because the number of subdivisions is odd.

1. If $[1, 4]$ is divided into 3 equal subintervals, find the
   (a) width h of each subinterval.
   (b) subdivision points.

2. True or false:
   (a) When the Trapezoidal Rule is used, the number of subdivisions, n, must be even.
   (b) When Simpson's Rule is used, the number of subdivisions, n, must be even.

3. We know that $\int_0^2 x \, dx = 2$. Use $n = 4$ subdivisions to find the

   (a) Trapezoidal Rule approximation.
   (b) Simpson's Rule approximation.

■

One advantage of both these methods is that they may be used when only functional values at the subdivision points are known, and the function formula itself is not known. This can be especially useful in applied problems.

EXAMPLE 3   A pharmaceutical company tests the body's ability to assimilate a drug. The test is done by administering a 200 mg dose and then, every half-hour, monitoring the rate of assimilation. The table below gives the data; t is time (in hr) and $R(t)$ is the rate of assimilation (in mg/hr).

t	0	0.5	1.0	1.5	2.0	2.5	3.0
$R(t)$	0.0	15.3	32.3	51.0	74.8	102.0	130.9

To find the total amount of the drug (in mg) that is assimilated in the first 3 hours, the company must find

$$\int_0^3 R(t) \, dt.$$

Use Simpson's Rule to approximate this definite integral.

Solution The values of t correspond to the endpoints of the subintervals and the values of $R(t)$ correspond to functional values at those endpoints. From the table we see that $h = \frac{1}{2}$ and $n = 6$ (even); thus Simpson's Rule is applied as follows.

$$\int_0^3 R(t)\, dt \approx \frac{h}{3}[R(t_0) + 4R(t_1) + 2R(t_2) + 4R(t_3) + 2R(t_4) + 4R(t_5) + R(t_6)]$$

$$= \frac{1}{6}[0 + 4(15.3) + 2(32.3) + 4(51.0) + 2(74.8) + 4(102.0) + 130.9]$$

$$\approx 169.7 \text{ mg}$$

Thus at the end of 3 hours, the body had assimilated approximately 169.7 mg of the 200 mg dosage.

Notice in Example 3 that the Trapezoidal Rule could also be used since it relies only on the values of $R(t)$ at the subdivision endpoints.

In practice, these kinds of approximations are usually done with a computer, where the computations can be done quickly, even for large values of n. In addition, numerical methods (and hence computer programs) exist that approximate the errors, even in cases like Example 3, where the function is not known. We leave any discussion of error approximation formulas and additional numerical techniques for a more advanced course.

TECHNOLOGY CORNER

Let $f(x) = (\ln x)^2$ on $[1, 5]$.

1. Graph the function.

2. Develop a table of values of $f(x)$ for 8 equal subdivisions on $[1, 5]$.

3. Find a Trapezoidal Rule approximation for $\int_1^5 (\ln x)^2\, dx$.

4. Find a Simpson's Rule approximation for this integral.

5. (a) Find $f''(x)$ and graph it on $[1, 5]$.

   (b) From your graph, estimate the maximum value of $f''(x)$ on $[1, 5]$.

6. Use the result of problem (5) to bound the error for the Trapezoidal Rule approximation of $\int_1^5 (\ln x)^2\, dx$.

7. Find $f^{(4)}(x)$, graph it on $[1, 5]$, and bound the error for the Simpson's Rule approximation of $\int_1^5 (\ln x)^2\, dx$.

CHECKPOINT
SOLUTIONS

1. (a) $h = \dfrac{b-a}{n} = \dfrac{4-1}{3} = 1$

   (b) $x_0 = 1, x_1 = 2, x_2 = 3, x_3 = 4$

2. (a) False. With the Trapezoidal Rule, n can be even or odd.
   (b) True

3. (a) $\dfrac{0.5}{2}[0 + 2(0.5) + 2(1) + 2(1.5) + 2] = 2$

   (b) $\dfrac{0.5}{3}[0 + 4(0.5) + 2(1) + 4(1.5) + 2] = 2$ ∎

EXERCISE 6.8

For each interval $[a, b]$ and value of n given in problems 1–6, find h and the values of $x_0, x_1, \ldots x_n$.

1. $[0, 2]$ $n = 4$ 2. $[0, 4]$ $n = 8$
3. $[1, 4]$ $n = 6$ 4. $[2, 5]$ $n = 9$
5. $[-1, 4]$ $n = 5$ 6. $[-1, 2]$ $n = 6$

For each integral in problems 7–12,
(a) approximate its value by using the Trapezoidal Rule.
(b) approximate its value by using Simpson's Rule.
(c) find its exact value by integration.
(d) state which approximation is more accurate. (Round each result to 2 decimal places.)

7. $\displaystyle\int_0^3 x^2\,dx; \quad n = 6$ 8. $\displaystyle\int_0^1 x^3\,dx; \quad n = 4$

9. $\displaystyle\int_1^2 \frac{1}{x^2}\,dx; \quad n = 4$ 10. $\displaystyle\int_1^4 \frac{1}{x}\,dx; \quad n = 6$

11. $\displaystyle\int_0^4 x^{1/2}\,dx; \quad n = 8$ 12. $\displaystyle\int_0^2 x^{3/2}\,dx; \quad n = 8$

In problems 13–18, approximate each integral by
(a) the Trapezoidal Rule.
(b) Simpson's Rule.
Use $n = 4$ and round answers to 3 decimal places.

13. $\displaystyle\int_0^2 \sqrt{x^3 + 1}\,dx$ 14. $\displaystyle\int_0^2 \frac{dx}{\sqrt{4x^3 + 1}}$

15. $\displaystyle\int_0^1 e^{-x^2}\,dx$

16. $\displaystyle\int_0^1 e^{x^2}\,dx$

17. $\displaystyle\int_1^5 \ln(x^2 - x + 1)\,dx$

18. $\displaystyle\int_1^5 \ln(x^2 + x + 2)\,dx$

Use the table of values given in each of problems 19–22 to approximate $\displaystyle\int_a^b f(x)\,dx$. Use Simpson's Rule whenever n is even; otherwise use the Trapezoidal Rule. Round answers to 1 decimal place.

19. Find $\displaystyle\int_1^4 f(x)\,dx$.   20. Find $\displaystyle\int_1^2 f(x)\,dx$.

x	$f(x)$	x	$f(x)$
1	1	1	1
1.6	2.2	1.2	0.5
2.2	1.8	1.4	0.3
2.8	2.9	1.6	0.1
3.4	4.6	1.8	0.8
4.0	2.1	2.0	0.1

21. Find $\int_{1.2}^{3.6} f(x)\, dx$.

22. Find $\int_{0}^{1.8} f(x)\, dx$.

x	$f(x)$
1.2	6.1
1.6	4.8
2.0	3.1
2.4	2.0
2.8	2.8
3.2	5.6
3.6	9.7

x	$f(x)$
0	8.8
0.3	4.6
0.6	1.5
0.9	0
1.2	0.7
1.5	2.8
1.8	7.6

APPLICATIONS

In problems 23–32, round all calculations to 2 decimal places.

23. **Total income** Suppose that the production from an assembly line can be considered as a continuous income stream with annual rate of flow given by

$$f(t) = 100\,\frac{e^{0.1t}}{t+1} \qquad \text{(in thousands of dollars).}$$

Use Simpson's Rule with $n = 4$ to approximate the total income over the first 2 years, given by

$$\text{Total income} = \int_{0}^{2} 100\,\frac{e^{0.1t}}{t+1}\, dt.$$

24. **Present value** Suppose that the rate of flow of a continuous income stream is given by $f(t) - 500t$ (in thousands of dollars). If money is worth 7% compounded continuously, then the present value of this stream over the next 5 years is given by

$$\text{Present value} = \int_{0}^{5} 500t\, e^{-0.07t}\, dt.$$

Use the Trapezoidal Rule with $n = 5$ to approximate this present value.

25. **Cost** Suppose that a company's cost of producing x items is given by $C(x) = (x^2 + 1)^{3/2} + 1000$. Use the Trapezoidal Rule with $n = 3$

to approximate the average cost for the production of $x = 30$ to $x = 33$ items.

26. **Demand** Suppose that the demand for a certain product is given by

$$p = 850 + \frac{100}{q^2 + 1}.$$

Use Simpson's Rule with $n = 6$ to approximate the average price as demand ranges from 3 to 9 items.

Supply and demand Use the following supply and demand schedules in problems 27 and 28.

Supply schedule		Demand schedule	
x	p	x	p
0	120	0	2400
10	260	10	1500
20	380	20	1200
30	450	30	950
40	540	40	800
50	630	50	730
60	680	60	680
70	720	70	640

27. Use Simpson's Rule to approximate the producer's surplus at market equilibrium. Note that market equilibrium can be found from the tables.

28. Use Simpson's Rule to approximate consumer's surplus at market equilibrium.

29. **Production** Suppose that the rate of production of a product (in units per week) is measured at the end of each of the first 5 weeks after startup, and the following data are obtained.

Weeks t	Rate $R(t)$	Weeks t	Rate $R(t)$
0	250.0	3	243.3
1	247.6	4	241.3
2	245.4	5	239.5

Approximate the total number of units produced in the first 5 weeks.

30. ***Drug levels in the blood*** The manufacturer of a medicine wants to test how a new 300 mg capsule is released into the bloodstream. After a volunteer is given a capsule, blood samples are drawn every half-hour and the number of milligrams of the drug in the bloodstream is calculated. The results obtained are as follows.

Time t (hr)	$N(t)$ (mg)	Time t (hr)	$N(t)$ (mg)
0	0	2.0	178.3
0.5	247.3	2.5	113.9
1.0	270	3.0	56.2
1.5	236.4	3.5	19.3

Approximate the *average* number of milligrams in the bloodstream during the first $3\frac{1}{2}$ hours.

31. ***Pollution monitoring*** Suppose that the presence of phosphates in certain waste products dumped into a lake promotes the growth of algae. Rampant growth of algae affects the oxygen supply in the water, so an environmental group wishes to estimate the area of algae growth. They measure across the algae growth (see Figure 6.28) and obtain the following data (in feet):

x	Width w	x	Width w
0	0	50	27
10	15	60	24
20	18	70	23
30	18	80	0
40	30		

Use Simpson's Rule to approximate the area of the algae growth.

FIGURE 6.28

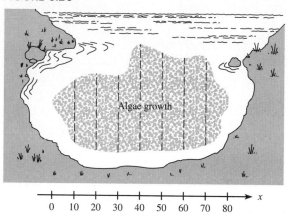

32. ***Development costs*** A land developer is planning to dig a small lake and build a group of homes around it. To estimate the cost of the project, the area of the lake must be calculated from the proposed measurements (in feet) given in Figure 6.29 and in the table below.

x	Width $w(x)$
0	0
100	300
200	200
300	400
400	0

Use Simpson's Rule to approximate the area of the lake.

FIGURE 6.29

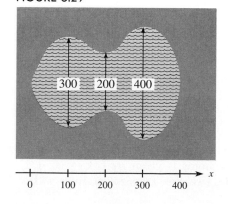

KEY TERMS
& FORMULAS

SECTION	KEY TERM	FORMULA

6.1   Sigma notation

$$\sum_{i=1}^{n} 1 = n; \quad \sum_{i=1}^{n} i = \frac{n(n+1)}{2}$$

$$\sum_{i=1}^{n} i^2 = \frac{n(n+1)(2n+1)}{6}$$

Area

    Right-hand endpoints

$$\lim_{n \to \infty} \sum_{i=1}^{n} f(x_i) \frac{b-a}{n}$$

    Left-hand endpoints

$$\lim_{n \to \infty} \sum_{i=1}^{n} f(x_{i-1}) \frac{b-a}{n}$$

6.2   Riemann sum

$$\sum_{i=1}^{n} f(x_i^*) \, \Delta x_i$$

Definite integral

$$\int_a^b f(x) \, dx = \lim_{\substack{\max \Delta x_i \to 0 \\ (n \to \infty)}} \sum_{i=1}^{n} f(x_i^*) \, \Delta x_i$$

Fundamental Theorem of Calculus

$$\int_a^b f(x) \, dx = F(b) - F(a), \text{ where } F'(x) = f(x)$$

$$\int_a^a f(x) \, dx = 0$$

$$\int_a^b f(x) \, dx = -\int_b^a f(x) \, dx$$

$$\int_a^b [f(x) \pm g(x)] \, dx = \int_a^b f(x) \, dx \pm \int_a^b g(x) \, dx$$

$$\int_a^b c \cdot f(x) \, dx = c \int_a^b f(x) \, dx$$

$$\int_a^c f(x) \, dx + \int_c^b (x) \, dx = \int_a^b f(x) \, dx$$

Area under $f(x)$, where $f(x) \geq 0$

$$A = \int_a^b f(x) \, dx$$

6.3   Area between $f(x)$ and $g(x)$, where $f(x) \geq g(x)$

$$A = \int_a^b [f(x) - g(x)] \, dx$$

Average value over $[a, b]$

$$\frac{1}{b-a} \int_a^b f(x) \, dx$$

SECTION	KEY TERM	FORMULA
6.4	Consumer's surplus [demand is $f(x)$]	$CS = \displaystyle\int_0^{x_1} f(x)\, dx - p_1 x_1$
	Producer's surplus [supply is $g(x)$]	$PS = p_1 x_1 - \displaystyle\int_0^{x_1} g(x)\, dx$
	Continuous income streams	
	Total income	$\displaystyle\int_0^k f(t)\, dt$ (for k years)
	Present value	$\displaystyle\int_0^k f(t)\, e^{-rt}\, dt$, where r is the interest rate (as a decimal)
6.5	Integration from tables	See Table 6.1.
6.6	Integration by parts	$\displaystyle\int u\, dv = uv - \int v\, du$
6.7	Improper integrals	$\displaystyle\int_a^\infty f(x)\, dx = \lim_{b \to \infty} \int_a^b f(x)\, dx$
		$\displaystyle\int_{-\infty}^b f(x)\, dx = \lim_{a \to \infty} \int_{-a}^b f(x)\, dx$
		$\displaystyle\int_{-\infty}^\infty f(x)\, dx = \int_{-\infty}^0 f(x)\, dx + \int_0^\infty f(x)\, dx$
	Capital value of a continuous income stream	$\displaystyle\int_0^\infty f(t)\, e^{-rt}\, dt$
6.8	Trapezoidal Rule for $\displaystyle\int_a^b f(x)\, dx$	$\approx \dfrac{h}{2}\left[f(x_0) + 2f(x_1) + \cdots + 2f(x_{n-1}) + f(x_n) \right]$ where $h = \dfrac{b-a}{n}$
	Error formula	$\lvert E \rvert \le \dfrac{(b-a)^3}{12n^2}\left[\max_{a \le x \le b} \lvert f''(x) \rvert \right]$
	Simpson's Rule for $\displaystyle\int_a^b f(x)\, dx$	$\approx \dfrac{h}{3}\left[f(x_0) + 4f(x_1) + 2f(x_2) + 4f(x_3) + \cdots + 2f(x_{n-2}) + 4f(x_{n-1}) + f(x_n) \right]$, where n is even and $h = \dfrac{b-a}{n}$
	Error formula	$\lvert E \rvert \le \dfrac{(b-a)^5}{180n^4}\left[\max_{a \le x \le b} \lvert f^{(4)}(x) \rvert \right]$

REVIEW
EXERCISES

6.1

1. Calculate $\sum\limits_{k=1}^{8} (k^2 + 1)$.

2. Use formulas to simplify

$$\sum_{i=1}^{n} \frac{3i}{n^3}.$$

3. Use 6 subintervals of the same size to approximate the area under the graph of $y = 3x^2$ from $x = 0$ to $x = 1$. Use the right-hand endpoints of the subintervals to find the heights of the rectangles.

4. Use rectangles to find the area under the graph of $y = 3x^2$ from $x = 0$ to $x = 1$. Use n equal subintervals.

6.2

5. Use a definite integral to find the area under the graph of $y = 3x^2$ from $x = 0$ to $x = 1$.

6. Find the area between the graph of $y = x^3 - 4x + 5$ and the x-axis from $x = 1$ to $x = 3$.

Evaluate the following integrals.

7. $\int_{1}^{4} 4\sqrt{x^3}\, dx$

8. $\int_{-3}^{2} (x^3 - 3x^2 + 4x + 2)\, dx$

9. $\int_{0}^{5} (x^3 + 4x)\, dx$

10. $\int_{-2}^{3} (x + 2)^2\, dx$

11. $\int_{-3}^{-1} (x + 1)\, dx$

12. $\int_{2}^{3} \frac{x^2}{2x^3 - 7}\, dx$

13. $\int_{-1}^{2} (x^2 + x)\, dx$

14. $\int_{1}^{4} \left(\frac{1}{x} + \sqrt{x}\right) dx$

15. $\int_{0}^{4} (2x + 1)^{1/2}\, dx$

16. $\int_{0}^{1} \frac{x}{x^2 + 1}\, dx$

17. $\int_{0}^{1} e^{-2x}\, dx$

18. $\int_{0}^{1} xe^{x^2}\, dx$

6.3

Find the areas between the curves in problems 19–22.

19. $y = x^2 - 3x + 2$ and $y = x^2 + 1$ from $x = 0$ to $x = 5$

20. $y = x^2$ and $y = 4x + 5$

21. $y = x^3$ and $y = x$ from $x = -1$ to $x = 0$

22. $y = x^3 - 1$ and $y = x - 1$

6.5

Use integral tables to evaluate the integrals in problems 23–26.

23. $\int \sqrt{x^2 - 4}\, dx$

24. $\int_{0}^{1} 3^x\, dx$

25. $\int x \ln x^2\, dx$

26. $\int \frac{dx}{x(3x + 2)}$

6.6   Use integration by parts to evaluate the following.

27. $\int x^5 \ln x \, dx$

28. $\int xe^{-2x} \, dx$

29. $\int \dfrac{x \, dx}{\sqrt{x+5}}$

30. $\int_1^e \ln x \, dx$

6.7   Evaluate the following improper integrals.

31. $\int_1^\infty \dfrac{1}{x} \, dx$

32. $\int_{-\infty}^{-1} \dfrac{200}{x^3} \, dx$

33. $\int_0^\infty 5e^{-3x} \, dx$

34. $\int_{-\infty}^0 \dfrac{x}{(x^2+1)^2} \, dx$

6.8   35. Evaluate $\int_1^3 \dfrac{2}{x^3} \, dx$

    (a) exactly.
    (b) by using the Trapezoidal Rule with $n = 4$ (to 3 decimal places).
    (c) by using Simpson's Rule with $n = 4$ (to 3 decimal places).

36. Use the Trapezoidal Rule with $n = 5$ to approximate

$$\int_0^1 \dfrac{4 \, dx}{x^2 + 1}.$$

Round your answer to 3 decimal places.

37. Use the table below to approximate

$$\int_1^{2.2} f(x) \, dx$$

by using Simpson's Rule. Round your answer to 1 decimal place.

x	$f(x)$
1	0
1.3	2.8
1.6	5.1
1.9	4.2
2.2	0.6

38. Suppose that a definite integral is to be approximated, and that to achieve a specified accuracy it is found that n must satisfy $n \geq 4.8$. What is the smallest n that can be used, if
    (a) the Trapezoidal Rule is used?
    (b) Simpson's Rule is used?

Applications

6.2   39. **Cost** Maintenance costs for buildings increase as the buildings age. If the rate of increase in maintenance costs for a building is

$$M'(t) = \frac{14,000}{\sqrt{t + 16}},$$

where M is in dollars and t is time in years, $0 \le t \le 15$, find the total maintenance cost for the first 9 years ($t = 0$ to $t = 9$).

6.3   40. **Compound amount** The compound amount of a $1000 investment in a savings account at 10%, compounded continuously, is $A = 1000e^{0.1t}$, where t is in years. Find the average amount in the savings account during the first 5 years.

41. **Income** Suppose that the total income from a video machine is given by

$$I = 50e^{0.2t}, \ 0 \le t \le 4, \quad t \text{ in hours.}$$

Find the average income over this 4-hour period.

6.4   42. **Consumer's surplus** The demand function for a product under pure competition is $p = \sqrt{64 - 4x}$, and the supply function is $p = x - 1$.
(a) Find the market equilibrium.
(b) Find the consumer's surplus at market equilibrium.

43. **Producer's surplus** Find the producer's surplus at market equilibrium for problem 42.

44. **Total income** Find the total income over the next 10 years from a continuous income stream that has an annual flow rate at time t given by

$$f(t) = 125e^{0.05t},$$

in thousands of dollars.

45. **Present value** Suppose that a machine's production is considered as a continuous income stream with an annual rate of flow at time t given by

$$f(t) = 150e^{-0.2t},$$

in thousands of dollars. If money is worth 8%, compounded continuously, find the present value of the machine over the next 5 years.

6.5   46. **Cost** Suppose that the cost function for a product is given by $C(x) = \sqrt{40,000 + x^4}$. Find the average cost over the first 150 units.

6.6   47. **Present value** Suppose that the present value of a continuous income stream over the next 5 years is given by

$$P = 9000 \int_0^5 te^{-0.08t} \, dt, \quad P \text{ in dollars, } t \text{ in years.}$$

Find the present value.

48. **Cost** If the marginal cost for a product is $\overline{MC} = 3 + x \ln(x + 1)$ and if the fixed cost is $2000, find the total cost function.

6.7

49. ***Capital value*** A service company considers its income as a continuous stream with an annual rate of flow at time t given by

$$f(t) = 150e^{-0.4t}$$

in thousands of dollars. If money is worth 10% compounded continuously, find the capital value of this company.

6.8

50. ***Total income*** Suppose that a continuous income stream has an annual rate of flow $f(t) = 100e^{-0.01t^2}$ (in thousands of dollars). Use Simpson's Rule with $n = 4$ to approximate the total income from this stream over the next 2 years.

51. ***Revenue*** A company has the following data from the sale of its product.

x	$\overline{MR}$
0	0
2	480
4	720
6	720
8	480
10	0

If x represents hundreds of units, approximate the total revenue from the sale of 1000 units by evaluating

$$\int_0^{10} \overline{MR}\, dx.$$

RETIREMENT PLANNING

A 52-year old client asks an accountant how to plan for his future retirement at age 62. He expects income from Social Security in the amount of $16,000 per year and a retirement pension of $30,000 per year from his employer. He wants to make monthly contributions to an investment plan that pays 8% compounded monthly for 10 years so that he will have a total income of $62,000 per year for 30 years. What will the size of the monthly contributions have to be to accomplish this goal, if it is assumed that money will be worth 8%, compounded continuously throughout the period after he is 62?

To help you answer this question, complete the following.

1. How much money must the client withdraw annually from his investment plan during his retirement so that his total income goal is met?

2. How much money S must the client's account contain when he is 62 so that it will generate this annual amount for 30 years? *Hint:* S can be considered as the present value over 30 years of a continuous income stream with the amount found in (1) as its annual rate of flow.

3. The monthly contribution R that would, after 10 years, amount to the present value S found in question 2 can be obtained from the formula

$$R = S\left[\frac{i}{(1 + i)^n - 1}\right],$$

with i representing the monthly interest rate and n the number of months. Find the client's monthly contribution, R.

PREREQUISITE PROBLEM TYPE	REVIEW SECTION/ANSWER
SECTION 7.1	Section 1.1, Functions
(a) If $y = f(x)$, x is the independent variable and y is the _____ variable.	(a) Dependent
(b) What is the domain of $f(x) = \dfrac{3x}{x-1}$?	(b) All reals except $x = 1$
(c) If $C(x) = 5 + 5x$, what is $f(0.20)$?	(c) 6
SECTIONS 7.5, 7.6	Section 1.6, Systems of equations
(a) Solve for x and y: $\begin{cases} 0 = 50 - 2x - 2y \\ 0 = 60 - 2x - 4y \end{cases}$	(a) $y = 5$, $x = 20$
(b) Solve for x and y: $\begin{cases} x = 2y \\ x + y - 9 = 0 \end{cases}$	(b) $x = 6$, $y = 3$
SECTIONS 7.2, 7.4, 7.5, 7.6	Sections 2.4, 2.6, 4.3, 4.4, Derivatives
(a) If $z = 4x^2 + 5x^3 - 7$, what is $\dfrac{dz}{dx}$?	(a) $\dfrac{dz}{dx} = 8x + 15x^2$
(b) If $f(x) = (x^2 - 1)^2$, what is $f'(x)$?	(b) $f'(x) = 4x(x^2 - 1)$
(c) If $z = 10y - \ln y$, what is $\dfrac{dz}{dy}$?	(c) $\dfrac{dz}{dy} = 10 - \dfrac{1}{y}$
(d) If $z = 5x^2 + e^x$, what is $\dfrac{dz}{dx}$?	(d) $\dfrac{dz}{dx} = 10x + e^x$
(e) Find the slope of the tangent to $y = 4x^3 - 4e^x$ at $(0, -4)$.	(e) -4
SECTION 7.7	Sections 5.1, 5.2, 5.3, 6.5, 6.6, Integration
Integrate:	
(a) $\displaystyle\int_2^5 (4x^3 - 2x + 1)\, dx$	(a) 591
(b) $\displaystyle\int 2e^{-3x}\, dx$	(b) $-\frac{2}{3}e^{-3x} + C$

7 | FUNCTIONS OF TWO OR MORE VARIABLES

Although we have been dealing primarily with functions of one variable, many real-life situations involve variables that are functions of two or more variables. For example, the grade you receive in a course is a function of several test grades. The cost of manufacturing a product may involve the cost of labor, the cost of materials, and overhead expenses. The concentration of a substance at any point in a vein after an injection is a function of time since the injection t, the velocity of the blood v, and the distance the point is from the point of injection.

In this chapter we will extend our study to functions of two or more variables. We will extend the derivative concept to functions of several variables by taking partial derivatives, and we will learn how to maximize functions of two variables. We will use these concepts to solve problems in the management, social, and life sciences. In particular, we will discuss joint cost functions, marginal cost, marginal productivity, and marginal demand functions. As an application of max-min techniques, we will derive the formulas for linear regression, a technique for finding the linear equation that best fits a set of data. We will use Lagrange multipliers to maximize functions of two variables subject to a condition that constrains the variables. In addition, we will define the double integral of a function of two variables over a closed and bounded region and show that if the function is above the xy-plane over the region, then this double integral is equal to the volume of the solid bounded below by this region and above by the function.

7.1 | FUNCTIONS OF TWO OR MORE VARIABLES

OBJECTIVES

- To find the domain and range of a function of two or more variables
- To evaluate a function of two or more variables given values for the independent variables

The relations we have studied up to this point have been limited to two variables, with one of the variables assumed to be a function of the other. But there are many instances where one variable may depend on two or more other variables. For example, the output or production Q (for quantity) of a company can be modeled according to the equation

$$Q = AK^\alpha L^{1-\alpha},$$

where A is a constant, K is the company's capital investment, L is the size of the labor force (in work hours), and α is a constant with $0 < \alpha < 1$. Functions of this type are called **Cobb-Douglas production functions,** and they are frequently used in economics. In addition, the demand function for a commodity frequently depends on the price of the commodity, available income, and prices of competing goods. Other examples from economics will be presented later in this chapter.

We write $z = f(x, y)$ to state that z is a function of both x and y. The variables x and y are called the **independent variables** and z is called the **dependent variable.** Thus the function f associates with each pair of possible values for the independent variables (x and y) exactly one value of the dependent variable (z).

The equation $z = x^2 - xy$ defines z as a function of x and y. We can denote this by writing $z = f(x, y) = x^2 - xy$. The domain of the function is the set of all ordered pairs (of real numbers) and the range is the set of all real numbers.

EXAMPLE 1

Give the domain of the function

$$g(x, y) = \frac{x^2 - 3y}{x - y}.$$

Solution The domain of the function is the set of ordered pairs that do not give a 0 denominator. That is, the domain is the set of all ordered pairs where the first and second elements are not equal (that is, where $x \neq y$).

CHECKPOINT

1. Find the domain of the function

$$f(x, y) = \frac{2}{\sqrt{x^2 - y^2}}$$

We graph the function $z = f(x, y)$ by using three dimensions. We can construct a three-dimensional coordinate space by drawing three mutually perpendicular axes as in Figure 7.1. By setting up a scale of measurement along the three axes from the origin 0, we can determine the three coordinates (x, y, z) for any point P. The point shown in Figure 7.1 is $+2$ units in the x-direction, $+3$ units in the y-direction, and $+4$ units in the z-direction, so the coordinates of the point are $(2, 3, 4)$.

FIGURE 7.1

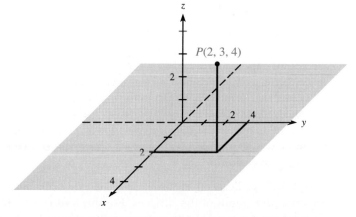

The pairs of axes determine the three **coordinate planes;** the xy-plane, the yz-plane, and the xz-plane. The planes divide the space into eight **octants.** The point $P(2, 3, 4)$ is in the first octant.

If we are given a function $z = f(x, y)$, we can find the z-value corresponding to $x = a$ and $y = b$ by evaluating $f(a, b)$.

EXAMPLE 2   If $z = f(x, y) = x^2 - 4xy + xy^3$, find the following.

(a) $f(1, 2)$ (b) $f(2, 5)$ (c) $f(-1, 3)$

Solution

(a) $f(1, 2) = 1^2 - 4(1)(2) + (1)(2)^3 = 1$

(b) $f(2, 5) = 2^2 - 4(2)(5) + (2)(5)^3 = 214$

(c) $f(-1, 3) = (-1)^2 - 4(-1)(3) + (-1)(3)^3 = -14$

CHECKPOINT   2. If $f(x, y, z) = x^2 + 2y - z$, find $f(2, 3, 4)$.   ■

EXAMPLE 3   The cost of manufacturing a Wosh is given by

$$C(x, y) = 5 + 5x + 2y,$$

where x represents the cost of one ounce of material used and y represents the cost of labor in dollars per hour. If the material cost is \$.20 per ounce and labor costs are \$3.50 per hour, what is the cost of manufacturing one Wosh?

Solution The cost is

$$C(0.20, 3.50) = 5 + 5(0.20) + 2(3.50)$$
$$= 13 \text{ (dollars)}.$$

For a given function $z = f(x, y)$, we can construct a table of values by assigning values to x and y and finding the corresponding values of z. To each pair of values for x and y there corresponds a unique value of z, and thus a unique point in space. From a table of values such as this, a finite number of points can be plotted. All points that satisfy the equation form a "surface" in space. Since z is a function of x and y, lines parallel to the z-axis will intersect such a surface in at most one point. The graph of the equation $z = 4 - x^2 - y^2$ is a surface like that shown in Figure 7.2. The portion of the surface above the xy-plane is like a bullet and is called a **paraboloid.**

In practical applications of functions of two variables, we will have little need to construct the graphs of the surfaces. For this reason, we will not discuss methods of sketching the graphs. Although you will not be asked to sketch graphs of these surfaces, the fact that the graphs do *exist* will be used in studying relative maxima and minima of functions of two variables.

The properties of functions of one variable can be extended to functions of two variables. The precise definition of continuity for functions of two variables is technical, and may be found in more advanced books. We will limit our study to functions that are continuous and have continuous derivatives in the domain of interest to us. We may think of continuous functions as functions whose graphs consist of surfaces without "holes" or "breaks" in them.

Let the function $U = f(x, y)$ represent the **utility** (that is, satisfaction) derived by a consumer from the consumption of two goods, X and Y, where x and y represent the amounts of X and Y, respectively. Since we will assume that the utility function is continuous, a given level of utility can be derived from an infinite number of combinations of x and y. The graph of all points (x, y) that give the same utility is called an **indifference curve.** A set of indifference curves corresponding to different levels of utility is called an **indifference map** (see Figure 7.3).

FIGURE 7.2

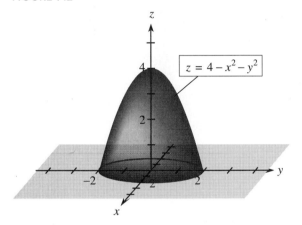

FIGURE 7.3

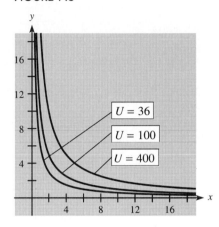

EXAMPLE 4

Suppose that the utility function for two goods, X and Y, is $U = x^2y^2$ and a consumer purchases 10 units of X and 2 units of Y.

(a) If the consumer purchases 5 units of X, how many units of Y must be purchased to retain the same level of utility?

(b) Graph the indifference curve for this level of utility.

(c) Graph the indifference curves for this utility function if $U = 100$ and if $U = 36$.

Solution

(a) If $x = 10$ and $y = 2$ satisfy the utility function, then $U = 10^2 \cdot 2^2 = 400$. Thus if x is 5, y must satisfy $400 = 5^2y^2$; so $y = 4$.

(b) The indifference curve for $U = 400$ is $400 = x^2y^2$. The graph for positive x and y is shown in Figure 7.3.

(c) The indifference map in Figure 7.3 contains these indifference curves.

TECHNOLOGY CORNER

The following investigations require 3-dimensional graphics capabilities. These capabilities are usually available with computer graphics software, but usually not with graphics calculators.

1. Suppose that $z = f(x, y) = \sqrt{16 - x^2 - y^2}$.

   (a) Graph the surface given by this function. Use $-4 \leq x \leq 4$ and $-4 \leq y \leq 4$.

   (b) Use the graph to identify the domain of the function. You may want to write a verbal description of the domain.

   (c) Use the graph to identify the range of the function.

   (d) Does the function appear to have a maximum point? Where?

2. Suppose that $z = f(x, y) = \dfrac{-1}{\sqrt{x^2 + y^2}}$.

   (a) Graph the surface given by this function. Use $-1 \leq x \leq 1$ and $-1 \leq y \leq 1$.

   (b) Use the graph to identify the domain of the function.

   (c) What behavior does the surface exhibit near any restrictions on the domain?

   (d) Use the graph to identify the range of the function.

CHECKPOINT
SOLUTIONS

1. The domain is the set of ordered pairs of real numbers where $x^2 - y^2 > 0$ or $x^2 > y^2$, that is, where $|x| > |y|$.

2. $f(2, 3, 4) = 4 + 6 - 4 = 6$ ■

EXERCISE 7.1

Give the domain of each of the following functions.

1. $z = x^2 + y^2$

2. $z = 4x - 3y$

3. $z = \dfrac{4x - 3}{y}$

4. $z = \dfrac{x + y^2}{\sqrt{x}}$

5. $z = \dfrac{4x^3 y - x}{2x - y}$

6. $z = \sqrt{x - y}$

7. $q = \sqrt{p_1} + 3p_2$

8. $q = \dfrac{p_1 + p_2}{\sqrt{p_1}}$

Evaluate the following functions at the given values of the independent variables.

9. $z = x^3 + 4xy + y^2$; $x = 1, y = -1$

10. $z = 4x^2 - 3xy^3$; $x = 2, y = 2$

11. $z = \dfrac{x - y}{x + y}$; $x = 4, y = -1$

12. $z = \dfrac{x^2 + xy}{x - y}$; $x = 3, y = 2$

13. $C(x_1, x_2) = 600 + 4x_1 + 6x_2$; $x_1 = 400, x_2 = 50$

14. $C(x_1, x_2) = 500 + 5x_1 + 7x_2$; find $C(200, 300)$.

15. $q_1(p_1, p_2) = \dfrac{p_1 + 4p_2}{p_1 - p_2}$; find $q_1(40, 35)$.

16. $q_1(p_1, p_2) = \dfrac{5p_1 - p_2}{p_1 + 3p_2}$; find $q_1(50, 10)$.

17. $z(x, y) = xe^{x+y}$; find $z(3, -3)$.

18. $f(x, y) = ye^{2x} + y^2$; find $f(0, 7)$.

19. $f(x, y) = \dfrac{\ln (xy)}{x^2 + y^2}$; find $f(-3, -4)$.

20. $z(x, y) = x \ln y - y \ln x$; find $z(1, 1)$.

21. $w = \dfrac{x^2 + 4yz}{xyz}$ at $(1, 3, 1)$

22. $u = f(w, x, y, z) = \dfrac{wx - yz^2}{xy - wz}$ at $(2, 3, 1, -1)$

APPLICATIONS

23. **Utility** Suppose that the utility function for two goods X and Y is given by $U = xy^2$, and a consumer purchases 9 units of X and 6 units of Y.
    (a) If the consumer purchases 9 units of Y, how many units of X must be purchased to retain the same level of utility?
    (b) If the consumer purchases 81 units of X, how many units of Y must be purchased to retain the same level of utility?

24. **Utility** Suppose that an indifference curve for two goods, X and Y, has equation $xy = 400$. If 20 units of X are purchased, how many units of Y must be purchased to remain on this indifference curve?

25. **Production** Suppose that the number of units of a good produced, z, is given by $z = 20xy$, where x is the number of machines working properly and y is the average number of work-hours per machine. Find the production for a week in which
    (a) 12 machines are working properly and the average number of work-hours per machine is 30.
    (b) 10 machines are working properly and the average number of work-hours per machine is 25.

26. **Profit** The Kirk Kelly Kandy Company makes two kinds of candy, Kisses and Kreams. The profit function for the company is

    $$P(x, y) = 100x + 64y - 0.01x^2 - 0.25y^2,$$

    where x is the number of pounds of Kisses sold per week and y is the number of pounds of Kreams. What is their profit if they sell
    (a) 20 pounds of Kisses and 10 pounds of Kreams?
    (b) 100 pounds of Kisses and 16 pounds of Kreams?
    (c) 10,000 pounds of Kisses and 256 pounds of Kreams?

27. **Epidemic** The cost per day to society of an epidemic is

    $$C(x, y) = 20x + 200y,$$

    where C is in dollars, x is the number of people infected on a given day, and y is the number of people who die on a given day. If 14,000 people are infected and 20 people die on a given day, what is the cost to society?

28. **Pesticide** An area of land is to be sprayed with two brands of pesticide: x liters of brand 1 and y liters of brand 2. If the number of insects killed is given by

    $$f(x, y) = 10{,}000 - 6500e^{-0.01x} - 3500e^{-0.02y},$$

    how many insects would be killed if 80 liters of brand 1 and 120 liters of brand 2 were used?

29. **Investment** The amount S of an investment earning 6%, compounded continuously, is a

function of the principal P and the length of time t that the principal has been invested, and is given by

$$S = f(P, t) = Pe^{0.06t}.$$

Find $f(2000, 20)$, and interpret your answer.

30. **Gas law** Suppose that a gas satisfies the universal gas law, $V = nRT/P$, with n equal to 10 moles of the gas and R, the universal gas constant, equal to 0.082054. What is V if $T = 10$ K (degrees kelvin) and $P = 1$ atmosphere?

31. **Production** Suppose that a company's production is given by the Cobb-Douglas production function

$$Q = 30K^{1/4} L^{3/4}.$$

(a) Find Q if $K = \$10,000$ and $L = 625$ hours.
(b) Show that if *both* K and L are doubled, then the output is doubled.

32. **Production** Suppose that the production of a company is given by the Cobb-Douglas production function

$$Q = 70K^{2/3} L^{1/3}.$$

(a) Find Q if $K = \$64,000$ and $L = 512$ hours.
(b) Show that if both K and L are halved, then Q is also halved.

7.2 | PARTIAL DIFFERENTIATION

OBJECTIVES

- To find partial derivatives of functions of two or more variables
- To evaluate partial derivatives of functions of two or more variables at given points
- To use partial derivatives to find slopes of tangents to surfaces

We have used derivatives to find the rate of change of cost with respect to the quantity produced (in Chapter 2). If cost is given as a function of two variables (such as material costs x and labor costs y), we can find the rate of change of cost with respect to *one* of these independent variables. This is done by finding the **partial derivative** of the function with respect to one variable, while holding the other one constant.

For example, suppose that the cost of manufacturing a good is given by

$$C(x, y) = 5 + 5x + 2y,$$

where x represents the cost of one ounce of material used and y represents the labor cost in dollars per hour. To find the rate at which the cost changes with respect to material used x, we treat the y variable as though it were a constant and take the derivative of C with respect to x. This derivative is

$$\frac{\partial C}{\partial x} = 0 + 5 + 0, \quad \text{or} \quad \frac{\partial C}{\partial x} = 5.$$

Note that the partial derivative of $2y$ with respect to x is 0 because y is treated as a constant. Since the partial derivative is a new type of derivative, we use a new symbol to denote it, $\partial C / \partial x$.

The partial derivative $\partial C / \partial x = 5$ tells us that a change of \$1 in the cost of materials will cause an increase of \$5 in total costs, *if* labor costs remain constant. To see the rate at which total cost changes with respect to labor costs, we find $\partial C / \partial y = 0 + 0 + 2$, or $\partial C / \partial y = 2$. Thus if material costs are held constant, an increase of \$1 in labor costs will cause an increase of \$2 in the total cost of the good.

In general, if $z = f(x, y)$ we denote the partial derivative of z with respect to x as $\partial z / \partial x$ and the partial derivative of z with respect to y as $\partial z / \partial y$. Note that dz/dx represents the derivative of a function of one variable, x, and that $\partial z / \partial x$ represents the partial derivative of a function of two or more variables.

Other notations used to represent the partial derivative of $z = f(x, y)$ with respect to x are

$$\frac{\partial f}{\partial x}, \quad \frac{\partial}{\partial x} f(x, y), \quad f_x(x, y), \quad f_x, \quad \text{and} \quad z_x.$$

If x is held constant in the function $z = f(x, y)$ and the derivative is taken with respect to y, we have the partial derivative of z with respect to y, denoted by

$$\frac{\partial z}{\partial y}, \quad \frac{\partial f}{\partial y}, \quad \frac{\partial}{\partial y} f(x, y), \quad f_y(x, y), \quad f_y, \quad \text{or} \quad z_y.$$

EXAMPLE 1 | If $z = 4x^2 + 5x^2y^2 + 6y^3 - 7$, find $\partial z / \partial x$ and $\partial z / \partial y$.

Solution

$$\frac{\partial z}{\partial x} - 8x + 10y^2x$$

$$\frac{\partial z}{\partial y} = 10x^2y + 18y^2$$

EXAMPLE 2 | If $z = x^2y + e^x - \ln y$, find z_x and z_y.

Solution

$$z_x = \frac{\partial z}{\partial x} = 2yx + e^x$$

$$z_y = \frac{\partial z}{\partial y} = x^2 - \frac{1}{y}$$

EXAMPLE 3 If $f(x, y) = (x^2 - y^2)^2$, find the following.

(a) f_x (b) f_y

Solution

(a) $f_x = 2(x^2 - y^2)2x = 4x^3 - 4xy^2$

(b) $f_y = 2(x^2 - y^2)(-2y) = -4x^2y + 4y^3$

CHECKPOINT

1. If $z = 100x + 10xy - y^2$, find

(a) z_x.

(b) $\dfrac{\partial z}{\partial y}$.

EXAMPLE 4 If $q = \dfrac{p_1 p_2 + 2p_1}{p_1 p_2 - 2p_2}$, find $\partial q / \partial p_1$.

Solution

$$
\begin{aligned}
\frac{\partial q}{\partial p_1} &= \frac{(p_1 p_2 - 2p_2)(p_2 + 2) - (p_1 p_2 + 2p_1)p_2}{(p_1 p_2 - 2p_2)^2} \\
&= \frac{p_1 p_2{}^2 + 2p_1 p_2 - 2p_2{}^2 - 4p_2 - p_1 p_2{}^2 - 2p_1 p_2}{(p_1 p_2 - 2p_2)^2} \\
&= \frac{-2p_2{}^2 - 4p_2}{p_2{}^2(p_1 - 2)^2} \\
&= \frac{-2p_2(p_2 + 2)}{p_2{}^2(p_1 - 2)^2} \\
&= \frac{-2(p_2 + 2)}{p_2(p_1 - 2)^2}
\end{aligned}
$$

We may evaluate partial derivatives by substituting values for x *and* y in the same manner we did with derivatives of functions of one variable. For example, if $\partial z / \partial x = 2x - xy$, the value of the derivative at $x = 2$, $y = 3$ is

$$
\frac{\partial z}{\partial x}\bigg|_{(2,\,3)} = 2(2) - 2 \cdot 3 = -2.
$$

Other notations used to denote evaluation of partial derivatives with respect to x at (a, b) are

$$
\frac{\partial}{\partial x} f(a, b) \quad \text{and} \quad f_x(a, b).
$$

We denote the evaluation of partial derivatives with respect to y at (a, b) by

$$\frac{\partial z}{\partial y}\bigg|_{(a, b)}, \quad \frac{\partial}{\partial y}f(a, b), \quad \text{or} \quad f_y(a, b).$$

EXAMPLE 5

Find the partial derivative of $f(x, y) = x^2 + 3xy + 4$ with respect to x at the point $(1, 2, 11)$.

Solution

$$f_x(x, y) = 2x + 3y$$
$$f_x(1, 2) = 2(1) + 3(2) = 8$$

CHECKPOINT

2. If $g(x, y) = 4x^2 - 3xy + 10y^2$, find

   (a) $\dfrac{\partial g}{\partial x}(1, 3)$

   (b) $g_y(4, 2)$

EXAMPLE 6

Suppose that a company's sales are related to its television advertising by

$$s = 20{,}000 + 10nt + 20n^2,$$

where n is the number of commercials per day and t is the length of the commercials in seconds. Find the partial derivative of s with respect to n and use the result to find the instantaneous rate of change of sales with respect to the number of commercials per day, if they are currently running ten 30-second commercials.

Solution The partial derivative of s with respect to n is $\partial s / \partial n = 10t + 40n$. At $n = 10$ and $t = 30$, the rate of change in sales is approximately

$$\frac{ds}{dn}\bigg|_{\substack{n = 10 \\ t = 30}} = 10(30) + 40(10) = 700.$$

Thus increasing the number of commercials by one would result in approximately 700 additional sales.

We have seen that the partial derivative $\partial z / \partial x$ is found by holding y constant and taking the derivative of z with respect to x and the partial derivative $\partial z / \partial y$ is found by holding x constant and taking the derivative of z with respect to y. We now give formal definitions of these partial derivatives.

We have already stated that the graph of $z = f(x, y)$ is a surface in three dimensions. The partial derivative with respect to x of such a function may be thought of as the slope of the tangent to the surface at a point (x, y, z) on the surface *in the direction of the x-axis*. That is, if a plane parallel to the xz-plane cuts the surface, passing through the point (x_0, y_0, z_0), the line in the plane that is tangent to the surface will have a slope equal to $\partial z / \partial x$ evaluated at the point. Thus

$$\frac{\partial z}{\partial x} \bigg|_{(x_0, y_0)}$$

represents the slope of the tangent to the surface in the direction of the x-axis (see Figure 7.4).

FIGURE 7.4

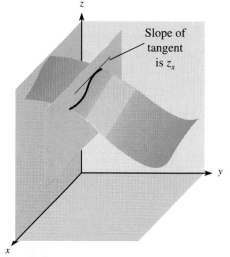

Slope of tangent is z_x

Similarly,

$$\frac{\partial z}{\partial y} \bigg|_{(x_0, y_0)} = \frac{\partial}{\partial y} f(x_0, y_0)$$

represents the slope of the tangent to the surface at (x_0, y_0, z_0) in the direction of the y-axis (see Figure 7.5).

FIGURE 7.5

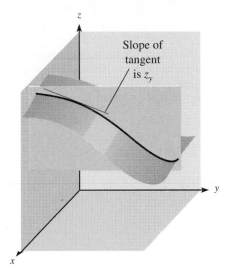

EXAMPLE 7

Find the slope of the tangent in the x-direction to the surface

$$z = 4x^3 - 4e^x + 4y^2$$

at the point $(0, 2, 12)$ on the surface.

Solution

$$\frac{\partial z}{\partial x} = 12x^2 - 4e^x$$

Evaluating the partial derivative at the given point, we find the slope of the tangent.

$$\frac{\partial z}{\partial x}\bigg|_{(0,\,2)} = 12(0)^2 - 4e^0 = -4$$

This tells us that z is *decreasing* at a rate of approximately 4 units for each increase of 1 unit in x at this point. That is, the slope of the tangent to the surface in the x-direction is negative at $(0, 2, 12)$.

EXAMPLE 8

Using the same function and point as that of Example 7, find the slope of the tangent in the y-direction to the surface at the point.

Solution

$$\frac{\partial z}{\partial y} = 8y$$

$$\frac{\partial z}{\partial y}\bigg|_{(0,\,2)} = 8(2) = 16$$

So the slope of the tangent in the y-direction is increasing at a rate of 16 units in the z-value for each unit change in y.

Up to this point we have considered derivatives of functions of two variables. We can easily extend the concept to functions of three or more variables. We can find the partial derivative with respect to any one independent variable by taking the derivative of the function with respect to that variable while holding all other independent variables constant.

EXAMPLE 9

If $u = f(w, x, y, z) = 3x^2y + w^3 - 4xyz$, find the following.

(a) $\dfrac{\partial u}{\partial w}$ (b) $\dfrac{\partial u}{\partial x}$ (c) $\dfrac{\partial u}{\partial y}$ (d) $\dfrac{\partial u}{\partial z}$

Solution

(a) $\dfrac{\partial u}{\partial w} = 3w^2$ (b) $\dfrac{\partial u}{\partial x} = 6xy - 4yz$

(c) $\dfrac{\partial u}{\partial y} = 3x^2 - 4xz$ (d) $\dfrac{\partial u}{\partial z} = -4xy$

EXAMPLE 10

If $C = 4x_1 + 2x_1^2 + 3x_2 - x_1x_2 + x_3^2$, find the following.

(a) $\dfrac{\partial C}{\partial x_1}$ (b) $\dfrac{\partial C}{\partial x_2}$ (c) $\dfrac{\partial C}{\partial x_3}$

Solution

(a) $\dfrac{\partial C}{\partial x_1} = 4 + 4x_1 - x_2$ (b) $\dfrac{\partial C}{\partial x_2} = 3 - x_1$ (c) $\dfrac{\partial C}{\partial x_3} = 2x_3$

CHECKPOINT

3. If $f(w, x, y, z) = 8xy^2 + 4yz - xw^2$, find

(a) $\dfrac{\partial f}{\partial x}$.   (b) $\dfrac{\partial f}{\partial w}$.

(c) $\dfrac{\partial f}{\partial y}(1, 2, 1, 3)$.   (d) $\dfrac{\partial f}{\partial z}(0, 2, 1, 3)$.

TECHNOLOGY CORNER

The following investigations require 3-dimensional graphics capabilities. These capabilities are usually available with computer graphics software, but usually not with graphics calculators.

1. Suppose that $z = f(x, y) = \dfrac{-4x}{x^2 + y^2 + 1}$.

   (a) Find the partial derivatives z_x and z_y.

   (b) Graph the surfaces given by z_x and z_y. Use $-3 \leq x \leq 3$ and $-3 \leq y \leq 3$.

   (c) Identify where both $z_x = 0$ and $z_y = 0$.

   (d) Graph the surface given by $z = f(x, y)$. Use the same ranges for x and y.

   (e) What features does the surface $z = f(x, y)$ have at the points where both $z_x = 0$ and $z_y = 0$?

2. Suppose that $z = f(x, y) = 4xy - x^4 - y^4$.

   (a)–(d) Repeat parts (a)–(d) in question 1. Use $-1.5 \leq x \leq 1.5$ and $-1.5 \leq y \leq 1.5$.

   (e) The point at the origin of the surface $z = f(x, y)$ is a maximum point in the x-direction and a minimum point in the y-direction. Does this point correspond to a point where both $z_x = 0$ and $z_y = 0$?

   (f) At the other points where both $z_x = 0$ and $z_y = 0$, what features does the surface $z = f(x, y)$ have?

CHECKPOINT
SOLUTIONS

1. (a) $z_x = 100 + 10y$

   (b) $\dfrac{\partial z}{\partial y} = 10x - 2y$

2. (a) $\dfrac{\partial g}{\partial x} = 8x - 3y$ and $\dfrac{\partial g}{\partial x}(1, 3) = 8(1) - 3(3) = -1$

   (b) $g_y = -3x + 20y$ and $g_y(4, 2) = -3(4) + 20(2) = 28$

3. (a) $\dfrac{\partial f}{\partial x} = 8y^2 - w^2$ (b) $\dfrac{\partial f}{\partial w} = -2xw$

   (c) $\dfrac{\partial f}{\partial y} = 16xy + 4z$ and $\dfrac{\partial f}{\partial y}(1, 2, 1, 3) = 16(2)(1) + 4(3) = 44$

   (d) $\dfrac{\partial f}{\partial z} = 4y$ and $\dfrac{\partial f}{\partial z}(0, 2, 1, 3) = 4(1) = 4$

EXERCISE 7.2

1. Find $\dfrac{\partial z}{\partial x}$ if $z = x^4 - 5x^2 + 4x + 3y^3 - 5y$.

2. Find $\dfrac{\partial z}{\partial y}$ if $z = x^5 - 6x + 4y^3 - y$.

3. Find $\dfrac{\partial z}{\partial x}$ if $z = x^2 - 5y + y$.

4. Find $\dfrac{\partial z}{\partial y}$ if $z = x^2 - 5y + y$.

5. If $z = x^3 + 4xy + 6y$, find z_y.
6. If $z = x^2 + 4xy + y$, find z_x.
7. If $z = 4x^2 - 5xy + 6y^2$, find z_y.
8. If $z = 4x^2 + 6xy^2 - y$, find z_x.
9. If $z = xy + y^2$, find z_x.
10. If $z = xy + y^2$, find z_y.

11. If $z = e^x + y \ln x$, find $\dfrac{\partial z}{\partial x}$.

12. If $z = e^x + y \ln x$, find $\dfrac{\partial z}{\partial y}$.

13. If $z = e^{xy}$, find z_y.
14. If $z = \ln(xy)$, find z_x.

15. If $z = (x^3 + y^2)^3$, find $\dfrac{\partial z}{\partial x}$.

16. If $z = \sqrt{x - y}$, find z_y.

17. If $f(x, y) = (xy + y)^2$, find $\dfrac{\partial f}{\partial y}$.

18. If $f(x, y) = x\sqrt{y - x}$, find $\dfrac{\partial f}{\partial x}$.

19. If $C(x, y) = 600 - 4xy + 10x^2 y$, find $\dfrac{\partial C}{\partial x}$.

20. If $C(x, y) = 1000 - 4x + xy^2$, find $\dfrac{\partial C}{\partial y}$.

21. If $q = \dfrac{5p_1 + 4p_2}{p_1 + p_2}$, find $\dfrac{\partial q}{\partial p_1}$.

22. If $q = \dfrac{5p_1 + 4p_2}{p_1 + p_2}$, find $\dfrac{\partial q}{\partial p_2}$.

23. If $Q(x, y) = 1500 + x^2 + 4xy + y^2$, find $\dfrac{\partial Q}{\partial x}$.

24. If $Q(x, y) = 1500 + x^2 + 4xy + y^2$, find $\dfrac{\partial Q}{\partial y}$.

25. Find the partial derivative of
$$f(x, y) = 4x^3 - 5xy + y^2$$
with respect to x at the point $(1, 2, -2)$.

26. Find the partial derivative of
$$f(x, y) = 3x^2 + 4x + 6xy$$
with respect to y at $x = 2$, $y = -1$.

27. Find the slope of the tangent in the x-direction to the surface $z = 5x^3 - 4xy$ at the point $(1, 2, -3)$.

28. Find the slope of the tangent in the y-direction to the surface $z = x^3 - 5xy$ at $(2, 1, -2)$.

29. Find the slope of the tangent in the y-direction to the surface $z = e^{xy}$ at $(0, 1, 1)$.

30. Find the slope of the tangent in the x-direction to the surface $z = \ln(xy)$ at $(1, 1, 0)$.

31. If $u = f(w, x, y, z) = y^2 - x^2 z + 4x$, find the following.
   (a) $\dfrac{\partial u}{\partial w}$ (b) $\dfrac{\partial u}{\partial x}$ (c) $\dfrac{\partial u}{\partial y}$ (d) $\dfrac{\partial u}{\partial z}$

32. If $u = x^2 + 3xy + xz$, find the following.
   (a) u_x (b) u_y (c) u_z

33. If $C(x_1, x_2, x_3) = 4x_1{}^2 + 5x_1 x_2 + 6x_2{}^2 + x_3$, find the following.
   (a) $\dfrac{\partial C}{\partial x_1}$ (b) $\dfrac{\partial C}{\partial x_2}$ (c) $\dfrac{\partial C}{\partial x_3}$

34. If $f(x, y, z) = 2x\sqrt{yz - 1} + x^2 z^3$, find the following.
   (a) $\dfrac{\partial f}{\partial x}$ (b) $\dfrac{\partial f}{\partial y}$ (c) $\dfrac{\partial f}{\partial z}$

APPLICATIONS

35. **Mortgage** When a homeowner has a 25-year variable rate mortgage loan, the monthly payment R is a function of the amount of the loan A and the current interest rate i (as a decimal);

that is, $R = f(A, i)$. Interpret each of the following.

(a) $f(100,000, 0.08) = 1289$

(b) $\dfrac{\partial f}{\partial i}(100,000, 0.08) = 62.51$

36. **Cost** Suppose that the total cost of producing a product is $C(x, y) = 25 + 2x^2 + 3y^2$, where x is the cost per pound for material and y is cost per hour for labor.

(a) If material costs are held constant, at what rate will the total cost increase for each \$1 per hour increase in labor?

(b) If the labor costs are held constant, at what rate will the total cost increase for each increase of \$1 in material cost?

37. **Pesticide** Suppose that the number of insects killed by two brands of pesticide is given by

$$f(x, y) = 10,000 - 6500e^{-0.01x} - 3500e^{-0.02y},$$

where x is the number of liters of brand 1 and y is the number of liters of brand 2.

(a) What is the rate of change of insect deaths with respect to the number of liters of brand 1?

(b) What is the rate of change of insect deaths with respect to the number of liters of brand 2?

38. **Profit** Suppose that the profit from the sale of Kisses and Kreams is given by

$$P(x, y) = 100x + 64y - 0.01x^2 - 0.25y^2,$$

where x is the number of pounds of Kisses and y is the number of pounds of Kreams.

(a) Find $\partial P/\partial x$, and give the approximate rate of change of profit with respect to the number of pounds of Kisses if present sales are 20 pounds of Kisses and 10 pounds of Kreams.

(b) Find $\partial P/\partial y$, and give the approximate rate of change of profit with respect to the number of pounds of Kreams that are sold if 100 pounds of Kisses and 16 pounds of Kreams are currently being sold.

39. **Utility** If $U = f(x, y)$ is the utility function for goods X and Y, the *marginal utility* of X is

$\partial U/\partial x$ and the *marginal utility* of Y is $\partial U/\partial y$. If $U = x^2y^2$, find the marginal utility of

(a) X. (b) Y.

40. **Utility** If the utility function for goods X and Y is $U = xy + y^2$, find the marginal utility of

(a) X. (b) Y.

41. **Production** Suppose that the output Q (in thousands of units) of a certain company is $Q = 75K^{1/3}L^{2/3}$, where K is the capital expenditures in thousands of dollars and L is the number of labor hours. Find $\partial Q/\partial K$ and $\partial Q/\partial L$ when capital expenditures are \$729,000 and the labor hours total 1728.

42. **Production** Suppose that the production Q (in hundreds of gallons of paint) of a paint manufacturer can be modeled by $Q = 140K^{1/2}L^{1/2}$, where K is the company's capital expenditures in thousands of dollars and L is the size of the labor force (in hours worked). Find $\partial Q/\partial K$ and $\partial Q/\partial L$ when capital expenditures are \$250,000 and the labor hours are 1225.

Wind chill factor Dr. Paul Siple conducted studies testing the effect of wind on the formation of ice at various temperatures, and developed the concept of the wind chill factor, which we hear reported during winter weather reports. The wind chill temperatures for selected air temperatures and wind speeds are shown in the table below. For example, the table shows that an air temperature of 15°F together with a wind speed of 35 mph feels the same as when the air temperature is -27°F and there is no wind.

Air temperature (°F)

Wind speed (mph)	35	25	15	5	-5	-15	-25
5	33	21	12	0	-10	-21	-31
15	16	2	-11	-25	-38	-51	-65
25	8	-7	-22	-36	-51	-66	-81
35	4	-12	-27	-43	-58	-74	-89
45	2	-14	-30	-46	-62	-78	-93

Source: *World Almanac*, 1991.

One form of the formula that meteorologists use to

calculate wind chill temperatures is

$$WC = 48.064 + 0.474t - 0.020ts - 1.85s$$
$$+ 0.304t\sqrt{s} - 27.74\sqrt{s},$$

where s is wind speed and t is the actual air temperature. Use this equation to answer problems 43 and 44.

43. (a) To see how the wind chill temperature changes with wind speed, find $\partial WC/\partial s$.

(b) Find $\partial WC/\partial s$ when the temperature is 10°F and the wind speed is 25 mph. What does this mean?

44. (a) To see how wind chill temperature changes with temperature, find $\partial WC/\partial t$.

(b) Find $\partial WC/\partial t$ when the temperature is 10°F and the wind speed is 25 mph. What does this mean?

7.3 | APPLICATIONS OF FUNCTIONS OF TWO VARIABLES IN BUSINESS AND ECONOMICS

OBJECTIVES

- To evaluate cost functions at given levels of production
- To find marginal costs from total cost and joint cost functions
- To find marginal productivity for given production functions
- To find marginal demand functions from demand functions for a pair of related products

JOINT COST AND MARGINAL COST

Suppose that a firm produces two commodities using the same inputs in different proportions. In such a case the **joint cost function** is of the form $C = Q(x, y)$, where x and y represent the quantities of each commodity and C represents the total cost for the two commodities. Then $\partial C/\partial x$ is the **marginal cost** with respect to product x, and $\partial C/\partial y$ is the **marginal cost** with respect to product y.

EXAMPLE 1

If the joint cost function for two products is

$$C = Q(x, y) = 50 + x^2 + 8xy + y^3,$$

find the marginal cost with respect to

(a) x.   (b) y.   (c) x at $(5, 3)$.   (d) y at $(5, 3)$.

Solution

(a) The marginal cost with respect to x is $\partial C/\partial x = 2x + 8y$.

(b) The marginal cost with respect to y is $\dfrac{\partial C}{\partial y} = 8x + 3y^2$

(c) $\dfrac{\partial C}{\partial x}\bigg|_{(5,\,3)} = 2(5) + 8(3) = 34$

Thus if 5 units of product x and 3 units of product y are produced, the total cost will increase approximately \$34 for each unit increase in product x if y is held constant.

(d) $\dfrac{\partial C}{\partial y}\bigg|_{(5,\,3)} = 8(5) + 3(3)^2 = 67$

Thus if 5 units of product x and 3 units of product y are produced, the total cost will increase approximately \$67 for each unit increase in product y if x is held constant.

PRODUCTION FUNCTIONS

An important problem in economics concerns how the factors necessary for production determine the output of a product. For example, the output of a product depends on available labor, land, capital, material, and machines. If the amount of output z of a product depends on the amounts of two inputs x and y, then the quantity z is given by the **production function** $z = f(x, y)$.

EXAMPLE 2

Suppose that it is known that z bushels of a crop can be harvested according to the function

$$z = (21)\frac{6xy - 4x^2 - 3y}{2x + 0.01y}$$

when $100x$ work-hours of labor are employed on y acres of land.

What would be the output (in bushels) if 200 work-hours were used on 300 acres?

Solution Since $z = f(x, y)$,

$$f(2, 300) = (21)\frac{6(2)(300) + 4(2)^2 - 3(300)}{2(2) + 3}$$

$$= (21)\frac{3600 + 16 - 900}{7} = 8148 \text{ (bushels)}.$$

If $z = f(x, y)$ is a production function, $\partial z/\partial x$ represents the change in the output z with respect to input x while input y remains constant. This partial derivative is called the **marginal productivity of x.** The partial derivative $\partial z/\partial y$ is the **marginal productivity of y,** and measures the rate of change of z with respect to input y.

Marginal productivity (for either input) will be positive over a wide range of inputs, but it increases at a decreasing rate, and may eventually reach a point where it no longer increases, and begins to decrease.

EXAMPLE 3

If a production function is given by $z = 5x^{1/2}y^{1/4}$, find the marginal productivity of

(a) x.   (b) y.

Solution

(a) $\dfrac{\partial z}{\partial x} = \dfrac{5}{2}x^{-1/2}y^{1/4}$ (b) $\dfrac{\partial z}{\partial y} = \dfrac{5}{4}x^{1/2}y^{-3/4}$

Note that the marginal productivity of x is positive for all values of x, but that it decreases as x gets larger (because of the negative exponent). The same is true for the marginal productivity of y.

DEMAND FUNCTIONS

Suppose that two products are sold at prices p_1 and p_2, respectively, on a competitive market consisting of a fixed number of consumers with given tastes and incomes. Then the amount of each *one* of the products demanded by the consumers is dependent on the prices of *both* products on the market. If q_1 represents the demand for the first product, then $q_1 = f(p_1, p_2)$ is the **demand function** for that product. The graph of such a function is called a **demand surface.** An example of a demand function in two variables is $q_1 = 400 - 2p_1 - 4p_2$. Here q_1 is a function of two variables p_1 and p_2. If $p_1 = \$10$ and $p_2 = \$20$, the demand would equal $400 - 2(10) - 4(20) = 300$.

EXAMPLE 4

The demand functions for two products are

$q_1 = 50 - 5p_1 - 2p_2$
$q_2 = 100 - 3p_1 - 8p_2$.

What is the demand for each of the products if the price of the first is $p_1 = \$5$ and the price of the second is $p_2 = \$8$?

Solution

$q_1 = 50 - 5(5) - 2(8) = 9$
$q_2 = 100 - 3(5) - 8(8) = 21$

Thus if these are the prices, the demand for product 2 is higher than the demand for product 1.

EXAMPLE 5 | Using the demand equations in Example 4, find a pair of prices p_1 and p_2 such that the demands for product 1 and product 2 are equal.

Solution We want q_1 to equal q_2. Setting $q_1 = q_2$, we see that

$$50 - 5p_1 - 2p_2 = 100 - 3p_1 - 8p_2$$
$$6p_2 - 50 = 2p_1$$
$$p_1 = 3p_2 - 25$$

Now, any pair of positive values that satisfies this equation will make the demands equal. Letting $p_2 = 10$, we see that $p_1 = 5$ will satisfy the equation. Thus the prices $p_1 = 5$ and $p_2 = 10$ will make the demands equal. The prices $p_1 = 2$ and $p_2 = 9$ will also make the demands equal. Many pairs of values (that is, all those satisfying $p_1 = 3p_2 - 25$) will equalize the demands.

If the demand functions for a pair of related products, product 1 and product 2, are $q_1 = f(p_1, p_2)$ and $q_2 = g(p_1, p_2)$, respectively, then the partial derivatives of q_1 and q_2 are called **marginal demand functions.**

$\dfrac{\partial q_1}{\partial p_1}$ is the marginal demand of q_1 with respect to p_1.

$\dfrac{\partial q_1}{\partial p_2}$ is the marginal demand of q_1 with respect to p_2.

$\dfrac{\partial q_2}{\partial p_1}$ is the marginal demand of q_2 with respect to p_1.

$\dfrac{\partial q_2}{\partial p_2}$ is the marginal demand of q_2 with respect to p_2.

For typical demand functions, if the price of product 2 is fixed, the demand for product 1 will decrease as its price p_1 increases. In this case the marginal demand of q_1 with respect to p_1 will be negative; that is, $\partial q_1/\partial p_1 < 0$. Similarly, $\partial q_2/\partial p_2 < 0$.

But what about $\partial q_2/\partial p_1$ and $\partial q_1/\partial p_2$? If $\partial q_2/\partial p_1$ and $\partial q_1/\partial p_2$ are both positive, the two products are **competitive** because an increase in price p_1 will result in an increase in demand for product 2 (q_2) if the price p_2 is held constant, while an increase in price p_2 will increase the demand for product 1 if p_1 is held constant. Stated more simply, an increase in the price of one of the two products will result in an increased demand for the other, so the products are in competition. For example, an increase in the price of a Japanese automobile will result in an increase in demand for an American automobile if the price of the American automobile is held constant.

If $\partial q_2/\partial p_1$ and $\partial q_1/\partial p_2$ are both negative, the products are **complementary** because an increase in the price of one product will cause a decrease in demand for the other product if the price of the second product doesn't change. Under these conditions, a *decrease* in the price of product 1 would result in an *increase* in the demand for product 2, and a decrease in the price of product 2 would result in an increase in the demand for product 1. For example, a decrease in the price of gasoline would result in an increase in the demand for large automobiles.

If the signs of $\partial q_2/\partial p_1$ and $\partial q_1/\partial p_2$ are different, the products are neither competitive nor complementary. This situation rarely occurs, but is possible.

EXAMPLE 6

The demand functions for two related products, product 1 and product 2, are given by

$$q_1 = 400 - 5p_1 + 6p_2$$
$$q_2 = 250 + 4p_1 - 5p_2$$

(a) Determine the four marginal demands.

(b) Are product 1 and product 2 complementary or competitive?

Solution

(a) $\dfrac{\partial q_1}{\partial p_1} = -5 \qquad \dfrac{\partial q_2}{\partial p_2} = -5$

$\dfrac{\partial q_1}{\partial p_2} = 6 \qquad \dfrac{\partial q_2}{\partial p_1} = 4$

(b) Since $\partial q_1/\partial p_2$ and $\partial q_2/\partial p_1$ are both positive, products 1 and 2 are competitive.

CHECKPOINT

1. If the joint cost function for two products is

$$C = 100 + 3x + 10xy + y^2,$$

find the marginal cost with respect to

(a) x.   (b) y at $(7, 3)$.

2. If the production function for a product is

$$P = 10x^{1/4}y^{1/2},$$

find the marginal productivity of x.

3. If the demand functions for two products are

$$q_1 = 200 - 3p_1 - 4p_2 \quad \text{and} \quad q_2 = 50 - 6p_1 - 5p_2,$$

what is the marginal demand of

(a) q_1 with respect to p_1?

(b) q_2 with respect to p_2?

TECHNOLOGY CORNER

For these questions, use either a computer or a graphics calculator.
Suppose that the Cobb-Douglas production function for a company is given by

$$z = 100x^{1/4}y^{3/4},$$

where x is the company's capital investment and y is the size of the labor force (in work-hours). Note that $x \geq 0$ and $y \geq 0$.

1. (a) Find z_x.
   (b) If the current labor force is 625 work-hours, then substitute $y = 625$ into z_x and graph the resulting function of x. Use $x \geq 0$.
   (c) Use the graph in (b) to determine whether $z_x(x, 625)$ is ever negative or zero. What does $z_x(x, 625) > 0$ tell you about the effect that additional capital investments have on production?

2. (a) Find z_y.
   (b) If current capital investment is $10,000, then substitute $x = 10,000$ into z_y and graph the resulting function of y. Use $y \geq 0$.
   (c) From the graph in (b) you can see that $z_y(10,000, y) > 0$. What does this tell you about the effect that additional work-hours have on production?

CHECKPOINT
SOLUTIONS

1. (a) $\dfrac{\partial C}{\partial x} = 3 + 10y$

   (b) $\dfrac{\partial C}{\partial y} = 10x + 2y$

   $\dfrac{\partial C}{\partial y}(7, 3) = 10(7) + 2(3) = 76$

2. $\dfrac{\partial P}{\partial x} = \dfrac{2.5y^{1/2}}{x^{3/4}}$

3. (a) $\dfrac{\partial q_1}{\partial p_1} = -3$ (b) $\dfrac{\partial q_2}{\partial p_2} = -5$

Joint Cost and Marginal Cost

1. The cost of manufacturing one item is given by

$$C(x, y) = 30 + 3x + 5y,$$

where x is the cost of one hour of labor and y is the cost of one pound of material. If the hourly cost of labor is $4, and the material costs $3 per pound, what is the cost of manufacturing one of these items?

2. The manufacture of one unit of a product has its cost given by

$$C(x, y, z) = 10 + 8x + 3y + z,$$

where x is the cost of one pound of one raw material, y is the cost of one pound of a second material, and z is the cost of one work-hour of labor. If the cost of the first raw material is $16 per pound, the cost of the second raw material is $8 per pound, and labor costs $8 per work-hour, what will it cost to produce one unit of the product?

3. The total cost of producing one unit of a product is

$$C(x, y) = 30 + 2x + 4y + \frac{xy}{50},$$

where x is the cost per pound of raw materials and y is the cost per hour of labor.
(a) If labor costs are held constant, at what rate will the total cost increase for each increase of $1 per pound in material cost?
(b) If material costs are held constant, at what rate will the total cost increase for each $1 per hour increase in labor costs?

4. The total cost of producing an item is

$$C(x, y) = 40 + 4x + 6y + \frac{x^2 y}{100},$$

where x is the cost per pound of raw materials and y is the cost per hour for labor. How will

an increase of
(a) $1 per pound of raw materials affect the total cost?
(b) $1 per hour in labor costs affect the total cost?

5. The total cost of producing one unit of a product is given by

$$C(x, y) = 20x + 70y + \frac{x^2}{1000} + \frac{xy^2}{100},$$

where x represents the cost per pound of raw materials and y represents the hourly rate for labor. The present cost for raw materials is $10 per pound and the present hourly rate for labor is $4. How will an increase of
(a) $1 per pound for raw materials affect the total cost?
(b) $1 per hour in labor costs affect the total cost?

6. The total cost of producing one unit of a product is given by

$$C(x, y) = 30 + 10x^2 + 20y - xy,$$

where x is the hourly labor rate and y is the cost per pound of raw materials. The current hourly rate is $5, and the raw materials cost $6 per pound. How will an increase of
(a) $1 per pound for the raw materials affect the total cost?
(b) $1 in the hourly labor rate affect the total cost?

7. The joint cost function for two products is

$$C(x, y) = 30 + x^2 + 3y + 2xy,$$

where x represents the quantity of product X produced and y represents the quantity of product Y produced. Find the marginal cost with respect to
(a) x if 8 units of product X and 10 units of product Y are produced.
(b) y if 8 units of product X and 10 units of product Y are produced.

8. The joint cost function for products X and Y is

$$C(x, y) = 40 + 3x^2 + y^2 + xy,$$

where x represents the quantity of X and y represents the quantity of Y. Find the marginal cost with respect to
    (a) x if 20 units of product X and 15 units of product Y are produced.
    (b) y if 20 units of X and 15 units of Y are produced.

9. If the joint cost function for two products is

$$C(x, y) = x\sqrt{y^2 + 1},$$

    (a) Find the marginal cost (function) with respect to x.
    (b) Find the marginal cost with respect to y.

10. Suppose the joint cost function for x units of product X and y units of product Y is given by

$$C(x, y) = 2500\sqrt{xy + 1}.$$

Find the marginal cost with respect to
    (a) x.   (b) y.

11. Suppose that the joint cost function for two products is

$$C(x, y) = 1200 \ln (xy + 1) + 10,000.$$

Find the marginal cost with respect to
    (a) x.   (b) y.

12. Suppose that the joint cost function for two products is

$$C(x, y) = y \ln (x + 1).$$

Find the marginal cost with respect to
    (a) x.   (b) y.

PRODUCTION FUNCTIONS

13. Suppose that the production function for a product is $z = \sqrt{4xy}$, where x represents the number of work-hours per month and y is the number of available machines. Determine the marginal productivity of
    (a) x.   (b) y.

14. Suppose the production function for a product is

$$z = 60x^{2/5}y^{3/5},$$

where x is the capital expenditures and y is the number of work-hours. Find the marginal productivity of
    (a) x.   (b) y.

15. Suppose that the production function for a product is $z = \sqrt{x} \ln (y + 1)$, where x represents the number of work-hours and y represents the available capital (per week). Find the marginal productivity of
    (a) x.
    (b) y.

16. Suppose that a company's production function for a certain product is

$$z = (x + 1)^{1/2} \ln (y^2 + 1),$$

where x is the number of work-hours of unskilled labor and y is the number of work-hours of skilled labor. Find the marginal productivity of
    (a) x.
    (b) y.

For problems 17–19, suppose that the production function for an agricultural product is given by

$$z = \frac{11xy - 0.0002x^2 - 5y}{0.03x + 3y},$$

where x is the number of hours of labor and y is the number of acres of the crop.

17. Find the output when $x = 300$ and $y = 500$.

18. Find the marginal productivity of the number of acres of the crop (y) when $x = 300$ and $y = 500$.

19. Find the marginal productivity of the number of hours of labor (x) when $x = 300$ and $y = 500$.

20. If a production function is given by $z = 12x^{3/4}y^{1/3}$, find the marginal productivity of
    (a) x.
    (b) y.

DEMAND FUNCTIONS

21. The demand functions for two products are given by

$$q_1 = 300 - 8p_1 - 4p_2$$
$$q_2 = 400 - 5p_1 - 10p_2.$$

Find the demand for each of the products if the price of the first is $p_1 = 10$ and the price of the second is $p_2 = 8$.

22. The demand functions for two products are given by

$$q_1 = 900 - 9p_1 + 2p_2$$
$$q_2 = 1200 + 6p_1 - 10p_2.$$

Find the demands q_1 and q_2 if $p_1 = \$10$ and $p_2 = \$12$.

23. Find a pair of prices p_1 and p_2 such that the demands for the two products in problem 21 will be equal.

24. Find a pair of prices p_1 and p_2 such that the demands for the two products in problem 22 will be equal.

In problems 25–28, the demand functions for two related products, A and B, are given. Complete parts (a)–(e) for each problem.

(a) Find the marginal demand of q_A with respect to p_A.

(b) Find the marginal demand of q_A with respect to p_B.

(c) Find the marginal demand of q_B with respect to p_B.

(d) Find the marginal demand of q_B with respect to p_A.

(e) Are the two goods competitive or complementary?

25. $\begin{cases} q_A = 400 - 3p_A - 2p_B \\ q_B = 250 - 5p_A - 6p_B \end{cases}$

26. $\begin{cases} q_A = 600 - 4p_A + 6p_B \\ q_B = 1200 + 8p_A - 4p_B \end{cases}$

27. $\begin{cases} q_A = 5000 - 50p_A - \dfrac{600}{p_B + 1} \\ q_B = 10{,}000 - \dfrac{400}{p_A + 4} + \dfrac{400}{p_B + 4} \end{cases}$

28. $\begin{cases} q_A = 2500 + \dfrac{600}{p_A + 2} - 40p_B \\ q_B = 3000 - 100p_A + \dfrac{400}{p_B + 5} \end{cases}$

7.4 | HIGHER-ORDER PARTIAL DERIVATIVES

OBJECTIVE

- To find and evaluate second and higher-order partial derivatives of functions of two variables

Just as each derivative of a function of one variable in turn may have second, third, and higher derivatives, partial derivatives may also have partial derivatives. A function of two variables, such as $z = f(x, y)$ has *four* second partial derivatives. The notations for these second partial derivatives follow.

Second Partial Derivatives

$z_{xx} = \dfrac{\partial^2 z}{\partial x^2} = \dfrac{\partial}{\partial x}\left(\dfrac{\partial z}{\partial x}\right)$: both derivatives taken with respect to x.

$z_{yy} = \dfrac{\partial^2 z}{\partial y^2} = \dfrac{\partial}{\partial y}\left(\dfrac{\partial z}{\partial y}\right)$: both derivatives taken with respect to y.

$z_{xy} = \dfrac{\partial^2 z}{\partial y\,\partial x} = \dfrac{\partial}{\partial y}\left(\dfrac{\partial z}{\partial x}\right)$: first derivative taken with respect to x, second with respect to y.

$z_{yx} = \dfrac{\partial^2 z}{\partial x\,\partial y} = \dfrac{\partial}{\partial x}\left(\dfrac{\partial z}{\partial y}\right)$: first derivative taken with respect to y, second with respect to x.

EXAMPLE 1   If $z = x^3 y - 3xy^2 + 4$, find each of the second partial derivatives of the function.

Solution Since

$$z_x = 3x^2 y - 3y^2 \quad \text{and} \quad z_y = x^3 - 6xy,$$

$$z_{xx} = \frac{\partial}{\partial x}(3x^2 y - 3y^2) = 6xy$$

$$z_{xy} = \frac{\partial}{\partial y}(3x^2 y - 3y^2) = 3x^2 - 6y$$

$$z_{yy} = \frac{\partial}{\partial y}(x^3 - 6xy) = -6x$$

$$z_{yx} = \frac{\partial}{\partial x}(x^3 - 6xy) = 3x^2 - 6y.$$

Note that z_{xy} and z_{yx} are equal for the function in Example 1. This will always occur if the derivatives of this function are continuous.

$z_{xy} = z_{yx}$

If the second partial derivatives z_{xy} and z_{yx} of a function $z = f(x, y)$ are continuous at a point, they are equal there.

EXAMPLE 2   Find each of the second partial derivatives of $z = x^2 y + e^{xy}$.

Solution Since $z_x = 2xy + e^{xy} \cdot y$,

$$z_{xx} = 2y + e^{xy} \cdot y^2 = 2y + y^2 e^{xy}$$
$$z_{xy} = 2x + (e^{xy} \cdot 1 + ye^{xy} \cdot x)$$
$$= 2x + e^{xy} + xye^{xy}.$$

Since $z_y = x^2 + e^{xy} \cdot x$,

$$z_{yx} = 2x + (e^{xy} \cdot 1 + xe^{xy} \cdot y)$$
$$= 2x + e^{xy} + xye^{xy}$$
$$z_{yy} = 0 + xe^{xy} \cdot x = x^2 e^{xy}.$$

EXAMPLE 3 | If $z = x^2 y + \ln x$, find $z_{xy}|_{(1, 1)}$.

Solution

$$z_x = 2xy + \frac{1}{x}$$

$$z_{xy} = 2x$$
$$z_{xy}|_{(1, 1)} = 2(1) = 2$$

CHECKPOINT

1. If $z = 4x^3 y^4 + 4xy$, find:
   (a) z_{xx} (b) z_{yy}
   (c) z_{xy} (d) z_{yx}

2. If $z = x^2 + 4e^{xy}$, find z_{xy}.

We can find partial derivatives of order higher than the second. For example, we can find the third-order partial derivatives z_{xyx} and z_{xyy} for the function in Example 1 from the second derivative $z_{xy} = 3x^2 - 6y$:

$$z_{xyx} = 6x$$
$$z_{xyy} = -6.$$

EXAMPLE 4 | If $z = x^3 y^2 + 4 \ln x$, find z_{xyy}.

Solution

$$z_x = 3x^2 y^2 + 4 \cdot \frac{1}{x}$$
$$z_{xy} = 3x^2(2y) + 0 = 6x^2 y$$
$$z_{xyy} = 6x^2$$

1. $z_x = 12x^2y^4 + 4y$ and $z_y = 16x^3y^3 + 4x$

    (a) $z_{xx} = 24xy^4$ (b) $z_{yy} = 48x^3y^2$
    (c) $z_{xy} = 48x^2y^3 + 4$ (d) $z_{yx} = 48x^2y^3 + 4$

2. $z_x = 2x + 4e^{xy}(y) = 2x + 4ye^{xy}$
   Calculation of z_{xy} requires the Product Rule.

   $$z_{xy} = 0 + (4y)(e^{xy}x) + (e^{xy})(4) = 4xye^{xy} + 4e^{xy}$$

EXERCISE 7.4

1. If $z = x^2 + 4x - 5y^3$, find the following.
   (a) z_{xx} (b) z_{xy} (c) z_{yx} (d) z_{yy}

2. If $z = x^3 - 5y^2 + 4y + 1$, find the following.
   (a) z_{xx} (b) z_{xy} (c) z_{yx} (d) z_{yy}

3. If $z = x^2y - 4xy^2$, find the following.
   (a) z_{xx} (b) z_{xy} (c) z_{yx} (d) z_{yy}

4. If $z = xy^2 + 4xy - 5$, find the following.
   (a) z_{xx} (b) z_{xy} (c) z_{yx} (d) z_{yy}

5. If $z = x^2 - xy + 4y^3$, find z_{xyx}.

6. If $z = x^3 - 4x^2y + 5y^3$, find z_{yyx}.

7. If $z = x^4 + x \ln y + y^2$, find z_{xyy}.

8. If $z = x^2y^3 + ye^x - y^2$, find z_{yxy}.

9. If $f(x, y) = x^3y + 4xy^4$, find $\left.\dfrac{\partial^2}{\partial x^2} f(x, y)\right|_{(1, -1)}$.

10. If $f(x, y) = x^4y^2 + 4xy$, find $\left.\dfrac{\partial^2}{\partial y^2} f(x, y)\right|_{(1, 2)}$.

11. If $f(x_1, x_2) = 3x_1^2 - 2x_1x_2$, find the following.
    (a) $\left.\dfrac{\partial^2 f(x_1, x_2)}{\partial x_1^2}\right|_{(0, 2)}$ (b) $\left.\dfrac{\partial^2 f(x_1, x_2)}{\partial x_2^2}\right|_{(3, 2)}$

12. If $f(x, y) = x^3y^2 + 4xy^3$, find the following.
    (a) $\left.\dfrac{\partial^2 f(x, y)}{\partial x^2}\right|_{(1, 3)}$ (b) $\left.\dfrac{\partial^2 f(x, y)}{\partial y^2}\right|_{(1, 3)}$

13. If $z = x^2y + ye^{x^2}$, find $z_{yx}|_{(1, 2)}$.

14. If $z = xy^3 + x \ln y^2$, find $z_{xy}|_{(2, 1)}$.

15. If $f(x, y) = x^2 + e^{xy}$, find the following.
    (a) $\dfrac{\partial^2 f}{\partial x^2}$ (b) $\dfrac{\partial^2 f}{\partial y \, \partial x}$ (c) $\dfrac{\partial^2 f}{\partial x \, \partial y}$ (d) $\dfrac{\partial^2 f}{\partial y^2}$

16. If $z = xe^{xy}$, find the following.
    (a) z_{xx} (b) z_{yy} (c) z_{xy} (d) z_{yx}

17. If $f(x, y) = y^2 - \ln xy$, find the following.
    (a) $\dfrac{\partial^2 f}{\partial x^2}$ (b) $\dfrac{\partial^2 f}{\partial y \, \partial x}$ (c) $\dfrac{\partial^2 f}{\partial x \, \partial y}$ (d) $\dfrac{\partial^2 f}{\partial y^2}$

18. If $f(x, y) = x^3 + \ln(xy - 1)$, find the following.
    (a) $\dfrac{\partial^2 f}{\partial x^2}$ (b) $\dfrac{\partial^2 f}{\partial y^2}$ (c) $\dfrac{\partial^2 f}{\partial x \, \partial y}$ (d) $\dfrac{\partial^2 f}{\partial y \, \partial x}$

19. If $z = \dfrac{\ln(x^2 + y^2)}{x^2}$, find z_{yy}.

20. If $z = \ln(x^2 + 4y^2)$, find z_{xx}.

21. If $z = \sqrt{4x^2 + y^2}$, find z_{xx}.

22. If $z = \ln(x^2 + 4y^2)$, find z_{yy}.

23. If $w = 4x^3y + y^2z + z^3$, find the following.
    (a) w_{xxy} (b) w_{xyx} (c) w_{xyz}

24. If $w = 4xyz + x^3y^2z + x^3$, find the following.
    (a) w_{xyz} (b) w_{xzz} (c) w_{yyz}

7.5 | MAXIMA AND MINIMA; LINEAR REGRESSION

OBJECTIVES

- To find relative maxima, minima, and saddle points of functions of two variables
- To write the equation of the line that is the best fit for a set of data points

MAXIMA AND MINIMA

In our study of differentiable functions of one variable, we saw that for a relative maximum or minimum to occur at a point, the tangent line to the curve had to be horizontal at that point. The function $z = f(x, y)$ describes a surface in three dimensions. If all partial derivatives of $f(x, y)$ exist, then the surface described by $z = f(x, y)$ must have a horizontal plane tangent to the surface at a point in order to have a relative maximum or minimum at that point (see Figure 7.6). But if the plane tangent to the surface at the point is horizontal, then all the tangent lines to the surface at that point must also be horizontal, for they lie in the tangent plane. In particular, the tangent line in the direction of the x-axis will be horizontal, so $\partial z/\partial x = 0$ at the point; and the tangent line in the direction of the y-axis will be horizontal, so $\partial z/\partial y = 0$ at the point. Thus we can determine the *critical points* for a surface by finding those points where *both* $\partial z/\partial x = 0$ and $\partial z/\partial y = 0$.

FIGURE 7.6   (a)

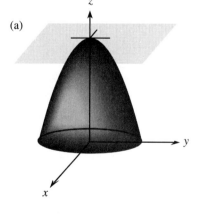

(b)

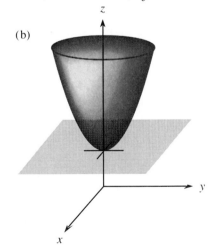

How can we determine whether a critical point is a relative maximum or relative minimum, or neither of these? Finding that $\partial^2 z/\partial x^2 < 0$ and $\partial^2 z/\partial y^2 < 0$ is not enough to tell us that we have a relative maximum. The "second derivative" test we must use involves the values of the second partial derivatives and the value of D at the critical point (a, b), where D is defined as follows:

$$D = \frac{\partial^2 z}{\partial x^2} \cdot \frac{\partial^2 z}{\partial y^2} - \left(\frac{\partial^2 z}{\partial x \, \partial y}\right)^2.$$

We shall state, without proof, the result that determines whether there is a relative maximum or minimum, or neither, at a point (a, b).

Test for Maxima and Minima

Let $z = f(x, y)$ be a function for which

$$\frac{\partial z}{\partial x} = \frac{\partial z}{\partial y} = 0 \quad \text{at a point } (a, b),$$

and suppose that all second partial derivatives are continuous there. For

$$D = \frac{\partial^2 z}{\partial x^2} \cdot \frac{\partial^2 z}{\partial y^2} - \left(\frac{\partial^2 z}{\partial x \partial y}\right)^2$$

(a) If $D > 0$ and $\partial^2 z/\partial x^2 > 0$ at (a, b), then a relative minimum occurs at (a, b). In this case, $\partial^2 z/\partial y^2 > 0$ at (a, b) also.

(b) If $D > 0$ and $\partial^2 z/\partial x^2 < 0$ at (a, b), then a relative maximum occurs at (a, b). In this case, $\partial^2 z/\partial y^2 < 0$ at (a, b) also.

(c) If $D < 0$ at (a, b), there is neither a relative maximum nor minimum at (a, b).

(d) If $D = 0$ at (a, b), then the test fails; the function must be investigated near the point.

We can test for relative maxima and minima by using the following procedure.

MAXIMA AND MINIMA OF $z = f(x, y)$

PROCEDURE	EXAMPLE
To find relative maxima and minima of $z = f(x, y)$.	Test $z = 4 - 4x^2 - y^2$ for relative maxima and minima.
1. Find $\partial z/\partial x$ and $\partial z/\partial y$.	1. $\dfrac{\partial z}{\partial x} = -8x;$ $\dfrac{\partial z}{\partial y} = -2y$
2. Find the point(s) that satisfy *both* $\partial z/\partial x = 0$ and $\partial z/\partial y = 0$. These are the critical points.	2. $\dfrac{\partial z}{\partial x} = 0$ if $x = 0$. $\dfrac{\partial z}{\partial y} = 0$ if $y = 0$. The critical point is $(0, 0, 4)$.
3. Find all second partial derivatives.	3. $\dfrac{\partial^2 z}{\partial x^2} = -8;$ $\dfrac{\partial^2 z}{\partial y^2} = -2$ $\dfrac{\partial^2 z}{\partial x \partial y} = \dfrac{\partial^2 z}{\partial y \partial x} = 0$
4. Evaluate D at the critical point(s).	4. At $(0, 0)$, $D = (-8)(-2) - 0^2 = 16$.
5. Use the test for maxima and minima to determine if relative maxima or minima occur.	5. $D > 0$, $\partial^2 z/\partial x^2 < 0$, and $\partial^2 z/\partial y^2 < 0$. A relative maximum occurs at $(0, 0)$. The graph is shown in Figure 7.7 on the following page.

FIGURE 7.7

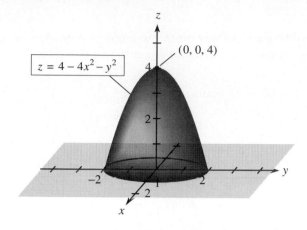

$z = 4 - 4x^2 - y^2$

$(0, 0, 4)$

EXAMPLE 1

Test $z = x^2 + y^2 - 2x + 1$ for relative maxima and minima.

Solution

1. $\dfrac{\partial z}{\partial x} = 2x - 2;$ $\qquad \dfrac{\partial z}{\partial y} = 2y$

2. $\dfrac{\partial z}{\partial x} = 0$ if $x = 1.$

$\dfrac{\partial z}{\partial y} = 0$ if $y = 0.$

Both are 0 if $x = 1$ *and* $y = 0$, so the critical point is $(1, 0, 0)$.

3. $\dfrac{\partial^2 z}{\partial x^2} = 2;$ $\qquad \dfrac{\partial^2 z}{\partial y^2} = 2$

$\dfrac{\partial^2 z}{\partial x\, \partial y} = \dfrac{\partial^2 z}{\partial y\, \partial x} = 0$

4. At $(1, 0)$, $D = 2 \cdot 2 - 0^2 = 4.$

5. $D > 0$, $\partial^2 z/\partial x^2 > 0$, and $\partial^2 z/\partial y^2 > 0$. A relative minimum occurs at $(1, 0)$. (See Figure 7.8.)

FIGURE 7.8

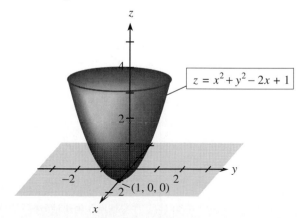

$z = x^2 + y^2 - 2x + 1$

$(1, 0, 0)$

EXAMPLE 2

Test $z = y^2 - x^2$ for relative maxima and minima.

Solution

1. $\dfrac{\partial z}{\partial x} = -2x; \qquad \dfrac{\partial z}{\partial y} = 2y$

2. $\dfrac{\partial z}{\partial x} = 0$ if $x = 0; \qquad \dfrac{\partial z}{\partial y} = 0$ if $y = 0$.

   So both equal 0 if $x = 0$, $y = 0$. The critical point is $(0, 0, 0)$.

3. $\dfrac{\partial^2 z}{\partial x^2} = -2; \qquad \dfrac{\partial^2 z}{\partial y^2} = 2; \qquad \dfrac{\partial^2 z}{\partial x\, \partial y} = \dfrac{\partial^2 z}{\partial y\, \partial x} = 0$

4. $D = (-2)(2) - 0 = -4$

5. $D < 0$, so the critical point is neither a relative maximum nor minimum. As Figure 7.9 shows, the surface formed has the shape of a saddle. For this reason, critical points that are neither relative maxima nor minima are called **saddle points.**

FIGURE 7.9

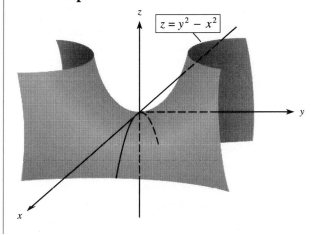

$z = y^2 - x^2$

The following example involves a surface with two critical points.

EXAMPLE 3

Test $z = x^3 + y^3 + 6xy$ for relative maxima and minima.

Solution

1. $\dfrac{\partial z}{\partial x} = 3x^2 + 6y; \qquad \dfrac{\partial z}{\partial y} = 3y^2 + 6x$

2. $\dfrac{\partial z}{\partial x} = 0$ if $0 = 3x^2 + 6y$; that is, if $y = -\frac{1}{2}x^2$.

   $\dfrac{\partial z}{\partial y} = 0$ if $0 = 3y^2 + 6x$; that is, if $x = -\frac{1}{2}y^2$.

Since *both* conditions must be satisfied, we can substitute $-\frac{1}{2}y^2$ for x in

$y = -\frac{1}{2}x^2$, and obtain

$$y = -\frac{1}{2}\left(-\frac{1}{2}y^2\right)^2,$$

$$y = -\frac{1}{8}y^4$$

$$y + \frac{1}{8}y^4 = 0$$

$$y(8 + y^3) = 0.$$

So $y = 0$ or $y^3 = -8$; thus, $y = 0$ or $y = -2$. If $y = 0$, $x = -\frac{1}{2}(0)^2 = 0$, so one critical point is $(0, 0, 0)$. If $y = -2$, $x = -\frac{1}{2}(-2)^2 = -2$, so the second critical point is $(-2, -2, 8)$.

3. $\dfrac{\partial^2 z}{\partial x^2} = 6x;\quad \dfrac{\partial^2 z}{\partial y^2} = 6y;\quad \dfrac{\partial^2 z}{\partial x\,\partial y} = \dfrac{\partial^2 z}{\partial y\,\partial x} = 6$

   Thus $D = (6x)(6y) - (6)^2$.

4. At $(0, 0)$, $D = 0 \cdot 0 - (6)^2 = -36 < 0$.
   At $(-2, -2)$, $D = (-12)(-12) - 36 = 108 > 0$.

5. At $(0, 0)$, $D < 0$, so a saddle point occurs at $(0, 0, 0)$.
   At $(-2, -2)$, $D > 0$, $\partial^2 z/\partial x^2 = 6(-2) = -12$, and $\partial^2 z/\partial y^2 = 6(-2) = -12$, so a relative maximum occurs at $(-2, -2)$. It is 8.

CHECKPOINT

Suppose that $z = 4 - x^2 - y^2 + 2x - 4y$.

1. Find z_x and z_y.

2. Solve $z_x = 0$ and $z_y = 0$ simultaneously to find the critical point(s) for the graph of this function.

3. Test the point(s) for relative maxima and minima.

EXAMPLE 4

Maximize the profit if the demand functions for products X and Y are $p_1 = 50 - x$ and $p_2 = 60 - 2y$, and if the joint cost function for the products is $C(x, y) = 2xy$.

Solution The profit function is $P(x, y) = p_1x + p_2y - C(x, y)$, so

$$P(x, y) = (50 - x)x + (60 - 2y)y - 2xy$$
$$= 50x - x^2 + 60y - 2y^2 - 2xy.$$

To maximize the profit, we proceed as follows.

$$P_x = 50 - 2x - 2y \quad \text{and} \quad P_y = 60 - 4y - 2x.$$

Solving simultaneously $P_x = 0$ and $P_y = 0$, we have

$$\begin{cases} 0 = 50 - 2x - 2y \\ 0 = 60 - 2x - 4y \end{cases}.$$

Subtraction gives $-10 + 2y = 0$, so $y = 5$. Thus $0 = 40 - 2x$, so $x = 20$. Now $P_{xx} = -2$, $P_{yy} = -4$, and $P_{xy} = -2$, and

$$D = (P_{xx})(P_{yy}) - (P_{xy})^2 = (-2)(-4) - (-2)^2 = +4.$$

Since $P_{xx} < 0$, $P_{yy} < 0$, and $D > 0$, the values $x = 20$ and $y = 5$ yield maximum profit. Therefore, when $x = 20$ and $y = 5$, $p_1 = 30$, $p_2 = 50$, and the maximum profit is

$$P(20, 5) = 600 + 250 - 200 = 650 \text{ (dollars)}.$$

Linear Regression

In this text we have used equations and functions to model cost, revenue, profit, demand, and supply, and we have used calculus to study the behavior of these functions, finding, for example, marginal cost, marginal revenue, producer's surplus, and so on. But how do we develop the equations that are used to model the concept? One method is to use previous experience and knowledge to provide a theoretical base for the model. A second method is to use empirical data and information about the form of the model to find the curve that "best fits" the data.

The formulas used to find the equation of the straight line that is the best fit for a set of data are developed using max-min techniques for functions of two variables. This line is called the **regression line.** Consider the table below, which shows a product's marginal costs at different levels of production. If we plot the points (x, y) for this set of data, we have the *scatter diagram* in Figure 7.10.

x (units)	y (marginal cost)
100	2400
200	4100
300	6000
400	8500

FIGURE 7.10

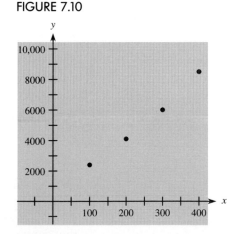

Although the points on the scatter diagram do not fit exactly on a line, we can see a trend that is nearly linear and in which the marginal cost y increases as the number of units x increases. Because the plot of the data (see Figure 7.10) is so close to linear, we might ask how we could find the equation of the line that is the best fit for these data.

In Figure 7.11, we define line ℓ to be the best fit for the data points (that is, the regression line) if the sum of the squares of the differences between the actual y-values of the data points and the y-values of the points on the line is a minimum.

In general, to find the equation of the regression line, we assume that the relationship between x and y is approximately linear, and that we can find a straight line with equation

$$\hat{y} = a + bx$$

where the values of $\hat{y}$ will approximate the y-values of the points we know. That is, for each given value of x, the point $(x, \hat{y})$ will be on the line. For any given x-value, x_i, we are interested in the deviation between the y-value of the data point (x_i, y_i) and the $\hat{y}$-value from the equation, $\hat{y}_i$, that results when x_i is substituted for x. These deviations are of the form

$$d_i = \hat{y}_i - y_i, \qquad \text{for } i = 1, 2, \ldots, n$$

(see Figure 7.11 for a general case with the deviations exaggerated).

FIGURE 7.11

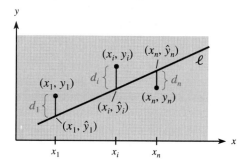

To measure the deviations in a way that accounts for the fact that some of the y-values will be above the line and some will be below the line, we will say that the line that is the best fit for the data is the one for which the sum of the squares of the deviations is a minimum. That is, we seek the a and b in the equation

$$\hat{y} = a + bx$$

such that the sum of the squares of the deviations,

$$S = \sum_{i=1}^{n} (\hat{y}_i - y_i)^2 = \sum_{i=1}^{n} [(bx_i + a) - y_i]^2$$
$$= (bx_1 + a - y_1)^2 + (bx_2 + a - y_2)^2 + \ldots + (bx_n + a - y_n)^2,$$

is a minimum.

We seek the values of b and a that make S a minimum, so we find the values that make

$$\frac{\partial S}{\partial b} = 0 \quad \text{and} \quad \frac{\partial S}{\partial a} = 0.$$

$$\frac{\partial S}{\partial b} = 2(bx_1 + a - y_1)x_1 + 2(bx_2 + a - y_2)x_2 + \ldots + 2(bx_n + a - y_n)x_n$$

$$\frac{\partial S}{\partial a} = 2(bx_1 + a - y_1) + 2(bx_2 + a - y_2) + \ldots + 2(bx_n + a - y_n)$$

Setting each equation equal to 0, dividing by 2, and using sigma notation gives the following:

$$0 = b \sum_{i=1}^{n} x_i^2 + a \sum_{i=1}^{n} x_i - \sum_{i=1}^{n} x_i y_i \qquad (1)$$

$$0 = b \sum_{i=1}^{n} x_i + a \sum_{i=1}^{n} 1 - \sum_{i=1}^{n} y_i \qquad (2)$$

We can write equations (1) and (2) as follows:

$$\sum_{i=1}^{n} x_i y_i = a \sum_{i=1}^{n} x_i + b \sum_{i=1}^{n} x_i^2 \qquad (3)$$

$$\sum_{i=1}^{n} y_i = an + b \sum_{i=1}^{n} x_i \qquad (4)$$

Multiplying equation (3) by n and equation (4) by $\sum_{i=1}^{n} x_i$ permits us to begin to solve for b:

$$n \sum_{i=1}^{n} x_i y_i = na \sum_{i=1}^{n} x_i + nb \sum_{i=1}^{n} x_i^2 \qquad (5)$$

$$\sum_{i=1}^{n} x_i \sum_{i=1}^{n} y_i = na \sum_{i=1}^{n} x_i + b \left(\sum_{i=1}^{n} x_i \right)^2 \qquad (6)$$

Subtracting equation (5) from equation (6) gives

$$\sum_{i=1}^{n} x_i \sum_{i=1}^{n} y_i - n \sum_{i=1}^{n} x_i y_i = b \left(\sum_{i=1}^{n} x_i \right)^2 - nb \sum_{i=1}^{n} x_i^2$$

$$= b \left[\left(\sum_{i=1}^{n} x_i \right)^2 - n \sum_{i=1}^{n} x_i^2 \right].$$

Thus
$$b = \frac{\sum_{i=1}^{n} x_i \sum_{i=1}^{n} y_i - n \sum_{i=1}^{n} x_i y_i}{\left(\sum_{i=1}^{n} x_i \right)^2 - n \sum_{i=1}^{n} x_i^2},$$

and, from equation (4),
$$a = \frac{\sum_{i=1}^{n} y_i - b \sum_{i=1}^{n} x_i}{n}.$$

It can be shown that these values for b and a give a minimum value for S, and so we have the following.

Linear Regression Equation

Given a set of data points (x_1, y_1), (x_2, y_2), ... , (x_n, y_n), the equation of the line that is the best fit for these data is

$$\hat{y} = a + bx$$

where

$$b = \frac{\Sigma x \cdot \Sigma y - n\Sigma xy}{(\Sigma x)^2 - n\Sigma x^2}, \qquad a = \frac{\Sigma y - b\Sigma x}{n},$$

and each summation is taken over the entire data set (that is, from 1 to n).

EXAMPLE 5

The following data show the relation between the diameter of a partial roll of blue denim material at MacGregor Mills and the actual number of yards remaining on the roll. Use linear regression to find the linear equation that gives the number of yards as a function of the diameter.

Diameter (inches)	Yds/roll	Diameter (inches)	Yds/roll
14.0	120	22.5	325
15.0	145	24.0	360
16.5	170	24.5	380
17.75	200	25.25	405
18.5	220	26.0	435
19.8	255	26.75	460
20.5	270	27.0	470
22.0	305	28.0	500

Solution Let x be the diameter of the partial rolls and y be the yards on a roll. Before finding the values for a and b, we evaluate some parts of the formulas:

$$n = 16$$
$$\Sigma x = 348.05$$
$$\Sigma x^2 = 7871.48$$
$$\Sigma y = 5070$$
$$\Sigma xy = 118{,}312.25$$
$$b = \frac{\Sigma x\Sigma y - n\Sigma xy}{(\Sigma x)^2 - n\Sigma x^2}$$
$$= \frac{(348.05)(5070) - 16(118{,}312.25)}{(348.05)^2 - 16(7871.48)} = 26.7192$$
$$a = \frac{\Sigma y - b\Sigma x}{n}$$
$$= \frac{(5070) - (26.7192)(348.05)}{16} = -264.3511$$

Thus the linear equation that can be used to estimate the number of yards of denim remaining on a roll is

$$\hat{y} = -264.35 + 26.72x.$$

We can use the equation developed in Example 5 to compare the estimate with the actual measurement. For example, if $x = 20.5$, the equation gives $\hat{y} = 283.41$ and the actual y-value is 270.

CHECKPOINT 4. Use linear regression (least squares) to determine a linear equation for the marginal costs, if the following table gives the marginal costs for a product at different levels of production.

x (units)	100	200	300	400
$\overline{MC}$ (marginal cost)	2400	4100	6000	8500

TECHNOLOGY CORNER

The following investigations require 3-dimensional graphics capabilities. These capabilities are usually available with computer graphics software, but usually not with graphics calculators.

1. Suppose that $z = 16y^2 - 8y^4 - x^2$.
   (a) Graph the surface given by this function. Use $-7 \leq x \leq 7$ and $-1.5 \leq y \leq 1.5$.
   (b) If the graph in part (a) shows evidence of relative maxima, relative minima, or saddle points, approximate their locations from the graph.
   (c) Precisely locate the critical points by finding where both $z_x = 0$ and $z_y = 0$. This may be done by graphing them and determining points of intersection.

2. Suppose that $z = (x^2 + 4y^2)e^{1-x^2-2y^2/3}$.
   (a)–(c) Repeat parts (a)–(c) from question 1. Use $-2 \leq x \leq 2$ and $-2 \leq y \leq 2$.

1. $z_x = -2x + 2$, $z_y = -2y - 4$

2. $-2x + 2 = 0$ gives $x = 1$
   $-2y - 4 = 0$ gives $y = -2$
   Thus the critical point is $(1, -2, 9)$.

3. $z_{xx} = -2$, $z_{yy} = -2$, and $z_{xy} = 0$, so
$$D(x, y) = (-2)(-2) - (0)^2 = 4.$$

   Hence, at $(1, -2, 9)$ we have $D > 0$ and $z_{xx} < 0$, so $(1, -2, 9)$ is a relative minimum.

4. $\Sigma x = 100 + 200 + 300 + 400 = 1000$
   $\Sigma x^2 = 10{,}000 + 40{,}000 + 90{,}000 + 160{,}000 = 300{,}000$
   $\Sigma y = 2400 + 4100 + 6000 + 8500 = 21{,}000$
   $\Sigma xy = 240{,}000 + 820{,}000 + 1{,}800{,}000 + 3{,}400{,}000 = 6{,}260{,}000$
$$b = \frac{1000(21{,}000) - 4(6{,}260{,}000)}{1000^2 - 4(300{,}000)} = \frac{21{,}000{,}000 - 25{,}040{,}000}{1{,}000{,}000 - 1{,}200{,}000} = 20.2$$
$$a = \frac{21{,}000 - (20.2)(1000)}{4} = \frac{800}{4} = 200$$

   Thus the linear equation that best predicts marginal cost (and best fits the data) is
$$\overline{MC} = 20.2x + 200.$$

In the following problems, test for relative maxima and minima.

1. $z = 9 - x^2 - y^2$
2. $z = 16 - 4x^2 - 9y^2$
3. $z = x^2 + y^2 + 4$
4. $z = x^2 + y^2 - 4$
5. $z = x^2 + y^2 - 2x + 4y + 5$
6. $z = 4x^2 + y^2 + 4x + 1$
7. $z = x^2 + 6xy + y^2 + 16x$
8. $z = x^2 - 4xy + y^2 - 6y$
9. $z = \dfrac{x^2 - y^2}{9}$
10. $z = \dfrac{y^2}{4} - \dfrac{x^2}{9}$
11. $z = 24 - x^2 + xy - y^2 + 36y$

12. $z = 46 - x^2 + 2xy - 4y^2$
13. $z = x^2 + xy + y^2 - 4y + 10x$
14. $z = x^2 + 5xy + 10y^2 + 8x - 40y$
15. $z = x^3 + y^3 - 6xy$
16. $z = x^3 + y^3 + 3xy$

In problems 17–20, use the points given in each table to write the equation of the line that is the best fit for the points.

17.

x	y
3	15
4	22
5	28
6	32

18.

x	y
0	6
1	8
2	12
3	15

19.	x	y
	10	2
	20	6
	30	5
	40	6

20.	x	y
	60	10
	70	20
	80	31
	90	38

APPLICATIONS

21. **Profit** Suppose that the profit from the sale of Kisses and Kreams is given by

$$P(x, y) = 100x + 64y - 0.01x^2 - 0.25y^2,$$

where x is the number of pounds of Kisses and y is the number of pounds of Kreams. Selling how many pounds of Kisses and Kreams will maximize profit?

22. **Profit** The profit from the sales of two products is given by

$$P(x, y) = 20x + 70y - x^2 - y^2,$$

where x is the number of units of product 1 sold and y is the number of units of product 2. Selling how much of each product will maximize profit?

23. **Nutrition** A new food is designed to add weight to mature beef cattle. The increase in weight is given by $W = xy(20 - x - 2y)$, where x is the number of units of the first ingredient and y is the number of units of the second ingredient. How many units of each ingredient will maximize the weight gain?

24. **Profit** The profit for a grain crop is related to fertilizer and labor. If the profit per acre is

$$P = 100x + 40y - 5x^2 - 2y^2,$$

where x is the number of units of fertilizer and y is the number of work-hours, what values of x and y will maximize the profit?

25. **Production** Suppose that

$$P = 3.78x^2 + 1.5y^2 - 0.09x^3 - 0.01y^3$$

is the production function for a product with x

units of one input and y units of a second input. Find the values of x and y that will maximize production.

26. **Production** Suppose that x units of one input and y units of a second input result in

$$P = 40x + 50y - x^2 - y^2 - xy$$

units of a product. Determine the inputs x and y that will maximize P.

27. **Production** Suppose that a manufacturer produces two brands of a product, brand 1 and brand 2. If the demand for brand 1 is $p_1 = 10 - x$, for brand 2, $p_2 = 40 - 2y$, and if the joint cost function is $C = xy$, how many of each brand should be produced to maximize profit?

28. **Production** Suppose that a firm produces two products, A and B, that sell for $\$a$ and $\$b$, respectively, with the total cost of producing x units of A and y units of B equal to $C(x, y)$. Show that profit from these products is maximized when

$$\frac{\partial C}{\partial x}(x, y) = a \quad \text{and} \quad \frac{\partial C}{\partial y}(x, y) = b.$$

29. **Manufacturing** Find the values for each of the dimensions of an open-top box of length x, width y, and height $500,000/(xy)$ such that the box requires the least amount of material to make.

30. **Manufacturing** Find the values for each of the dimensions of a closed-top box of length x, width y, and height z if the volume equals 27,000 cubic inches and the box requires the least amount of material to make. (*Hint:* First write z in terms of x and y as in problem 25.)

31. **Profit** A company manufactures two products, A and B. If x is the number of units of A and y is the number of units of B, then the cost and revenue functions are

$$C(x, y) = 2x^2 - 2xy + y^2 - 7x + 10y + 11$$
$$R(x, y) = 5x + 4y.$$

Find the number of each type of product that should be manufactured to maximize profit.

32. ***Production*** Let x be the number of work-hours required and y be the amount of capital required to produce z units of a product. Show that the average production per work-hour, z/x, is maximized when

$$\frac{\partial z}{\partial x} = \frac{z}{x}.$$

Use $z = f(x, y)$ and assume a maximum exists.

33. ***Earnings and gender*** The following table shows the 1986 median weekly earnings of men and women in various occupations.
    (a) Write the linear regression equation that is the best fit for the data.
    (b) Use the equation found in part (a) to see how well it predicts the 1986 median weekly earnings for a woman in a job where a man earned $472 (technical sales).

	Earnings	
Occupation	Men (x)	Women (y)
Management	$666	$465
Technical sales	472	305
Service	299	208
Crafts, repair	446	302
Operators, fabricators	352	238
Fish, farm, forestry	234	201

Source: U.S. Bureau of Labor Statistics.

34. ***Profit*** The following table shows the 1988 sales and profits for several of the largest U.S. corporations. Write the linear regression equation that is the best fit for the data.

35. ***Gestation*** The following data show the gestation period (in days) and the average longevity (in years) of several North American mammals in captivity. Write the linear regression equation that best fits these data.

Animal	Gestation (x) (in days)	Longevity (y) (in years)
Grizzly bear	225	25
Beaver	122	5
Cow	284	15
Elk	250	15
Red fox	52	7
White-tailed deer	201	8
Horse	330	20
Moose	240	12
Sheep	154	12

Source: *1990 World Almanac and Book of Facts*, by Pharos Books.

36. ***Training and productivity*** Suppose that a company purchased a new software package to handle their word processing, payroll, inventory, and accounting needs. After a few employees had received some training with the new system, their work with it was monitored and the following data were gathered.

Hours of training (x)	Number of errors (y)	Hours of training (x)	Number of errors (y)
1	8	12	0
2	7	7	3
10	2	6	3
8	2	4	4
6	8	4	6

Corporation	Sales (x) (in billions)	Profit (y) (in millions)	Corporation	Sales (x) (in billions)	Profit (y) (in millions)
GM	$121.1	$4,856	Pepsico	13.0	762
IBM	59.7	5,806	Coca-Cola	8.3	1,044
Chrysler	35.5	1,050	Philips Petroleum	11.3	650
Philip Morris	25.9	2,337	GE	49.4	3,386
Boeing	17.0	614	Du Pont	32.5	2,190

Source: *Fortune Magazine.*

(a) Develop the linear regression equation for these data.

(b) Use the equation developed in part (a) to determine the number of hours of training needed for the predicted number of errors to equal 0.

37. **Supply and demand** The data below give the number of color television sets (in thousands) sold in 15 different years, along with the corresponding average price per set for the year. Use linear regression to find the best linear equation defining the demand function $q = f(p)$.

Price (p) (in dollars)	Quantity sold (q) (in thousands)
471.56	9793
487.79	10236
487.32	9107
510.78	7700
504.39	6485
466.29	8411
449.81	10071
509.86	7908
524.96	6349
514.10	4822
515.43	5962
520.82	5981
525.01	5777
462.32	5892
560.09	2646

Source: U.S. Bureau of the Census, Statistical Abstract of the United States, Washington, D.C.

38. **Research expenditures and profits** The data below give the money spent in 1990 on research and development (R & D) in 18 different aerospace industries, along with the corresponding profits for the year. Find the linear regression equation for the line that is the best fit for the data, with profit as a function of R & D.

R & D (in millions)	Profit (in millions)
$ 827	$1972
2.7	7.3
0.7	−15.5
36	82
390	−988
11.8	−10.3
9.9	32.8
450	430
212.4	48.8
620	402
155.7	49.8
2.6	−5.5
6.9	1.8
22.7	75.1
124.0	189.5
10.3	68.2
1021.4	1291.2
12.4	46.2

Source: *Business Week,* Jan 15, 1992.

7.6 | MAXIMA AND MINIMA OF FUNCTIONS SUBJECT TO CONSTRAINTS; LAGRANGE MULTIPLIERS

OBJECTIVE

- To find the maximum or minimum value of a function of two or more variables subject to a condition that constrains the variables

Many practical problems require that a function of two or more variables be maximized or minimized subject to certain conditions, or constraints, that limit the variables involved. For example, a firm will want to maximize its profits within the limits (constraints) imposed by its production capacity. Similarly, a city planner may want to locate a new building to maximize access to public transportation, yet may be constrained by the availability and cost of building sites.

We can obtain maxima and minima for a function $z = f(x, y)$ subject to the constraint $g(x, y) = 0$ by using the method of **Lagrange multipliers,** named for the famous eighteenth century mathematician Joseph Louis Lagrange. Lagrange multipliers can be used with functions of two or more variables when the constraints are given by an equation.

In order to find the critical values of a function $f(x, y)$ subject to the constraint $g(x, y) = 0$, we will use the new variable λ to form the **objective function**

$$F(x, y, \lambda) = f(x, y) + \lambda g(x, y).$$

It can be shown that the critical values of $F(x, y, \lambda)$ will satisfy the constraint $g(x, y)$ and will also be critical points of $f(x, y)$. Thus we need only find the critical points of $F(x, y, \lambda)$ to find the required critical points.

To find the critical points of $F(x, y, \lambda)$, we must find the points that make all the partial derivatives equal to 0. That is, the points must satisfy

$$\partial F/\partial x = 0, \quad \partial F/\partial y = 0, \quad \text{and} \quad \partial F/\partial \lambda = 0.$$

Since $F(x, y, \lambda) = f(x, y) + \lambda g(x, y)$, these equations may be written as

$$\frac{\partial f}{\partial x} + \lambda \frac{\partial g}{\partial x} = 0$$

$$\frac{\partial f}{\partial y} + \lambda \frac{\partial g}{\partial y} = 0$$

$$g(x, y) = 0.$$

Finding the values of x and y that satisfy these three equations simultaneously gives the critical values.

This method will not tell us if the critical points correspond to maxima or minima, but this can be determined either from the physical setting for the problem or by testing according to a procedure similar to that used for unconstrained maxima and minima. The following examples will illustrate the use of Lagrange multipliers.

EXAMPLE 1

Find the maximum value of $z = x^2y$ subject to $x + y = 9$, $x \geq 0$, $y \geq 0$.

Solution The function to be maximized is $f(x, y) = x^2y$.
The constraint is $g(x, y) = 0$, where $g(x, y) = x + y - 9$.
The objective function is

$$F(x, y, \lambda) = f(x, y) + \lambda g(x, y),$$

or

$$F(x, y, \lambda) = x^2y + \lambda(x + y - 9).$$

Thus

$$\frac{\partial F}{\partial x} = 2xy + \lambda(1) = 0, \quad \text{or} \quad 2xy + \lambda = 0$$

$$\frac{\partial F}{\partial y} = x^2 + \lambda(1) = 0, \quad \text{or} \quad x^2 + \lambda = 0$$

$$\frac{\partial F}{\partial \lambda} = 0 + 1(x + y - 9) = 0, \quad \text{or} \quad x + y - 9 = 0.$$

Solving the first two equations for λ and substituting gives

$$\lambda = -2xy$$
$$\lambda = -x^2$$
$$2xy = x^2$$
$$2xy - x^2 = 0$$
$$x(2y - x) = 0.$$

So

$$x - 0 \quad \text{or} \quad x = 2y.$$

Since $x = 0$ could not make $z = x^2y$ a maximum, we substitute $x = 2y$ into $x + y - 9 = 0$.

$$2y + y = 9$$
$$y = 3$$
$$x = 6$$

Thus the function $z = x^2y$ is maximized at 108 when $x = 6$, $y = 3$, if the constraint is $x + y = 9$. Testing values near $x = 6$, $y = 3$, and satisfying the constraint shows that the function is maximized there. (Try $x = 5.5$, $y = 3.5$, $x = 7$, $y = 2$, and so on.)

EXAMPLE 2

Find the minimum value of the function $z = x^3 + y^3 + xy$ subject to the constraint $x + y - 4 = 0$.

Solution The function to be minimized is $f(x, y) = x^3 + y^3 + xy$.
The constraint function is $g(x, y) = x + y - 4$.
The objective function is

$$F(x, y, \lambda) = f(x, y) + \lambda g(x, y),$$

or

$$F(x, y, \lambda) = x^3 + y^3 + xy + \lambda(x + y - 4).$$

Then

$$\frac{\partial F}{\partial x} = 3x^2 + y + \lambda = 0$$

$$\frac{\partial F}{\partial y} = 3y^2 + x + \lambda = 0$$

$$\frac{\partial F}{\partial \lambda} = x + y - 4 = 0.$$

Solving the first two equations for λ and substituting gives the following.

$$\lambda = -(3x^2 + y)$$
$$\lambda = -(3y^2 + x)$$
$$3x^2 + y = 3y^2 + x$$

Solving $x + y - 4 = 0$ for y gives $y = 4 - x$. Substituting for y in the equation above, we get

$$3x^2 + (4 - x) = 3(4 - x)^2 + x$$
$$3x^2 + 4 - x = 48 - 24x + 3x^2 + x$$
$$22x = 44 \quad \text{or} \quad x = 2.$$

Thus when $x + y - 4 = 0$, $x = 2$ and $y = 2$ give the minimum value $z = 20$.

EXAMPLE 3

Find the maximum value of the function $z = 2xy - 2x^2 - 2y^2$ subject to the constraint $2x + y = 7$.

Solution The constraint function is $g(x, y) = 2x + y - 7$, so the objective function is

$$F(x, y, \lambda) = 2xy - 2x^2 - 2y^2 + \lambda(2x + y - 7).$$

Then

$$\frac{\partial F}{\partial x} = 2y - 4x + 2\lambda = 0$$

$$\frac{\partial F}{\partial y} = 2x - 4y + \lambda = 0$$

$$\frac{\partial F}{\partial \lambda} = 2x + y - 7 = 0.$$

Solving the first two equations for λ gives

$$\lambda = -y + 2x$$
$$\lambda = -2x + 4y$$
$$-y + 2x = -2x + 4y$$
$$4x = 5y$$
$$x = \frac{5y}{4}.$$

Substituting for x in $2x + y - 7 = 0$ gives $\frac{5}{2}y + y - 7 = 0$, or $y = 2$. Thus the critical values are $y = 2$, $x = \frac{5}{2}$. Testing values near $x = \frac{5}{2}$, $y = 2$, shows that the function has a relative maximum there. The maximum value is $-21/2$.

CHECKPOINT

Find the minimum value of $f(x, y) = x^2 + y^2 - 4xy$, subject to the constraint $x + y = 10$, by:

1. forming the objective function $F(x, y, \lambda)$;

2. finding $\dfrac{\partial F}{\partial x}$, $\dfrac{\partial F}{\partial y}$, and $\dfrac{\partial F}{\partial \lambda}$;

3. setting the three partial derivatives (from question 2) equal to 0, and solving the equations simultaneously for x and y;

4. finding the value of $f(x, y)$ at the critical values of x and y, and testing other values of x and y that satisfy the constraint to verify that the value is a minimum. ∎

We can also use Lagrange multipliers to find the maxima and minima of functions of three (or more) variables subject to two (or more) constraints. The method involves using two multipliers, one for each constraint, to form an objective function $F = f + \lambda g_1 + \mu g_2$. We leave further discussion for more advanced courses.

We can easily extend the method to functions of three or more variables, as the following example shows.

EXAMPLE 4

Find the minimum value of the function $w = x + y^2 + z^2$, subject to the constraint $x + y + z = 1$.

Solution The function to be minimized is $f(x, y, z) = x + y^2 + z^2$. The constraint is $g(x, y, z) = 0$, where $g(x, y, z) = x + y + z - 1$.

The objective function is

$$F(x, y, z, \lambda) = f(x, y, z) + \lambda g(x, y, z),$$

or

$$F(x, y, z, \lambda) = x + y^2 + z^2 + \lambda(x + y + z - 1).$$

Then

$$\frac{\partial F}{\partial x} = 1 + \lambda = 0$$

$$\frac{\partial F}{\partial y} = 2y + \lambda = 0$$

$$\frac{\partial F}{\partial z} = 2z + \lambda = 0$$

$$\frac{\partial F}{\partial \lambda} = x + y + z - 1 = 0.$$

Solving the first three equations simultaneously gives

$$\lambda = -1$$

$$y = \frac{1}{2}$$

$$z = \frac{1}{2}.$$

Substituting these values in the fourth equation (which is the constraint), we get $x + \frac{1}{2} + \frac{1}{2} - 1 = 0$, so $x = 0, y = \frac{1}{2}, z = \frac{1}{2}$. Thus $w = \frac{1}{2}$ is the minimum value since other values of x, y, and z satisfying $x + y + z = 1$ give larger values for w.

EXAMPLE 5

Suppose that the utility function for commodities X and Y is given by $U = x^2 y^2$, where x and y are the amounts of X and Y, respectively. If p_1 and p_2 represent the prices of X and Y, respectively, and I represents the consumer's income available to purchase these two commodities, the equation $p_1 x + p_2 y = I$ is called the *budget constraint*. If the price of X is \$2, the price of Y is \$4, and the income available is \$40, find x and y that maximize utility.

Solution The utility function is $U = x^2 y^2$ and the budget constraint is

$2x + 4y = 40$. The objective function is

$$F(x, y, \lambda) = x^2y^2 + \lambda(2x + 4y - 40).$$
$$\frac{\partial F}{\partial x} = 2xy^2 + 2\lambda, \qquad \frac{\partial F}{\partial y} = 2x^2y + 4\lambda, \qquad \frac{\partial F}{\partial \lambda} = 2x + 4y - 40$$

Setting these partial derivatives equal to 0 and solving gives

$$-\lambda = xy^2 = x^2y/2, \quad \text{or} \quad xy^2 - x^2y/2 = 0,$$

so

$$xy(y - x/2) = 0$$

yields $x = 0$, $y = 0$, or $x = 2y$. Neither $x = 0$ nor $y = 0$ maximizes utility. If $x = 2y$, we have

$$0 = 4y + 4y - 40.$$

Thus $y = 5$ and $x = 10$.

Testing values near $x = 10$, $y = 5$ shows that these values maximize utility, at $U = 2500$.

TECHNOLOGY CORNER

For these questions, use either a graphics calculator or a computer.

Suppose that the Cobb-Douglas production function for a certain manufacturer gives the number of units of production z according to

$$z = f(x, y) = 100x^{4/5}y^{1/5},$$

where x is the number of units of labor and y is the number of units of capital. Suppose further that labor costs $160 per unit, capital costs $200 per unit, and the total cost for capital and labor is limited to $100,000. This means that production is constrained by

$$160x + 200y = 100{,}000.$$

1. Graph the constraint equation. Use $0 \le x \le 950$ and $0 \le y \le 640$.

2. If $z = 30{,}000$ units of production, then the production function becomes
$$30{,}000 = 100x^{4/5}y^{1/5}.$$

(a) Graph this equation on the same set of axes as the constraint equation from problem 1.

(b) Any points of intersection of these two graphs mark points where production is 30,000 units and the cost constraint is satisfied. Approximate any such points.

3. (a) Let $z = 36{,}000$ and $z = 40{,}000$, and graph the resulting production functions on the same set of axes with the other two graphs.

(b) Do both of the functions graphed in part (a) intersect the cost constraint?

4. (a) Describe how you could use graphical methods to maximize
$$z = 100x^{4/5}y^{1/5}$$

subject to the constraint
$$160x + 200y = 100{,}000.$$

(b) Apply your method from part (a) to approximate the numbers of units of labor and of capital that give the maximum value of z.

5. (a) Use the method of Lagrange multipliers to check the solution you found in problem 4(b).

(b) In problems like this one, economists call the value of the Lagrange multiplier λ the **marginal productivity of money.** Find the value of λ.

CHECKPOINT
SOLUTIONS

1. $F(x, y, \lambda) = x^2 + y^2 - 4xy + \lambda(10 - x - y)$

2. $\dfrac{\partial F}{\partial x} = 2x - 4y - \lambda, \quad \dfrac{\partial F}{\partial y} = 2y - 4x - \lambda, \quad \dfrac{\partial F}{\partial \lambda} = 10 - x - y$

3. $0 = 2x - 4y - \lambda$ (1)
$0 = 2y - 4x - \lambda$ (2)
$0 = 10 - x - y$ (3)
From equations (1) and (2) we have the following:
$$\lambda = 2x - 4y \quad \text{and} \quad \lambda = 2y - 4x$$

So

$$2x - 4y = 2y - 4x$$
$$6x = 6y \quad \text{or} \quad x = y$$

Using $x = y$ in equation (3) gives $0 = 10 - x - x$, or $2x = 10$. Thus $x = 5$ and $y = 5$.

4. $f(5, 5) = 25 + 25 - 100 = -50$ is a relative minimum.
$f(6, 4) = f(4, 6) = -44$, $f(1, 9) = f(9, 1) = 46$,
$f(0, 10) = f(10, 0) = 100$, so -50 is an absolute minimum for f.

EXERCISE 7.6

1. Find the minimum value of $z = x^2 + y^2$ subject to the condition $x + y = 6$.

2. Find the minimum value of $z = 4x^2 + y^2$ subject to the constraint $x + y = 5$.

3. Find the minimum value of $z = 3x^2 + 5y^2 - 2xy$ subject to the constraint $x + y = 5$.

4. Find the maximum value of $z = 2xy - 3x^2 - 5y^2$ subject to the constraint $x + y = 5$.

5. Find the maximum value of $z = x^2 y$ subject to $x + y = 6$, $x \geq 0$, $y \geq 0$.

6. Find the maximum value of the function $z = x^3 y^2$ subject to $x + y = 10$, $x \geq 0$, $y \geq 0$.

7. Find the maximum value of the function $z = 2xy - 2x^2 - 4y^2$ subject to the condition $x + 2y = 8$.

8. Find the minimum value of $z = 2x^2 + y^2 - xy$ subject to the constraint $2x + y = 8$.

9. Find the minimum value of $z = x^2 + y^2$ subject to the condition $2x + y + 1 = 0$.

10. Find the minimum value of $z = x^2 + y^2$ subject to the condition $xy = 1$.

11. Find the minimum value of the function $w = x^2 + y^2 + z^2$ subject to the constraint $x + y + z = 3$.

12. Find the minimum value of the function $w = x^2 + y^2 + z^2$ subject to the condition $2x - 4y + z = 21$.

13. Find the maximum value of $w = xz + y$ subject to the constraint $x^2 + y^2 + z^2 = 1$.

14. Find the maximum value of $w = x^2 yz$ subject to $4x + y + z = 4$, $x \geq 0$, $y \geq 0$, and $z \geq 0$.

APPLICATIONS

15. **Utility** Suppose that the utility function for two commodities is given by $U = x^2 y$ and that the budget constraint is $3x + 6y = 18$. What values of x and y will maximize utility?

16. **Utility** Suppose that the budget constraint in problem 15 is $5x + 20y = 80$. What values of x and y will maximize $U = x^2y$?

17. **Utility** Suppose that the utility function for two products is given by $U = x^2y$, and the budget constraint is $2x + 3y = 120$. Find the values of x and y that maximize utility.

18. **Utility** Suppose that the utility function for two commodities is given by $U = x^2y^3$, and the budget constraint is $10x + 15y = 250$. Find the values of x and y that maximize utility.

19. **Cost** A firm has two plants, X and Y. Suppose that the cost of producing x units at plant X is $x^2 + 1200$ and the cost of producing y units of the same product at plant Y is given by $3y^2 + 800$. If they have an order for 1200 units, how many should they produce at each plant to fill this order and minimize the cost of production?

20. **Cost** Suppose that the cost of producing x units at plant X is $(3x + 4)x$ and that the cost of producing y units of the same product at plant Y is $(2y + 8)y$. If the firm owning the plants has an order for 149 units, how many should it

produce at each plant to fill this order and minimize its cost of production?

21. **Revenue** On the basis of past experience a company has determined that its sales revenue is related to its advertising according to the formula $s = 20x + y^2 + 4xy$, where x is the amount spent in radio advertising and y is the amount spent in television advertising. If the company plans to spend \$30,000 on these two means of advertising, how much should it spend on each method to maximize its sales revenue?

22. **Manufacturing** Find the dimensions x, y, and z of the rectangular box with the largest volume that satisfies

$$3x + 4y + 12z = 12.$$

23. **Manufacturing** Find the dimensions of the box with square base, open top, and volume 500,000 cc that requires the least materials.

24. **Manufacturing** Show that a box with a square base, an open top, and a fixed volume requires the least material to build if it has a height equal to one-half the length of one side of the base.

7.7 | DOUBLE INTEGRALS

OBJECTIVES

- To find antiderivatives of functions of two variables
- To evaluate double integrals
- To solve applied problems involving double integrals

In Section 7.2, we found partial derivatives of functions of two or more variables. We can use a similar process to find the antiderivative, with respect to one variable, of a function of two or more variables.

For example,

$$\int (3x^2y^2 + 4xy + 5)\, dy$$

indicates that we should integrate with respect to y (because of the dy) and treat x as a constant. This gives

$$3x^2\left(\frac{y^3}{3}\right) + 4x\left(\frac{y^2}{2}\right) + 5(y) + C(x),$$

or

$$x^2y^3 + 2xy^2 + 5y + C(x).$$

We write the constant of integration as $C(x)$ in this case because any function of x alone is a constant *relative to the variable y*.

We can verify that this function is the antiderivative of $3x^2y^2 + 4xy + 5$ by taking its partial derivative with respect to y.

$$\frac{\partial}{\partial y}[x^2y^3 + 2xy^2 + 5y + C(x)] = 3x^2y^2 + 4xy + 5$$

EXAMPLE 1 | Evaluate $\int (6x^5y + 7x^3 + y^2 + 2xy)\, dx$.

Solution The dx indicates that we are to integrate with respect to the *variable x* while holding y constant.

$$\int (6x^5y + 7x^3 + y^2 + 2xy)\, dx = x^6y + \frac{7}{4}x^4 + xy^2 + x^2y + C(y)$$

EXAMPLE 2 | Evaluate $\int_0^3 x\sqrt[3]{x^2 - y^3}\, dx$.

Solution We integrate with respect to x by letting $u = x^2 - y^3$ and $du = 2x\, dx$. We first find the antiderivative.

$$\int x\sqrt[3]{x^2 - y^3}\, dx = \frac{1}{2}\int (x^2 - y^3)^{1/3}(2x\, dx)$$

$$= \frac{1}{2}\int u^{1/3}\, du$$

$$= \frac{1}{2}\cdot\frac{u^{4/3}}{4/3} + C(y)$$

Simplifying, substituting for u, and evaluating the definite integral gives:

$$\int_0^3 x\sqrt[3]{x^2 - y^3}\, dx = \frac{3}{8}(x^2 - y^3)^{4/3} + C(y)\ \Big|_0^3$$

$$= \left[\frac{3}{8}(9 - y^3)^{4/3} + C(y)\right] - \left[\frac{3}{8}(-y^3)^{4/3} + C(y)\right]$$

$$= \frac{3}{8}\left[(9 - y^3)^{4/3} - y^4\right].$$

Notice in Example 2 that the constant of integration subtracts out and need not be written.

Note that in evaluating the definite integral in Example 2, we eliminated the variable x, leaving a function of the single variable y. This suggests that we could evaluate an integral of the form

$$\int_c^d \left[\int_a^b f(x, y)\, dx\right] dy$$

by evaluating the integral inside the bracket first and then integrating the resulting function with respect to y. This process of repeated integration is called **iteration,** and is illustrated in Example 3.

EXAMPLE 3

Evaluate $\int_0^1 \left(\int_0^2 6xy^3 \, dx \right) dy$.

Solution Evaluating the integral inside the parentheses first gives

$$\int_0^1 \left(\int_0^2 6xy^3 \, dx \right) dy = \int_0^1 \left(3x^2y^3 \, \Big|_0^2 \right) dy$$

$$= \int_0^1 [(12y^3) - 0] \, dy$$

$$= \int_0^1 12y^3 \, dy.$$

$$= 3y^4 \, \Big|_0^1$$

$$= 3 - 0$$

$$= 3.$$

CHECKPOINT

1. Evaluate the double integral

$$\int_4^6 \left[\int_{-1}^2 (x^2 - 4xy^2) \, dx \right] dy.$$

Recall that a definite integral of a function in one variable is defined if the function is defined and continuous over an interval. If a function of two variables is defined on a closed and bounded region of the xy plane, it is possible to define a (definite) **double integral.** For example,

$$\int_a^b \int_c^d f(x, y) \, dx \, dy \quad \text{or equivalently} \quad \int_a^b \left[\int_c^d f(x, y) \, dx \right] dy,$$

is the double integral of the function $f(x, y)$ over a region R determined by the limits of integration. If in this integral a, b, c, and d are constants, then the region is bounded below by $y = a$, above by $y = b$, on the left by $x = c$, and on the right by $x = d$. Thus the region R is a rectangle (see Figure 7.12). Similarly, in Example 3 the region was bounded by $x = 0$, $x = 2$, $y = 0$, and $y = 1$ (see Figure 7.13).

We sometimes write a double integral in the form

$$\iint_R f(x, y) \, dA,$$

where dA represents either $dx \, dy$ or $dy \, dx$ and R represents the region over which the integration is taking place.

FIGURE 7.12   FIGURE 7.13

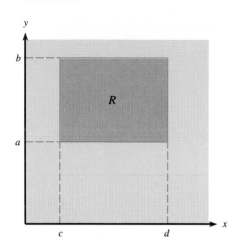   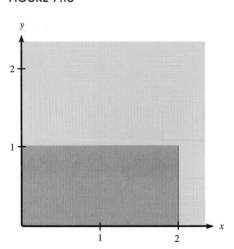

We formally define the double integral over a rectangular region as follows.

Double Integral Over a Rectangle

The double integral of a function $f(x, y)$ over a rectangular region R in the xy plane is

$$\iint_R f(x, y)\, dA = \int_a^b \int_c^d f(x, y)\, dy\, dx = \int_c^d \int_a^b f(x, y)\, dx\, dy.$$

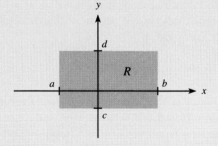

EXAMPLE 4

Evaluate the integral of Example 3 with the order of integration reversed. That is, evaluate

$$\int_0^2 \int_0^1 6xy^3\, dy\, dx.$$

Solution

$$\int_0^2 \int_0^1 6xy^3 \, dy \, dx = \int_0^2 \left(\int_0^1 6xy^3 \, dy \right) dx$$

$$= \int_0^2 \left[6x \left(\frac{y^4}{4} \right) \right]_0^1 dx$$

$$= \int_0^2 \left[6x \left(\frac{1}{4} \right) - 6x(0) \right] dx$$

$$= \int_0^2 \frac{3}{2} x \, dx$$

$$= \frac{3}{2} \left(\frac{x^2}{2} \right) \Big|_0^2$$

$$= \frac{3}{4} (2)^2 - \frac{3}{4} (0)^2$$

$$= 3$$

As the definition of a double integral indicates, reversing the order of integration gives the same value.

Just as the definite integral $\displaystyle\int_a^b f(x) \, dx$

can be used to find the area under the curve $y = f(x)$ if $f(x) \geq 0$ on $[a, b]$, the double integral

$$\iint_R f(x, y) \, dy \, dx$$

can be used to find the volume under the surface $z = f(x, y)$ if the surface is above the xy-plane over the region R.

In a manner similar to that used to approximate the area under a curve by adding the areas of a large number of small rectangles, the volume under the surface can be approximated by finding the volumes of a large number of small rectangular solids and adding these volumes together (see Figure 7.14).

Clearly, as the number of rectangular solids increases and the base of each one becomes smaller, the sum of their volumes more accurately approximates the volume under the surface. As might be expected, this limiting process gives us the double integral

$$\iint_R f(x, y) \, dx \, dy.$$

Thus the volume under the surface is the double integral over the region if $f(x, y)$ lies above the xy-plane over R.

FIGURE 7.14

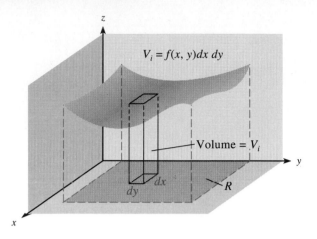

$$V_i = f(x, y)dx\, dy$$

Volume $= V_i$

Volume

If $z = f(x, y)$ and $z \geq 0$ over a region R in the xy-plane, then the volume of the solid bounded by the region R, by the xy-plane below and by $z = f(x, y)$ above is

$$\iint_R f(x, y)\, dx\, dy = \iint_R f(x, y)\, dy\, dx.$$

EXAMPLE 5

Find the volume of the solid bounded by the xy-plane with $0 \leq x \leq 2$ and $0 \leq y \leq 1$ and by $z = 9 - x^2 - y^2$. (See Figure 7.15.)

FIGURE 7.15

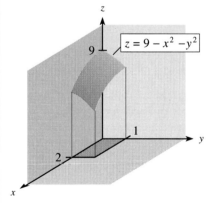

$$z = 9 - x^2 - y^2$$

Solution The volume is found by evaluating the double integral

$$\iint_R (9 - x^2 - y^2)\, dx\, dy = \int_0^1 \left[\int_0^2 (9 - x^2 - y^2)\, dx \right] dy$$

$$= \int_0^1 \left[9x - \frac{x^3}{3} - y^2 x \right]_0^2 dy$$

$$= \int_0^1 \left[(18 - \frac{8}{3} - 2y^2) - (0) \right] dy$$

$$= \int_0^1 \left[\frac{46}{3} - 2y^2 \right] dy$$

$$= \frac{46}{3}y - 2\frac{y^3}{3} \Big|_0^1$$

$$= \left(\frac{46}{3} - \frac{2}{3} \right) - 0$$

$$= \frac{44}{3}.$$

We have seen that the average value of a continuous function f over an interval $[a, b]$ is given by

$$\text{Average value} = \frac{1}{b - a} \int_a^b f(x) \, dx.$$

In a similar manner, we can find the average value of a function of two variables.

Average Value

The average value of a function of two variables $z = f(x, y)$ over a rectangular region in the xy-plane is

$$\text{Average value} = \frac{1}{A} \iint_R f(x, y) \, dx \, dy,$$

where A is the area of the rectangular region in the plane.

EXAMPLE 6

Find the average value of $z = x^3 + xy^2$ over the region $1 \le x \le 4$, $0 \le y \le 2$.

Solution The region in the xy-plane is $2 - 0 = 2$ units wide and $4 - 1 = 3$ units long, so $A = 2 \cdot 3 = 6$. The average value of z is

$$\frac{1}{6} \int_0^2 \int_1^4 (x^3 + xy^2) \, dx \, dy = \frac{1}{6} \int_0^2 \left[\frac{x^4}{4} + \frac{x^2}{2}y^2 \right]_1^4 dy$$

$$= \frac{1}{6} \int_0^2 \left[(64 + 8y^2) - \left(\frac{1}{4} + \frac{y^2}{2} \right) \right] dy$$

$$= \frac{1}{6} \int_0^2 \left[\frac{255}{4} + \frac{15}{2}y^2 \right] dy$$

$$= \frac{1}{6} \left[\frac{255}{4}y + \frac{15}{2} \cdot \frac{y^3}{3} \right] \Big|_0^2$$

$$= \frac{1}{6}\left[\left(\frac{255}{2} + 20\right) - (0)\right]$$

$$= \frac{295}{12}.$$

If a double integral has the form

$$\int_c^d \int_{f_1(x)}^{f_2(x)} f(x, y)\, dy\, dx$$

then the limits on the inner integral represent functions of x. In this case, $y = f_1(x)$ is a curve that forms the lower boundary of the region and $y = f_2(x)$ is a curve that forms the upper boundary of the region (see Figure 7.16).

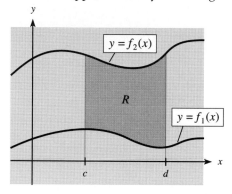

A double integral of this type can also be evaluated by using iteration.

$$\int_c^d \int_{f_1(x)}^{f_2(x)} f(x, y)\, dy\, dx = \int_c^d \left[\int_{f_1(x)}^{f_2(x)} f(x, y)\, dy\right] dx$$

When the inner integral is evaluated, the limit functions $f_1(x)$ and $f_2(x)$ are substituted for y so that the result is a function of x alone. Thus the result of the first integration is a single integral in one variable.

EXAMPLE 7 Evaluate $\int_0^1 \int_{x^2}^x [4 - (x^2 + y^2)]\, dy\, dx$.

Solution We begin by evaluating the inner integral.

$$\int_0^1 \left[\int_{x^2}^x [4 - (x^2 + y^2)]\, dy\right] dx = \int_0^1 \left[4y - x^2 y - \frac{y^3}{3}\right]_{x^2}^x dx$$

$$= \int_0^1 \left[\left(4x - x^3 - \frac{x^3}{3}\right) - \left(4x^2 - x^4 - \frac{x^6}{3}\right)\right] dx$$

$$= \int_0^1 \left(4x - 4x^2 - \frac{4}{3}x^3 + x^4 + \frac{x^6}{3}\right) dx$$

$$= 2x^2 - \frac{4}{3}x^3 - \frac{x^4}{3} + \frac{x^5}{5} + \frac{x^7}{21}\Big|_0^1$$

$$= 2 - \frac{4}{3} - \frac{1}{3} + \frac{1}{5} + \frac{1}{21} - 0$$

$$= \frac{61}{105}$$

CHECKPOINT 2. Evaluate the double integral

$$\int_{-1}^0 \int_x^{x^3} (x^2 + y^2)\, dy\, dx.$$

A double integral of the form

$$\int_c^d \int_{g_1(y)}^{g_2(y)} f(x, y)\, dx\, dy$$

can also be evaluated by using iteration. In this case the region R is bounded on the left and right by the curves $x = g_1(y)$ and $x = g_2(y)$, respectively, with the y values limited from $y = c$ to $y = d$. In Example 8 we evaluate the double integral of $z = 4xy + 6$ over the region in the xy-plane shown in Figure 7.17.

FIGURE 7.17

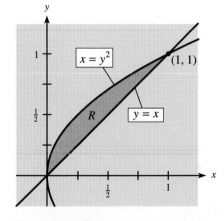

EXAMPLE 8 | Evaluate $\displaystyle\int_0^1 \left[\int_{y^2}^y (4xy + 6)\, dx \right] dy.$

Solution $\displaystyle\int_0^1 \left[\int_{y^2}^y (4xy + 6)\, dx \right] dy = \int_0^1 \left(2x^2 y + 6x \Big|_{y^2}^y \right) dy$

$$= \int_0^1 \left[(2y^3 + 6y) - (2y^5 + 6y^2) \right] dy$$

$$= 2 \cdot \frac{y^4}{4} + 6 \cdot \frac{y^2}{2} - 2 \cdot \frac{y^6}{6} - 6 \cdot \frac{y^3}{3} \bigg|_0^1$$

$$= \left(\frac{1}{2} + 3 - \frac{1}{3} - 2 \right) - 0$$

$$= \frac{7}{6}$$

TECHNOLOGY CORNER

The following investigations require 3-dimensional graphics capabilities. These capabilities are usually available with computer graphics software, but usually not with graphics calculators.

We have seen that if $f(x) \geq 0$ over the interval $[a, b]$, then

$$\int_a^b f(x) \, dx$$

can be interpreted as the area between $f(x)$ and the x-axis from $x = a$ to $x = b$. Similarly, if $f(x, y) \geq 0$ over some region R in the xy-plane, then

$$\int_R \int f(x, y) \, dA$$

can be interpreted as the volume of the solid between $f(x, y)$ and the xy-plane within the region R.

In order to get a visual sense for this relationship, consider the following.

1. (a) Graph the surface $z = 4$ over $0 \leq x \leq 3$ and $0 \leq y \leq 2$.

   (b) The double integral

$$\int_0^3 \int_0^2 4 \, dy \, dx$$

   gives the volume of the solid between the surface $z = 4$ and the xy-plane over the region $0 \leq x \leq 3$ and $0 \leq y \leq 2$. Evaluate this integral to find the volume.

   (c) Use the graph in part (a) and a formula from geometry to find the volume in a different way.

2. (a) Graph the surface $z = 16 - 4x^2 - y^2$ over $0 \leq x \leq 1$ and $0 \leq y \leq 3$.

   (b) The graph in part (a) shows the solid that lies above the xy-plane and whose volume is given by

$$\int_0^1 \int_0^3 (16 - 4x^2 - y^2) \, dy \, dx.$$

Evaluate this integral to find the volume.

3. (a) Graph the solid that lies above the *xy*-plane and whose volume is given by

$$\int_0^1 \int_0^3 \frac{12}{(x + 2)(y + 1)} \, dy \, dx.$$

Use the region *R* as the ranges for *x* and *y*.

(b) Evaluate the integral in part (a) to find the volume of this solid.

**CHECKPOINT
SOLUTIONS**

1. $\displaystyle\int_4^6 \left[\int_{-1}^2 (x^2 - 4xy^2) \, dx \right] dy = \int_4^6 \left[\frac{x^3}{3} - 2x^2y^2 \right]_{-1}^2 dy$

$$= \int_4^6 (3 - 6y^2) \, dy$$

$$= \left[3y - 2y^3 \right]_4^6 = -298$$

2. $\displaystyle\int_{-1}^0 \left[\int_x^{x^3} (x^2 + y^2) \, dy \right] dx = \int_{-1}^0 \left[x^2y + \frac{y^3}{3} \right]_x^{x^3} dx$

$$= \int_{-1}^0 \left(\frac{x^9}{3} + x^5 - \frac{4}{3}x^3 \right) dx$$

$$= \left[\frac{x^{10}}{30} + \frac{x^6}{6} - \frac{x^4}{3} \right]_{-1}^0$$

$$= -\left(\frac{1}{30} + \frac{1}{6} - \frac{1}{3} \right) = \frac{2}{15}$$

EXERCISE 7.7

In problems 1–6, find the antiderivatives.

1. $\displaystyle\int (12x^2y + y) \, dx$

2. $\displaystyle\int (2x - 3y^2) \, dx$

3. $\displaystyle\int (12x^2y + y) \, dy$

4. $\displaystyle\int (3x^2 + 2xy - 3) \, dy$

5. $\displaystyle\int y^3(x^2 - y^4)^5 \, dy$

6. $\displaystyle\int x\sqrt{3x^2 - y^3} \, dx$

In problems 7–10, evaluate the definite integrals.

7. $\int_2^4 (x^2 + xy^3)\, dy$

8. $\int_0^1 (x - 3x^2y^2)\, dx$

9. $\int_0^y (4x^2y^2 - 5)\, dx$

10. $\int_0^{x^2} (x - 3xy^2)\, dy$

In problems 11–24, evaluate the integrals.

11. $\int_0^1 \int_0^2 (x + y)\, dy\, dx$

12. $\int_0^2 \int_0^1 (x^2 - y)\, dy\, dx$

13. $\int_0^2 \int_0^1 (x + y)\, dx\, dy$

14. $\int_0^1 \int_0^2 (x^2 - y)\, dx\, dy$

15. $\int_1^4 \int_3^6 (xy + y^2)\, dy\, dx$

16. $\int_1^6 \int_1^4 (xy - 10)\, dx\, dy$

17. $\int_0^1 \int_0^y (x^2 + y^2)\, dx\, dy$

18. $\int_0^2 \int_0^{y^2} (xy + y)\, dx\, dy$

19. $\int_0^3 \int_1^x xy\, dy\, dx$

20. $\int_0^1 \int_2^x (x - y^3)\, dy\, dx$

21. $\int_1^3 \int_0^x 2\sqrt[3]{x^2 - 1}\, dy\, dx$

22. $\int_0^1 \int_0^y (y^2 - 1)^3\, dx\, dy$

23. $\int_0^2 \int_y^{y^2} xy\, dx\, dy$

24. $\int_0^1 \int_{x^2}^x (x^2 + y)\, dy\, dx$

In problems 25–28, use both orders of integration to evaluate each double integral over the given rectangular region R.

25. $\iint_R xy\, dA;$ $R: 0 \le x \le 2, 0 \le y \le 1$

26. $\iint_R (x^2 + y^2)\, dA;$ $R: 0 \le x \le 1, 0 \le y \le 3$

27. $\iint_R y\sqrt{x}\, dA;$ $R: 1 \le x \le 3, 1 \le y \le 2$

28. $\iint_R e^{x+y}\, dA;$ $R: 0 \le x \le 1, 0 \le y \le 2$

In problems 29–32, find the volume of each solid under the given surface over the given rectangular region.

29. $f(x, y) = 8 - x - y;$ $R: 0 \le x \le 4, 0 \le y \le 4$

30. $f(x, y) = 9 - x;$ $R: 0 \le x \le 5, 0 \le y \le 5$

31. $f(x, y) = 4 - y^2;$ $R: 0 \le x \le 2, 0 \le y \le 2$

32. $f(x, y) = 8 - x^2 - y^2;$ $R: 0 \le x \le 2,$
$0 \le y \le 2$

In problems 33–36, find the average value of the function over the given rectangular region in the xy-plane.

33. $f(x, y) = 4xy;$ $R: 0 \le x \le 6, 0 \le y \le 4$

34. $f(x, y) = x^2y;$ $R: 0 \le x \le 3, 0 \le y \le 2$

35. $f(x, y) = x - 9;$ $R: 4 \le x \le 10, 3 \le y \le 5$

36. $f(x, y) = \dfrac{x}{y};$ $R: -1 \le x \le 1, 1 \le y \le 2$

APPLICATIONS

37. **Cost** A company manufactures two products, A and B. If x is the number of units of A and y is the number of units of B, then the cost in thousands of dollars is given by

$$C(x, y) = 2x^2 - 2xy + y^2 - 7x + 10y + 11.$$

If the number of units of A varies from 1 to 10 and if the number of units of B varies from 2 to 10 units, what is the average cost for the products?

38. **Profit** A product has profit described by $P(x, y) = 100,000 - (x - 500)^2 - (y - 300)^2$, where x represents the number of units of product 1 produced and sold and y represents the number of units of product 2. If the monthly production and sales of product 1 varies between 200 and 500 units and the monthly production and sales of product 2 varies between 100 and 300 units, find the

average monthly profit for the products.

39. **Production** For a particular company, the monthly Cobb-Douglas production function is given by $N(x, y) = 35x^{0.75}y^{0.25}$, where x represents the number of hundreds of labor-hours and y represents the investment in millions of dollars. If $16 \leq x \leq 18$ and $0.5 \leq y \leq 1$, find the average number of units produced over these ranges for x and y.

40. **Production** The Krug Company has a Cobb-Douglas production function given by

$$N(x, y) = 70x^{2/3}y^{1/3},$$

where x is the number of work-hours and y is the capital investment in thousands of dollars. Find the average production if x varies from 1000 to 1728 and y varies from 27 to 125.

41. **Population growth** Suppose that the concentration of population in a rectangular county is given by

$$C = 250 - (x^2 + y^2)$$

in thousands/square mile, where $x = 0$, $y = 0$ is the center of the county. If the county extends 12 miles to the north and south of the center and 9 miles to the east and west, what is the average population per square mile of the county?

42. **Population growth** The total population of the county in problem 41 can be estimated by evaluating

$$\int_{-12}^{12} \int_{-9}^{9} [250 - (x^2 + y^2)] \, dx \, dy.$$

Estimate this population.

43. **Surveying** The sheer face of a mountain can be described by the equation

$$z = 300 - 0.5x - y$$

[see Figure 7.18(a)], with the region under the cliff shown in Figure 7.18(b). What is the average height of the cliff above this triangular region?

FIGURE 7.18

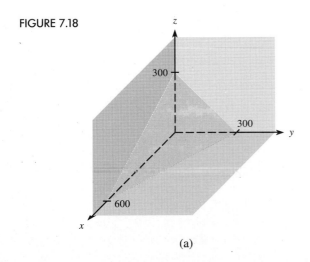

(a)

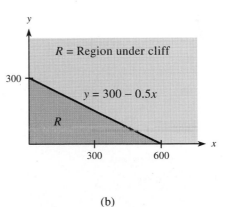

(b)

KEY TERMS
& FORMULAS

SECTION	KEY TERM	FORMULA

7.1 Function of two variables
　　　Variables: independent, dependent
　　　Domain
　　Coordinate planes
　　Utility
　　　Indifference curve
　　　Indifference map

7.2 Partial derivative

　　　With respect to x　　　　　　　$z_x = \dfrac{\partial z}{\partial x}$

　　　With respect to y　　　　　　　$z_y = \dfrac{\partial z}{\partial y}$

7.3 Joint cost function　　　　　　$C = Q(x, y)$
　　Marginal cost
　　Marginal productivity
　　Demand function
　　Marginal demand function
　　Competitive products
　　Complementary products

7.4 Higher-order partial derivatives
　　　Second partial derivatives　　　$z_{xx}, z_{yy}, z_{xy},$ and z_{yx}

7.5 Critical values for maxima and minima　　Solve simultaneously $\begin{cases} z_x = 0 \\ z_y = 0 \end{cases}$

　　Test for critical values　　　Use $D(x, y) = (z_{xx})(z_{yy}) - (z_{xy})^2$
　　Linear regression　　　　　$\hat{y} = a + bx$, where

$$b = \frac{\Sigma x \Sigma y - n\Sigma xy}{(\Sigma x)^2 - n\Sigma x^2},$$

$$a = \frac{\Sigma y - b\Sigma x}{n}$$

7.6 Maxima and minima subject to constraints
　　Lagrange multipliers
　　Objective function

SECTION	KEY TERM	FORMULA

7.7   Double integrals

$$\iint_R f(x, y) \, dA = \int_a^b \int_c^d f(x, y) \, dydx$$

$$= \int_c^d \int_a^b f(x, y) \, dxdy$$

Volume under $z = f(x, y)$ over R,
if $z \geq 0$

$$\iint_R f(x, y) \, dydx = \iint_R f(x, y) \, dxdy$$

Average value of a function

$$\text{Average value} = \frac{1}{A} \iint_R f(x, y) \, dxdy$$

REVIEW
EXERCISES

7.1

1. What is the domain of $z = \dfrac{3}{2x - y}$?

2. What is the domain of $z = \dfrac{3x + 2\sqrt{y}}{x^2 + y^2}$?

3. If $w(x, y, z) = x^2 - 3yz$, find $w(2, 3, 1)$.

4. If $Q(K, L) = 70K^{2/3}L^{1/3}$, find $Q(64{,}000, 512)$.

7.2

5. Find $\dfrac{\partial z}{\partial x}$ if $z = 5x^3 + 6xy + y^2$.

6. Find $\dfrac{\partial z}{\partial y}$ if $z = 12x^5 - 14x^3y^3 + 6y^4 - 1$.

In problems 7–12, find z_x and z_y.

7. $z = 4x^2y^3 + \dfrac{x}{y}$

8. $z = \sqrt{x^2 + 2y^2}$

9. $z = (xy + 1)^{-2}$

10. $z = e^{x^2y^3}$

11. $z = e^{xy} + y \ln x$

12. $z = e^{\ln xy}$

13. Find the partial derivative of $f(x, y) = 4x^3 - 5xy^2 + y^3$ with respect to x at the point $(1, 2, -8)$.

14. Find the slope of the tangent in the x-direction to the surface $z = 5x^4 - 3xy^2 + y^2$ at $(1, 2, -3)$.

7.4

In problems 15–18, find the second partials
(a) z_{xx} (b) z_{yy} (c) z_{xy} (d) z_{yx}.

15. $z = x^2y - 3xy$

16. $z = 3x^3y^4 - \dfrac{x^2}{y^2}$

17. $z = x^2e^{y^2}$

18. $z = \ln(xy + 1)$

7.5   19. Test $z = 16 - x^2 - xy - y^2 + 24y$ for maxima and minima.

20. Test $z = x^3 + y^3 - 3xy$ for maxima and minima.

7.6   21. Find the minimum value of $z = 4x^2 + y^2$ subject to the constraint $x + y = 10$.

22. Find the maximum value of $z = x^4 y^2$ subject to $x + y = 9$, $x \geq 0$, $y \geq 0$.

7.7   In problems 23–28, evaluate the integrals

23. $\int_0^1 \int_0^1 (x + y) \, dx \, dy$

24. $\int_0^1 \int_1^2 (x^2 y - 1) \, dy \, dx$

25. $\int_0^2 \int_2^4 \frac{x}{(y - 1)^2} \, dy \, dx$

26. $\int_1^2 \int_1^4 (x^3 y - y) \, dx \, dy$

27. $\int_0^1 \int_0^y (3x^2 - y) \, dx \, dy$

28. $\int_0^3 \int_0^{\sqrt{x^2 - 1}} \frac{1}{\sqrt{x^2 - 1}} \, dy \, dx$

APPLICATIONS

7.1   29. **Utility** Suppose that the utility function for two goods X and Y is given by $U = x^2 y$, and a consumer purchases 6 units of X and 15 units of Y. If the consumer purchases 60 units of Y, how many units of X must be purchased to retain the same level of utility?

30. **Utility** Suppose that an indifference curve for two products, X and Y, has the equation $xy = 1600$. If 80 units of X is purchased, how many units of Y must be purchased?

7.3   31. **Cost** The joint cost function for two products is $C(x, y) = x^2 \sqrt{y^2 + 13}$. Find the marginal cost with respect to
(a) x if 20 units of x and 6 units of y are produced.
(b) y if 20 units of x and 6 units of y are produced.

32. **Production** Suppose that the production function for a company is given by

$$Q = 80K^{1/4}L^{3/4},$$

where Q is the output (in hundreds of units), K is the capital expenditures (in thousands of dollars), and L is the labor-hours. Find $\partial Q/\partial K$ and $\partial Q/\partial L$ when expenditures are $625,000 and total labor hours are 4096.

33. **Marginal demand** The demand functions for two related products, product A and product B, are given by

$$q_A = 400 - 2p_A - 3p_B$$
$$q_B = 300 - 5p_A - 6p_B.$$

(a) Find the marginal demand of q_A with respect to p_A.
(b) Find the marginal demand of q_B with respect to p_B.
(c) Are the two products complementary or competitive?

34. **Marginal demand** Suppose that the demand functions for two related products, A and B,

are given by

$$q_A = 800 - 40p_A - \frac{2}{p_B + 1}$$

$$q_B = 1000 - \frac{10}{p_A + 4} - 30p_B.$$

Determine whether the products are competitive or complementary.

7.5   35. **Profit** The profit from the sale of two products is given by $P(x, y) = 40x + 80y - x^2 - y^2$, where x is the number of units of product 1 and y is the number of units of product 2. Selling how much of each product will maximize profit?

36. **Taxes** The following data show U.S. national personal income and personal taxes for selected years.
    (a) Write the linear regression equation that best fits these data.
    (b) Use the equation found in part (a) to see how well it predicts the taxes for the income from 1980.

Year	Income (x) (in billions)	Taxes (y) (in billions)
1974	$1168.6	$170.2
1976	1391.2	196.8
1978	1732.7	258.7
1980	2165.3	336.5
1982	2584.6	404.1
1984	3108.7	440.2
1986	3526.2	512.9
1988	4064.5	586.6

Source: Bureau of Economic Analysis, U.S. Commerce Dept.

7.6   37. **Utility** If the utility function for two commodities is $U = x^2y$, and the budget constraint is $4x + 5y = 60$, find the values of x and y that maximize utility.

7.7   38. **Volume** Find the volume between $z = 16 - (x^2 + y^2)$ and the xy-plane above the region given by $R: 0 \le x \le 2, \quad 2 \le y \le 3$.

39. **Population** The concentration of population of a deer herd (in deer/square mile) in a national forest is described by

$$C = 200 - x - 2y.$$

If the forest is in the shape of a rectangle that is 12 miles by 30 miles (that is, $0 \le x \le 12$ and $0 \le y \le 30$), what is the average deer population per square mile?

ADVERTISING

To model sales of its tires, the manufacturer of GRIPPER tires used the quadratic equation $S = a_0 + a_1x + a_2x^2 + b_1y$, where S is regional sales in millions of dollars, x is TV advertising expenditures in millions of dollars, and y is other promotional expenditures in millions of dollars. (See the Consultant's Corner Marginal Return to Sales, on page 253.)

Although this model represents the relationship between advertising and sales dollars for small changes in advertising expenditures, it is clear to the vice president of advertising that it does not apply to large expenditures for TV advertising on a national level. He knows from experience that increased expenditures for TV advertising do result in more sales, but at a decreasing rate of return for the product.

The vice president is aware that some advertising agencies model the relationship between advertising and sales by the function

$$S = b_0 + b_1(1 - e^{-ax}) + c_1y,$$

where $a > 0$, S is sales in millions of dollars, x is TV advertising expenditures in millions of dollars, and y is other promotional expenditures in millions of dollars.* The equation

$$S_n = 24.58 + 325.18(1 - e^{-x/14}) + b_1y$$

has the form mentioned previously as being used by some advertising agencies. For TV advertising expenditures up to $20 million, this equation closely approximates

$$S_1 = 30 + 20x - 0.4x^2 + b_1y$$

which, in the Consultant's Corner on page 253, was used with fixed promotional expenses to describe advertising and sales in Region 1.

To help the vice president decide if this is a better model for large expenditures, answer the following questions.

1. What is $\partial S_1/\partial x$? Does this indicate that sales might actually decline after some amount x is spent on TV advertising? If so, what is this amount?

2. Does the quadratic model $S_1(x, y)$ indicate that sales will become negative after some amount is spent on TV advertising? Does this model cease to be useful in predicting sales after a certain point?

3. What is $\partial S_n/\partial x$? Does this indicate that sales will continue to rise if additional money is devoted to TV advertising? Is S_n growing at a rate that is increasing or decreasing when promotional sales are held constant? Is S_n a better model for large expenditures?

4. If this model does describe the relationship between advertising and sales, and if promotional expenditures are held constant at y_0, is there an upper limit to the sales, even if an unlimited amount of money is spent on TV advertising? If so, what is it?

*Mansfield, Edwin, *Managerial Economics*, W. W. Norton and Co., 1990.

APPENDIX

Table I Exponential functions

x	e^x	e^{-x}	x	e^x	e^{-x}
0.0	1.000	1.000	3.0	20.09	0.0498
0.1	1.105	0.9048	3.1	22.20	0.0450
0.2	1.221	0.8187	3.2	24.53	0.0408
0.3	1.350	0.7408	3.3	27.11	0.0369
0.4	1.492	0.6703	3.4	29.96	0.0334
0.5	1.649	0.6065	3.5	33.12	0.0302
0.6	1.822	0.5488	3.6	36.60	0.0273
0.7	2.014	0.4966	3.7	40.45	0.0247
0.8	2.226	0.4493	3.8	44.70	0.0224
0.9	2.460	0.4066	3.9	49.40	0.0202
1.0	2.718	0.3679	4.0	54.60	0.0183
1.1	3.004	0.3329	4.1	60.34	0.0166
1.2	3.320	0.3012	4.2	66.69	0.0150
1.3	3.669	0.2725	4.3	73.70	0.0136
1.4	4.055	0.2466	4.4	81.45	0.0123
1.5	4.482	0.2231	4.5	90.02	0.0111
1.6	4.953	0.2019	4.6	99.48	0.0101
1.7	5.474	0.1827	4.7	109.9	0.0091
1.8	6.050	0.1653	4.8	121.5	0.0082
1.9	6.686	0.1496	4.9	134.3	0.0074
2.0	7.389	0.1353	5.0	148.4	0.0067
2.1	8.166	0.1225	5.1	164.0	0.0061
2.2	9.025	0.1108	5.2	181.3	0.0055
2.3	9.974	0.1003	5.3	200.3	0.0050
2.4	11.02	0.0907	5.4	221.4	0.0045
2.5	12.18	0.0821	5.5	244.7	0.0041
2.6	13.46	0.0743	5.6	270.4	0.0037
2.7	14.88	0.0672	5.7	298.9	0.0033
2.8	16.44	0.0608	5.8	330.3	0.0030
2.9	18.17	0.0550	5.9	365.0	0.0027
			6.0	403.4	0.0025
			7.0	1097	0.0009
			8.0	2981	0.0003
			9.0	8103	0.0001

Table II Selected values of ln x

x	ln x	x	ln x	x	ln x
.002	− 6.215	1.40	0.336	600	6.397
.004	− 5.521	1.50	0.405	700	6.551
.010	− 4.605	2	0.693	800	6.685
.015	− 4.200	3	1.099	900	6.802
.018	− 4.017	5	1.609	1000	6.908
.020	− 3.912	7	1.946	1300	7.170
.023	− 3.772	10	2.303	1600	7.378
.027	− 3.612	20	2.996	2000	7.601
.030	− 3.507	30	3.401	2300	7.741
.040	− 3.219	50	3.912	2600	7.863
.045	− 3.101	80	4.382	3000	8.006
.050	− 2.996	100	4.605	3500	8.161
.080	− 2.526	110	4.700	4000	8.294
.10	− 2.303	130	4.868	4600	8.434
.20	− 1.609	150	5.011	5100	8.537
.30	− 1.204	170	5.136	5700	8.648
.40	− 0.916	200	5.298	6300	8.748
.41	− 0.892	230	5.438	6900	8.839
.48	− 0.734	250	5.521	7500	8.923
.50	− 0.693	280	5.635	8100	9.000
.52	− 0.654	300	5.704	8700	9.071
.60	− 0.511	350	5.858	9300	9.138
.70	− 0.357	400	5.991	10000	9.210
.80	− 0.223	410	6.016	11000	9.306
.90	− 0.105	460	6.131	12000	9.363
1.00	0.0	500	6.215	13000	9.473
1.30	0.262	520	6.254	14000	9.547
1.35	0.300	580	6.363	15000	9.616

ANSWERS TO SELECTED EXERCISES

Following are the answers to odd-numbered Section Exercises and to all Chapter Review Exercises.

CHAPTER 0

Exercise 0.1

1. $\in$ **3.** $\notin$ **5.** $D \subseteq C$ **7.** $\emptyset \subseteq A$
9. A and B, B and D, C and D **11.** $\{3, 8\}$
13. $\{2, 3, 4, 6, 8, 10\}$ **15.** $\{4, 6, 9, 10\}$
17. $\{1, 2, 3, 5, 7, 9\}$ **19. (a)** irrational
(b) rational, integer   **(c)** rational, integer, natural
(d) meaningless   **21.** $<$ **23.** $>$ **25.** -4
27. 4   **29.** $\frac{-4}{3}$ **31.** 3   **33.** entire line
35. $(1, 3]$ **37.** $(2, 10)$ **39.** $x \le 5$ **41.** $x > 4$
43. $(-3, 4)$

45. $(4, +\infty)$

47. $[-1, +\infty)$

49. $(-\infty, 0) \cup (7, +\infty)$

51. -0.000038585 **53.** 9122.387471
55. 398.73507

Exercise 0.2

1. -64 **3.** -16 **5.** $\frac{1}{9}$ **7.** $-\frac{9}{4}$ **9.** 6^8
11. $\frac{1}{10}$ **13.** 3^9 **15.** $(\frac{3}{2})^2 = \frac{9}{4}$ **17.** $1/x^6$
19. x/y^2 **21.** x^7 **23.** $x^{-2} = 1/x^2$
25. $2^{-7} = (\frac{1}{2})^7$ **27.** x^4 **29.** y^{12} **31.** x^{12}
33. $x^2 y^2$ **35.** $16/x^4$ **37.** $x^8/(16y^4)$
39. $-16a^2/b^2$ **41.** $2/(xy^2)$ **43.** $1/(x^9 y^6)$
45. $(a^{18} c^{12})/b^6$ **47.** x^{-1} **49.** $8x^3$ **51.** $\frac{1}{4} x^{-2}$
53. $-\frac{1}{8} x^3$ **55.** 2.0736 **57.** -7776
59. $A = \$2114.81; I = \$914.81$
61. $A = \$9607.70; I = \$4607.70$

Exercise 0.3

1. $\frac{16}{3}$ **3.** -8 **5.** -2 **7.** 8   **9.** $-\frac{1}{3}$
11. $\frac{9}{4}$ **13.** $m^{3/2}$ **15.** $(m^2 n^5)^{1/4}$ **17.** $\sqrt[4]{x^7}$
19. $-1/(4\sqrt[4]{x^5})$ **21.** $y^{3/4}$ **23.** $z^{19/4}$
25. $1/y^{5/2}$ **27.** x **29.** $1/y^{21/10}$ **31.** $x^{1/2}$
33. $1/x$ **35.** $8x^2$ **37.** $8x^2 y^2 \sqrt{2y}$
39. $2x^2 y \sqrt[3]{5x^2 y^2}$ **41.** $6x^2 y \sqrt{x}$ **43.** $42x^3 y^2 \sqrt{x}$
45. $2xy^5/3$ **47.** $2b\sqrt[4]{b}/(3a^2)$ **49.** $\sqrt{6}/3$
51. $\sqrt{mx}/x$ **53.** $\sqrt[3]{mx^2}/x^2$ **55.** $-\frac{2}{3} x^{-2/3}$
57. $3x^{3/2}$ **59.** $(3\sqrt{x})/2$ **61.** $1/(2\sqrt{x})$
63. 74 kg   **65.** 39,491   **67.** 10

Exercise 0.4

1. (a) 2   **(b)** -1 **(c)** 10   **(d)** one
3. (a) 5   **(b)** -14 **(c)** 0   **(d)** several
5. $11x^2 + 19x - 6$ **7.** $7x^2 y^2 - 4x^3$
9. $a + 8b - c$ **11.** $-q - 1$ **13.** $x^2 - 1$
15. $35x^5$ **17.** $3rs$ **19.** $2m^2 x^3$
21. $2ax^4 + a^2 x^3 + a^2 bx^2$ **23.** $6y^2 - y - 12$
25. $2 - 5x^2 + 2x^4$ **27.** $16x^2 + 24x + 9$
29. $x^4 - x^2 + \frac{1}{4}$ **31.** $4x^2 - 1$ **33.** $0.01 - 16x^2$
35. $x^3 - 8$ **37.** $x^8 + 3x^6 - 10x^4 + 5x^3 + 25x$
39. $3 + m + 2m^2 n$
41. $8x^3 y^9/3 + 5/(3y) - 2x^7/(3y)$
43. $x^3 + 3x^2 + 3x + 1$ **45.** $8x^3 - 36x^2 + 54x - 27$
47. $0.1x^2 - 1.995x - 0.1$
49. $x^2 - 2x + 5 - 11/(x + 2)$
51. $x^2 + 3x - 1 + (-4x + 2)/(x^2 + 1)$
53. $x + 2x^2$ **55.** $x - x^{1/2} - 2$ **57.** $x - 9$
59. $4x^2 + 4x$ **61.** $(15 - 2x)(10 - 2x)x$
63. (a) $10 - x$ **(b)** $.20x$ **(c)** $.05(10 - x)$
(d) $.20x + .05(10 - x) = .5 + .15x$

Exercise 0.5

1. $3b(3a - 4a^2 + 6b)$ **3.** $2x(2x + 4y^2 + y^3)$
5. $(5 - x^2)(y - 4)$ **7.** $(6 + y)(x - m)$
9. $(x + 2)(x + 6)$ **11.** $(x - 3)(x + 2)$
13. $2(x - 7)(x + 3)$ **15.** $(7x + 4)(x - 2)$
17. $(x - 5)^2$ **19.** $(7a + 12b)(7a - 12b)$
21. $2x(x - 2)^2$ **23.** $(2x - 3)(x + 2)$
25. $3(x + 4)(x - 3)$ **27.** $2x(x + 2)(x - 2)$
29. $(5x + 2)(2x + 3)$ **31.** $(5x - 1)(2x - 9)$
33. $(3x - 1)(3x + 8)$
35. $(y^2 + 4x^2)(y + 2x)(y - 2x)$
37. $(x + 2)^2(x - 2)^2$
39. $(2x + 1)(2x - 1)(x + 1)(x - 1)$ **41.** $(x + 1)^3$
43. $(x - 4)^3$ **45.** $(x - 4)(x^2 + 4x + 16)$
47. $(3 + 2x)(9 - 6x + 4x^2)$ **49.** $x + 1$
51. $1 + x$ **53.** $7x - 3x^3$ **55.** $4x(4 - x)^2$

Exercise 0.6

1. $2y^3/z$ **3.** $\frac{1}{3}$ **5.** $(x - 1)/(x - 3)$
7. $(2xy^2 - 5)/(y + 3)$ **9.** $20x/y$ **11.** $\frac{32}{3}$
13. $2x^2 - 7x + 6$
15. $-(x + 1)(x + 3)/[(x - 1)(x - 3)]$
17. $15bc^2/2$ **19.** $5y/(y - 3)$
21. $\dfrac{-x(x - 3)(x + 2)}{x + 3}$ **23.** $\dfrac{4a - 4}{a(a - 2)}$
25. $(x^2 + 3x + 1)/(x + 1)$ **27.** $\dfrac{16a + 15a^2}{12(x + 2)}$
29. $\dfrac{-5x + 17}{(x - 4)(x - 1)(x - 5)}$ **31.** $\dfrac{79x + 9}{30(x - 2)}$
33. $\dfrac{-4y}{(x - 2y)^2(x + 2y)}$ **35.** $\dfrac{9x + 4}{(x - 2)(x + 2)(x + 1)}$
37. $(7x - 3x^3)/\sqrt{3 - x^2}$ **39.** $\frac{1}{6}$ **41.** $\dfrac{y + x}{y - x}$
43. $\dfrac{x + 1}{x^2}$ **45.** $\dfrac{1}{\sqrt{a}} = \dfrac{\sqrt{a}}{a}$ **47.** $\dfrac{x - 2}{(x - 3)\sqrt{x^2 + 9}}$
49. $2b - a$ **51.** $\dfrac{x^3 + y^3}{x^2y^2(x + y)} = \dfrac{x^2 - xy + y^2}{x^2y^2}$
53. $(\sqrt{5} + 3)/(-4)$ **55.** $(1 - 2\sqrt{x} + x)/(1 - x)$
57. $1/(\sqrt{x + h} + \sqrt{x})$ **59.** $(bc + ac + ab)/abc$

Exercise 0.7

1. $x = 0$ **3.** $x = -\frac{5}{4}$ **5.** $x = 9$ **7.** $x = \frac{5}{2}$
9. $x = \frac{17}{13}$ **11.** $x = \frac{13}{5}$ **13.** $x = 40$
15. $x = -\frac{29}{2}$ **17.** $x = 1$ **19.** $x = 0$
21. $x \approx -0.279$ **23.** $y = -3x/2 + 20$
25. $y = x - 1$
27. $x \le -4$
$(-\infty, -4]$

29. $x < 2$
$(-\infty, 2)$

31. $x < \frac{3}{2}$
$(-\infty, \frac{3}{2})$

33. $x \ge -16$
$[-16, +\infty)$

35. $-1 < x < \frac{1}{3}$
$(-1, \frac{1}{3})$

37. $-\frac{9}{2} \le x \le -4$
$[-\frac{9}{2}, -4]$

39. (a) approx. 3333   **(b)** 15,873   **41. (a)** 132 lb
(b) $73\frac{7}{11}$ in.   **43.** 9000   **45. (a)** $T = (7n - 52)/12$
(b) 61°F   **47.** \$4000   **49.** \$307   **51.** \$246
53. \$300   **55.** \$8800   **57.** $x > 1100$
59. (a) $0 \le I \le 20,350$
  $20,350 < I \le 49,300$
  $I > 49,300$
(b) $0 \le T \le 3052.50$
  $3052.50 < T \le 11,158.50$
  $T > 11,158.50$

Chapter 0 Review Exercises

1. yes   **2.** no   **3.** no
4. $\{1, 2, 3, 5, 6, 7, 8, 9, 10\}$ **5.** $\{1, 3\}$
6. $\{4, 5, 6, 7, 8, 10\}$ **7. (a)** irrational
(b) rational, integer   **(c)** meaningless
8. (a) $>$ **(b)** $<$ **(c)** $>$ **9.** 6   **10.** 142
11. $\frac{13}{4}$ **12.** $\frac{5}{4}$ **13.** 9   **14.** -29
15. (a) $[0, 5]$; closed

(b) $[-3, 7)$; half-open

(c) $(-4, 0)$; open

16. (a) $-1 < x < 16$ **(b)** $-12 \le x \le 8$
(c) $x < -1$ **17. (a)** 1 **(b)** $2^7 = 128$ **(c)** 4^6
(d) 7 **18. (a)** $1/x^2$ **(b)** x^{10} **(c)** x^9 **(d)** $1/y^8$
(e) y^6 **19.** $9y^8/(4x^4)$ **20.** $y^2/(4x^4)$
21. $-x^8z^4/y^4$ **22.** $3x/(y^7z)$ **23. (a)** 4 **(b)** $\frac{2}{7}$
24. (a) $x^{1/2}$ **(b)** $x^{2/3}$ **(c)** $x^{-1/4}$ **25. (a)** $\sqrt[3]{x^2}$
(b) $1\sqrt{x} = \sqrt{x}/x$ **(c)** $-x\sqrt{x}$ **26. (a)** $5y\sqrt{2x}/2$
(b) $\sqrt[3]{x^2y}/x^2$ **27.** $x^{5/6}$ **28.** y **29.** $x^{17/4}$
30. $x^{11/3}$ **31.** $x^{2/5}$ **32.** x^2y^8 **33.** $2xy^2\sqrt{3xy}$
34. $25x^3y^4\sqrt{2y}$ **35.** $6x^2y^4\sqrt[3]{5x^2y^2}$ **36.** $8a^2b^4\sqrt{2a}$
37. $2xy$ **38.** $4x\sqrt{x}/(y^3\sqrt{3y}) = 4x\sqrt{3xy}/(3y^4)$
39. $-x - 2$ **40.** $-x^2 - x$
41. $4x^3 + xy + 4y - 4$ **42.** $24x^5y^5$
43. $3x^2 - 7x + 4$ **44.** $3x^2 + 5x - 2$
45. $4x^2 - 7x - 2$ **46.** $6x^2 - 11x - 7$
47. $4x^2 - 12x + 9$ **48.** $16x^2 - 9$
49. $2x^4 + 2x^3 - 5x^2 + x - 3$
50. $8x^3 - 12x^2 + 6x - 1$ **51.** $x^3 - y^3$
52. $(2/y) - (3xy/2) - 3x^2$
53. $3x^2 + 2x - 3 + (-3x + 7)/(x^2 + 1)$
54. $x^3 - x^2 + 2x + 7 + 21/(x - 3)$ **55.** $x^2 - x$
56. $2x - a$ **57.** $x^3(2x - 1)$
58. $2(x^2 + 1)^2(1 + x)(1 - x)$ **59.** $(2x - 1)^2$
60. $(4 + 3x)(4 - 3x)$ **61.** $2x^2(x + 2)(x - 2)$
62. $(x - 7)(x + 3)$ **63.** $(3x + 2)(x - 1)$
64. $(4x + 3)(3x - 8)$ **65.** $(2x + 3)^2(2x - 3)^2$
66. $x^{2/3} + 1$ **67. (a)** $x/(x + 2)$ **(b)** $\dfrac{2xy(2 - 3xy)}{2x - 3y}$

68. $\dfrac{x^2 - 4}{x(x + 4)}$ **69.** $(x + 3)/(x - 3)$

70. $\dfrac{x^2(3x - 2)}{(x - 1)(x + 2)}$ **71.** $(6x^2 + 9x - 1)/(6x^2)$

72. $\dfrac{4x - x^2}{4(x - 2)}$ **73.** $-\dfrac{x^2 + 2x + 2}{x(x - 1)^2}$

74. $\dfrac{x(x - 4)}{(x - 2)(x + 1)(x - 3)}$ **75.** $\dfrac{(x - 1)^3}{x^2}$ **76.** $\dfrac{1 - x}{1 + x}$

77. $3(\sqrt{x} + 1)$ **78.** $2/(\sqrt{x} + \sqrt{x - 4})$ **79.** $x = 7$
80. $x = \frac{31}{3}$ **81.** -13 **82.** $-\frac{29}{8}$ **83.** $x = -\frac{1}{9}$
84. $x = 10.05$ **85.** $x = \frac{2}{5}$ **86.** $x \approx 1.11$
87. $(-\infty, 3]$

88. $[-25, +\infty)$

89. $(-\infty, -\frac{3}{2}]$

90. $(-1, 5)$

91. 40,000 mi. He would normally drive more than 40,000 mi in 5 years so he should buy diesel.
92. (a) $x > 340$ **(b)** $x = 340$

CHAPTER 1

Exercise 1.1

1. yes **3.** no **5.** yes **7.** no **9. (a)** -10
(b) 6 **(c)** -34 **(d)** 2.8 **11. (a)** -3 **(b)** 1
(c) 13 **(d)** 6 **13. (a)** $63/8$ **(b)** 6 **(c)** -6
15. (a) 13 **(b)** $x^2 + 3x + 3$
(c) $x^2 + 2xh + h^2 + x + h + 1$
17. (a) $-2x^2 - 4xh - 2h^2 + x + h$
(b) $-4xh - 2h^2 + h$ **(c)** $-4x - 2h + 1$
19. yes **21.** no **23.** 2 **25.** 0
27. (a) $b = a^2 - 4a$ **(b)** $(1, -3)$, yes
(c) $(3, -3)$, yes **(d)** $x = 0, x = 4$, yes

29. (a) $3x + x^3$ **(b)** $3x - x^3$ **(c)** $3x^4$ **(d)** $\dfrac{3}{x^2}$

31. (a) $\sqrt{2x} + x^2$ **(b)** $\sqrt{2x} - x^2$ **(c)** $x^2\sqrt{2x}$
(d) $\dfrac{\sqrt{2x}}{x^2}$ **33. (a)** $-8x^3$ **(b)** $1 - 2(x - 1)^3$

(c) $[(x - 1)^3 - 1]^3$ **(d)** $(x - 1)^6$ **35. (a)** $2\sqrt{x^4 + 5}$
(b) $16x^2 + 5$ **(c)** $2\sqrt{2\sqrt{x}}$ **(d)** $4x$ **37.** D: all
reals; R: reals $y \ge 4$ **39.** D: reals $x \ge 1$; R: reals
$y \ge 0$ **41.** all reals except $x = 0$ **43.** reals $x \ge 1$
and $x \ne 2$ **45. (a)** yes **(b)** $v \ge -\frac{1}{4}$
(c) $v \ge 0$ **47. (a)** yes **(b)** all reals
(c) D: $32° \le F \le 212°$; R: $0° \le C \le 100°$ **(d)** 4.44°C
49. (a) 6 **(b)** 20 **(c)** 42 **51. (a)** $N(2) = 48\frac{2}{3}$;
number is 48 **(b)** $N(10) = 248\frac{2}{51}$; number is 248
53. (a) $0 \le p < 100$ **(b)** \$5972.73 **(c)** \$65,700
(d) \$722,700 **(e)** \$1,817,700 **55. (a)** yes
(b) $A(2) = 96; A(30) = 600$ **(c)** $0 < x < 50$

57. (a) $(p \circ x)(t) = 180(1000 + 10t) - \dfrac{(1000 + 10t)^2}{100} - 200$

(b) $x = 1150$, $p = \$193{,}575$ **59.** $L = 2x + 3200/x$

61. $R = (30 + x)(10 - 0.20x)$

Exercise 1.2

1.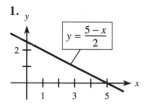
$y = \dfrac{5 - x}{2}$

3.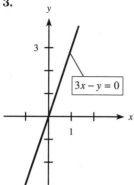
$3x - y = 0$

5.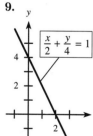
$y = 3$

7.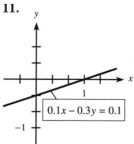
$x = -4$

9.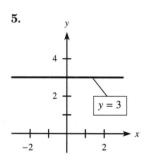
$\dfrac{x}{2} + \dfrac{y}{4} = 1$

11.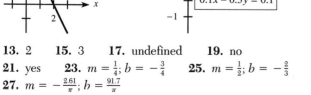
$0.1x - 0.3y = 0.1$

13. 2   **15.** 3   **17.** undefined   **19.** no

21. yes   **23.** $m = \frac{1}{4}$; $b = -\frac{3}{4}$ **25.** $m = \frac{1}{2}$; $b = -\frac{2}{3}$

27. $m = -\dfrac{2.61}{\pi}$; $b = \dfrac{91.7}{\pi}$

29.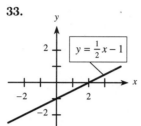
$y = \frac{1}{2}x + 3$

31.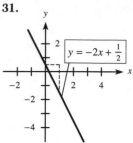
$y = -2x + \frac{1}{2}$

33.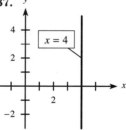
$y = \frac{1}{2}x - 1$

35.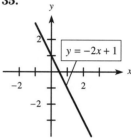
$y = -2x + 1$

37.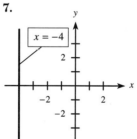
$x = 4$

39. $y = \frac{1}{13}x + \frac{32}{13}$ **41.** $y = 2$ **43.** l_2 and l_3

45. $y = 0$ **47.** $y = -\frac{3}{5}x - \frac{41}{5}$

49. $y = -\frac{6}{5}x + \frac{23}{5}$ **51.** $y = -\frac{8}{5}x + \frac{128}{5}$

53. $F = \frac{9}{5}C + 32$

55.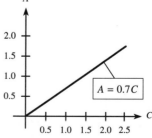
$A = 0.7C$

57. $N = 280l - 8000$ **59.** $y = 0.48x - 71$

61. $y = -\frac{1}{4}x + \frac{25}{2}$

63. (a)   **(b)** $R = 4.98x$ **(c)** $x \geq 0$

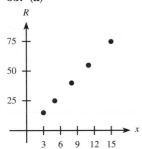

65. (a) 2055   **(b)** 2008

Exercise 1.3

1. (a) $C(x) = 17x + 3400$ **(b)** $C(200) = \$6800$

3. (a) $R(x) = 34x$ **(b)** $R(300) = \$10,200$

5. (a) $P(x) = 17x - 3400$ **(b)** $P(300) = \$1700$

(c) 200   **7. (a)** $m = 5; b = 250$

(b) $MC = 5 =$ cost of producing one more item

(c) \$250   **(d)** $MC = m = 5; b =$ fixed costs $= \$250$

(e) \$5; \$5   **9. (a)** $m = 51; b = -710$

(b) $MP = 51 =$ profit from the sale of one more item

(c) loss of \$710 when no units are sold   **(d)** \$310

(e) \$51   **11. (a)** $MP = -11.95$, so the firm loses

\$11.95 on each item sold.   **(b)** The firm should shut

down and take the loss of fixed costs only.

13. $P(x) = 50x - 46,000$ **15. (a)** Revenue passes

through the origin.   **(b)** \$2000   **(c)** 400 units

(d) $MC = 2.5; MR = 7.5$ **17.** 33

19. (a) $R(x) = 12x; C(x) = 8x + 1600$ **(b)** 400

21. (a) $P(x) = 4x - 1600$ **(b)** $x = 400$ [same as 19(b)]

23. 20,000 units   **25. (a)** 600   **(b)** 200   **(c)** shortage

27. 16 demanded; 25 supplied; surplus   **29.** (30, \$25)

31.   **33.**

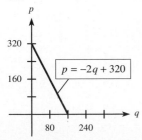

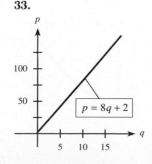

35. $q = 31.8$ units; $p = \$256.40$

37. $q = 10; p = \$180$ **39.** $q = 100, p = \$325$

41. (a) \$15   **(b)** $q = 100, p = \$100$

(c) $q = 50, p = \$110$ **(d)** yes   **43.** $q = 8, p = \$188$

45. $q = 500, p = \$40$ **47.** $R = \frac{5}{2}t + 1$

49. $y = \frac{30}{7}x - \frac{914}{7}$ or $y \approx 4.29x - 130.6$

51. (a) $T = 0.15x$

(b) $T = 11{,}158.50 + 0.31(x - 49{,}300)$

53. (a) $\dfrac{C - s}{n} = d$ **(b)** $D = \left(\dfrac{C - s}{n}\right)t$

55. (a) $A = 1000 + 60t$ **(b)** \$1090

57. $y = 5.19 + 0.5191x$ **59. (a)** $y = 1.05x$

(b) $y = 1.1025x$

61. (a) $p = -0.0104N + 574.96$

(b) For the first six data points, the model predicts
$p = 473.11, 468.51, 480.25, 494.88, 507.52,$
$487.49,$ and 470.22. The model is only fairly
good because some predicted p-values are
within a few dollars of the actual value while
others are off by more than \$20.

Exercise 1.4

1. $(-1, -\frac{1}{2})$; min   **3.** $(1, 9)$; max   **5. (a)** $x = 3$

(b) $f(3) = 9$ **7. (a)** $x = -1$ **(b)** $f(-1) = -4$

9. zeros $(-2, 0), (0, 0)$

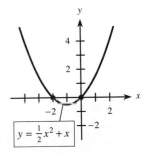

11. zeros $(-2, 0), (4, 0)$

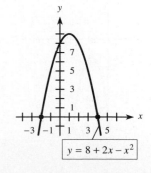

13. vertex $(0, -4)$,
zeros $(-2, 0)$, $(2, 0)$

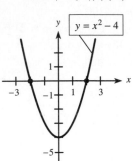

15. vertex $(2, 1)$;
zeros $(0, 0)$, $(4, 0)$

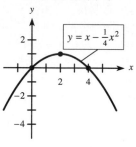

29. no zeros, vertex $(-1, \frac{8}{5})$

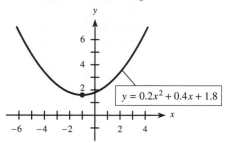

31. (a) zero $(0, 0)$; vertex $(0, 0)$
(b) zero $(0, 0)$; vertex $(0, 0)$

17. vertex $(-2, 0)$;
zero $(-2, 0)$

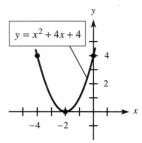

19. vertex $(-\frac{5}{2}, -\frac{9}{4})$;
zeros $(-1, 0)$, $(-4, 0)$

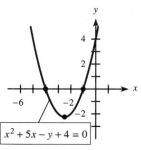

(a)

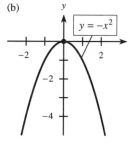

(b)

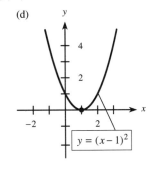

(c) zeros $(-1, 0)$, $(1, 0)$; vertex $(0, -1)$
(d) zero $(1, 0)$; vertex $(1, 0)$

21. vertex $(-2, 3)$;
no zeros

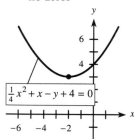

23. no zeros; vertex $(0, 5)$

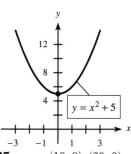

(c)

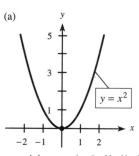

(d)

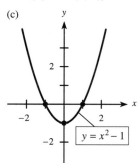

25. no zeros;
vertex $(\frac{7}{8}, -\frac{15}{16})$

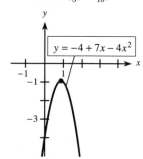

27. zeros $(10, 0)$, $(30, 0)$;
vertex $(20, 10)$

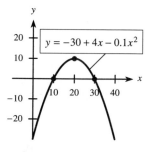

33. (a) 80 units   **(b)** $540

35.

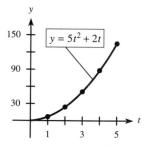

37.

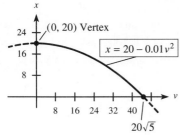

39.

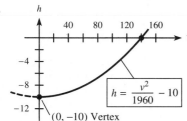

41. $x = 500$; $S = 250,000$ (max)   **43.** $x = \frac{3}{2}$

45. Equation (a): $(384.62, 202.31)$; Equation (b): $(54, 46)$; Projectile (a) goes higher   **47.** $41,173.61

49. $x = 40$ units, $x = 50$ units   **51.** The first goes farther.   **53.** (a) $651,041.67

(b) $P(x) = 1028x - x^2 - 28,000$; max profit = $236,196

(c) no   **55.** $A = \dfrac{900x - 3x^2}{4}$; max $A = 16,875$ sq ft

57. **(a), (b)**

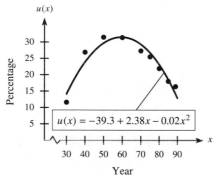

$u(x) = -39.3 + 2.38x - 0.02x^2$

59. **(a)** 1999 and 1919   **(b)** after 1999 and before 1919, when the percentage is less than 0

Exercise 1.5

1. (m)   **3.** (i)   **5.** (k)   **7.** (e)   **9.** (t)

11. (q)   **13.** (a)   **15.** (d)   **17.** (h)   **19.** (o)

21. **(a)** -1 **(b)** 1   **(c)** 1   **(d)** no   **23.** **(a)** 7

(b) undefined   **(c)** 2.99   **(d)** 1.9   **25.** **(a)** 37

(b) undefined   **(c)** 2.99   **(d)** 1.81   **27.** **(a)** 2

(b) 4   **(c)** 0   **(d)** 2

29.

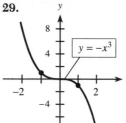

$y = -x^3$

31.

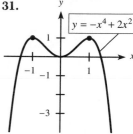

$y = -x^4 + 2x^2$

33.

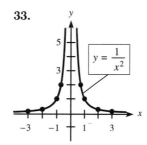

$y = \dfrac{1}{x^2}$

35.

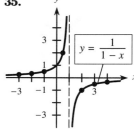

$y = \dfrac{1}{1-x}$

37.

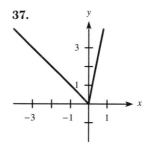

$$y = \begin{cases} -x & \text{if } x < 0 \\ 5x & \text{if } x \geq 0 \end{cases}$$

39.

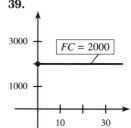

$FC = 2000$

41. **(a)**   **(b)** 11,664

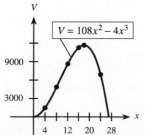

$V = 108x^2 - 4x^3$

43.

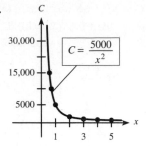

45. (a)   **(b)** 4 plates

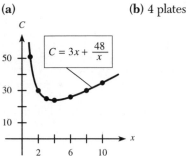

47.

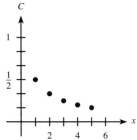

49. (a) $x = 0.30, f(0.30) = 18$
(b) $x = 30, f(30) = 19$
(c) $x = 40, f(40) = 20$
(d)

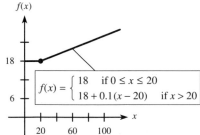

51. (a) -5 **(b)** 0   **(c)** 50   **(d)** 100   **(e)** 105
(f) changing state from ice to water

Exercise 1.6

1. $x = 40$ units; $x = 50$ units   **3.** $x = 50; x = 300$
5. $x = 15$ units; reject $x = 100$ **7.** Break-even at
$x = 100.$ $P > 0$ is impossible.   **9.** $x = 28$ units;
$x = 1000$ units
11. (a), (b) See graph.
    (c) See E on graph.
    (d) $q = 4, p = \$14$

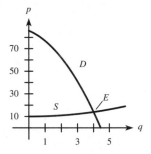

13. (a), (b) See graph.
    (c) See E on graph.
    (d) $q = 4, p = \$6.60$

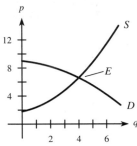

15. $q = 10, p = \$196$ **17.** $p = \$27.08, q = 216\frac{2}{3}$
19. $p = \$40, q = 30$ **21.** $q = 90, p = \$50$
23. $q = 70, p = \$62$

Chapter 1 Review Exercises

1. yes   **2.** no   **3.** yes   **4.** $D: x \leq 9; R: y \geq 0$
5. $x \geq -3; x \neq 0$ **6. (a)** 2   **(b)** 37   **(c)** 7.25
7. (a) 0   **(b)** $\frac{9}{4}$ **(c)** 10.01   **8. (a)** 0   **(b)** 10,000
(c) -25 **(d)** $\frac{1}{10}$ **9. (a)** -36 **(b)** $8 + 7x - x^2$
(c) $9x + 9h - x^2 - 2xh - h^2$ **10.** $-1 - 4x - 2h$
11. yes   **12.** no   **13.** 4   **14.** 0, 4   **15.** ± 1
16. 4   **17. (a)** $\dfrac{2}{x^3} + 3x^4$ **(b)** $\dfrac{2}{x^3} - 3x^4$

(c) $6x; x \neq 0$ **(d)** $\dfrac{2}{(3x^7)}$ **18. (a)** $2/(27x^{12})$
(b) $48/x^{12}$ **(c)** $243x^{16}$ **(d)** $9x^8$

19.

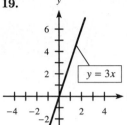

20.

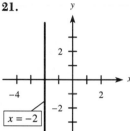

39. vertex $(\frac{1}{2}, \frac{25}{4})$;
zeros $(-2, 0)$, $(3, 0)$

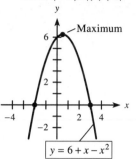

40. vertex $(2, 1)$;
no real zeros

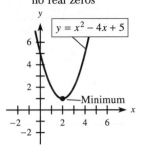

21.

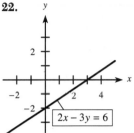

22.

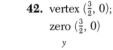

41. vertex $(-3, 0)$;
zero $(-3, 0)$

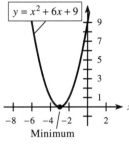

42. vertex $(\frac{3}{2}, 0)$;
zero $(\frac{3}{2}, 0)$

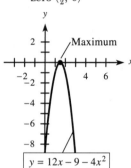

23.

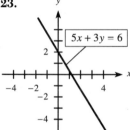

43. vertex $(-1, 1)$; no real zeros

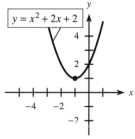

24. $-\frac{3}{4}$ **25.** 1   **26.** undefined
27. $m = -\frac{2}{5}; b = 2$ **28.** $m = -\frac{4}{3}; b = 2$
29. $y = 4x + 2$ **30.** $y = -\frac{1}{2}x + 3$ **31.** $y = \frac{2}{5}x + \frac{9}{5}$
32. $y = -x - 5$ **33.** $y = -\frac{11}{8}x + \frac{17}{4}$ **34.** $x = -1$
35. $y = 4x + 2$ **36.** $y = \frac{4}{3}x + \frac{10}{3}$
37. vertex $(-2, -2)$;
zeros $(0, 0)$, $(-4, 0)$

38. vertex $(0, 4)$;
zeros $(4, 0)$, $(-4, 0)$

44. vertex $(\frac{7}{2}, \frac{9}{4})$; zeros $(2, 0)$, $(5, 0)$

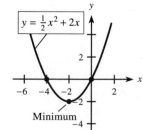

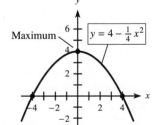

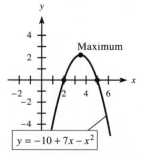

45. vertex $(100, 1000)$; zeros $(0, 0)$, $(200, 0)$

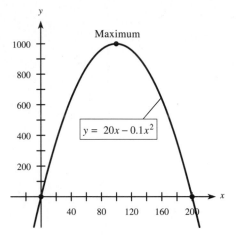

46. vertex $(75, -6.25)$; zeros $(50, 0)$, $(100, 0)$

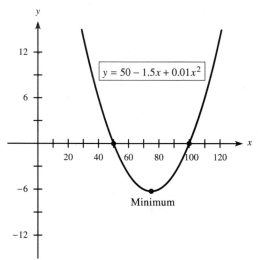

47.

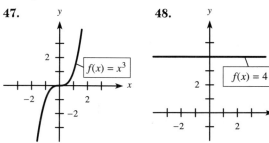

$f(x) = x^3$

48.

$f(x) = 4$

49.

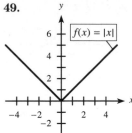

$f(x) = |x|$

50.

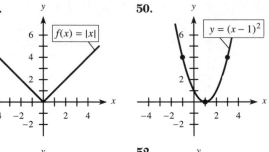

$y = (x - 1)^2$

51.

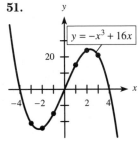

$y = -x^3 + 16x$

52.

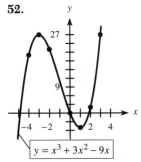

$y = x^3 + 3x^2 - 9x$

53.

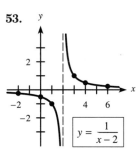

$y = \dfrac{1}{x - 2}$

54.

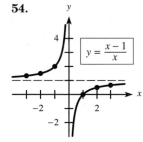

$y = \dfrac{x - 1}{x}$

55.

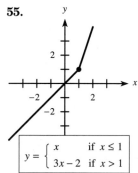

$y = \begin{cases} x & \text{if } x \le 1 \\ 3x - 2 & \text{if } x > 1 \end{cases}$

56.

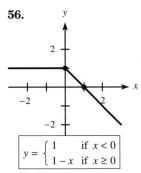

$y = \begin{cases} 1 & \text{if } x < 0 \\ 1 - x & \text{if } x \ge 0 \end{cases}$

57. Costs equal at 40,000 mi; diesel is the better buy.
58. **(a)** 12 supplied, 14 demanded   **(b)** shortfall
(c) increase   **59.** **(a)** $C(x) = 2x + 500$
(b) $C(100) = 700$ **60.** **(a)** $R(x) = 4x$
(b) $R(100) = 400$ **61.** **(a)** $P(x) = 2x - 500$
(b) $P(100) = -300$ (loss of \$300)   **(c)** 250 units

62. $100,000 at 9.5%; $50,000 at 11%

63.

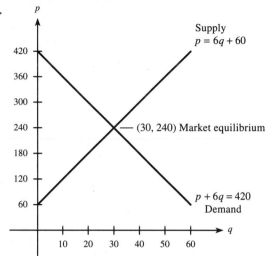

64. (a) $MC = 38.80$ (b) $MR = 61.30$
(c) $MP = 22.50$ (d) 200 units
65. (a) $C(x) = 22x + 1500$ (b) $R(x) = 52x$
(c) $P(x) = 30x - 1500$ (d) $MC = 22$ (e) $MR = 52$
(f) $MP = 30$ (g) $x = 50$ units   **66.** $p = \$150$
67. (a) $x = 200$ ft   (b) $A = 30,000$ sq ft
68. (a)   (b) $p = 41$, $q = 20$

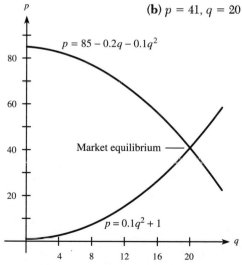

69. $p = 400$, $q = 10$ **70.** $p = 10$, $q = 20$
71. $x = 46 + 2\sqrt{89}$, $x = 46 - 2\sqrt{89}$
72. $(15, 1275)$, $(60, 2400)$ **73.** max revenue = $2500;
max profit = $506.25

74. max profit = 12.25; break-even $x = 100$, $x = 30$

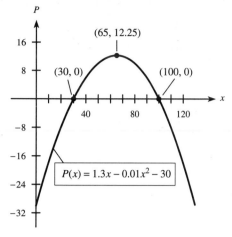

75. $x = 50$, $P(50) = 640$
76. (a) $C = 15,000 + 140x + 0.04x^2$; $R = 300x - 0.06x^2$
(b) 100, 1500   (c) 2500
(d) $P = 160x - 15,000 - 0.1x^2$; max at 800
(e) at 2500: $P = -240,000$; at 800: $P = 49,000$

CHAPTER 2

Exercise 2.1
1. (a) 1   (b) 1   **3.** (a) -8 (b) -8
5. (a) 10   (b) does not exist   **7.** (a) 0   (b) -6
9. (a) does not exist $(+\infty)$ (b) does not exist $(+\infty)$
(c) does not exist $(+\infty)$ (d) does not exist
11. (a) 3   (b) -6 (c) does not exist   (d) -6

13.

x	$f(x)$
1.9	-0.0526
1.99	-0.0050
1.999	-0.0005
↓	↓
2	0
↑	↑
2.001	0.0005
2.01	0.0050
2.1	0.0476

$\lim\limits_{x \to 2} f(x) = 0$

15.

x	$f(x)$
0.9	-1.9
0.99	-1.99
0.999	-1.999
↓	↓
1	-2
↑	↑
1.001	-2.001
1.01	-2.01
1.1	-2.1

$\lim\limits_{x \to 1} f(x) = -2$

17. 9   **19.** -1 **21.** 6   **23.** -4 **25.** 0
27. -2 **29.** 6   **31.** 0   **33.** -2

35. 1/30   **37.** does not exist

39. does not exist   **41.** does not exist   **43.** $3x^2$

45.

a	$(1 + a)^{1/a}$
0.1	2.5937
0.01	2.7048
0.001	2.7169
0.0001	2.7181
0.00001	2.71827
$\downarrow$	$\downarrow$
0	≈ 2.718

47. (a) 2   **(b)** 6   **(c)** -8 **(d)** $-\frac{1}{2}$

49. \$150,000   **51. (a)** \$32 thousands

(b) \$55.04 thousands   **53. (a)** \$2800   **(b)** \$700

(c) \$560   **55. (a)** 1.52 units/hr   **(b)** 0.85 units/hr

(c) lunch   **57. (a)** \$90/unit   **(b)** \$100/unit

59. (a) \$29,200   **(b)** does not exist ($+\infty$)   **(c)** no

Exercise 2.2

1. (a) continuous   **(b)** discontinuous; $f(1)$ does not exist   **(c)** discontinuous; $\lim_{x\to 3} f(x)$ does not exist

(d) discontinuous; $f(0)$ does not exist and $\lim_{x\to 0} f(x)$ does not exist   **3.** continuous   **5.** continuous

7. discontinuous; $f(-3)$ does not exist

9. discontinuous; $f(-1)$ and $\lim_{x\to -1} f(x)$ do not exist

11. continuous   **13.** discontinuous; $\lim_{x\to 1} f(x)$ does not exist   **15.** continuous   **17.** discontinuity at $x = -2$; $g(-2)$ does not exist   **19.** discontinuity at $x = -2$; $g(-2)$ and $\lim_{x\to -2} g(x)$ do not exist

21. continuous   **23.** continuous   **25.** discontinuity at $x = 3$; $\lim_{x\to 3} f(x)$ does not exist   **27. (a)** $x = -2$

(b) 0   **(c)** 0   **(d)** $y = 0$ (x-axis)

29. (a) $x = -2, x = 3$ **(b)** 2   **(c)** 2   **(d)** $y = 2$

31. 0   **33.** 1   **35.** $\frac{5}{3}$ **37.** 0   **39.** does not exist ($+\infty$)   **41. (a)** yes   **(b)** yes

43. (a) yes, $q = -1$ **(b)** yes

45. (a) discontinuity at $x - 0$ **(b)** change of state occurs at $x = 0$ **47.** yes, $0 \le p \le 100$ **49.** 100%; no   **51.** $A = R/i$ **53.** yes   **55. (a)** 18

(b) yes   **57. (a)** \$0.75   **(b)** \$0.75   **(c)** \$0.98

(d) does not exist   **(e)** \$0.98

Exercise 2.3

1. (a) 32   **(b)** 32   **(c)** (4, 64)   **3.** $f'(x) = -6$

5. $f'(x) = 8x - 2$ **7. (a)** $p'(q) = 2q + 4$

(b) $p'(5) = 14$ **9. (a)** $C'(x) = 28x + 5$

(b) $C'(4) = 117$ **11. (a)** $f'(x) = 2x + 1$

(b) $f'(2) = 5$ **(c)** $y = 5x - 4$ **13. (a)** $f'(x) = 3x^2$

(b) $f'(1) = 3$ **(c)** $y = 3x + 1$ **15. (a)** $P(1, 1)$,

$A(3, 0)$ **(b)** $-\frac{1}{2}$ **(c)** $-\frac{1}{2}$ **(d)** $-\frac{1}{2}$

17. (a) $P(1, 3)$, $A(0, 3)$ **(b)** 0   **(c)** 0   **(d)** 0

19. $f'(-3) = \frac{5}{2}; f(-3) = -9$ **21.** $y = 3x - 4$

23. (a) a, b, d **(b)** c **(c)** A, C, E

25. (a) A, B, C, D   **(b)** A, D

27. (a) -32 ft/sec   **(b)** the ball is falling, so S is decreasing   **29. (a)** $\dfrac{-100}{3}$ **(b)** $\dfrac{-4}{3}$ **31.** 68 mph

33. (a) 200   **(b)** 100   **(c)** 0   **(d)** changing from increasing to decreasing   **35.** 200   **37. (a)** 100

(b) -100 **39. (a)** 5 g/hr   **(b)** 7.5 g/hr

(c) 18.75 g/hr   **(d)** 30 g/hr   **41.** 48 mph

Exercise 2.4

1. 0   **3.** 1   **5.** $3x^2$ **7.** $15x^4$ **9.** $40q^7$

11. 3   **13.** $18x^5 - 24x$ **15.** $15q^2 + 8q$

17. $-3x^{-4}$ **19.** $-2x^{-3} = -2/x^3$

21. $\frac{2}{3}x^{-1/3} = 2/(3x^{1/3})$ **23.** $-\frac{4}{5}x^{-9/5} = -4/(5x^{9/5})$

25. $\frac{3}{4}q^{-1/4} = 3/(4\sqrt[4]{q})$ **27.** $-4x^{-9/5} + \frac{2}{5}x^{-4/5}$

29. $9x^2 + 10/x^6$ **31.** $-9/x^4 + 1(3x^{4/3}) - 5/(2\sqrt{x})$

33. $1/\sqrt{x} + 6\sqrt{x}$ **35.** 19   **37.** 0

39. $y = 8x - 3$ **41.** $y = 3$

43. (a) $y' = 3x^2; u'(x) = 1; v'(x) = 2x$ **(b)** no

(c) No, it fails for u and v given in part (a).

45. (a) 40, revenue increasing   **(b)** -20, revenue decreasing   **47. (a)** 920   **(b)** 926

49. (a) 0.005   **(b)** 0.024   **51. (a)** 1500

(b) 3000   **53. (a)** $\overline{C(x)}' = \dfrac{-4000}{x^2} + 0.1$ **(b)** 200

55. $-120,000$ **57.** $\dfrac{dy}{dt} = 8t + 2$ **59.** 70 gal/min

61. (a) -0.78% per year   **(b)** -0.82% per year

Exercise 2.5

1. $y' = 3x^2 + 2x - 6$ **3.** $dp/dq = 9q^2 - 2q + 6$
5. $f'(x) = (x^{12} + 3x^4 + 4)(12x^2) + (4x^3 - 1)(12x^{11} + 12x^3)$
7. $R'(x) = 18x^2 - 4x + 300$ **9.** $y' = (3x + 1)/(2\sqrt{x})$
11. $y' = (4\sqrt{x} + 3/x)(1/\sqrt[3]{x^2} + 10/x^3) +$
$(3\sqrt[3]{x} - 5/x^2 - 5^2)(2/\sqrt{x} - 3/x^2)$
13. -8 **15.** $y' = (-x^2 - 1)/(x^2 - 1)^2$
17. $\dfrac{dp}{dq} = (q^2 - 4q - 1)/(q - 2)^2$
19. $y' = (-x^6 - 4x^3 - 3x^2)/(x^3 + 1)^2$
21. $dp/dq = (2q + 1)/[\sqrt[3]{q^2}(1 - q)^2]$
23. $y' = (2x^3 - 6x^2 - 8)/(x - 2)^2$ **25.** $\frac{3}{4}$
27. $\frac{3}{5}$ **29.** $y = \frac{10}{3}x - \frac{10}{3}$
31. $(\frac{1}{3}, -\frac{50}{27})$ and $(1, -2)$

33. $f'(x) = \lim\limits_{h \to 0} \dfrac{\dfrac{u(x + h)}{v(x + h)} - \dfrac{u(x)}{v(x)}}{h}$

$= \lim\limits_{h \to 0} \dfrac{u(x + h)\, v(x) - u(x)\, v(x + h)}{h \cdot v(x)\, v(x + h)}$

$= \lim\limits_{h \to 0} \dfrac{u(x + h)\, v(x) - u(x)\, v(x) + u(x)\, v(x) - u(x)\, v(x + h)}{h \cdot v(x)\, v(x + h)}$

$= \lim\limits_{h \to 0} \dfrac{v(x)\left[\dfrac{u(x + h) - u(x)}{h}\right] - u(x)\left[\dfrac{v(x + h) - v(x)}{h}\right]}{v(x)\, v(x + h)}$

$= \dfrac{v(x)\, u'(x) - u(x)\, v'(x)}{[v(x)]^2}$

35. $C'(p) = 810{,}000/(100 - p)^2$
37. $R'(x) = (12x^2 + 12x - 27)/(2x + 1)^2$
39. $S = 1000x - x^2$ **41. (a)** 5   **(b)** 20/9
43. (a) 0.012   **(b)** With 1 more hour of training, monthly sales would change by approximately $0.012 (thousand).
45. $\dfrac{dP}{dt} = \dfrac{10{,}000}{(t + 10)^2}$ **47.** $\dfrac{dR}{dn} = \dfrac{r(1 - r)}{[1 + (n - 1)r]^2}$

Exercise 2.6

1. $6x(x^2 + 1)^2$
3. $4(8x - 4)(4x^2 - 4x + 1)^3 = 16(2x - 1)^7$
5. $-6x/(x^2 + 2)^4$ **7.** $-4(x + 2)(x^2 + 4x)^{-3}$
9. $-3(2x + 3)(x^2 + 3x + 4)^{-4}$
11. $\dfrac{-3(6x^2 + 3)}{4(2x^3 + 3x + 5)^{7/4}}$ **13.** $(x + 2)/\sqrt{x^2 + 4x + 5}$

15. $(6 - 4x)/\sqrt{3x - x^2}$ **17.** $16x(x^2 - 3)^4$
19. $\dfrac{15(3x + 1)^4 - 3}{7}$ **21.** 96,768   **23.** 2
25. $y = -3x + 4$ **27.** $9x - 5y = 2$
29. $x = 0, x = -2, x = 2$ **31. (a)** $y' = 2x^2$
(b) $y' = -2/x^4$ **(c)** $y' = 2(2x)^2$ **(d)** $y' = \dfrac{-18}{(3x)^4}$

33. 0.97   **35. (a)** $\dfrac{dy}{dt} = 4t(t^2 + 1)$ **(b)** 4040
37. 10 ft/sec   **39.** -0.114 (approx.)
41. $-\$3.20$ per unit   **43.** $\dfrac{dy}{dx} = \left(\dfrac{8k}{5}\right)(x - x_0)^{3/5}$
45. $\$1499.85$ (approx.)   **47.** $\dfrac{dp}{dq} = \dfrac{-100}{(2q + 1)^{3/2}}$
49. (a) $\$658.75$ **(b)** $\$2156.94$

Exercise 2.7

1. 0   **3.** $4(-4x^{-5})$; $-16/x^5$
5. $15x^2 + 4(-x^{-2})$; $15x^2 - 4/x^2$
7. $(x^2 - 2)1 + (x + 4)(2x)$; $3x^2 + 8x - 2$
9. $\dfrac{x^2(3x^2) - (x^3 + 1)(2x)}{(x^2)^2}$; $(x^3 - 2)/x^3$
11. $(3x^2 - 4)(x^3 - 4x)^9$
13. $\frac{5}{3}x^3[3(4x^5 - 5)^2(20x^4)] + (4x^5 - 5)^3(5x^2)$;
$5x^2(4x^5 - 5)^2(24x^5 - 5)$
15. $(x - 1)^2(2x) + (x^2 + 1)\, 2(x - 1)$;
$2(x - 1)(2x^2 - x + 1)$
17. $\dfrac{(x^2 + 1)\, 3(x^2 - 4)^2(2x) - (x^2 - 4)^3(2x)}{(x^2 + 1)^2}$;
$\dfrac{2x(x^2 - 4)^2(2x^2 + 7)}{(x^2 + 1)^9}$
19. $3[(q + 1)(q^3 - 3)]^2[(q + 1)\, 3q^2 + (q^3 - 3)1]$;
$3(4q^3 + 3q^2 - 3)[(q + 1)(q^3 - 3)]^2$
21. $4[x^2(x^2 + 3x)]^3[x^2(2x + 3) + (x^2 + 3x)(2x)]$;
$4x^2(4x + 9)[x^2(x^2 + 3x)]^3$
23. $4\left(\dfrac{2x - 1}{x^2 + x}\right)^3\left[\dfrac{(x^2 + x)2 - (2x - 1)(2x + 1)}{(x^2 + x)^2}\right]$;
$\dfrac{4(-2x^2 + 2x + 1)(2x - 1)^3}{(x^2 + x)^5}$

25. $(8x^4 + 3)^2 \, 3(x^3 - 4x)^2(3x^2 - 4) +$
$(x^3 - 4x)^3 \, 2(8x^4 + 3)(32x^3);$
$(8x^4 + 3)(x^3 - 4x)^2(136x^6 - 352x^4 + 27x^2 - 36)$

27. $\dfrac{(4 - x^2)\frac{1}{3}(x^2 + 5)^{-2/3}(2x) - (x^2 + 5)^{1/3}(-2x)}{(4 - x^2)^2};$

$\dfrac{2x(2x^2 + 19)}{3\sqrt[3]{(x^2 + 5)^2}\,(4 - x^2)^2}$

29. $(x^2)\frac{1}{4}(4x - 3)^{-3/4}(4) + (4x - 3)^{1/4}(2x);$
$(9x^2 - 6x)/\sqrt[4]{(4x - 3)^3}$

31. $(2x)\frac{1}{2}(x^3 + 1)^{-1/2}(3x^2) + (x^3 + 1)^{1/2}(2);$
$(5x^3 + 2)/\sqrt{x^3 + 1}$

33. (a) $F_1'(x) = 12x^3(x^4 + 1)^4$ **(b)** $F_2'(x) = \dfrac{-12x^3}{(x^4 + 1)^6}$

(c) $F_3'(x) = 12x^3(3x^4 + 1)^4$ **(d)** $F_4'(x) = \dfrac{-300x^3}{(5x^4 + 1)^6}$

35. $dP/dx = 90(3x + 1)^2$ **37. (a)** \$59,900
(b) it is increasing **39.** $C'(y) = 1/\sqrt{y + 1} + 0.4$
41. $dV/dx = 144 - 96x + 12x^2$ **43.** -1.6

Exercise 2.8

1. $24x - 30$ **3.** $60x - 2$ **5.** $6x - 2x^{-3}$

7. $6x + \frac{1}{4}x^{-3/2}$ **9.** $20x^3 + \frac{1}{4}x^{-3/2}$ **11.** $\dfrac{-1}{4(x - 1)^{3/2}}$

13. $\dfrac{4}{(x^2 + 4)^{3/2}}$ **15.** $\dfrac{-2}{(x + 1)^3}$ **17.** $60x^2 - 96$

19. $1008x^6 - 720x^3$ **21.** $-6/x^4$ **23.** $\frac{3}{8}x^{-5/2}$
25. $\frac{3}{8}(x + 1)^{-5/2}$ **27.** $-12x(x^2 + 4)^{-5/2}$ **29.** 0
31. $-15/(16x^{7/2})$ **33.** 26 **35.** $a = 20.12$
37. -0.02 **39. (a)** $f'(x) = 290x - 90x^2$
(b) $f'(1) = 200; f'(3) = 60$ **(c)** $f''(1) = 110;$
$f''(3) = -250$ **41.** 0.0009 (approx.)

43. (a) $S' = \dfrac{-3}{(t + 3)^2} + \dfrac{36}{(t + 3)^3}$ **(b)** $S''(15) = 0$

Exercise 2.9

1. $\overline{MC} = 8$ **3.** $\overline{MC} = 13 + 2x$
5. $\overline{MC} = 3x^2 - 12x + 24$ **7.** $\overline{MC} = 27 + 3x^2$
9. (a) \$10; the cost will increase by \$10. **(b)** \$11
11. \$46; the cost will increase by \$46.

13.

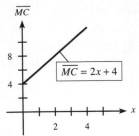

15. (a) $\overline{MR} = 4$ **(b)** The sale of each additional
item brings in \$4 revenue at all levels of production.
17. (a) \$3500; this is revenue from the sale of 100 units.
(b) $\overline{MR} = 36 - 0.02x$ **(c)** \$34; Revenue will increase
by \$34. **(d)** Actual revenue from the sale of the 101st
item is \$33.99.
19. (a) $\overline{MR} = 36 - 0.02x$ **(b)** $x = 1800$ **(c)** \$32,400

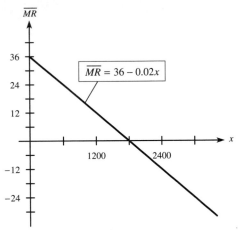

21. $\overline{MP} = 5$
23. (a) \$0 **(b)** $\overline{MP} = 30 - 2x$ **(c)** $-$\$10; profit
will decrease by \$10 if one additional unit is sold
(d) The sale of the 21st item results in a loss of \$11.
25. (a) **(b)** 15 **(c)** 15 **(d)** \$25

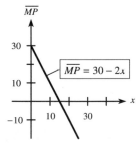

27. 70 **29.** \$200

Chapter 2 Review Exercises

1. (a) 2 **(b)** 2 **2.** (a) 0 **(b)** 0 **3.** (a) 2
(b) 1 **4.** (a) 2 **(b)** does not exist
5. (a) does not exist **(b)** 2 **6.** (a) does not exist
(b) does not exist **7.** 55 **8.** 0 **9.** -2
10. 6 **11.** $\frac{1}{2}$ **12.** $\frac{1}{5}$ **13.** no limit **14.** 0
15. 4 **16.** no limit **17.** 6x **18.** $1 - 4x$
19. (a) yes **(b)** no **20.** (a) yes **(b)** no
21. 2 **22.** no limit **23.** 1 **24.** no
25. yes **26.** yes **27.** discontinuity at $x = 5$
28. discontinuity at $x = 2$ **29.** continuous
30. discontinuity at $x = 1$ **31.** (a) $x = 0, x = 1$
(b) 0 **(c)** 0 **32.** (a) $x = -1, x = 0$ **(b)** $\frac{1}{2}$
(c) $\frac{1}{2}$ **33.** -2 **34.** 0 **35.** true **36.** false
37. $f'(x) = 6x + 2$ **38.** $f'(x) = 1 - 2x$
39. (a) no **(b)** no **40.** (a) yes **(b)** no
41. $20x^4 - 18x^2$ **42.** 8x **43.** 3 **44.** $1/(2\sqrt{x})$
45. 0 **46.** $-4/(3\sqrt[3]{x^4})$ **47.** $\dfrac{-1}{x^2} + \dfrac{1}{2\sqrt{x^3}}$
48. $\dfrac{-3}{x^3} - \dfrac{1}{3\sqrt[3]{x^2}}$ **49.** $y = 15x - 18$
50. $y = 34x - 48$ **51.** $x = 0, x = 2$
52. $x = 0, x = 2, x = -2$ **53.** $9x^2 - 26x + 4$
54. $15x^4 + 9x^2 + 2x$ **55.** $\dfrac{2(1 - q)}{q^3}$
56. $\dfrac{1 - 3t}{[2\sqrt{t}(3t + 1)^2]}$ **57.** $\dfrac{9x + 2}{2\sqrt{x}}$
58. $\dfrac{5x^6 + 2x^4 + 20x^3 - 3x^2 - 4x}{(x^3 + 1)^2}$
59. $(9x^2 - 24x)(x^3 - 4x^2)^2$
60. $6(30x^5 + 24x^3)(5x^6 + 6x^4 + 5)^5$
61. $(9x^2 - 24x)(x^3 - 4x^2)^2$ **62.** $\dfrac{(3x^2 - 4)}{2\sqrt{(x^3 - 4x)^3}}$
63. $2x(2x^4 + 5)^7(34x^4 + 5)$ **64.** $\dfrac{-2(3x + 1)(x + 12)}{(x^2 - 4)^2}$
65. $36[(3x + 1)(2x^3 - 1)]^{11}(8x^3 + 2x^2 - 1)$
66. $\dfrac{3}{(1 - x)^4}$ **67.** $\dfrac{(2x^2 - 4)}{\sqrt{x^2 - 4}}$ **68.** $\dfrac{2x - 1}{(3x - 1)^{4/3}}$
69. $y'' = \frac{-1}{4}x^{-3/2} - 2$ **70.** $y'' = 12x^2 - 2/x^3$
71. $\dfrac{d^5y}{dx^5} = 0$ **72.** $\dfrac{d^5y}{dx^5} = -30(1 - x)$
73. $\dfrac{d^3y}{dx^3} = -4/[(x^2 - 4)^{3/2}]$ **74.** $\dfrac{d^4y}{dx^4} = \dfrac{2x(x^2 - 3)}{(x^2 + 1)^3}$

75. (a) -1 **(b)** $-\frac{1}{4}$ **76.** $\dfrac{dq}{dp} = \dfrac{-p}{\sqrt{0.02p^2 + 500}}$
77. $\frac{1}{6}$ **78.** (a) $\overline{MC} = 6x + 6$ **(b)** 186 **79.** 53
80. (a) $\overline{MR} = 40 - 0.04x$ **(b)** $x = 1000$ units
81. 48 **82.** (a) $\overline{MR} = 80 - 0.08x$ **(b)** 72
83. $\dfrac{120x(x + 1)}{(2x + 1)^2}$ **84.** $\overline{MP} = 4500 - 3x^2$
85. $\overline{MP} = 16 - 0.2x$

CHAPTER 3

Exercise 3.1

1. (a) $dy/dx = x - 1$ **(b)** $x = 1$ **(c)** $(1, -\frac{1}{2})$
(d) rel min **3.** (a) $dy/dx = 3x^2 - 3$ **(b)** $x = 1, -1$
(c), (d) $(1, -2)$ rel min; $(-1, 2)$ rel max
5. (a) $dy/dx = 3x^2 + 6x + 3$ **(b)** $x = -1$
(c) $(-1, -1)$ **(d)** horizontal point of inflection
7. (a) $\dfrac{dy}{dx} = \dfrac{2}{3x^{1/3}}$ **(b)** $x = 0$ **(c)** $(0, 0)$
(d) rel min **9.** (a) $dy/dx = x^2 + x - 2$
(b) $x = -2, x = 1$ **(c)** $(-2, \frac{13}{3})$, $(1, -\frac{1}{6})$
(d) $(-2, \frac{13}{3})$ rel max;
$(1, -\frac{1}{6})$ rel min
(e)

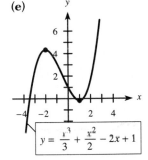

11. (a) $dy/dx = 3x^2 - 6x$ **(b)** $x = 0, x = 2$
(c) $(0, 0)$, $(2, -4)$ **(d)** $(0, 0)$ rel max; $(2, -4)$ rel min
(e)

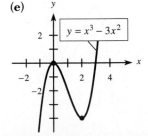

13. $(1, 1)$ rel max;
$(0, 0)$, $(2, 0)$ rel min

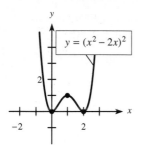

17. $(3, 4)$ rel max;
$(5, 0)$ rel min;
HPI $(0, 0)$

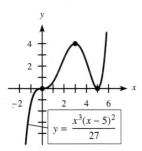

21. HPI $(1, \frac{4}{3})$
no max or min

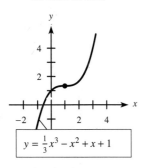

25. $(0, 4)$ rel max;
$(2, 0)$ rel min

15. $(\frac{1}{2}, -\frac{27}{16})$ min;
HPI $(2, 0)$

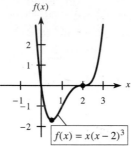

19. $(0, 0)$ rel max;
$(2, -4.8)$ rel min

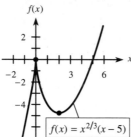

23. HPI $(0, 0)$;
$(3, -27)$ min

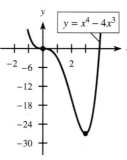

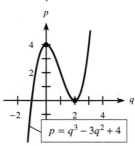

27. $(\frac{4}{3}, -\frac{95}{27})$ rel min;
$(-2, 15)$ rel max

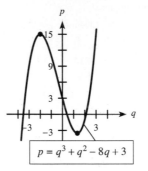

31. decreases for $t \geq 0$
33. **(a)** $2 \pm \sqrt{13}$
(b) $2 + \sqrt{13} \approx 5.6$
(c) $0 \leq t < 2 + \sqrt{13}$

29. $(-1, 3)$ rel max;
$(1, -1)$ rel min;
HPI $(0, 1)$

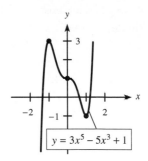

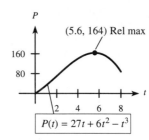

35. **(a)** $t = 6$ **(b)** 6 weeks   **37.** **(a)** at a:
increasing $(f'(a) > 0)$; at b: rate $= 0$ $(f'(b) = 0)$; at c:
decreasing $(f'(c) < 0)$ **(b)** (a, b) **39.** **(a)** 10
(b) Jan 1   **41.** **(a)** 1973   **(b)** yes

Exercise 3.2

1. $(1, -2)$ **3.** $(0, 0)$ **5.** none   **7.** $(2, 0)$
9. $(-2, -9)$ and $(1, \frac{3}{4})$ **11.** $(3, -54)$ **13.** $(0, 0)$
15. $(0, 0)$ and $(-2, 7.6)$ **17.** $(0, 0)$, $(\sqrt{3}, \sqrt{3})$, and
$(-\sqrt{3}, -\sqrt{3})$
19. points of inflection: $(0, 1)$ and $(\frac{2}{3}, \frac{11}{27})$; min: $(1, 0)$

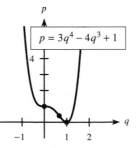

21. $(-2, 64)$ rel max; $(2, -64)$ rel min; and points of inflection: $(-\sqrt{2}, 39.6)$, $(0, 0)$, and $(\sqrt{2}, -39.6)$

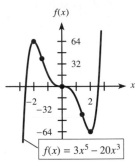

$f(x) = 3x^5 - 20x^3$

23. $(1, -3)$ min; points of inflection: $(-2, 7.6)$ and $(0, 0)$

25. no points of inflection; $(2, -2)$ min

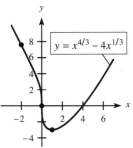

$y = x^{4/3} - 4x^{1/3}$

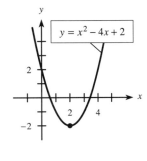

$y = x^2 - 4x + 2$

27. $(0, 6)$ rel max; $(2, 2)$ rel min; point of inflection: $(1, 4)$

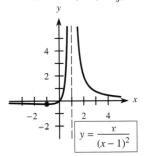

$y = x^3 - 3x^2 + 6$

29. $(0, 0)$ rel max; $(2\sqrt{2}, -64)$, $(-2\sqrt{2}, -64)$ min; points of inflection: $(2\sqrt{6}/3, -320/9)$ and $(-2\sqrt{6}/3, -320/9)$

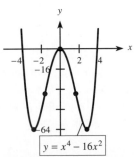

$y = x^4 - 16x^2$

31. no points of inflection; $(0, -4)$ min

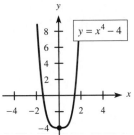

$y = x^4 - 4$

33. (a) $P'(t)$ (b) B (c) C **35.** (a) C
(b) right (c) yes **37.** (a) in an 8-hour shift, max when $t = 8$ (b) 4 hr **39.** 5000
41. (a) 9 days (b) 15 days

Exercise 3.3

0. (a) $x = -2$ (b) 0 (c) $y = 0$ (d) 0
3. (a) $x = -2, x = 3$ (b) 2 (c) $y = 2$ (d) 2
5. HA: $y = 2$; VA: $x = 3$
7. HA: $y = 0$; VA: $x = 2, x = -2$
9. HA: none; VA: $x = \frac{5}{2}$ **11.** HA: $y = 0$; VA: none
13. HA: $y = 0$; VA: $x = 1$; **15.** VA: $x = 3$; $(2, -1)$
$(-1, -\frac{1}{4})$ rel min; point rel max; $(4, 7)$ rel min
of inflection: $(-2, -\frac{2}{9})$

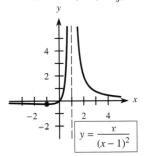

$y = \dfrac{x}{(x - 1)^2}$

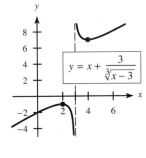

$y = x + \dfrac{3}{\sqrt[3]{x - 3}}$

17. HA: $y = 0$; VA: $x = -1$; $(2, 1.6)$ rel max; $(0, 0)$ rel min; points of inflection: $(-0.12, 0.84)$ and $(4.12, 1.51)$

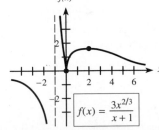

$f(x) = \dfrac{3x^{2/3}}{x + 1}$

19. HA: $y = 0$; VA: $x = 0$ **21.** HA: $y = 0$; VA: $x = 1$

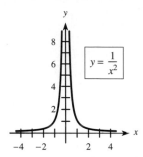

$y = \dfrac{1}{x^2}$

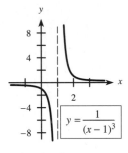

$y = \dfrac{1}{(x-1)^3}$

23. VA: $x = 0$; $(-2, -4)$ rel max; $(2, 4)$ rel min

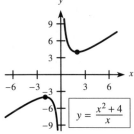

$y = \dfrac{x^2 + 4}{x}$

25. VA: $x = -1$; HA: $y = 0$; $(0, 0)$ rel min; $(2, 4)$ rel max; points of inflection: $(2 + \sqrt{3}, 3.55)$ and $(2 - \sqrt{3}, 0.95)$

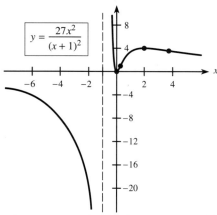

$y = \dfrac{27x^2}{(x+1)^2}$

27. HA: $y = 0$; $(1, 8)$ rel max; $(-1, -8)$ rel min; points of inflection: $(0, 0)$, $(-\sqrt{3}, -4\sqrt{3})$, and $(\sqrt{3}, 4\sqrt{3})$

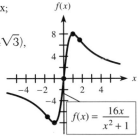

$f(x) = \dfrac{16x}{x^2 + 1}$

29. **(a)** none   **(b)** $C \geq 0$ **(c)** $p = 100$ **(d)** no

31. **(a)**

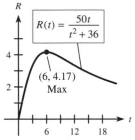

$R(t) = \dfrac{50t}{t^2 + 36}$

$(6, 4.17)$ Max

(b) 6 weeks

(c) 22 weeks after its release

33. 5 years   **35.** **(a)** $P = C$ **(B)** C **(C)** $P' = 0$ **(d)** 0

Exercise 3.4

1. $x = 1800$ units, $R = \$32,400$

3. $x = 20$ units, $R = \$24,000$ **5.** 40 people

7. $p = \$15$, $R = \$22,500$ **9.** **(a)** max $= \$2100$

(b) $x = 10$ **11.** $x = 5$ units, $\overline{C} = \$23$

13. $x = 10$ units, $\overline{C} = \$20$

15. 200 units $(x = 2)$, $\overline{C} = \$108$ **17.** $x = 5$

19. $x = 80$ units, $P = \$280,000$

21. $x = 10\sqrt{15} \approx 39$ units, $P \approx \$71,181$ (using $x = 39$)

23. $x = 1000$ units, $P = \$39,700$

25. 39 units; $P(39) = \$71,181$ **27.** **(a)** 60

(b) $570   **(c)** $9000   **29.** **(a)** 15   **(b)** $9450

31. 2000 units priced at $90/unit; max profit is $90,000/wk   **33.** rent $= \$430$ **35.** $12/item

37. $t = \$350$ **39.** $115/item

41. $483/item; $40,100   **43.** $1100/item

Exercise 3.5

1. **(a)** $x_1 = \$25$ million, $x_2 = \$30$ million

(b) $55 million   **3.** $x = 500$ **5.** 400 trees

7. **(a)** 5   **(b)** 237.5   **9.** $50   **11.** 1 week

13. $t = 8$, $p = 45\%$ **15.** 240 ft   **17.** $300' \times 150'$

19. 20 ft long, $6\frac{2}{3}$ ft across (dividers run across)

21. $4'' \times 8'' \times 8''$ high   **23.** 30,000   **25.** 12,000

27. $x = 2$ **29.** 3 weeks from now   **31.** 25 plates

33. 72.3 ft

Exercise 3.6

1. $\Delta y = 63$ **3.** $\Delta y \approx 0.171$ **5.** $dy = (16x - 1)\,dx$

7. $dy = (x^3 - 4x^2)\,dx$ **9.** $dy = \left(\dfrac{-2}{x^3} + \dfrac{2}{x^2}\right)dx$

11. $dy = \dfrac{60x^3}{(3x^4 + 5)^2}\,dx$ **13.** $\dfrac{-x^3\,dx}{\sqrt{4 - 3x^4}}$

15. $(x^2 + 2x + 1)^{10}(2x + 2)\,dx$

17. $\Delta y = 6.75$; $dy = 6.5$; $dx = 0.5$

19. $\Delta y \approx 0.364$; $dy = 0.375$; $dx = 0.5$

21. $dV = 0.32\pi(\text{in.})^3 \approx 1.01$ (in.)^3 **23.** 6%   **25.** 3%

27. (a) $dq = -2$ units   (b) $dq = 3.2$ units

29. (a) $dp \approx 0.00024$ tons   (b) $dp \approx 0.00067$ tons

31. $dC = \$101{,}250$ **33.** $dA = \$28.19$

35. $dR \approx -12.5$ (thousand dollars)

Exercise 3.7

1. $-x/(2y)$ **3.** $-(2x + 4)/(2y - 3)$ **5.** $-x/y$

7. $-(2x + 3y)/(3x)$ **9.** $-p/q$ **11.** $\dfrac{2x(1 - 5x^3)}{3y^2(7 + 4y)}$

13. $\dfrac{2x + 6xy^4}{1 - 12x^2y^3}$ **15.** $\dfrac{20x^3y^3 - 2x - 2y}{2x + 2y - 15x^4y^2}$

17. $(4x^3 + 9x^2y^2 - 8x - 12y)/(18y + 12x - 6x^3y + 10y^4)$

19. undefined   **21.** 1   **23.** $y = \frac{1}{2}x + 1$

25. $y = 4x + 5$ **27.** horizontal: $(2, \sqrt{2})$, $(2, -\sqrt{2})$;
vertical: $(2 + 2\sqrt{2}, 0)$, $(2 - 2\sqrt{2}, 0)$

31. yes, because $x^2 + y^2 = 4$ **33.** $1/(2x\sqrt{x})$

35. $\frac{1}{2}$ **37.** $-\frac{243}{128}$ **39.** At $p = \$80$, $q = 49$ and
$dq/dp = -\frac{5}{16}$, which means that if the price is
increased to \$81, quantity demanded will decrease by
approximately $\frac{5}{16}$ units.   **41.** (a) 1   (b) no change

43. (a) 84   (b) revenue will decrease

45. (a) $\frac{100}{99}$ (b) elastic   (c) decrease

47. (a) 0.81   (b) inelastic   (c) increase

49. $dR/dp = p(dq/dp) + q$: $\eta = 1 \Rightarrow dq/dp = -q/p$;
$\therefore dR/dp = p(-q/p) + q = -q + q = 0$

51. $dR/dp = p(dq/dp) + q$: $\eta < 1$
$\Rightarrow (-p/q)(dq/dp) < 1 \Rightarrow dq/dp > -q/p$;
$\therefore dR/dp = p(dq/dp) + q > p(-q/p) + q = 0$
so $dR/dp > 0$

Exercise 3.8

1. $-\frac{24}{5}$ **3.** $\frac{7}{6}$ **5.** -5 if $z = 5$, -10 if $z = -5$

7. -80 units/sec   **9.** 12π ft^2/min   **11.** $\frac{16}{27}$ in./sec

13. $\dfrac{1}{4\pi}$ micrometers/day   **15.** 36π mm^3/month

17. $\dfrac{\dfrac{dW}{dt}}{W} = 3\left(\dfrac{\dfrac{dL}{dt}}{L}\right)$ **19.** $\dfrac{\dfrac{dC}{dt}}{C} = 1.54\left(\dfrac{\dfrac{dW}{dt}}{W}\right)$

21. \$1798/day   **23.** \$0.42/day

25. 430 units/month   **27.** $\frac{13}{4}$ ft/min

29. 8 ft/min   **31.** 25 knots   **33.** $\dfrac{50}{81\pi}$ in./min

Chapter 3 Review Exercises

1. $(0, 0)$ max   **2.** $(2, -9)$ min   **3.** HPI $(1, 0)$

4. $(1, \frac{3}{2})$ max, $(-1, -\frac{3}{2})$ min

5. (a) $\frac{1}{3}, -1$

(b) $(-1, 0)$ rel max,
$(\frac{1}{3}, -\frac{32}{27})$ rel min

(c) none

(d)

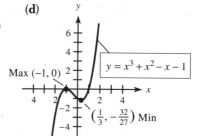

$y = x^3 + x^2 - x - 1$

Max $(-1, 0)$

$\left(\frac{1}{3}, -\frac{32}{27}\right)$ Min

6. (a) 3, 0

(b) $(3, 27)$ max

(c) $(0, 0)$

(d)

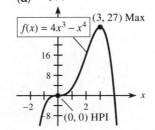

$f(x) = 4x^3 - x^4$

$(3, 27)$ Max

$(0, 0)$ HPI

7. **(a)** $-1, 6$

(b) $(-1, 11)$ rel max,

$(6, -160.5)$ rel min

(c) none

(d)

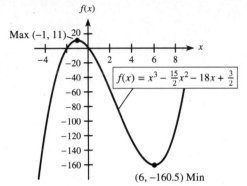

Max $(-1, 11)$

$f(x) = x^3 - \frac{15}{2}x^2 - 18x + \frac{3}{2}$

$(6, -160.5)$ Min

8. **(a)** $0, \pm 1$

(b) $(-1, 1)$ rel max,

$(1, -3)$ rel min

(c) $(0, -1)$

(d)

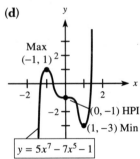

Max $(-1, 1)$

$(0, -1)$ HPI

$(1, -3)$ Min

$y = 5x^7 - 7x^5 - 1$

9. **(a)** 0

(b) $(0, -1)$ min

(c) none

(d)

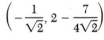

$y = x^{2/3} - 1$

$(0, -1)$ Min
Vertical tangent

10. **(a)** $0, 1, 4$

(b) $(0, 0)$ rel min,

$(1, 9)$ rel max,

$(4, 0)$ rel min

(c) none

(d)

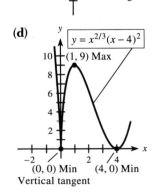

$y = x^{2/3}(x - 4)^2$

$(1, 9)$ Max

$(0, 0)$ Min $(4, 0)$ Min
Vertical tangent

11. concave up

12. $(-1, -3); (2, -42)$

13. $(-1, 15)$ rel max; $(3, -17)$ rel min; point of inflection $(1, -1)$

14. $(-2, 16)$ rel max;

$(2, -16)$ rel min;

point of inflection $(0, 0)$

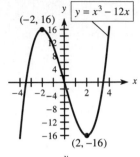

$y = x^3 - 12x$

$(-2, 16)$

$(2, -16)$

15. $(1, 4)$ rel max;

$(-1, 0)$ rel min;

points of inflection:

$\left(\dfrac{1}{\sqrt{2}}, 2 + \dfrac{7}{4\sqrt{2}}\right)$,

$(0, 2)$, and

$\left(-\dfrac{1}{\sqrt{2}}, 2 - \dfrac{7}{4\sqrt{2}}\right)$

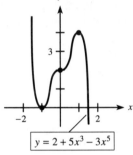

$y = 2 + 5x^3 - 3x^5$

16. **(a)** $x = 1$ **(b)** $y = 0$ **(c)** 0 **(d)** 0

17. **(a)** $x = -1$ **(b)** $y = \frac{1}{2}$ **(c)** $\frac{1}{2}$ **(d)** $\frac{1}{2}$

18. HA: $y = \frac{3}{2}$; VA: $x = 2$

19. HA: $y = -1$; VA: $x = 1, x = -1$

20. **(a)** HA: $y = 3$;

VA: $x = -2$

(b) No max nor min

(c)

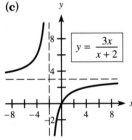

$y = \dfrac{3x}{x + 2}$

21. **(a)** HA: $y = 0$;

VA: $x = 0$

(b) $(4, 1)$ max

(c)

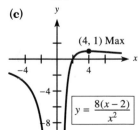

$(4, 1)$ Max

$y = \dfrac{8(x - 2)}{x^2}$

22. **(a)** HA: none;
 VA: $x = 1$
(b) $(0, 0)$ rel max;
 $(2, 4)$ rel min

(c)

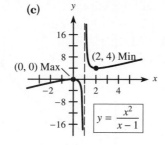

23. **(a)** $(0, 0)$ absolute min; $(140, 19{,}600)$ absolute max
 (b) $(0, 0)$ absolute min; $(100, 18{,}000)$ absolute max
24. **(a)** $(50, 233{,}333)$ absolute max; $(0, 0)$ absolute min
 (b) $(64, 248{,}491)$ absolute max; $(0, 0)$ absolute min

25. $dy = \dfrac{2x\,dx}{(1 - x^2)^2}$ **26.** $dy = 3(3x + 4)^7\,dx$

27. 240   **28.** 0.048   **29.** $dy/dx = 2/y$

30. $\dfrac{dy}{dx} = \dfrac{2(x + 1)}{3(1 - 2y)}$ **31.** $y' = \dfrac{6x(1 + xy^2)}{y(5y^3 - 4x^3)}$

32. $d^2y/dx^2 = -(x^2 + y^2)/y^3$ **33.** $\frac{5}{9}$

34. $(-2, \pm \sqrt{\frac{2}{3}})$ **35.** $\frac{3}{4}$ **36.** 11 sq. units/min

37. $x = 5$ units, $\overline{C} = \$45$

38. $x = 1600$ units, $R = \$25{,}600$

39. $P = \$54{,}000$ at $x = 100$ units   **40.** $x = 3$ units

41. $x = 152$ units   **42.** $x = 7$ units   **43.** $300

44. selling 175 sets at $425 each

45. \$93,625 at 325 units   **46. (a)** 150   **(b)** \$650

47. \$208,490.67 at 64 units   **48.** yes

49. $t = 1446.67$ **50.** \$880   **51.** $x = 1000$ units

52. 10:00 A.M.   **53.** 325 in 1995

54. 20 mi from A, 10 mi from B **55.** 4 ft $\times$ 4 ft

56. $8\frac{3}{4}'' \times 10''$ **57.** 500   **58.** $\frac{29}{18}$ **59.** 24,000

60. (a) 0.35 (thousand) = \$350   **(b)** $dS = \$320$

61. $dR = \$2$ (million)   **62. (a)** 1   **(b)** no change

63. $\frac{25}{12}$, elastic   **64.** $1/(25\pi)$ mm/min

65. $\frac{48}{25}$ ft/min   **66.** $\dfrac{dS/dt}{S} = \dfrac{1}{3}\left(\dfrac{dA/dt}{A}\right)$

11.

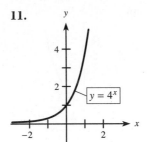

13.

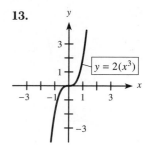

15.

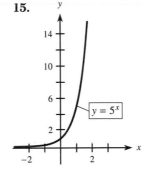

17.

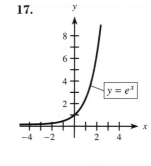

19.

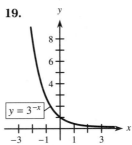

21.

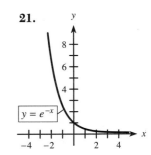

23.

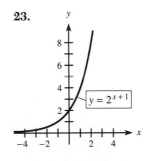

25.

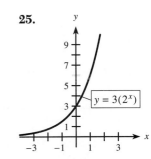

Chapter 4

Exercise 4.1

1. 3.162278   **3.** 0.01296525   **5.** 1.44225
7. 7.3891   **9.** 0.04979

27.

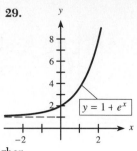

$y + 1 = 2^x$

29.

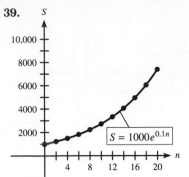

$y = 1 + e^x$

39.

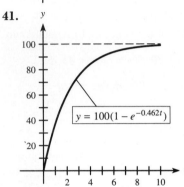

$S = 1000e^{0.1n}$

31. identical shape, 1 unit higher

33. N

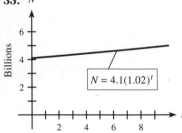

$N = 4.1(1.02)^t$

41.

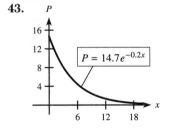

$y = 100(1 - e^{-0.462t})$

35. N

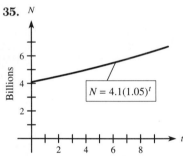

$N = 4.1(1.05)^t$

43. P

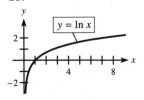

$P = 14.7e^{-0.2x}$

37. y

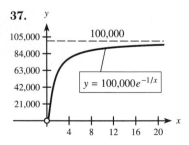

$y = 100{,}000e^{-1/x}$

Exercise 4.2

1. $2^4 = 16$ **3.** $4^{1/2} = 2$ **5.** $x = 8$ **7.** $x = \frac{1}{2}$

9. $\log_2 32 = 5$ **11.** $\log_4\left(\frac{1}{4}\right) = -1$

13.

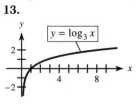

$y = \log_3 x$

15.

$y = \ln x$

17.

$y = \log_2(-x)$

19. 3 **21.** $\frac{1}{2}$ **23.** 4 **25.** x **27.** 1
29. 2 **31.** x **33.** 2 **35.** 1.0792
37. 0.5118 **39.** -2.4082 **41.** 8.3169
43. $\log x - \log(x+1)$ **45.** $\log_7 x + \frac{1}{3}\log_7(x+4)$
47. $\ln\left(\frac{x}{y}\right)$ **49.** $\log_5\left[x^{1/2}(x+1)\right]$ **51.** 4.0875
53. 2.5237 **55.** -6.6439
57. If $u = \log_a M$, then $a^u = M$.
$\log_a M^N = \log_a (a^u)^N = \log_a (a^{Nu}) = Nu$
$\therefore \log_a M^N = N \log_a M.$
59. (a) \$230.26 **(b)** 31 (nearest unit) **61.** 5.903
63. 15.8 **65.** 4:1 **67.** 140 decibels
69. 2512:1 **71. (a)** 7.4 **(b)** 4.2 **(c)** 2.2
73. (a) 0.001 **(b)** 1.62×10^{-8} **(c)** 0.0000001

Exercise 4.3

1. (a) $y' = 4/x$ **(b)** $y' = 4/x$

3. (a) $y' = \dfrac{-1}{x(x-1)}$ **(b)** $y' = \dfrac{1}{x} - \dfrac{1}{x-1}$

5. (a) $y' = \dfrac{2x}{3(x^2-1)}$ **(b)** $y' = \dfrac{2x}{3(x^2-1)}$

7. (a) $y' = \dfrac{-8x+3}{x(4x-1)}$ **(b)** $y' = \dfrac{4}{4x-1} - \dfrac{3}{x}$

9. (a) $y' = \dfrac{7x+6}{2x(x+1)}$ **(b)** $y' = \dfrac{3}{x} + \dfrac{1}{2(x+1)}$

11. $y' = 0$ **13.** $dp/dq = 2q/(q^2+1)$

15. $\dfrac{dp}{dq} = \dfrac{(q^2+1)}{q(q^2-1)}$ **17.** $\dfrac{dy}{dt} = -\dfrac{(3t^2-4t-3)}{2(1-t)(t^2+3)}$

19. $y' = \ln x$ **21.** $y' = (1 - \ln x)/x^2$

23. $y' = 8x^3/(x^4+3)$ **25.** $y' = \dfrac{4(\ln x)^3}{x}$

27. $y' = \dfrac{8x^3 \ln(x^4+3)}{x^4+3}$ **29.** $y' = \dfrac{1}{x \ln 4}$

31. $y' = \dfrac{4x^3 - 12x^2}{(x^4 - 4x^3 + 1)\ln 6}$ **33. (a)** $\overline{MC} = \dfrac{400}{2x+1}$

(b) $\dfrac{400}{401}$; at $x = 200$ units, producing one additional unit

costs about \$1. **35.** $\dfrac{dq}{dx} = \dfrac{150}{3x+1}$

37. $\dfrac{-1}{[H^+]\ln 10}$ **39. (a)** during 1914, at $x = 14.1$

(b) no **(c)** 0 **(d)** Although the model indicates
that life span will always be increasing, the rate of
increase is decreasing with time.

Exercise 4.4

1. $y' = 3x^2 e^{x^3}$ **3.** $y' = 36x e^{3x^2}$ **5.** $y' = e^{-1/x}/x^2$

7. $y' = 12x(x^2+1)^2 e^{(x^2+1)^3}$ **9.** $y' = \dfrac{2}{x^3}e^{-1/x^2} - 2xe^{-x^2}$

11. $ds/dt = te^t(t+2)$ **13.** $y' = 1$
15. $y' = e^{\frac{1}{2}x} + e^{\sqrt{x}}/(2\sqrt{x})$ **17.** $y' = 12e^{3x} - 12x^2 e^{x^3}$
19. $y' = 2e^{2x}/(e^{2x}+1)$
21. $y' = e^{-3x}/x - 3e^{-3x}\ln(2x)$
23. $y' = (2e^{5x} - 3)/e^{3x} = 2e^{2x} - 3e^{-3x}$
25. $y' = 30e^{3x}(e^{3x}+4)^9$ **27.** $y' = 6^x \ln 6$
29. $y' = 4^{x^2}(2x \ln 4)$ **31.** $y = e^{-1}$ **33.** $z = 0$
35. $z = 1, z = -1$ **37. (a)** 8.67 **(b)** 17.80

39. $\dfrac{dS}{dt} = -50{,}000\,e^{-0.5t}$ **41.** $100{,}000e^{-1/x}/x^2$

43. (a) $0.1(Pe^{0.1n})$ **(b)** $0.1(Pe^{0.1}) \approx 0.1105P$
(c) yes; because of the compounding
45. 29.107 **47.** $1200e$
49. $N'(t) = 3{,}535{,}000\,e^{-0.7t}/(1 + 100\,e^{-0.7t})^2$
51. (a) $d'(x) = 29 - 20.1891e^{x/100} + 0.044e^{x/10}$
(b) \$1.28 (billion/yr), \$198.01 (billion/yr)
(c) U.S. could not tolerate exponential growth in
its debt. The percent of federal expenditures
devoted to payment of interest on the debt
was too high.

Exercise 4.5

1. \$6655 **3.** \$18,772.72 **5.** \$9029.98

7. $6005.38   **9. (a)** $5469.03   **(b)** 7 years, 9 months (approx.)   **11. (a)** $5532.77   **(b)** 5 years, 2 months (approx.)   **13. (a)** 2038   **(b)** 4.9 months
15. (a) 69%   **(b)** 37,204 yrs (approx.)
17. 24.5 yrs   **19.** 128,402
21. (a) 600
    (b) 2119
    (c) 3000
    (d)

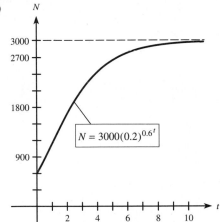

23. (a) 10   **(b)** 2.5   **25. (a)** 37   **(b)** 1.5 hrs
27. (a) 52   **(b)** tenth   **29. (a)** $4.98   **(b)** 8
31. $502   **33.** $420.09   **35.** $2707
37. (a) 2%   **(b)** 20 months   **39. (a)** 0.23 km^3
(b) 5.9 yrs   **41. (a)** 0 lb   **(b)** 29.95 lb
(c) 0.21 min   **43. (a)** $x = 16$; 0.2%
(b) 10.56 min   **(c)** 0.06%

Chapter 4 Review Exercises
1. (a) $\log_2 y = x$ **(b)** $\log_3 2x = y$
2. (a) $7^{-2} = \frac{1}{49}$ **(b)** $4^{-1} = x$
3.

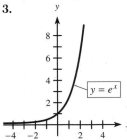

4.

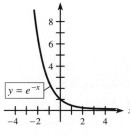

5.

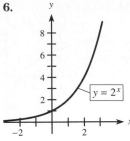

6.

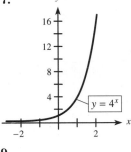

7.

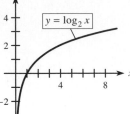

8.

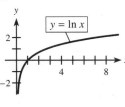

9.

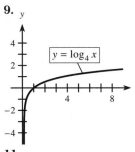

10.

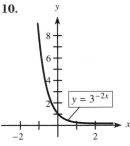

11.

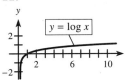

12.

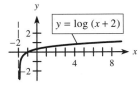

13.

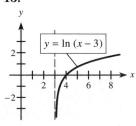

14.

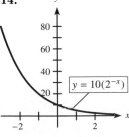

15. 0   **16.** 2   **17.** $\frac{1}{2}$ **18.** -1 **19.** 8

20. 1   **21.** 5   **22.** 3.15   **23.** 0.6020

24. 0.6021   **25.** 1.8062   **26.** 1.8063

27. $\log y + \log z$ **28.** $\frac{1}{2}\ln(x+1) - \frac{1}{2}\ln x$

29. $x^2 e^x + 2xe^x$ **30.** $2x$ **31.** $1/q - \left[\dfrac{2q}{(q^2-1)}\right]$

32. $dy/dx = 2xe^{x^2}$ **33.** $dy/dx = 3^{3x-3}\ln 3$

34. $y' = \dfrac{10(1+\ln x)^9}{x}$ **35.** $y' = \dfrac{1-\ln x}{x^2}$

36. $dy/dx = -2e^{-x}/(1-e^{-x})^2$

37. $dy/dx = \dfrac{2[1 - \ln(2x+1)]}{(2x+1)^2}$

38. $dx/dt = e^t(t^2+4)(t+2)^2$ **39.** $y' = \dfrac{-y}{x\ln x}$

40. $dy/dx = ye^{xy}/(1 - xe^{xy})$ **41. (a)** -3.9

(b) $0.14\,B_a$ **(c)** $0.004\,B_a$ **(d)** yes   **42.** 135.3

43. (a) 152.5   **(b)** 1.13 times faster

44. (a) $-0.00002876\,A_0$ **(b)** $-0.00002876\,A_0$

(c) less   **45.** $1200e$ **46.** \$11,239.42

47. \$372.79   **48.** \$1616.07   **49.** 3 years

50. 6 years   **51. (a)** 3000   **(b)** 8603

(c) 10,000   **52. (a)** \$27,440.58   **(b)** 12 weeks

53. \$1366.19

CHAPTER 5

Exercise 5.1

1. $x^4 + C$ **3.** $\frac{1}{7}x^7 + C$ **5.** $\frac{1}{8}x^8 + C$ **7.** $\frac{5}{4}x^4 + C$

9. $\frac{4}{3}x^6 + C$ **11.** $27x + \frac{1}{4}x^4 + C$ **13.** $\frac{2}{5}x^{5/2} + C$

15. $\frac{1}{5}x^5 - x^3 + C$ **17.** $\frac{2}{3}x^{3/2} + C$ **19.** $\frac{24}{5}x\sqrt[4]{x} + C$

21. $-5/(3x^3) + C$ **23.** $\frac{3}{2}\sqrt[3]{x} + C$

25. $\dfrac{1}{4}x^4 - 4x - \dfrac{1}{x^5} + C$ **27.** $\dfrac{1}{10}x^{10} + \dfrac{1}{2x^2} + 3x^{2/3} + C$

29. $\frac{1}{4}x^4 + \frac{10}{3}x^3 + \frac{25}{2}x^2 + C$ **31.** $\frac{16}{5}x^5 - \frac{8}{3}x^3 + x + C$

33. $-1/x - 1/(2x^2) + C$ **35.** $R(x) = 3x$

37. $R(x) = 2x^2 + 3x$ **39.** \$3800

41. $P(t) = \frac{1}{4}t^4 + \frac{4}{3}t^3 + 6t$ **43. (a)** $x = t^{7/4}/1050$

(b) 0.96 tons   **45. (a)** $x/4 + 100/x + 30$ **(b)** \$56

47. (a) $r = -t + 32$ **(b)** 174

(c) $r = 0$ at $t = 32$; 512 barrels

Exercise 5.2

1. $\frac{1}{4}(x^2+3)^4 + C$ **3.** $(15x^2+10)^5/5 + C$

5. $\frac{1}{3}(3x - x^3)^3 + C$ **7.** $\frac{1}{8}(x^2+5)^4 + C$

9. $\frac{7}{6}(x^4+6)^{3/2} + C$ **11.** $9x - 2x^3 + \frac{1}{5}x^5 + C$

13. $(4x-1)^7/4 + C$ **15.** $-\frac{1}{4}(x^2+1)^{-2} + C$

17. $\frac{1}{10}(x^2 - 2x)^5 + C$ **19.** $\frac{3}{8}(x^2+2x)^{4/3} + C$

21. $-1/[3(x^3-1)] + C$ **23.** $-1/[9(x^3-5)^3] + C$

25. $\frac{2}{3}\sqrt{x^3 - 6x^2} + C$ **27.** $-8/[3(x^3-4)] + C$

29. $-1/[8(x^4 - 4x)^2] + C$ **31.** 3720

33. $R(x) = 60,000x + \left[\dfrac{40,000}{(10+x)}\right] - 4000$

35. (a) $s = 10\sqrt{x+1}$ **(b)** 50

37. (a) $100/(t+10) - 1000/(t+10)^2$

(b) 2.5 million   **39.** 7400

Exercise 5.3

1. $\ln|x^3+4| + C$ **3.** $\ln|x^3 - 2x| + C$

5. $\frac{1}{4}\ln|x^4+1| + C$ **7.** $2\ln|x^2-4| + C$

9. $\frac{1}{4}\ln|4z+1| + C$ **11.** $\frac{1}{3}\ln|z^3+3z| + C$

13. $\frac{1}{3}x^3 + \ln|x-1| + C$ **15.** $x + \frac{1}{2}\ln|x^2+3| + C$

17. $e^{3x} + C$ **19.** $-e^{-x} + C$ **21.** $\frac{1}{12}e^{3x^4} + C$

23. $-\frac{3}{2}e^{-2x} + C$ **25.** $\frac{1}{18}e^{3x^6-2} + C$

27. $\frac{1}{4}e^{4x} + 6/e^{x/2} + C$ **29.** \$1030.97   **31.** $n = n_0 e^{-Kt}$

33. 55   **35. (a)** $Pe^{0.1n}$ **(b)** approx. 7 yrs

37. (a) $p = 95e^{-0.491t}$ **(b)** ≈ 90.45

Exercise 5.4

1. $C(x) = x^2 + 100x + 200$ **3.** $C(x) = 2x^2 + 2x + 80$

5. \$3750   **7. (a)** $x = 3$ units is optimal level

(b) $P(x) = -4x^2 + 24x - 200$ **(c)** loss of \$164

9. (a) \$2960   **(b)** 896

11. (a) $\overline{C}(x) = 6/x + x/6 + 266/15$ **(b)** \$21.37

13. $C(y) = 0.4y + 0.6\sqrt{y} + 5$

15. $C(y) = 0.3y + 0.4\sqrt{y} + 8$

17. $C = 2\sqrt{y+1} + 0.4y + 4$

19. $C = 0.7y + 0.5e^{-2y} + 5.15$

21. $C = 0.85y + 5.15$

23. $C = 0.8y + \dfrac{2\sqrt{3y+7}}{3} + 4.24$

Chapter 5 Review Exercises

1. $\frac{1}{7}x^7 + C$ **2.** $\frac{2}{3}x^{3/2} + C$

3. $\frac{1}{4}x^4 - x^3 + 2x^2 + 5x + C$ **4.** $\frac{1}{5}x^5 - \frac{2}{3}x^3 + x + C$

5. $\frac{1}{6}(x^2 - 1)^3 + C$ **6.** $\frac{1}{6}(x^3 - 3x^2)^2 + C$

7. $\frac{1}{8}x^8 + \frac{8}{5}x^5 + 8x^2 + C$ **8.** $\frac{1}{21}(x^3 + 4)^7 + C$

9. $\frac{1}{3}\ln|x^3 + 1| + C$ **10.** $\dfrac{-1}{3(x^3 + 1)} + C$

11. $\frac{1}{2}(x^3 - 4)^{2/3} + C$ **12.** $\frac{1}{3}\ln|x^3 - 4| + C$

13. $\dfrac{1}{2}x^2 - \dfrac{1}{x} + C$ **14.** $\frac{1}{3}x^3 + \frac{1}{2}x^2 - 2x - \ln|x - 1| + C$

15. $\frac{1}{3}e^{y^3} + C$ **16.** $x^3/3 - x^2 + x + C$

17. $\frac{1}{2}\ln|2x^3 - 7| + C$ **18.** $\dfrac{-5}{4e^{4x}} + C$

19. $x^4/4 - e^{3x}/3 + C$ **20.** $\frac{1}{2}e^{x^2 + 1} + C$

21. $\dfrac{-2}{x^3 + 1} + C$ **22.** $-\frac{7}{2}\sqrt{1 - x^4} + C$

23. $\frac{1}{4}e^{2x} - e^{-2x} + C$ **24.** $x^2/2 + 1/(x + 1) + C$

25. (a) $\frac{1}{10}(x^2 - 1)^5 + C$ **(b)** $\frac{1}{22}(x^2 - 1)^{11} + C$

(c) $\frac{3}{16}(x^2 - 1)^8 + C$ **(d)** $\frac{3}{2}(x^2 - 1)^{1/3} + C$

26. (a) $\ln|x^2 - 1| + C$ **(b)** $\dfrac{-1}{x^2 - 1} + C$

(c) $3\sqrt{x^2 - 1} + C$ **(d)** $\frac{3}{2}\ln|x^2 - 1| + C$ **27.** 0

28. 472   **29.** $400[1 - 5/(t + 5) + 25/(t + 5)^2]$

30. $p = 1990.099 - 100,000/(t + 100)$

31. (a) $y = -60e^{-0.04t} + 60$ **(b)** 23%

32. $R = 800\ln(x + 1)$ **33. (a)** \$1000

(b) $C(x) = 3x^2 + 4x + 1000$ **34.** 80 units, \$440

35. $C = \sqrt{2y + 16} + 0.6y + 4.5$

36. $C = 0.8y - 0.05e^{-2y} + 7.85$

CHAPTER 6

Exercise 6.1

1. 6.25   **3.** 8.3125   **5.** 4.25   **7.** 10.3125

9. $S_L(10) = 4.08$; $S_R(10) = 5.28$ **11.** both equal 14/3

13. It would lie between $S_L(10)$ and $S_R(10)$. It would equal 14/3.   **15.** 3   **17.** 42   **19.** -5

21. 180   **23.** 11,315

25. $3 - \dfrac{3(n + 1)}{n} + \dfrac{(n + 1)(2n + 1)}{2n^2} = \dfrac{2n^2 - 3n + 1}{2n^2}$

27. (a) $S = (n - 1)/2n$ **(b)** 9/20   **(c)** 99/200

(d) 999/2000   **(e)** $\frac{1}{2}$ **29. (a)** $S = \dfrac{(n + 1)(2n + 1)}{6n^2}$

(b) $77/200 = 0.385$ **(c)** $6767/20,000 \approx 0.3384$

(d) $667,667/2,000,000 \approx 0.3338$ **(e)** $\frac{1}{3}$ **31.** $\frac{20}{3}$

Exercise 6.2

1. 60   **3.** 33   **5.** 25   **7.** $12\sqrt[3]{25}$ **9.** 98

11. $\frac{7}{3}$ **13.** 12,960   **15.** 0   **17.** $8\sqrt{3} - \frac{7}{3}\sqrt{7}$

19. 0   **21.** $\frac{1}{6}\ln(112/31)$ **23.** A, C

25. $\int_0^4(2x - \frac{1}{2}x^2)\,dx$ **(b)** 16/3   **27. (a)** $\int_{-1}^0(x^3 + 1)\,dx$

(b) 3/4   **29.** $\frac{1}{6}$ **31.** $\frac{1}{2}(e^9 - e)$ **33.** same absolute values, opposite signs   **35.** 6   **37.** 20,405.39

39. 0.04 cm^3 **41.** 1222 (approx.)   **43.** \$450,000

45. (a) \$7007   **(b)** \$19,649

Exercise 6.3

1. (a) $\int_0^2(4 - x^2)\,dx$ **(b)** 16/3

3. (a) $\int_0^1[(2 - x) - \sqrt[3]{x}]\,dx$ **(b)** 3/4

5. (a) $\int_0^2[(4 - x^2) - (\frac{1}{4}x^3 - 2)]\,dx$ **(b)** 25/3

7. (a) $(-1, 1)$, $(2, 4)$ **(b)** $\int_{-1}^2[(x + 2) - x^2]\,dx$

(c) 9/2   **9. (a)** $(0, 0)$, $(\frac{5}{2}, -\frac{15}{4})$

(b) $\int_0^{5/2}[(x - x^2) - (x^2 - 4x)]\,dx$ **(c)** 125/24

11. (a) $(-2, -4)$, $(0, 0)$, $(2, 4)$

(b) $\int_{-2}^0[(x^3 - 2x) - 2x]\,dx + \int_0^2[2x - (x^3 - 2x)]\,dx$

(c) 8   **13.** 28/3   **15.** 1/4   **17.** 16/3   **19.** 1/3

21. 37/12   **23.** $4 - 3\ln 3$ **25.** 8/3   **27.** 6

29. 0   **31.** $-4/9$ **33. (a)** \$1402   **(b)** \$535,333.33

35. 102.5 units   **37.** \$513.86   **39.** 147 mg

Exercise 6.4

1. \$83.33   **3.** \$161.89   **5.** $(5, 56)$; \$83.33

7. \$11.50   **9.** \$204.17   **11.** \$2766.67

13. \$17,839.58   **15.** \$133.33   **17.** \$2.50

19. \$103.35   **21.** \$120,000   **23.** \$346,664 (nearest dollar)   **25.** \$506,000 (nearest thousand)

27. \$18,660 (nearest dollar)   **29.** \$82,155 (nearest dollar)   **31.** \$265,781 (nearest dollar)   **33.** \$190,519 (nearest dollar)   **35.** Gift shop: \$151,024; Video rental: \$141,093; Gift shop is a better buy.

Exercise 6.5

1. $\frac{1}{8}\ln|(4+x)/(4-x)| + C$ **3.** $\frac{1}{3}\ln[(3+\sqrt{10})/2]$

5. $w(\ln w - 1) + C$ **7.** $\frac{1}{3} + \frac{1}{4}\ln(\frac{3}{7})$

9. $3^x\log_3 e + C$ or $3^x/\ln 3 + C$

11. $\frac{1}{2}[7\sqrt{24} - 25\ln(7+\sqrt{24}) + 25\ln 5]$

13. $\dfrac{(6x-5)(4x+5)^{3/2}}{60} + C$ **15.** $\frac{1}{2}(5^{x^2})\log_5 e + C$

17. $\frac{1}{3}(13^{3/2} - 8)$ **19.** $\frac{-5}{\sqrt{8}}\ln\left|\dfrac{\sqrt{8} + \sqrt{8-x^2}}{x}\right| + C$

21. $\frac{1}{3}\ln|3x + \sqrt{9x^2 - 4}| + C$ **23.** $\frac{1}{8}\ln(\frac{9}{5})$

25. $\frac{1}{3}\ln|3x + 1 + \sqrt{(3x+1)^2 + 1}| + C$

27. $\frac{1}{4}[10\sqrt{109} - \sqrt{10} + 9\ln(10 + \sqrt{109}) -$
$9\ln(1 + \sqrt{10})]$ **29.** $-\frac{1}{6}\ln|7 - 3x^2| + C$

31. $\frac{1}{2}\ln|2x + \sqrt{4x^2 + 7}| + C$ **33.** $2e^{\sqrt{x-1}} + C$

35. $\frac{1}{32}[\ln|4x^2 + 5| + 5/(4x^2 + 5)] + C$ **37.** $\$3391.10$

39. $C = \frac{1}{2}x\sqrt{x^2 + 9} + \frac{9}{2}\ln\left|\dfrac{x + \sqrt{x^2+9}}{3}\right| + 300$

41. $CS = \$399$ approx.

Exercise 6.6

1. $\frac{1}{2}xe^{2x} - \frac{1}{4}e^{2x} + C$ **3.** $\frac{1}{3}x^3\ln x - \frac{1}{9}x^3 + C$

5. $\dfrac{104\sqrt{2}}{15}$ **7.** $e - 2$ **9.** $-(1 + \ln x)/x + C$

11. $\frac{1}{2}e^{x^2} + C$ **13.** $(x-3)^{1/2}(\frac{2}{3}x + 4) + C$ **15.** 1

17. $\dfrac{x^2}{2}\ln(2x-3) - \dfrac{1}{4}x^2 - \dfrac{3}{4}x - \dfrac{9}{8}\ln(2x-3) + C$

19. $\frac{1}{5}(q^2 - 3)^{3/2}(q^2 + 2) + C$ **21.** 282.4

23. $\frac{2}{3}x^{3/2}\ln x - \frac{4}{9}x^{3/2} + C$

25. $\frac{1}{4}x^4\ln^2 x - \frac{1}{8}x^4\ln x + \frac{1}{32}x^4 + C$ **27.** $\$2794.46$

29. $\$34,836.73$

Exercise 6.7

1. $1/e$ **3.** $\frac{1}{3}$ **5.** diverges   **7.** 10   **9.** diverges

11. diverges   **13.** diverges   **15.** 0   **17.** 0.5

19. $1/(2e)$ **21.** $3/2$ **23.** $\int_0^\infty Ae^{-rt}dt = A/r$

25. $\$2,400,000$ **27.** $\$700,000$

29. (a) $500\left[\dfrac{e^{-0.03b} + 0.03b - 1}{0.0009}\right]$ (b) limit $= \infty$

Exercise 6.8

1. $h = \frac{1}{2}$; $x_0 = 0$, $x_1 = \frac{1}{2}$, $x_2 = 1$, $x_3 = \frac{3}{2}$, $x_4 = 2$

3. $h = \frac{1}{2}$; $x_0 = 1$, $x_1 = \frac{3}{2}$, $x_2 = 2$, $x_3 = \frac{5}{2}$, $x_4 = 3$, $x_5 = \frac{7}{2}$,
$x_6 = 4$ **5.** $h = 1$; $x_0 = -1$, $x_1 = 0$, $x_2 = 1$, $x_3 = 2$,
$x_4 = 3$, $x_5 = 4$ **7.** (a) 9.13   (b) 9.00   (c) 9

(d) Simpson's   **9.** (a) 0.51   (b) 0.50   (c) $\frac{1}{2}$

(d) Simpson's   **11.** (a) 5.27   (b) 5.30   (c) 5.33

(d) Simpson's   **13.** (a) 3.283   (b) 3.240

15. (a) 0.743   (b) 0.747   **17.** (a) 7.132

(b) 7.197   **19.** 7.8   **21.** 10.3   **23.** 119.58 ($\$119,580$)

25. $\$32,389.76$ **27.** $\$14,133.33$

29. 1222.35 (1222 units)   **31.** 1586.67 sq ft

Chapter 6 Review Exercises

1. 212   **2.** $\dfrac{3(n+1)}{2n^2}$ **3.** 91/72   **4.** 1   **5.** 1

6. 14   **7.** 248/5   **8.** $-205/4$ **9.** 825/4

10. 125/3   **11.** -2 **12.** $\frac{1}{6}\ln 47 - \frac{1}{6}\ln 9$

13. 9/2   **14.** $\ln 4 + 14/3$ **15.** 26/3

16. $\frac{1}{2}\ln 2$ **17.** $(1 - e^{-2})/2$ **18.** $(e - 1)/2$

19. 95/2   **20.** 36   **21.** $\frac{1}{4}$ **22.** $\frac{1}{2}$

23. $\frac{1}{2}(x\sqrt{x^2 - 4} - 4\ln|x + \sqrt{x^2 - 4}|) + C$

24. $2\log_3 e$ **25.** $\frac{1}{2}x^2(\ln x^2 - 1) + C$

26. $\frac{1}{2}\ln|x| - \frac{1}{2}\ln|3x + 2| + C$

27. $\frac{1}{6}x^6\ln x - \frac{1}{36}x^6 + C$

28. $(-xe^{-2x}/2) - (e^{-2x}/4) + C$

29. $2x\sqrt{x+5} - \frac{4}{3}(x+5)^{3/2} + C$ **30.** 1   **31.** ∞

32. -100 **33.** $\frac{5}{3}$ **34.** $-\frac{1}{2}$ **35.** (a) 0.889

(b) 1.004   (c) 0.909   **36.** 3.135   **37.** 3.9

38. (a) $n = 5$ (b) $n = 6$ **39.** $\$28,000$

40. $\$1297.44$ **41.** $\$76.60$ **42.** (a) (7, 6)

(b) $\$7.33$ **43.** $\$24.50$ **44.** $\$1,621,803$

45. $\$403,609$ **46.** $\$217.42$ **47.** $\$86,557.41$

48. $-\dfrac{x^2}{4} + \dfrac{7}{2}x + \dfrac{x^2 - 1}{2}\ln(x + 1) + 2000$

49. $\$300,000$ **50.** $\$197,365$ **51.** $\$4800$

CHAPTER 7

Exercise 7.1

1. $\{(x, y): x \text{ and } y \text{ are real numbers}\}$
3. $\{(x, y): x \text{ and } y \text{ are real numbers and } y \neq 0\}$
5. $\{(x, y): x \text{ and } y \text{ are real numbers and } 2x - y \neq 0\}$
7. $\{(p_1, p_2): p_1 \text{ and } p_2 \text{ are real numbers and } p_1 \geq 0\}$
9. -2 **11.** $\frac{5}{3}$ **13.** 2500   **15.** 36   **17.** 3
19. $\frac{1}{25} \ln (12)$ **21.** $\frac{13}{3}$ **23. (a)** $x = 4$ **(b)** $y = 2$
25. (a) 7200   **(b)** 5000   **27.** \$284,000
29. \$6640.23; the amount that results when \$2000 is
invested for 20 years   **31. (a)** 37,500
(b) $30(2K)^{1/4}(2L)^{3/4} = 30(2^{1/4})(2^{3/4})K^{1/4}L^{3/4} = 2[30K^{1/4}L^{3/4}]$

Exercise 7.2

1. $4x^3 - 10x + 4$ **3.** $2x$ **5.** $4x + 6$
7. $12y - 5x$ **9.** y **11.** $e^x + y/x$ **13.** xe^{xy}
15. $9x^2(x^3 + y^2)^2$ **17.** $2y(x + 1)^2$
19. $-4y + 20xy$ **21.** $p_2/(p_1 + p_2)^2$
23. $2x + 4y$ **25.** 2   **27.** 7   **29.** 0
31. (a) 0   **(b)** $-2xz + 4$ **(c)** $2y$ **(d)** $-x^2$
33. (a) $8x_1 + 5x_2$ **(b)** $5x_1 + 12x_2$ **(c)** 1
35. (a) For a mortgage of \$100,000 and an 8% interest
rate, the monthly payment is \$1289.   **(b)** The rate of
change of the payment with respect to the interest rate
is \$62.51. That is, if the rate goes from 8% to 9% on a
\$100,000 mortgage, the approximate increase in the
monthly payment is \$62.51.   **37. (a)** $65e^{-0.01x}$
(b) $70e^{-0.02y}$ **39. (a)** $2xy^2$ **(b)** $2x^2y$
41. $\partial Q/\partial K = (44\frac{4}{9})\ \partial Q/\partial L = 37\frac{1}{2}$

43. (a) $\dfrac{\partial WC}{\partial s} = -0.020t - 1.85 + \dfrac{0.152t}{\sqrt{s}} - \dfrac{13.87}{\sqrt{s}}$

(b) at $t = 10$, $s = 25$, $\dfrac{\partial WC}{\partial s} = -0.20 - 1.85 + 0.304$

$- 2.774 = -4.52$

This means that the rate of change of WC with respect
to s is -4.52 if $t = 10°F$, $s = 25$ mph. An increase in
speed causes a decrease in wind chill temperature.

Exercise 7.3

1. 57   **3. (a)** $2 + y/50$ **(b)** $4 + x/50$
5. (a) 20.18   **(b)** 70.80   **7. (a)** 36   **(b)** 19
9. (a) $\sqrt{y^2 + 1}$ **(b)** $xy/\sqrt{y^2 + 1}$
11. (a) $1200y/(xy + 1)$ **(b)** $1200x/(xy + 1)$
13. (a) $\sqrt{y/x}$ **(b)** $\sqrt{x/y}$ **15. (a)** $\ln(y + 1)/(2\sqrt{x})$
(b) $\sqrt{x}/(y + 1)$ **17.** $z = 1092$ approx.   **19.** $z_x = 3.6$
21. $q_1 = 188$; $q_2 = 270$ **23.** any values for p_1 and p_2
that satisfy $6p_2 - 3p_1 = 100$ and that make q_1 and q_2
nonnegative, such as $p_1 = 10$, $p_2 = 21\frac{2}{3}$ **25. (a)** -3
(b) -2 **(c)** -6 **(d)** -5 **(e)** complementary
27. (a) -50 **(b)** $600/(p_B + 1)^2$ **(c)** $-400/(p_B + 4)^2$
(d) $400/(p_A + 4)^2$ **(e)** competitive

Exercise 7.4

1. (a) 2   **(b)** 0   **(c)** 0   **(d)** $-30y$ **3. (a)** $2y$
(b) $2x - 8y$ **(c)** $2x - 8y$ **(d)** $-8x$ **5.** 0
7. $-1/y^2$ **9.** -6 **11. (a)** 6   **(b)** 0
13. $2 + 2e$ **15. (a)** $2 + y^2e^{xy}$ **(b)** $xye^{xy} + e^{xy}$
(c) $xye^{xy} + e^{xy}$ **(d)** x^2e^{xy} **17. (a)** $1/x^2$ **(b)** 0
(c) 0   **(d)** $2 + 1/y^2$ **19.** $\dfrac{2x^2 - 2y^2}{x^2(x^2 + y^2)^2}$
21. $4y^2/(4x^2 + y^2)^{3/2}$ **23. (a)** $24x$ **(b)** $24x$ **(c)** 0

Exercise 7.5

1. max $(0, 0, 9)$ **3.** min $(0, 0, 4)$ **5.** min $(1, -2, 0)$
7. saddle $(1, -3, 8)$ **9.** saddle $(0, 0, 0)$
11. max $(12, 24, 456)$ **13.** min $(-8, 6, -52)$
15. saddle $(0, 0, 0)$; min $(2, 2, -8)$ **17.** $\hat{y} = 5.7x - 1.4$
19. $\hat{y} = .11x + 2$ **21.** $x = 5000$, $y = 128$
23. $x = \frac{20}{3}$, $y = \frac{10}{3}$ **25.** $x = 28$, $y = 100$
27. $x = 0$, $y = 10$ **29.** length $= 100$, width $= 100$,
height $= 50$ **31.** $x = 3$, $y = 0$
33. (a) $y = 27.0 + 0.631x$ **(b)** \$325 (to the
nearest dollar)   **35.** $y = 2.70 + 0.051x$
37. $\hat{q} = 34,726 - 55.09p$

Exercise 7.6

1. 18 at $(3, 3)$ **3.** 35 at $(3, 2)$ **5.** 32 at $(4, 2)$

7. -28 at $(3, \frac{5}{2})$ **9.** $\frac{1}{5}$ at $(-\frac{2}{5}, -\frac{1}{5})$

11. 3 at $(1, 1, 1)$ **13.** 1 at $(0, 1, 0)$

15. $x = 4, y = 1$ **17.** $x = 40, y = \frac{40}{3}$

19. $x = 900, y = 300$

21. $x = \$10,003.33, y = \$19,996.67$

23. length $= 100$ cm, width $= 100$ cm, height $= 50$ cm

24. $-1/2$ **25.** $4/3$ **26.** $729/8$ **27.** $-1/12$

28. 3   **29.** 3 units   **30.** 20   **31. (a)** 280

(b) 2400/7   **32.** $\partial Q/\partial K = 81.92$; $\partial Q/\partial L = 37.5$

33. (a) -2 **(b)** -6 **(c)** complementary

34. competitive   **35.** $x = 20, y = 40$

36. (a) $\hat{y} = 10.00 + 0.14x$ **(b)** $\hat{y} = 313.142$; actual $y = 336.5$ **37.** $x = 10, y = 4$

38. 370/3 cu. units   **39.** 164

Exercise 7.7

1. $4x^3y + xy + C(y)$ **3.** $6x^2y^2 + y^2/2 + C(x)$

5. $-\frac{1}{24}(x^2 - y^4)^6 + C(x)$ **7.** $2x^2 + 60x$

9. $\frac{4}{3}y^5 - 5y$ **11.** 3   **13.** 3   **15.** 1161/4

17. 1/3   **19.** 63/8   **21.** 12   **23.** 10/3

25. 1   **27.** $3^{3/2} - 1$ **29.** 64   **31.** 32/3

33. 24   **35.** -2 **37.** \$81,833   **39.** 271.69

(272 units)   **41.** 175,000   **43.** 100

Chapter 7 Review Exercises

1. $\{(x, y): x \text{ and } y \text{ are real numbers and } y \neq 2x\}$

2. $\{(x, y): x \text{ and } y \text{ are real numbers with } y \geq 0 \text{ and } (x, y) \neq (0, 0)\}$ **3.** -5 **4.** 896,000

5. $15x^2 + 6y$ **6.** $24y^3 - 42x^3y^2$

7. $z_x = 8xy^3 + 1/y$; $z_y = 12x^2y^2 - x/y^2$

8. $z_x = x/\sqrt{x^2 + 2y^2}$; $z_y = 2y/\sqrt{x^2 + 2y^2}$

9. $z_x = -2y/(xy + 1)^3$; $z_y = -2x/(xy + 1)^3$

10. $z_x = 2xy^3e^{x^2y^3}$; $z_y = 3x^2y^2e^{x^2y^3}$

11. $z_x = ye^{xy} + y/x$; $z_y = xe^{xy} + \ln x$

12. $z_x = y$; $z_y = x$ **13.** -8 **14.** 8

15. (a) $2y$ **(b)** 0   **(c)** $2x - 3$ **(d)** $2x - 3$

16. (a) $18xy^4 - 2/y^2$ **(b)** $36x^3y^2 - 6x^2/y^4$

(c) $36x^2y^3 + 4x/y^3$ **(d)** $36x^2y^3 + 4x/y^3$

17. (a) $2e^{y^2}$ **(b)** $4x^2y^2e^{y^2} + 2x^2e^{y^2}$ **(c)** $4xye^{y^2}$

(d) $4xye^{y^2}$ **18. (a)** $-y^2/(xy + 1)^2$ **(b)** $-x^2/(xy + 1)^2$

(c) $1/(xy + 1)^2$ **(d)** $1/(xy + 1)^2$

19. max $(-8, 16, 208)$ **20.** saddle $(0, 0, 0)$; min $(1, 1, -1)$

21. 80 at $(2, 8)$ **22.** 11,664 at $(6, 3)$ **23.** 1

INDEX

Index of Selected Applications (Continued)

Social Science

Additional Applications